FISHES of
Chesapeake Bay

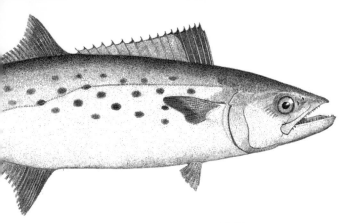

FISHES of

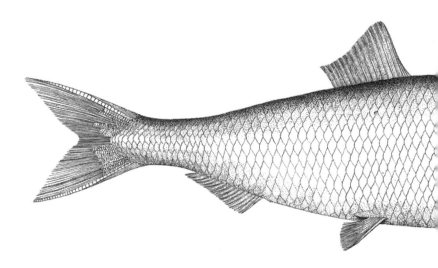

Chesapeake Bay

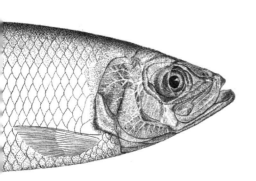

Edward O. Murdy
Ray S. Birdsong
John A. Musick

Smithsonian Institution Press
Washington and London

To the memory of our friend, colleague, and coauthor, Ray Birdsong. Tragically, Ray died before this book was completed. We miss him and the additional contributions he would have made to the final product. He was a good ichthyologist and an even better friend.

E.O.M. AND J.A.M.

To Becky, Kirby, and Kelly for their patience during this seemingly endless project, and especially to my parents, Olive and Ralph Murdy, who aided and abetted my interest in fishes.

E.O.M.

© 1997 by the Smithsonian Institution
All rights reserved

COPY EDITOR Rosemary Sheffield
PRODUCTION EDITOR Deborah L. Sanders
DESIGNER Linda McKnight

Library of Congress Cataloging-in-Publication Data
Murdy, Edward O.
    Fishes of Chesapeake Bay / by Edward O. Murdy, Ray S. Birdsong, and John A. Musick.
    p.   cm.
    Includes bibliographical references (p.   ) and indexes.
    ISBN 1-56098-638-7 (alk. paper)
    1. Fishes—Chesapeake Bay (Md. and Va.)   2. Fishes—Chesapeake Bay (Md. and Va.)—Identification.   3. Fishes—Chesapeake Bay (Md. and Va.)—Pictorial works.   I. Birdsong, Ray S.   II. Musick, John A. III. Title.
QL628.C5M87   1996
597.092′147—dc20   96-26586

British Library Cataloguing-in-Publication Data available

Manufactured in the United States of America
06 05 04 03 02 01 00 99 98 97   5 4 3 2 1

♾ The paper used in this publication meets the minimum requirements of the American National Standard for Permanence of Paper for Printed Library Materials Z39.48-1984.

For permission to reproduce illustrations appearing in this book, please correspond directly with the sources, as listed herein starting on page 311. The Smithsonian Institution Press does not retain reproduction rights for these illustrations individually or maintain a file of addresses for photo sources.

Cover design by Linda McKnight

Contents

 Acknowledgments

There are many persons who deserve our thanks for their assistance in preparing this book. Below, we acknowledge those who provided special help in diverse ways. We apologize for not mentioning everyone who assisted us, but the complete list would require a publication subsidy.

First, we thank Michael Fahay, who provided as complete and detailed a review as any author would desire. Mike's efforts, as well as those of an anonymous reviewer, resulted in numerous improvements. Prior to Mike's review, sections of the manuscript were reviewed by the following people, who also richly deserve our thanks: Steve Branstetter (Carcharhiniformes, Lamniformes, Squaliformes, Squatiniformes); Louis Daniel (Sciaenidae); Joe Desfosse (Clupeiformes); Carl Ferraris (Siluriformes); Bob Jenkins (Amiiformes, Centrarchidae, Cypriniformes, Salmoniformes, Siluriformes); Eddie Matheson (Gerreidae); John McEachran (Myliobatiformes, Pristiformes, Rajiformes, Triglidae); Tom Munroe (Pleuronectiformes); Bill Smith-Vaniz (Carangidae); Wayne Starnes (Centrarchidae, Cypriniformes, Priacanthidae, Salmoniformes); and Jim Tyler (Tetraodontiformes). In addition, Tom Orrell reviewed our key to the orders of Chesapeake Bay fishes and key to the families of Perciformes. Thanks to Tom, these keys are more user-friendly.

We relied on previously published artwork to illustrate this book, the majority of which came from the Division of Fishes, U.S. National Museum of Natural History, Smithsonian Institution (NMNH), and from the Food and Agricultural Organization of the United Nations (FAO). The NMNH artwork was provided with the cooperation and assistance of Lisa Palmer, Lynne Parenti, Victor Springer, and Stan Weitzman. Permission to use FAO art was facilitated by Kent Carpenter. The following persons either gave permission or helped obtain permission for the use of additional artwork: Dave Lee of the North Carolina State Museum; Eddie Matheson of the Florida Department of Environmental Protection; John D. McEachran of Texas A&M University; Larry Page of the Illinois Natural History Survey; Jon Moore of the Peabody Museum; Gerald Barnhart, Stephen Clarke, and Eileen Stegemann of the New York State Department of Environmental Conservation; Bruce Collette; and Ed Crossman. Wanda Cohen, Harold Burrell, and Kay Stubblefield of the art department of the Virginia Institute of Marine Science assisted in preparing figures for our use. David Hastings of the U.S. National Oceanic and Atmospheric Administration's National Geophysical Data Center provided the satellite image of the Chesapeake Bay region. Chip Clark generously photographed all of the original artwork from NMNH for reproduction here. Wanda Cohen, Harold Burrell, and Kay Stubblefield of the art department of the Virginia Institute of Marine Science electronically scanned numerous illustrations for our use.

Finally, we wish to thank the science acquisitions editor at the Smithsonian Institution Press, Peter Cannell. Peter patiently answered questions and guided us through the preparation of this book, which took far longer than anyone expected or planned.

Introduction
to Chesapeake Bay and Its Fishes

PHYSICAL AND CHEMICAL FEATURES OF THE BAY

Chesapeake Bay, the largest of the 850 estuaries that bracket the United States, is fed by more than 20 major tributaries that drain some 175,000 km² (67,000 mi²). The largest of these tributaries, the Susquehanna River, drains more than 70,000 km² (27,000 mi²) in Maryland, Pennsylvania, and New York State and provides more than 50% of the freshwater that flows into the bay. The main stem of the bay is approximately 320 km (200 mi) long and varies in width from 6.4 km (4 mi) near Annapolis to 48 km (30 mi) near the mouth of the Potomac River (Plate 1; Figure 1). The surface area of more than 11,000 km² (4,300 mi²) is about evenly divided between the main stem and the tidal tributaries. The surface area of the bay is shared nearly equally by Maryland and Virginia, with Virginia's portion being slightly larger.

The bay is a geologically young feature that had its beginnings some 10,000 years ago when the Pleistocene Susquehanna River, carrying the outflow from glaciers far to the north, cut its way down from the highlands, across the piedmont plateau, through the fall line, and across a coastal plain that was much broader than today's. Sea level was about 90 m (300 ft) lower, and the ancient Susquehanna carved out not only the great channels in the Chesapeake Basin but also the precipitous chasm at the edge of the continental margin known as Norfolk Submarine Canyon. As the glaciers receded, the sea slowly rose and progressed inland, burying the entire terrestrial, boreal biota along the coast beneath water. As sea level rose (a process that continues today), Chesapeake Bay was formed. Today the deepest part of the bay—53 m, or 174 ft—is located in Maryland waters south of Queen Annes County. The bay, however, is actually a shallow water body. Less than 10% of its area is 18 m (60 ft) deep, and approximately 50% is less than 6 m (20 ft) deep.

As the sea invaded the freshwater tributaries of the Chesapeake Basin, brackish habitats were created: marshes developed on the intertidal lowlands, aquatic grass beds flourished in the shallow, flooded flatlands, and oysters formed acres of subtidal hard-bottom reef habitat. Today the pulse of ocean tides pushes to the very fall line itself. Freshwater from the tributaries flows down the bay at the surface because it is less dense than salt water from the ocean. At the same time, seawater has a net flow along the bottom upstream into the bay and its tributaries. In between, at middepths, is a zone of mixing. This incoming "salt wedge," which transports larval crabs and fishes and other organisms into the bay from the ocean, is a critical mechanism by which many species travel from the coastal areas where they have been spawned to the productive estuarine nursery areas, where they may grow rapidly in relatively protected shallow habitats such as sea grass beds and marsh creeks. Most of the marine fishes that use Chesapeake Bay as a feeding or nursery ground spawn in the ocean. A few species, such as black drum and weakfish, may spawn in the lower portion of the bay on the eastern side where there is a deep channel and salinity is very high. The eastern side of the bay is saltier than the western because of the Coriolis effect associated with rotation of the earth and because of the inflow of many large freshwater tributaries on the bay's Western Shore. Salinity, which is expressed as grams of salt per liters of water, is denoted by the per-mille symbol, ‰.

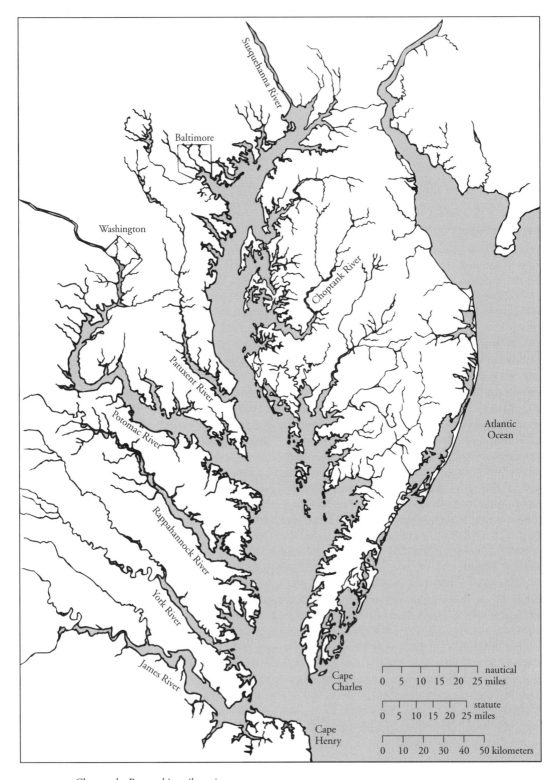

FIGURE I. Chesapeake Bay and its tributaries.

Typically, the bay's salinity is graded from near full seawater (32‰) at the mouth to freshwater (<0.5‰) at its northern extreme. Because of fluctuations in the amount of precipitation, the average salinity typically varies from month to month, season to season, and year to year. At any given location the salinity, temperature, turbidity, and other features of water quality are subject to small to large changes with the tides.

Chesapeake Bay has one of the most extreme annual temperature ranges known for coastal ecosystems in the world. Water temperatures in the bay and nearshore coastal waters may reach as high as 28°–30°C (82°–86°F) in late summer and dip as low as 1°–4°C (34°–39°F) in late winter. Temperature differences, as well as the vertical salinity gradient, contribute to the vertical stratification of bay waters. Because warm water is less dense than cold water, the water column becomes increasingly stratified as surface waters begin to warm during the spring. A layered structure is established, especially in the deeper portions of the bay, with lighter, warmer, less salty water in the upper water column separated from heavier, colder, saltier water in the lower water column. Between these two layers is a distinct boundary layer of sharp density change, the pycnocline. The transport of materials (oxygen, nutrients, and such) is reduced across this boundary layer.

An important result of stratification is that deep bottom waters become isolated from their oxygen source, the near-surface waters. In deep, dimly lit bottom waters, where photosynthesis is minimal, organic materials (mainly dead phytoplankton and zooplankton, fecal matter, and materials of human origin) sink down from the productive waters above. In the bottom waters the organic matter is broken down by microbial action, with the consumption of oxygen by microbial respiration. The greater the amount of organic matter introduced into the bottom waters, the greater the amount of oxygen consumed. The spring and summer conditions of pronounced stratification, low oxygen-carrying capacity of the water, and high organic production in the upper water column promote low levels of dissolved oxygen in bottom waters. During this period, oxygen levels may fall to near 0 mg/L, a level that causes extreme hypoxia in many aquatic organisms. Many fishes, mollusks, crustaceans, and other estuarine organisms show signs of distress when the dissolved-oxygen level falls below 2 mg/L, and some organisms are even more sensitive. Under extreme conditions these deep waters essentially become devoid of all but microbial life. The extent of bay waters subjected to these extreme conditions has been growing (a 15-fold increase since 1950) and now includes much of the bay north of the Rappahannock River that is deeper than 12 m (40 ft) from May through September. The southern quarter of the bay, which gets flushed more because of its proximity to the bay mouth, is less affected.

The cause of the decreasing levels of dissolved oxygen is the excessive input of nutrients (phosphorus and nitrogen compounds) that overstimulate phytoplankton growth. The excessive growth of phytoplankton reduces water clarity, and the reduction in light penetration in turn reduces the growth of submerged rooted aquatic plants. The sources of the nutrients are numerous, but primary among them are runoff from agricultural and residential lands and municipal discharges. Although the environmental problems besetting the bay are numerous and varied, overenrichment (eutrophication) is the most serious. The human population of the Chesapeake Bay watershed is projected to exceed 16 million shortly after the year 2000. Only the most concerted public effort will stem the continued degradation of the bay as the human population of the watershed grows.

GENERAL CHARACTERISTICS OF THE FISH FAUNA

The flora and fauna of Chesapeake Bay are particularly rich. Nearly 3,000 species of plants and animals have been reported from the bay's waters and tidal margins. Species richness is typical of ecotones, the boundary zones between different habitats. The bay is an ecotone between the Atlantic Ocean and the rivers and streams of Maryland and Virginia. The bay owes its species richness to the incorporation of biotic elements from both the ocean habitat and the freshwater habitat, along with an estuarine biota specifically adapted for life in waters of reduced salinity.

As the glaciers receded and the climate became warmer at the end of the Pleistocene, a diverse estuarine and marine fish fauna became established from warm-temperate and subtropical habitats to the south. Today these warmwater elements (such as the families Carangidae, Cyprinodontidae, Gobiidae, Paralichthyidae, and Sciaenidae) comprise the most abundant, diverse, and ecologically important groups of fishes in the bay. Many of these warm-temperate and subtropical species have great importance to the fisheries as well.

Five major categories of fishes occupy Chesapeake Bay: freshwater, estuarine, marine, anadromous, and catadromous. The first three categories are based on salinity regimes, whereas the last two categories comprise reproductively specialized fishes that migrate between freshwater and salt water (or vice versa) in order to reproduce.

Freshwater fishes inhabit the tributaries of the bay, with many of these species descending into tidal freshwaters. Some of these fishes can tolerate brackish waters with a salinity as high as 10‰. Salinity tolerance by freshwater fishes typically increases with decreasing temperature, and therefore their downstream penetration into brackish water is greatest in the winter. Only a few freshwater fishes ever enter the bay proper. In this book we treat only those freshwater fishes that are known at least occasionally to enter waters with salinities of 5‰ or greater.

Estuarine fishes typically inhabit tidal waters with salinities of 0–30‰. Given this wide salinity tolerance, estuarine fishes can be found anywhere in the bay. There is a general tendency for estuarine fishes to penetrate farther up the tributaries and be closer to shore in the warmer months and to retreat to deeper water during the colder months.

Marine fishes typically spend much of their lives and spawn in coastal or oceanic waters with salinities greater than 30‰. Only a few marine species penetrate the bay north of the Potomac River. All the marine species migrate to and from the bay in response to the extreme seasonal changes in temperature there.

Anadromous fishes migrate from ocean waters to freshwater to spawn. These fishes are often targeted by commercial fisheries because the habit of anadromy ensures that large numbers will arrive in inland waters at a predictable time. Notable anadromous fishes in the bay include the clupeids of the genus *Alosa* (shads and river herring) and the striped bass. Upstream migration may extend to nontidal freshwaters. After spawning, the adults return downstream to the bay and eventually out to sea. A variety of fishes move from waters of higher salinity to waters of lower salinity to spawn and can be categorized as semianadromous. These include fishes (such as the white perch) that move from brackish water to freshwater for spawning, as well as those (such as the black drum) that migrate from oceanic waters to the slightly reduced salinities just inside the bay mouth for spawning.

Catadromous fishes display a migration pattern that takes them from freshwater to the ocean for spawning. True catadromy is rare in the Northern Hemisphere, and in the bay only the American eel can be so categorized.

The habits of fishes and the ways in which they utilize the bay are diverse. Not all species can be easily placed in the simple categories just described.

DYNAMIC NATURE OF THE FISH FAUNA

The fish fauna of Chesapeake Bay is very dynamic because of the extreme seasonal temperature changes and the diversity of habitats within the bay. Fish diversity reaches a maximum in late summer and early autumn (August–September), when rarer tropical species may straggle into the bay to join warm-temperate and subtropical summer residents. With the onset of shorter day lengths in late summer, many marine species move toward the mouth of the bay. With the arrival of the first cool northerlies in early autumn, most marine species begin their migration coastally to the south around Cape Hatteras or to offshore waters or both. As large numbers of smaller sciaenids, Atlantic menhaden, mullets, and other small fishes leave the bay and migrate down the coast, they are accompanied by predators of moderate size, such as bluefish, weakfish, and young sandbar sharks. These in turn are consumed by larger sharks such as the sand tiger, larger sandbar sharks, and dusky, blacktip, and hammerhead sharks. In general, the larger the fish, the farther the migration. Large species migrate farther than small species, and young age-classes (smaller individuals) within a species migrate shorter distances than do the adults.

Some species or stocks within species may migrate offshore in winter rather than to the south. For example, clearnose skate, black sea bass, scup, butterfish, striped and northern searobins, and some summer flounder migrate eastward to the edge of the continental shelf to overwinter at depths of 90–180 m (300–600 ft). The shelf edge adjacent to Chesapeake Bay is influenced by an oceanic water mass (slope water), and bottom temperatures are moderate (8°–12°C, or 46°–54°F) year-round. These moderate temperatures represent the lower normal limit for many warm-temperate species and the upper limit for many boreal species. Thus the outer continental shelf can serve as a refuge not only for warm-temperate species in winter but also for boreal species in summer.

As autumn progresses in the bay, boreal species such as red, spotted, and silver hakes enter the lower bay to feed. But with the arrival of winter and cold temperatures (≤4°C, or ≤39°F), even these cold-adapted species move back out onto the continental shelf, where water temperatures are more moderate. In midwinter, many of the more mobile estuarine resident species such as white perch, smaller striped bass, and young-of-the-year Atlantic croakers move into the deeper channels of the tributaries, where water temperatures are more stable. Of all the sciaenids found in Chesapeake Bay, the Atlantic croaker is the last to spawn in the fall, and its young are generally too small to migrate south with the spot, the weakfish, and other sciaenids. In warm winters (≥5°C, or ≥41°F), young Atlantic croakers may have excellent survival, but in very cold winters (≤4°C, or ≤39°F), most of the new year-class may die. Thus Atlantic croaker year-class abundance in Chesapeake Bay may fluctuate widely from year to year. The same is true of most marine species that use the bay as a nursery, although the mechanisms that determine year-class survival may differ among species.

Because many marine species spawn in the coastal zone of the Chesapeake Bay region, year-class success often depends on critical wind direction immediately adjacent to the bay at the time the larvae are about to transform and settle to the bottom. If prevailing winds produce onshore currents, the pelagic larvae may be transported close to the mouth of the bay, where they transform and descend, and then they can be transported by the bottom currents up into the estuarine nursery grounds. Conversely, if prevailing winds produce offshore currents, larvae may be swept away from estuarine nurseries within the bay and descend somewhere in deep water out over the continental shelf, where food is less abundant than in the estuary and where predation is higher because there is less cover and shelter.

In midwinter, the diversity and density of demersal (bottom) fishes in Chesapeake Bay become quite low. However, winter flounder have been reported to be common at times in the upper bay, and pelagic boreal species such as Atlantic mackerel, Atlantic herring, and spiny dogfish often visit the lower bay in midwinter. By late winter and early spring (February–March), the anadromous alewife and American shad enter the bay and begin to ascend the tributaries on their spawning migrations. They are followed shortly by hickory shad, blueback herring, and striped bass. By late April some of the sciaenids and summer flounder have returned to the lower bay, and by late May most of the warm-temperate and subtropical summer residents have returned.

FISHERY TRENDS

Trends in the commercial and recreational landings of fishes in Chesapeake Bay since Hildebrand and Schroeder described them in 1928 have been extremely variable. This variability may be attributed to several factors. First, the boom-and-bust life history strategy of most of the fishes leads to highly variable natural recruitment (addition of individuals to a population) from year to year. Second, the explosive growth of the human population in the Chesapeake Bay region and the adjacent Mid-Atlantic Bight area has led to increased recreational and commercial fishing efforts, resulting in overexploitation of many fish species.

The development of offshore otter trawling during the winter, when demersal species such as summer flounder, Atlantic croaker, weakfish, black sea bass, and scup have emigrated from Chesapeake Bay, has adversely affected traditional bay fisheries such as pound netting and haul seining. Because the bay's marine fishes are migratory, fishermen from Massachusetts to North Carolina may compete with Chesapeake Bay fishermen for the same stocks of fish, but at different times of the year or at different times in a fish's life history. Conversely, Chesapeake Bay serves as an important nursery ground for several species—such as summer flounder, striped bass, bluefish, weakfish, and Atlantic menhaden—that may migrate to coastal areas as far north as Massachusetts and as far south as North Carolina as they grow older. Thus the environmental quality of the Chesapeake Bay region could affect survival, recruitment, and subsequent availability of fish to fisheries over a wide geographic area. From the 1930s to the 1980s, eutrophication due to both domestic and agricultural pollution led to greater phytoplankton production, greater turbidity, and reduced light in Chesapeake Bay. Insufficient light caused the vast beds of sea grasses, which provide shelter and food to many juvenile fishes, to decline drastically. Concerted efforts coordinated by the U.S. Environmental Protection Agency's Chesapeake Bay Program have reversed this trend in recent years. Water clarity has improved substantially in the 1990s, and the sea grass beds are well on their way to recovery.

The specter of overfishing and a resultant collapse of fish stocks has led to the creation of regional fishery management plans administered by the Atlantic States Marine Fisheries Commission within state waters (≤4.8 km, or ≤3 mi, off the coast) and the Mid-Atlantic Fishery Management Council (>4.8 to 322 km, or >3 to 200 mi, offshore). From 1985 through 1989, the striped bass was placed under a coast-wide fishery moratorium after several year-class failures and gross overharvesting, especially in Chesapeake Bay, where both the recreational and commercial fisheries traditionally landed very small fish. Striped bass stocks appear to be fully recovered, and the fishery has been reopened, but with stringent minimum-size limits, creel limits, a substantial closed season, and a commercial quota. Similar stringent regulations have been implemented for summer flounder, bluefish, weakfish, red drum, and other species. Recent federal legislation mandates that the coastal states must come into compliance with regional fishery management plans or face fishery closures. This act will greatly aid the cause of responsible fishery management in the states where local policies and short-term economic considerations often dictated fishery regulations in the past.

Scope of This Book

This book treats 267 fish species that are known to occur in Chesapeake Bay as delimited below. These fishes include permanent residents, spawning migrants, and seasonal visitors. Of these 267 species, only 32 are year-round residents of the bay (Table 1). The remaining species enter the bay from either freshwater or the Atlantic Ocean for periods from days to months to feed, reproduce, or seek refuge. (Sportfishing records of the largest fishes caught in Chesapeake Bay, by species, are presented in Appendix 1.)

Readers who are familiar with S. F. Hildebrand and W. C. Schroeder's *Fishes of Chesapeake Bay* (1928) will notice that although we have retained the same title, we have designed this book very differently from that earlier work. In establishing the scope of this book, we have attempted to avoid arbitrary limits. This has not been an easy task. Estuaries by definition are water bodies that grade from oceanic to freshwater. During times of flood, a number of freshwater fishes may be found in locations that we normally classify as estuarine. We have chosen to limit the inclusion of primary freshwater fishes to those that are commonly found in waters with salinities of 5‰ or higher. For readers wishing more information on freshwater species, we recommend *Freshwater Fishes of Virginia* (Jenkins and Burkhead 1994). The seaward limit of our coverage is a line between Cape Henry and Cape Charles. We have included only those species that have been taken west of this line and for which there is corroboration, normally a voucher specimen in the collections of the Virginia Institute of Marine Science or the U.S. National Museum of Natural History. The bay mouth is near the southern geographical limit of many northern species and the northern limit of many southern species; therefore the recorded fish fauna contains many uncommon to rare transient marine fishes. Species as dissimilar in their primary habitats as the tropical to subtropical spotfin butterflyfish and the cold-temperate to boreal Atlantic salmon are occasionally taken in the bay mouth.

Year-to-year fluctuations in climate can cause wide variations in the abundance or occurrence of species, especially the less common species. Very rare species or those for which Chesapeake Bay records are in question are listed in Table 2 and described in Appendix 2. Undoubtedly, there are other marine species not here included that enter the bay on rare occasion but for which no substantiated records exist. If you find a fish that should fall within the scope of this book but does not appear to be included, we urge you to make your find available to the Virginia Institute of Marine Science or one of the other marine institutes, laboratories, or universities around the bay.

ORGANIZATION

This book presents keys to the fishes of Chesapeake Bay: a key to the orders, keys to the families within orders, and keys to the species within families. An account of each species treated in the book is provided after the appropriate key to the species. If only one species within a family is treated, no species key is presented. In each species account, information on the geographic distribution, ecology, and fishing interest of the fish is provided, as well as the key features and other characteristics of the fish. For more information about a species, the reader is referred to pertinent literature citations. The systematic arrangement

TABLE I
Year-round resident fishes in Chesapeake Bay

COMMON NAME	SCIENTIFIC NAME	COMMON NAME	SCIENTIFIC NAME
anchovy, bay	*Anchoa mitchilli*	mummichog	*Fundulus heteroclitus*
bass, striped	*Morone saxatilis*	perch, silver	*Bairdiella chrysoura*
blenny, feather	*Hypsoblennius hentz*	perch, white	*Morone americana*
blenny, striped	*Chasmodes bosquianus*	perch, yellow	*Perca flavescens*
catfish, white	*Ameiurus catus*	pipefish, dusky	*Syngnathus floridae*
flounder, smallmouth	*Etropus microstomus*	pipefish, northern	*Syngnathus fuscus*
goby, green	*Microgobius thalassinus*	seahorse, lined	*Hippocampus erectus*
goby, naked	*Gobiosoma bosc*	silverside, Atlantic	*Menidia menidia*
goby, seaboard	*Gobiosoma ginsburgi*	silverside, inland	*Menidia beryllina*
hogchoker	*Trinectes maculatus*	silverside, rough	*Membras martinica*
killifish, banded	*Fundulus diaphanus*	skilletfish	*Gobiesox strumosus*
killifish, marsh	*Fundulus confluentus*	stargazer, northern	*Astroscopus guttatus*
killifish, rainwater	*Lucania parva*	stickleback, fourspine	*Apeltes quadracus*
killifish, spotfin	*Fundulus luciae*	toadfish, oyster	*Opsanus tau*
killifish, striped	*Fundulus majalis*	tonguefish, blackcheek	*Symphurus plagiusa*
minnow, sheepshead	*Cyprinodon variegatus*	windowpane	*Scophthalmus aquosus*

NOTE: The fish species listed here are considered year-round residents of Chesapeake Bay that complete all aspects of their natural history, including reproduction, in the bay's waters.

and taxonomy for orders and families follows that proposed in *Catalog of the Genera of Recent Fishes* (Eschmeyer 1990); genus and species classifications, and corresponding common names, follow the standards of the American Fisheries Society (Robins et al. 1991). Each species described herein is illustrated as a black-and-white figure; some species are also illustrated as a color plate. Most of the black-and-white line drawings were rendered by H. W. Todd, an illustrator who worked for the U.S. Bureau of Commercial Fisheries in the late 1800s. The majority of the color paintings were done by either Charles B. Hudson or Sherman Foote Denton, mostly in the 1880s and 1890s.

HOW TO IDENTIFY SPECIES OF FISHES IN THE BAY

To ensure proper identification of Chesapeake Bay fishes, we recommend the following procedure. (1) Familiarize yourself with the sections in this chapter entitled "Morphology" and "Basic Counts and Measurements" and with the glossary of selected technical terms at the end of the book, because this information is critical to understanding the technical language used in the keys. Words not defined in the glossary can be found in a standard dictionary. (2) To identify a particular fish, work your way through the keys, beginning with the most general key (the key to the orders) and ending with the most specific key (the key to the families or, if necessary, the key to the species) until you reach a species name and page number for the fish. See the section "How to Use the Keys," below. (3) Compare your fish with the text description and illustration of the species in the species account. If they correspond, your identification is probably correct.

How to Use the Keys

The keys provide a rather simple method for identifying a fish by eliminating, through a series of alternate choices, all groups of fishes (orders, families, and species) except the one in question. When all the possibilities have been tested, you will come to a common name and a scientific name for the fish that is being identified.

Each key consists of consecutively numbered couplets. Each couplet consists of a pair of choices

TABLE 2
Fish species rarely recorded from Chesapeake Bay

COMMON NAME	SCIENTIFIC NAME	COMMON NAME	SCIENTIFIC NAME
agujon	*Tylosurus acus*	mojarra, slender	*Eucinostomus jonesi*
amberjack, lesser	*Seriola fasciata*	mojarra, tidewater	*Eucinostomus harengulus*
barbu	*Polydactylus virginicus*	parrotfish, blue	*Scarus coeruleus*
batfish, longnose	*Ogcocephalus corniger*	porcupinefish	*Diodon hystrix*
blenny, seaweed	*Parablennius marmoreus*	puffer, checkered	*Sphoeroides testudineus*
catfish, hardhead	*Arius felis*	raven, sea	*Hemitripterus americanus*
cero	*Scomberomorus regalis*	ray, spotted eagle	*Aetobatis narinari*
chub, Bermuda	*Kyphosus sectatrix*	salmon, coho	*Oncorhynchus kisutch*
chub, yellow	*Kyphosus incisor*	sargassumfish	*Histrio histrio*
cowfish, scrawled	*Lactophrys quadricornis*	searobin, bighead	*Prionotus tribulus*
crappie, white	*Pomoxis annularis*	searobin, leopard	*Prionotus scitulus*
dolphin	*Coryphaena hippurus*	shark, blacktip	*Carcharhinus limbatus*
eel, speckled worm	*Myrophis punctatus*	shark, lemon	*Negaprion brevirostris*
flounder, yellowtail	*Pleuronectes ferrugineus*	shark, nurse	*Ginglymostoma cirratum*
flyingfish, Atlantic	*Cypselurus melanurus*	shark, tiger	*Galeocerdo cuvier*
goatfish, dwarf	*Upeneus parvus*	sharksucker, whitefin	*Echeneis neucratoides*
goatfish, red	*Mullus auratus*	sleeper, fat	*Dormitator maculatus*
goby, clown	*Microgobius gulosus*	sunfish, ocean	*Mola mola*
goby, code	*Gobiosoma robustum*	threadfin, Atlantic	*Polydactylus octonemus*
grunt, white	*Haemulon plumieri*	tomtate	*Haemulon aurolineatum*
hake, white	*Urophycis tenuis*	torpedo, Atlantic	*Torpedo nobiliana*
halibut, Atlantic	*Hippoglossus hippoglossus*	tuna, bluefin	*Thunnus thynnus*
marlinsucker	*Remora osteochir*	walleye	*Stizostedion vitreum*
mojarra, flagfin	*Eucinostomus melanopterus*	whalesucker	*Remora australis*

NOTE: The fish species listed here have been recorded from Chesapeake Bay, but in many instances their occurrence has been reported only once. A specimen that validates such an occurrence may or may not exist. Species listed here are not expected to be found in the bay in any abundance or with any regularity.

labeled "a" and "b." For example, begin with couplet 1 of the key to the orders, and read the choices (be sure to read both choices before reaching a conclusion). Select the "a" or "b" choice that best describes your fish, and proceed as indicated by the notation at the end of the choice. If that notation is a number, proceed in the same key to the couplet with that number, and make a choice as before. If the notation is the name of an order, then proceed to the indicated text page and continue your identification process in the key to the families of that order. Likewise, when you have successfully identified the family to which your fish belongs, proceed to the appropriate key to the species of that family and continue the process until your couplet selection yields the common and scientific names of a species and the page number of the species account. Note that when a family is represented by a single species in Chesapeake Bay waters, the common and scientific names of the species and the page number of the species account are provided in the family key, and no key to the species of the family is given.

If you have accurately compared the characters of your fish with those in the key couplets, your fish is correctly identified when you reach the species names. Your identification can be verified by referring to the more extensive description in the species account and to the illustration(s) provided. An additional tip: If neither choice within a couplet seems to match your specimen, or if the species account or illustration does not correspond to your fish, work backward through your couplet choices to ensure that you have correctly read each couplet and properly interpreted the characters in your specimen. If this process returns you to the same impasse, then follow each of the two choices in turn. Usually one of them will be quickly revealed as the wrong path. If you believe you have correctly followed the key but your fish does not accurately match all the characteristics of the identified species, then your fish may be new to the bay.

Please consult another identification guide or bring your fish to the attention of someone who specializes in the study of Chesapeake Bay fishes.

Morphology

In order to identify fishes, you must know something about their structure, especially the parts used in classification. The following general morphological terms apply to all animals.

> *Anterior*—in front of; the front end of the body or structure
> *Posterior*—behind; the back end of the body or structure
> *Dorsal*—toward, near, or pertaining to the back or upper surface
> *Ventral*—toward, near, or pertaining to the underpart or lower surface
> *Lateral*—toward, near, or pertaining to the side
> *Medial*—toward, near, or pertaining to the middle

The technical terms and principal measurements most commonly used in the identification of fishes are illustrated in Figures 2–5.

Fishes have both paired and unpaired (median) fins. In sharks, skates, and rays, the fins are covered by thick skin such that the skeletal supports are not visible without dissection. The skeletal supports in the fins of bony fishes, however, are easily visible and may be present as hard pointed spines, as flexible segmented rays, or as both. The number of spines and/or rays in a given fin is frequently a useful diagnostic character. The pectoral and pelvic fins, when present, are paired. The pectoral fins are usually located laterally near the gill openings, and the pelvic fins along the belly. Variations in the length and shape of these fins are useful characters in identification, as is the placement of the pelvic fins. The position of the pelvic fins is termed abdominal when they are inserted near the anus, thoracic when they are inserted near or directly ventral to the pectoral fins, and jugular when they are inserted anterior to the pectoral fins. The unpaired fins of fishes consist of the dorsal, anal, and caudal fins. The dorsal fin extends along the midline of the back and may be divided into several parts. A singular adipose fin or a series of finlets may be present posterior to the dorsal fin in some fishes. The adipose fin is fleshy and without spines or rays, whereas finlets are supported by a single soft ray. The anal fin is located along the ventral midline just posterior to the anus. The tail usually terminates in a caudal fin. There are many variations in the shape of the caudal fin. Based on the arrangement of the internal bony support, the caudal fin of most fishes may be categorized as either heterocercal or homocercal. In the heterocercal tail, the vertebral column extends into the upper portion of the fin, and the fin is asymmetrical, usually with the upper lobe much larger than the lower. In sharks and sturgeons the caudal fin is strongly heterocercal. The abbreviate heterocercal (hemicercal) tail found in the bowfin and in gars is less easily distinguished. Homocercal caudal fins have a variety of shapes but are typically symmetrical or nearly so, and the vertebral column does not extend into the tail.

The scales of bony fishes serve as an important tool in identification. Their presence or absence, type, and number along a given line are frequently utilized. The types of scales differentiated in these keys are ganoid, cycloid, and ctenoid. Ganoid scales are hard, thick, rhomboid or diamond-shaped, and barely overlapping. Cycloid scales are smooth, thin, rounded, and overlapping. Ctenoid scales are similar to cycloid scales, but the exposed portion of ctenoid scales bears tiny spines called ctenii. Ctenoid scales usually feel rough to the touch. Some bony fishes have an axillary scale, or axillary process, at the base of the pectoral and pelvic fins.

The head of a fish includes the gill region and corresponds to the head, neck, and throat of higher vertebrates. Many diagnostic characters are found in the head region. The snout is that portion of the head projecting forward from the anterior rim of the eye. It contains the nostrils, which are a pair of blind pits that detect odors. Each nostril usually has two openings, but in some fishes only one aperture is present. The upper jaw is ventral to the snout and in bony fishes comprises several paired bones. The front

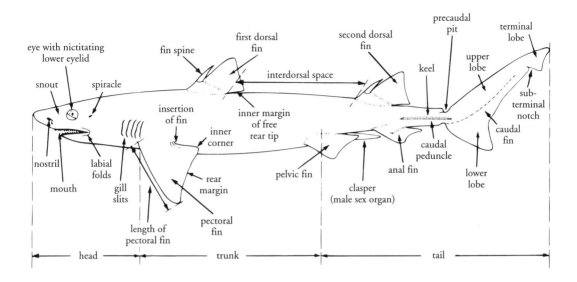

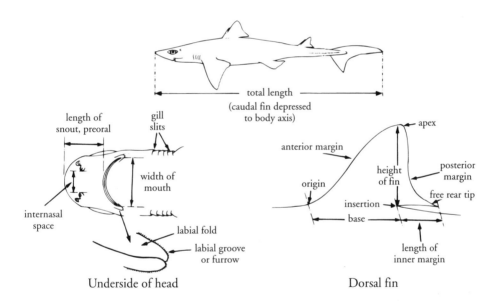

FIGURE 2. Technical terms and principal measurements for sharks.

pair are the premaxillae, which are followed by the spatula-shaped maxillae. A splintlike bone, the supra-maxilla, may be present on the upper edge of the maxilla. The lower jaw, or mandible, consists of several bones, the largest being paired dentary bones. In some bony fishes a prominent bone, the gular plate, is present ventrally between the arms of the lower jaw. Some fishes may have fleshy, threadlike structures called barbels around the mouth and snout regions of the head.

The gill area is an important region for fish differentiation. In sharks, skates, and rays each gill chamber has a separate opening to the outside, whereas the gills of bony fishes are usually enclosed in a

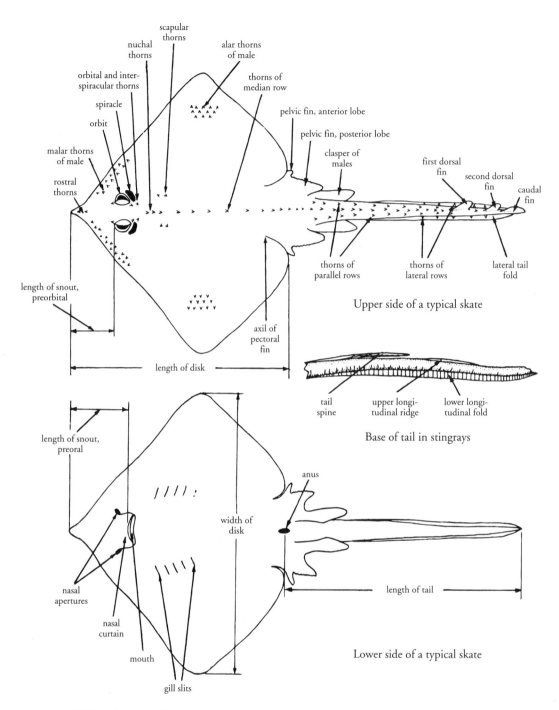

scapular
thorns

nuchal
thorns

alar thorns
of male

orbital and inter-
spiracular thorns

thorns of
median row

spiracle

pelvic fin, anterior lobe

orbit

pelvic fin, posterior lobe

malar thorns
of male

clasper of
males

first dorsal
fin

second dorsal
fin

rostral
thorns

caudal
fin

thorns of
parallel rows

thorns of
lateral rows

lateral tail
fold

length of snout,
preorbital

Upper side of a typical skate

axil of
pectoral
fin

length of disk

tail
spine

upper longi-
tudinal ridge

lower longi-
tudinal fold

Base of tail in stingrays

length of snout,
preoral

anus

width of
disk

nasal
apertures

length of tail

nasal
curtain

mouth

Lower side of a typical skate

gill slits

FIGURE 3. Technical terms and
principal measurements for skates
and rays.

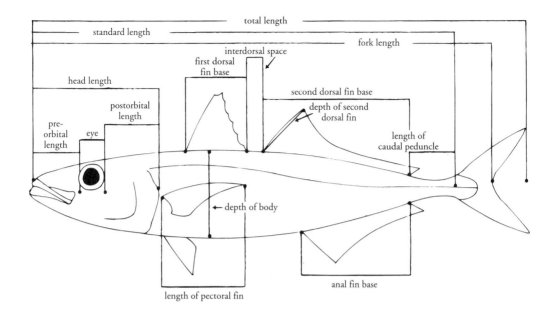

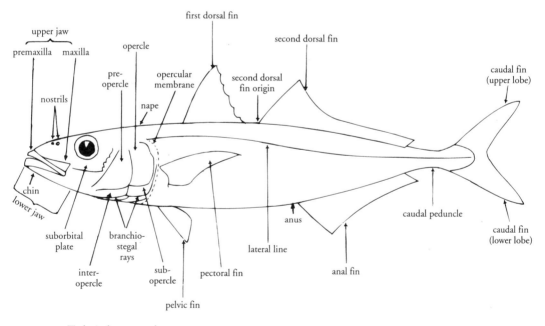

FIGURE 4. Technical terms and principal measurements for bony fishes.

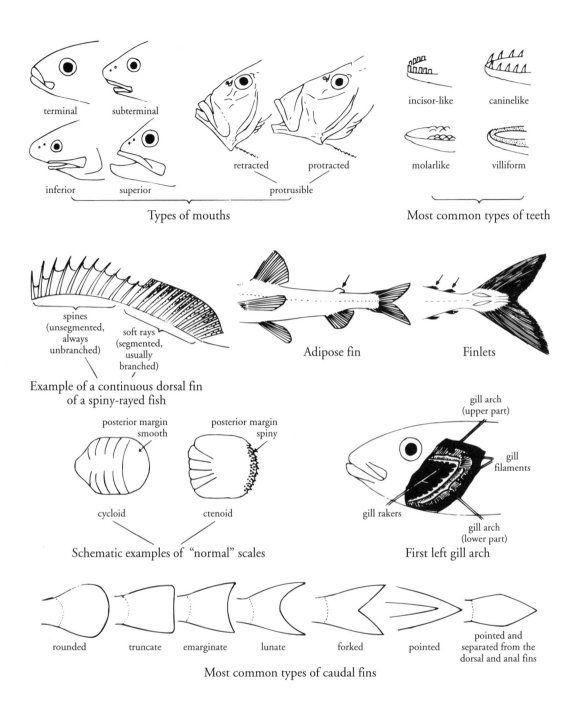

terminal subterminal

inferior superior

retracted protracted

protrusible

Types of mouths

incisor-like caninelike

molarlike villiform

Most common types of teeth

spines
(unsegmented,
always
unbranched)

soft rays
(segmented,
usually
branched)

Example of a continuous dorsal fin
of a spiny-rayed fish

Adipose fin

Finlets

posterior margin
smooth

posterior margin
spiny

cycloid ctenoid

Schematic examples of "normal" scales

gill arch
(upper part)

gill
filaments

gill rakers

gill arch
(lower part)

First left gill arch

rounded truncate emarginate lunate forked pointed pointed and
separated from the
dorsal and anal fins

Most common types of caudal fins

FIGURE 5. Examples of anatomical features in bony fishes.

chamber covered by a bony flap called the opercle, or operculum. The preopercular bone is located just anterior to the opercle. A thin membrane supported by a series of slender bones called branchiostegal rays connects the lower edge of the opercle to a region of the throat called the isthmus. This branchiostegal membrane may be nearly free from the isthmus or broadly joined. The gill chamber is located internal to the opercle and contains the gills. Each set of gills comprises a pair of bony arches (pharyngeal arches) that support a double row of red gill filaments on their outer edge and a row of knobby, hairy, or finger-like structures called gill rakers on their inner edge. Gill rakers range in shape from knoblike bumps to filamentous hairs. The number of gill rakers and their shape and size are useful in the identification of many fishes.

Fishes have an external set of sensory structures collectively known as the lateral line system. The most obvious part of this system is a series of pores extending in a line along the sides of the trunk and tail. The presence or absence, as well as the configuration, of the lateral line system is useful in identification.

Basic Counts and Measurements

The number of fin spines or rays is frequently used as a diagnostic character. For the purpose of this key, spines are unpaired structures without segmentation. They are usually stiff but may be rudimentary or flexible. Rays are usually branched, flexible, and segmented. When a fin contains both spines and rays, the spines are always anterior to the rays. In the dorsal and anal fins, the last two rays are usually close together and appear to arise from a single origin. These two rays are conventionally counted as a single ray. When counting the rays of paired fins, include the smallest ray at the lower or inner end of the fin base. This count may sometimes require some dissection to be accurate.

The most common scale count used in this book is the number of scales along the lateral line or along an imaginary line in the position that would normally be occupied by a typical lateral line. The count originates with the scale touching the shoulder girdle and ends at the base of the caudal fin. The base of the caudal fin is determined by the presence of a crease that is clearly visible when the tail is bent to either side. Lateral line scales behind the crease are not counted, and if a scale lies directly over the crease, it is not counted if the middle of the scale is posterior to the crease.

Gill raker counts are made on the first gill arch and may consist of all gill rakers or only those on the upper or lower limb, as designated in the key. Gill rakers that straddle the angle of the gill arch are included in the count for the lower limb. All rudimentary rakers are included in the count unless stated otherwise.

The most common measurements called for in this book are standard length, total length, fork length, head length, and body depth. The type of length measurement that is used to describe a fish often depends on the particular characteristics of the fish in question. Standard length (SL) is the greatest distance in a straight line from the tip of the snout to the base of the caudal fin. Total length (TL) is the greatest distance in a straight line from the tip of the snout to the posteriormost tip of the caudal fin. Fork length (FL) is the distance from the tip of the snout to the midpoint of the caudal fin margin. Head length is the greatest distance from the tip of the snout to the posteriormost point of the opercular membrane. Body depth is the greatest vertical distance in a straight line exclusive of fins or any fleshy or scaly structure associated with fin bases.

Other terms used in the text and keys may be found in the glossary or in a standard dictionary.

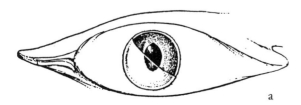

Key to the Orders
of Chesapeake Bay Fishes

Most of the orders treated in this key are morphologically diverse and are distributed worldwide. In many cases, the universal defining traits involve internal characteristics that require considerable amounts of knowledge and specimen preparation to evaluate. To make the key accessible to persons who have limited familiarity with fish anatomy or who lack the tools to use internal characteristics, we have limited the key characteristics to those that require minimal use of magnification and no dissection. The user should be aware that, by so limiting the characteristics, we have necessarily restricted the utility of the key to the species that inhabit Chesapeake Bay.

1a. Jaws absent; mouth in form of roundish, funnellike opening with horny, conical teeth; paired fins (pectoral and pelvic fins) absent; 7 pairs of gill openings present . . . . **lampreys—Petromyzontiformes** (p. 21)
1b. Jaws present; mouth not as above; paired fins present (1 or 2 pairs); fewer than 7 pairs of gill openings present **2**

2a. Single pair of gill openings present . . . . **(bony fishes) 11**
2b. Five pairs of gill openings present . . . . **(sharks, skates, and rays) 3**

3a. Gill openings located on lateral surface of head. **4**
3b. Gill openings located on ventral surface of head. **7**

4a. Anal fin absent; 1 stout anterior spine present on each dorsal fin . . . . **dogfish sharks—Squaliformes** (p. 34)
4b. Anal fin present; spines absent on dorsal fins. **5**

5a. Mouth entirely anterior to eye. . . **nurse sharks—Orectolobiformes: Ginglymostomatidae** (p. 283)
5b. Mouth terminating posterior to eye **6**

6a. Eye with nictitating membrane (Figure 6a) . . . . **ground sharks—Carcharhiniformes** (p. 25)
6b. Eye without nictitating membrane (Figure 6b) . . . . **mackerel sharks—Lamniformes** (p. 22)

FIGURE 6. *(a)* Eye of hammer-head shark, with nictitating membrane; *(b)* eye of smooth dogfish, which lacks nictitating membrane.

a   b

7a. Snout in form of flat blade with lateral teeth . . . . **sawfishes—Pristiformes** (p. 36)
7b. Snout not in form of flat blade with lateral teeth **8**

8a. Front margin of pectoral fin not fused to body (body sharklike); mouth terminal . . . .
. . . . **angel sharks—Squatiniformes** (p. 35)
8b. Front margin of pectoral fin fused to body (body raylike); mouth ventral (except in manta ray) . . . **9**

9a. Dorsal fin absent or single dorsal fin present; caudal fin absent; elongate serrated spine present on tail
(except in manta ray and smooth butterfly ray) . . . . . . **rays and mantas—Myliobatiformes** (p. 42)
9b. Two dorsal fins present; caudal fin usually present (may be obscure in some large skates); elongate
serrated spine absent on tail **10**

10a. Snout rounded; disk thick at margins, nearly circular . . . .
. . . . **electric rays—Torpediniformes: Torpedinidae** (p. 284)
10b. Snout pointed or forming pronounced angle; disk thin at margins, not circular . . . .
. . . . **skates—Rajiformes** (p. 37)

11a. Caudal fin heterocercal or abbreviate heterocercal **12**
11b. Caudal fin absent or not heterocercal **14**

12a. Caudal fin strongly heterocercal; 5 longitudinal rows of bony scutes present on body; snout projecting, with 4 ventral barbels; mouth ventral, with teeth absent or poorly developed . . . .
. . . . **sturgeons—Acipenseriformes** (p. 53)
12b. Caudal fin abbreviate heterocercal; scutes absent; snout not projecting; barbels absent; mouth termi-
nal, with teeth well developed **13**

13a. Jaws very elongate, with many small needlelike teeth; body covered with hard diamond-shaped scales;
dorsal fin short, located near caudal fin . . . . **gars—Lepisosteiformes** (p. 56)
13b. Jaws not elongate; body with cycloid scales; dorsal fin long, extending more than half the body length
. . . . **bowfins—Amiiformes** (p. 57)

14a. Both eyes on same side of head . . . . **flatfishes—Pleuronectiformes** (p. 269)
14b. Eyes bilateral **15**

15a. Body eellike **16**
15b. Body not eellike **17**

16a. Pelvic fin absent . . . . **eels—Anguilliformes** (p. 62)
16b. Pelvic fin present, far forward, and barbellike in appearance . . . **cusk-eels—Ophidiiformes** (p. 115)

17a. Adipose fin present **18**
17b. Adipose fin absent **20**

18a. Barbels present on head; spines present in dorsal and pectoral fins . . . .
. . . . **catfishes—Siluriformes** (p. 90)
18b. Barbels absent; spines absent in fins **19**

19a. Dorsal fin origin dorsoanterior to pelvic fin insertion . . . .
. . . . **salmon, trouts, and pickerels—Salmoniformes** (p. 97)
19b. Dorsal fin origin dorsoposterior to pelvic fin insertion . . . . **lizardfishes—Aulopiformes** (p. 79)

20a. Dorsal fin and/or anal fin with 1 or more spines **21**
20b. Dorsal fin and anal fin without apparent spines **29**

21a. Pelvic fin absent or represented by midventral spine or tubercle **22**
21b. Pelvic fin present **23**

22a. Gill opening in form of small vertical slit anterior to and approximately as long as pectoral fin base . . . . **puffers and triggerfishes—Tetraodontiformes** (p. 260)

22b. Gill opening typically much longer than pectoral fin base. . . . . **perchlike fishes, in part—Perciformes** (p. 147)

23a. Pelvic fin jugular in position, well anterior to pectoral fin **24**

23b. Pelvic fin thoracic or abdominal in position, perpendicular or posterior to pectoral fin **25**

24a. Anteriormost dorsal spine free, located on head, and tipped with esca (angling bait); gill opening in form of small hole located in pectoral fin axil . . . . **goosefishes—Lophiiformes** (p. 108)

24b. Dorsal spines stout and short, located on body, and not formed into angling device; gill opening located anterior to pectoral fin base; pectoral fin axil with small opening into blind pouch . . . . **toadfishes—Batrachoidiformes** (p. 106)

25a. More than 6 total elements (spines plus rays) present in each pelvic fin. . . . . **squirrelfishes—Beryciformes** (p. 133)

25b. Six or fewer elements present in each pelvic fin. **26**

26a. Spiny stay present on cheek below eye (extension of third infraorbital bone); pectoral fin greatly enlarged (except in lumpsuckers). . . . **searobins and sculpins—Scorpaeniformes, in part** (p. 141)

26b. Spiny stay absent on cheek below eye; pectoral fin typically not greatly enlarged. **27**

27a. First dorsal fin composed of 2–6 stout unconnected spines that are remote from second dorsal fin; pelvic fin subabdominal, with 1 stout spine and 0–2 rays . . . . **sticklebacks—Gasterosteiformes** (p. 134)

27b. Dorsal spines connected by membrane or, if unconnected, contiguous to remaining dorsal elements; pelvic fin abdominal to thoracic, usually with 1 spine and 5 rays (the combtooth blennies—Perciformes: Blenniidae—are a notable exception). **28**

28a. Pectoral fin high on body, with base mostly dorsal to lateral midline; pelvic fin abdominal; lateral line absent; body with prominent midlateral silvery stripe . . . . . . **silversides—Atheriniformes** (p. 130)

28b. Pectoral fin low on body, with base mostly or entirely ventral to lateral midline; pelvic fin thoracic; lateral line variously developed but present; body without prominent midlateral silvery stripe . . . . **perchlike fishes, in part—Perciformes** (p. 147)

29a. Mouth located at end of long, tubelike snout; body encased in series of bony rings; pelvic fin absent . . . . **pipefishes and cornetfishes—Syngnathiformes** (p. 137)

29b. Mouth not located at end of elongate snout; body not encased in bony rings; pelvic fin present **30**

30a. Elongate scale present in axil of pelvic and pectoral fins. **31**

30b. Elongate scale absent in axil of pelvic and pectoral fins **35**

31a. Bony gular plate present on underside of head between arms of lower jaw . . . . **tarpons and tenpounders—Elopiformes** (p. 59)

31b. Bony gular plate absent or not externally visible. **32**

32a. Belly with sharp-angled keel formed by median row of scutes. . . . . **shads and herrings—Clupeiformes, in part** (p. 65)

32b. Belly rounded, without median row of scutes **33**

33a. Mouth terminal or superior, with snout not overhanging . . . . **round herrings—Clupeiformes, in part** (p. 65)

33b. Mouth inferior, with snout overhanging **34**

34a. Mouth very large, extending almost to posterior limit of head; side with prominent midlateral silvery stripe . . . . **anchovies—Clupeiformes, in part** (p. 65)

34b. Mouth small, not extending as far as eye; side without prominent midlateral silvery stripe . . . . **bonefishes—Albuliformes** (p. 58)

35a. Belly with sucking disk partially or completely formed from pelvic fin **36**

35b. Belly without sucking disk **37**

36a. Head dorsoventrally flattened; body not globose or triangular in cross section; scales or tubercles absent on body . . . . **clingfishes—Gobiesociformes** (p. 107)

36b. Head not flattened; body globose and triangular in cross section; skin with bony tubercles or dermal warts . . . . **lumpsuckers—Scorpaeniformes, in part** (p. 145)

37a. Pelvic fin jugular or thoracic in position, typically more anterior than pectoral fin . . . . **cods and hakes—Gadiformes** (p. 110)

37b. Pelvic fin abdominal in position, well posterior to pectoral fin **38**

38a. Lower jaw or both jaws greatly elongated to form beak . . . . **needlefishes and halfbeaks—Beloniformes** (p. 116)

38b. Neither jaw elongated to form beak **39**

39a. Caudal fin rounded or truncate; lower jaw projecting; teeth present in jaws . . . . **killifishes and livebearers—Cyprinodontiformes** (p. 121)

39b. Caudal fin bilobed; lower jaw not projecting; teeth absent in jaws . . . . **suckers and minnows—Cypriniformes** (p. 80)

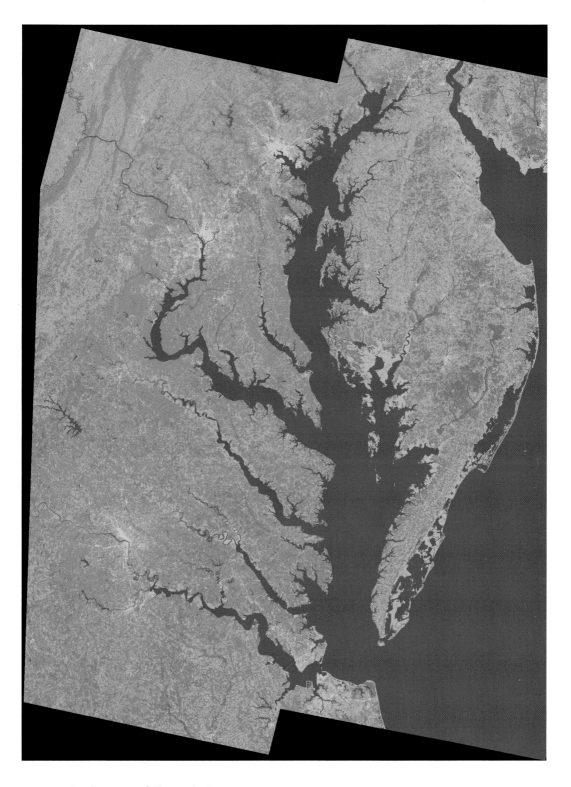

PLATE 1. Landsat image of Chesapeake Bay.

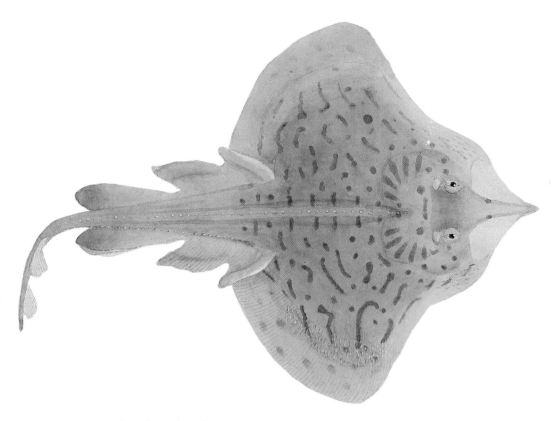

PLATE 2. Clearnose skate, *Raja eglanteria*.

PLATE 3. American eel, *Anguilla rostrata.*

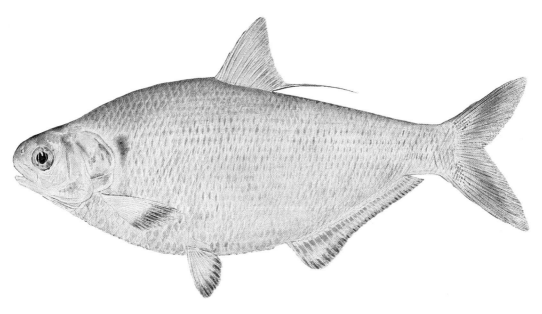

PLATE 4. Gizzard shad, *Dorosoma cepedianum.*

PLATE 5. Atlantic herring, *Clupea harengus.*

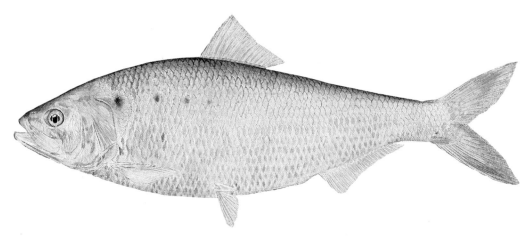

PLATE 6. American shad, *Alosa sapidissima.*

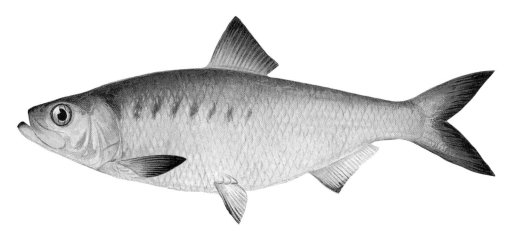

PLATE 7. Hickory shad, *Alosa mediocris.*

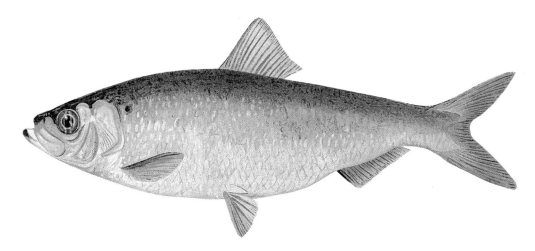

PLATE 8. Alewife, *Alosa pseudoharengus.*

PLATE 9. White sucker, *Catostomus commersoni.*

PLATE 10. Goldfish, *Carassius auratus*.

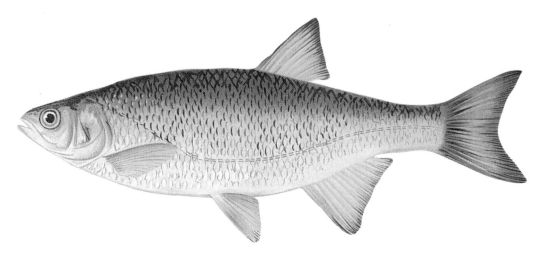

PLATE 11. Golden shiner, *Notemigonus crysoleucas*.

PLATE 12. Flathead catfish, *Pylodictis olivaris.*

PLATE 13. Yellow bullhead, *Ameiurus natalis.*

PLATE 14. Brown bullhead, *Ameiurus nebulosus.*

PLATE 15. Oyster toadfish, *Opsanus tau*.

PLATE 16. Pollock, *Pollachius virens*.

PLATE 17. Silver hake, *Merluccius bilinearis.*

a

b

PLATE 18. Striped killifish, *Fundulus majalis: (a)* male, *(b)* female.

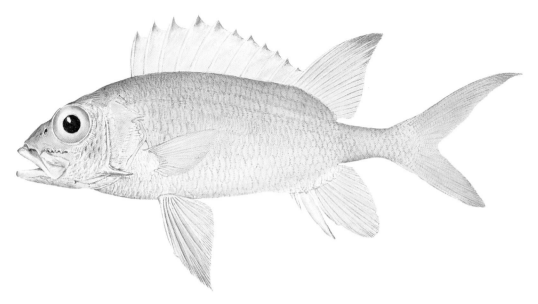

PLATE 19. Squirrelfish, *Holocentrus adscensionis.*

PLATE 20. Northern searobin, *Pr̲ ̲ ̲s carolinus.*

PLATE 21. Longhorn sculpin, *Myoxocephalus octodecemspinosus.*

PLATE 22. Butterfish, *Peprilus triacanthus.*

PLATE 23. Crevalle jack, *Caranx hippos.*

PLATE 24. Banded rudderfish, *Seriola zonata* (juvenile).

PLATE 25. Florida pompano, *Trachinotus carolinus.*

PLATE 26. Chub mackerel, *Scomber japonicus.*

PLATE 27. Spanish mackerel, *Scomberomorus maculatus.*

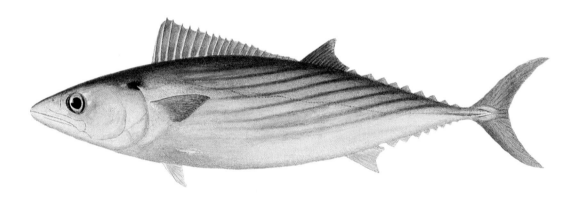

PLATE 28. Atlantic bonito, *Sarda sarda.*

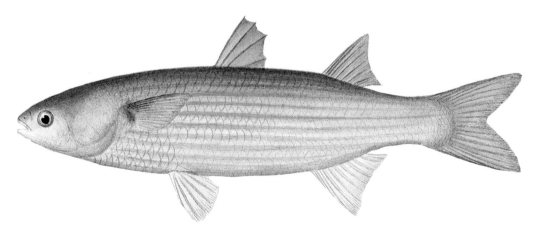

PLATE 29. Striped mullet, *Mugil cephalus.*

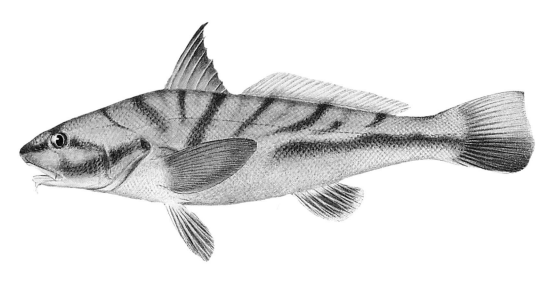

PLATE 30. Northern kingfish, *Menticirrhus saxatilis.*

PLATE 31. Weakfish, *Cynoscion regalis.*

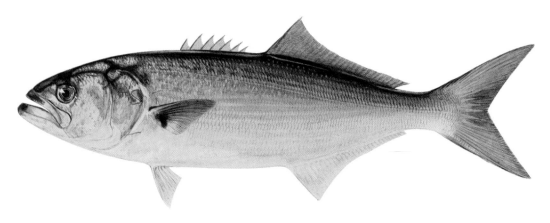

PLATE 32. Bluefish, *Pomatomus saltatrix.*

PLATE 33. White perch, *Morone americana.*

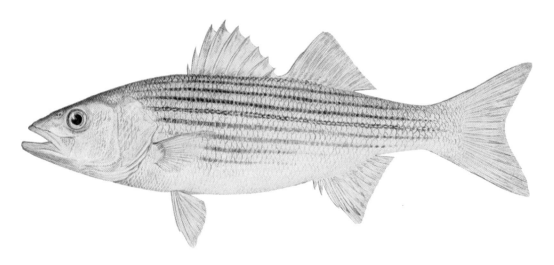

PLATE 34. Striped bass, *Morone saxatilis*.

PLATE 35. Yellow perch, *Perca flavescens*.

PLATE 36. Scup, *Stenotomus chrysops.*

PLATE 37. Sheepshead, *Archosargus probatocephalus.*

PLATE 38. Gray snapper, *Lutjanus griseus*.

PLATE 39. Bigeye, *Priacanthus arenatus*.

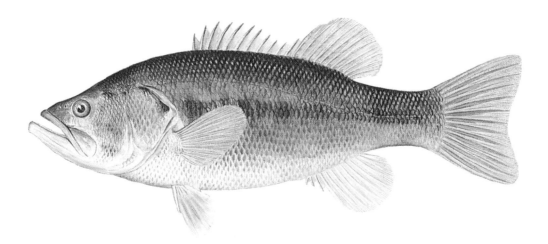

PLATE 40. Largemouth bass, *Micropterus salmoides.*

PLATE 41. Smallmouth bass, *Micropterus dolomieu.*

PLATE 42. Bluegill, *Lepomis macrochirus.*

PLATE 43. Cunner, *Tautogolabrus adspersus.*

PLATE 44. Tautog, *Tautoga onitis.*

PLATE 45. Black sea bass, *Centropristis striata.*

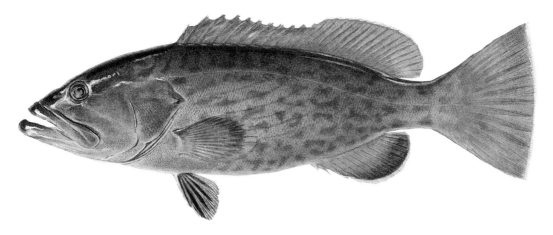

PLATE 46. Gag, *Mycteroperca microlepis.*

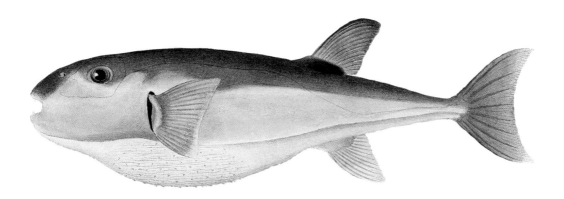

PLATE 47. Smooth puffer, *Lagocephalus laevigatus.*

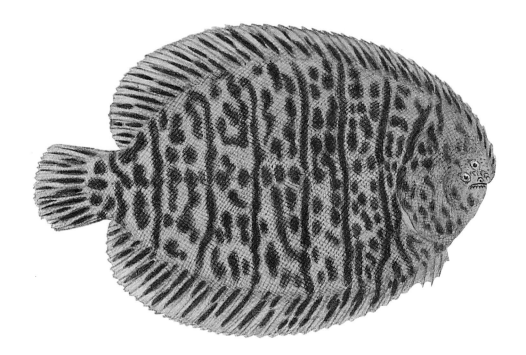

PLATE 48. Hogchoker, *Trinectes maculatus.*

PLATE 49. Winter flounder, *Pleuronectes americanus.*

Species Accounts
by Order and Family

Lampreys
ORDER PETROMYZONTIFORMES

The lamprey order contains a single family, which occurs in Chesapeake Bay.

Lampreys
FAMILY PETROMYZONTIDAE

Lampreys are primitive fishes that lack true bone. They are eel-shaped, cylindrical anteriorly and compressed posteriorly. The mouth is jawless and circular. Lampreys can be either parasitic or nonparasitic. The parasitic forms may be either freshwater or anadromous, whereas the nonparasitic lampreys are confined to freshwater. Anadromous forms have become landlocked in some instances. There are 9 genera and 31 species of lampreys worldwide, with 1 species recorded from Chesapeake Bay waters.

Sea lamprey
Petromyzon marinus Linnaeus, 1758

FIGURE 7. Sea lamprey, *Petromyzon marinus.*

KEY FEATURES Pointed teeth arranged in concentric circles in suctorial mouth; dorsal fin with obvious notch, separated into 2 lobes; pectoral and pelvic fins absent; anal fin represented by small fold.

OTHER CHARACTERISTICS Head depressed; body cylindrical anteriorly and compressed posteriorly; dorsal and anal fins continuous with caudal fin; origin of dorsal fin just posterior to midpoint of body; eye of moderate size; gill openings represented by 7 pairs of small lateral clefts. Brown or black mottling present dorsally; whitish or gray ventrally. Maximum adult size 84 cm SL (2.8 ft).

GEOGRAPHIC DISTRIBUTION Inhabiting the northern Atlantic coasts of Europe and North America, extending from Labrador to Florida in the western Atlantic. Although native to Lake

Ontario, the sea lamprey has extended its range to the other Great Lakes by way of ship canals.

ECOLOGY   Adult sea lampreys are parasitic on a variety of fishes and marine mammals and attach themselves by means of their suctorial mouth. Although sea lampreys are called parasites, their attacks are typically fatal to the prey. Sea lampreys are size-selective predators that actively seek the largest individuals of a species. Once attached, a sea lamprey opens wounds on its prey's skin with its rasping tongue and sharp teeth, sucking out blood and other bodily tissue. This lamprey is anadromous, ascending freshwaters in Maryland and Virginia from March to June to locate suitable spawning grounds. The female sea lamprey deposits numerous small eggs in nests constructed by males. Once spawning is complete, the adults soon die. Larvae (ammocoetes) spend 4–5 years in freshwater, feeding on microscopic plankton. Metamorphosis of sea lampreys from the larval to the juvenile stage occurs between July and November when larvae reach lengths of 11–16 cm (4.3–6.3 in). Metamorphosis is typically followed by migration out of the river system into the estuary or coastal marine environment. In the following spring and summer, juvenile anadromous sea lampreys return to rivers primarily as parasites of anadromous fishes. Smaller sea lampreys ($<$40 cm, or $<$1.3 ft) typically are bottom dwellers along coasts and out on the continental shelf. Larger sea lampreys ($\geq$40 cm, or $\geq$1.3 ft) typically occur along the edge of the shelf and over the continental slope. Anadromous sea lampreys larger than 40 cm (1.3 ft) occur in freshwater essentially only as nonfeeding adults during their spawning migration. Sea lampreys can live for at least 8 years.

FISHING INTEREST   None, except as a potential threat to species that are recreationally or commercially important in the Chesapeake Bay region. Invasion of the Great Lakes by the sea lamprey resulted in the decimation of important fish stocks in the 1950s. Restocking and widespread application of lamprey-specific pesticides corrected this situation in the 1960s. Although the sea lamprey is probably present in all major drainages of Chesapeake Bay during its spring spawning period, it is not present in sufficient numbers to be a major destructive force, even though it has been found attached to Atlantic menhaden, bluefish, and weakfish.

LITERATURE   Hildebrand and Schroeder 1928:43; Musick 1972; Eddy and Underhill 1978; Manooch 1984; Beamish and Medland 1988; Swink 1990, 1991; Halliday 1991; Jenkins and Burkhead 1994; Nelson 1994.

Mackerel Sharks
ORDER LAMNIFORMES

The order of mackerel sharks contains five families, of which two occur in Chesapeake Bay.

KEY TO THE FAMILIES OF MACKEREL SHARKS IN CHESAPEAKE BAY

1a. Strong keel present on caudal peduncle . . . . **basking sharks—Cetorhinidae** (p. 22)
1b. Keel absent on caudal peduncle . . . . **sand tigers—Odontaspididae** (p. 24)

Basking Sharks
FAMILY CETORHINIDAE

Basking sharks are very large, plankton-feeding, pelagic sharks. They are characterized by having five extremely long gill slits, a strong caudal keel, and a nearly symmetrical caudal fin. Slow but strong swimmers, basking sharks are found in boreal and warm-temperate waters. Although they filter their food by means of their gill rakers, basking sharks possess numerous minute teeth. Basking sharks reach an imposing size but nevertheless are no threat to humans. The family is monotypic, with the single species being found worldwide.

Basking shark
Cetorhinus maximus (Gunnerus, 1765)

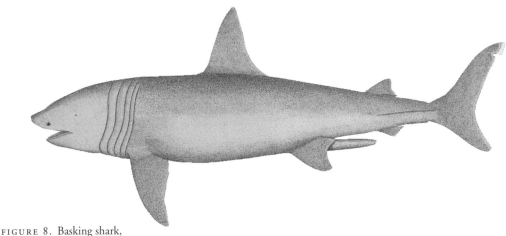

FIGURE 8. Basking shark,
Cetorhinus maximus.

KEY FEATURES   Five exceptionally large gill slits present, almost meeting dorsally; gill rakers long and bristlelike; caudal fin nearly symmetrical; caudal peduncle with strong keel on each side.

OTHER CHARACTERISTICS   Head long; snout conical and pointed; eye circular and relatively small; mouth very large, with numerous minute hooked teeth; trunk fusiform and stout; first dorsal fin triangular and located near midbody; second dorsal fin much smaller than first and with strongly concave posterior margin; caudal fin with strong ventral lobe; anal fin similar in shape to second dorsal fin and located somewhat ventroposterior to second dorsal fin; pelvic fin about one-half the size of first dorsal fin and located perpendicular to midpoint between first and second dorsal fins; pectoral fin large and originating immediately posterior to fifth gill slit. Grayish brown to gray or black dorsally; same or paler ventrally. Maximum adult size probably 10 m TL (33 ft); however, reports of basking sharks as long as 15 m TL (50 ft) are known. The basking shark is the second-largest shark (the whale shark, *Rhincodon typus,* is the largest).

GEOGRAPHIC DISTRIBUTION   Found coastally in cold to cooler waters of all oceans and seas.

ECOLOGY   Although primarily a boreal coastal species, the basking shark occasionally ventures inshore and enters large bays such as the Chesapeake. Sightings of the basking shark in Chesapeake Bay are usually during the early spring. The basking shark is so named because it is often observed swimming and feeding at the water's surface. Basking sharks are highly migratory, moving northward along the east coast of the United States with the vernal warming of the western Atlantic. The basking shark feeds by filtering planktonic organisms as it swims with its mouth agape and its gills distended. Gatherings of as many as 100 basking sharks have been reported; however, sightings of 1–3 individuals are more common. Dead and decomposing basking sharks occasionally wash up on beaches; it has been suggested that such carcasses may be the basis for certain "sea monster" stories. The basking shark is a live-bearer, and its size at birth is 1 m (3.3 ft) or greater.

FISHING INTEREST   Of no commercial or recreational value in the Chesapeake Bay area. Where the basking shark is more common, it is the subject of a small-scale harpoon fishery. The meat of the basking shark is used for human consumption, and the fins are used for soup. Its liver oil is used for tanning leather and as lamp oil, its hide for leather, and its carcass for fish meal. To its detriment, the basking shark shows no fright response to boats, and thus harpooners can approach it with impunity. Because of its long gesta-

tion period (3.5 years) and lengthy maturation (6–7 years), the basking shark is vulnerable to overfishing.

LITERATURE   Bigelow and Schroeder 1948; Musick 1972; Fischer 1978; Compagno 1984a.

Sand Tigers
FAMILY ODONTASPIDIDAE

Sand tigers are large slow sharks with a short head and a stout body that frequent tropical to cool-temperate waters. All species have two dorsal fins of about equal size. Sand tigers are known from inshore and deepwater areas of all seas and typically are bottom dwellers that feed on a variety of bony fishes, invertebrates, rays, and other sharks. Development is ovoviviparous. There are four species of sand tigers worldwide, with one species recorded from Chesapeake Bay waters.

Sand tiger
Odontaspis taurus (Rafinesque, 1810)

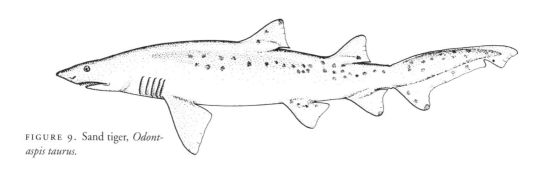

FIGURE 9. Sand tiger, *Odontaspis taurus.*

KEY FEATURES   Fifth (and last) gill slit markedly anterior to pectoral fin base; anterior teeth long, narrow, crooked, and unserrated; eye without nictitating fold or membrane.

OTHER CHARACTERISTICS   Body large and stout; mouth very long and angular, terminating posterior to eye; dorsal, anal, and pelvic fins about equal in size; first dorsal fin closer to pelvic fin than to pectoral fin. Light grayish brown dorsally; venter white; body often with dusky brown spots. Maximum adult size about 3.3 m TL (10 ft).

GEOGRAPHIC DISTRIBUTION   Known from the Atlantic and western Pacific oceans, as well as the Red Sea.

ECOLOGY   The sand tiger is a common visitor in the summer and fall to the lower Chesapeake

Bay, inhabiting shallow estuaries and coastal waters. This species is found most often on or near the bottom and is most active nocturnally, feeding primarily on small fishes, squids, and other sharks. The sand tiger is the principal predator of sandbar sharks in the vicinity of the bay mouth.

FISHING INTEREST   Caught often with hook and line.

ADDITIONAL REMARKS   The sand tiger looks dangerous because of its size and jagged teeth. However, no well-documented attacks on humans by this species have been reported. As with all sharks, it is best not to provoke the sand tiger.

LITERATURE   Musick 1972; Compagno 1984a; Robins et al. 1986.

Ground Sharks
ORDER CARCHARHINIFORMES

The order of ground sharks comprises eight families, three of which occur in Chesapeake Bay.

KEY TO THE FAMILIES OF GROUND SHARKS IN CHESAPEAKE BAY

1a. Head with lateral expansions or blades . . . . **hammerhead sharks—Sphyrnidae** (p. 25)
1b. Head normal, not expanded laterally **2**

2a. Precaudal pit present . . . . **requiem sharks—Carcharhinidae** (p. 29)
2b. Precaudal pit absent. . . . . **smoothhounds—Triakidae** (p. 33)

Hammerhead Sharks
FAMILY SPHYRNIDAE

The hammerhead sharks inhabit surface waters along tropical and warm-temperate coastlines. Hammerheads are easily distinguishable by the laterally expanded blades on the head, with the eyes located on the lateral edge of the blades. The lateral expansion of the head aids in maneuverability and provides forward lift. In addition, the expanded head may enhance bilateral sensory capacity. Hammerheads are versatile feeders that prey mainly on bony fishes, cephalopods, crustaceans, rays, and other sharks. Schools of hammerheads are common, sometimes consisting of hundreds of individuals. Development is viviparous. There are two genera and nine species of hammerheads worldwide, with one genus and three species recorded from Chesapeake Bay waters.

KEY TO THE SPECIES OF HAMMERHEAD SHARKS IN CHESAPEAKE BAY

1a. Head flattened dorsoventrally and shovel- or bonnet-shaped; anterior contour of head evenly rounded
at midline (Figure 10) . . . . **bonnethead, *Sphyrna tiburo*** (p. 26)
1b. Head broad and T-shaped; anterior contour of head moderately convex (Figure 11a,b) **2**

FIGURE 10. Ventral view of head of bonnethead.

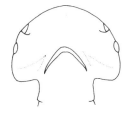

FIGURE 11. Ventral view of *(a)* head of scalloped hammerhead and *(b)* head of smooth hammerhead.

a   b

FIGURE 12. Lateral view of scalloped hammerhead.

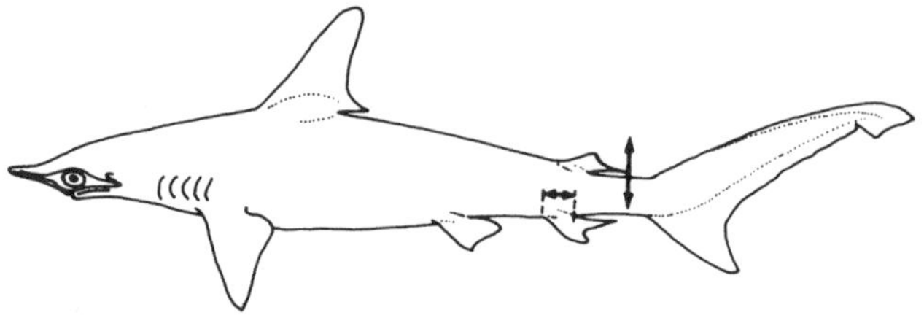

FIGURE 13. Lateral view of smooth hammerhead.

2a. Medial indentation present on anterior margin of snout; free rear tip of second dorsal fin nearly reaching origin of upper caudal fin; base of anal fin noticeably longer than base of second dorsal fin (Figure 12) . . . . **scalloped hammerhead,** *Sphyrna lewini* (p. 27)

2b. Medial indentation absent on anterior margin of snout; free rear tip of second dorsal fin terminating well anterior to origin of upper caudal fin; base of anal fin about as long as base of second dorsal fin (Figure 13) . . . . **smooth hammerhead,** *Sphyrna zygaena* (p. 28)

Bonnethead
Sphyrna tiburo (Linnaeus, 1758)

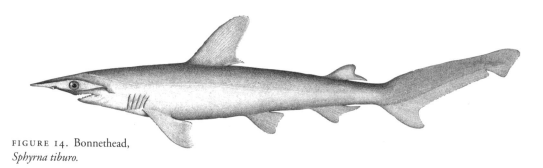

FIGURE 14. Bonnethead, *Sphyrna tiburo.*

KEY FEATURES   Head flattened dorsoventrally and shovel-shaped or bonnet-shaped; anterior contour of head evenly rounded at midline; inner narial grooves absent; lateral expansions of head relatively short.

OTHER CHARACTERISTICS   Body elongate and compressed; eye large; mouth strongly arched; teeth small and smooth-edged; first dorsal fin high, originating perpendicular to posterior tip of pectoral fin; second dorsal fin and anal fin about equal in height, but anal fin significantly longer; anal fin origin ventroanterior to origin of second dorsal fin; pelvic and pectoral fins with straight posterior margins. Gray or grayish brown dorsally; pale or almost white ventrally. Maximum adult size 1.5 m TL (5 ft).

GEOGRAPHIC DISTRIBUTION   Inhabiting both the western Atlantic and the eastern Pacific, ranging from New England to Argentina and from southern California to Ecuador.

ECOLOGY   Occasional summer visitors to the lower Chesapeake Bay, bonnetheads inhabit waters 10–25 m (30–82 ft) deep over sandy and muddy bottoms. In southern waters, where they are more common, bonnetheads are gregarious, and schools of a dozen individuals occur frequently. The bonnethead spends the nighttime hours on shallow grass flats, searching for nocturnally active invertebrate prey, and moves into deeper water during the day. Its food is primarily crustaceans such as crabs and shrimps.

FISHING INTEREST   Occasionally caught by shrimp trawls and trammel nets as well as by rod and reel.

LITERATURE   Hildebrand and Schroeder 1928:51; Musick 1972; Ellis 1975; Compagno 1984b; Parsons and Killam 1991.

Scalloped hammerhead
Sphyrna lewini (Griffith and Smith, 1834)

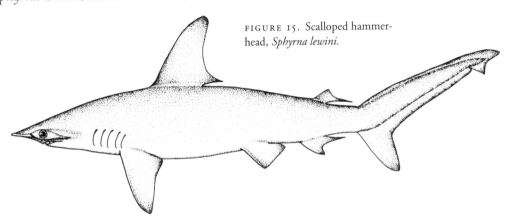

FIGURE 15. Scalloped hammerhead, *Sphyrna lewini.*

KEY FEATURES   Head very wide and T-shaped; anterior contour of head very broadly arched, with prominent medial and lateral indentations; inner narial grooves well developed; free rear tip of second dorsal fin nearly reaching origin of upper caudal fin; base of anal fin noticeably longer than base of second dorsal fin.

OTHER CHARACTERISTICS   Head greatly depressed and expanded laterally, but longitudinally short; body elongate and compressed; eye large; mouth strongly arched; teeth of upper jaw oblique; teeth of lower jaw erect and spiked; first dorsal fin high, originating perpendicular to posterior edge of pectoral fin; second dorsal fin small; anal fin with deeply concave posterior margin and slightly higher than second dorsal fin; pelvic fin with nearly straight posterior margin; pectoral fin broad. Brown to yellowish dorsally, shading to white ventrally; pectoral fin tipped with black or gray. Maximum adult size about 4.2 m TL (14 ft).

GEOGRAPHIC DISTRIBUTION   Inhabiting warm-temperate and tropical coastal waters of all oceans and seas. In the western Atlantic, the scalloped hammerhead is found from New Jersey to Brazil, including the Gulf of Mexico and the Caribbean Sea.

ECOLOGY   Although the scalloped hammerhead is common along the Virginia coast in summer, it rarely enters Chesapeake Bay. The only records of this species in the bay waters are from Kiptopeke/Cape Charles and near the bay mouth. This species spends the winter in the Gulf Stream from Cape Hatteras to Florida, then migrates to the continental shelf off Virginia in June. In autumn it migrates south along the coast, often in very shallow water, and feeds on migrating Atlantic menhaden, mullets, sciaenids, and flounders. Young individuals of this species often form large schools; adults sometimes congregate as well, particularly in winter and spring. The scalloped hammerhead feeds on a wide variety of fishes and invertebrates.

FISHING INTEREST   Utilized for human consumption where abundant. This species is landed with trawls, longlines, and handlines. On hook and line, the scalloped hammerhead is reported to be a dogged fighter.

ADDITIONAL REMARKS   The scalloped hammerhead is probably dangerous to humans and should be avoided. It is often confused with other large hammerhead sharks such as the smooth hammerhead.

LITERATURE   Compagno 1984b.

Smooth hammerhead
Sphyrna zygaena (Linnaeus, 1758)

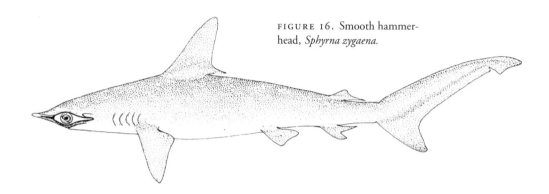

FIGURE 16. Smooth hammerhead, *Sphyrna zygaena*.

KEY FEATURES   Head very wide and T-shaped; anterior margin of head very broadly arched, with prominent lateral indentations; inner narial grooves well developed; free rear tip of second dorsal fin terminating well anterior to origin of upper caudal fin; second dorsal fin low, its height less than height of anal fin; base of anal fin about as long as base of second dorsal fin.

OTHER CHARACTERISTICS   Head greatly depressed and expanded laterally, but longitudinally short; body elongate and compressed; eye large; mouth strongly arched; teeth of both jaws oblique; first dorsal fin high, with origin dorsoanterior to posterior margin of pectoral fin; second dorsal fin with weakly concave posterior margin; anal fin with deeply notched posterior margin and slightly higher than second dorsal fin; pectoral and pelvic fins with straight or slightly concave posterior margin. Dusky gray dorsally; grayish white ventrally; underside of tip of pectoral fin dusky. Maximum adult size about 4.0 m TL (13 ft).

GEOGRAPHIC DISTRIBUTION   Inhabiting warm-temperate coastal waters of all oceans and seas and also known from certain tropical localities in the Atlantic, Pacific, and Indian oceans. In the western Atlantic, the smooth hammerhead is found from Nova Scotia to Florida, but it is not found in the Gulf of Mexico. It is also known from southern Brazil to southern Argentina.

ECOLOGY   The smooth hammerhead is a rare to occasional seasonal visitor to Chesapeake Bay, usually in the summer or fall, and has been recorded from as far north as the mouth of the Choptank River. The biology and distribution of the smooth hammerhead is not well known. Although it may generally be more of an inshore species than the scalloped hammerhead, the smooth hammerhead does occur in offshore waters. It is more tolerant of temperate waters than is the scalloped hammerhead. The smooth hammerhead feeds on a variety of bony fishes, as well as on rays and other sharks.

FISHING INTEREST   Utilized for human consumption where abundant. This species is landed with trawls, longlines, and handlines.

ADDITIONAL REMARKS   Large hammerhead sharks such as the smooth hammerhead have been reported in a small number of attacks on humans.

LITERATURE   Hildebrand and Schroeder 1928:50; Musick 1972; Compagno 1984b.

Requiem Sharks
FAMILY CARCHARHINIDAE

Requiem sharks are active, strong swimmers, occurring singly or in small to large schools. Many species are more active at night or at dawn and dusk than in the daytime. All species are voracious predators, feeding mainly on sharks, rays, bony fishes, turtles, seabirds, and occasionally even bottom-dwelling animals such as crabs. Development is either ovoviviparous or viviparous. The carcharhinids make up one of the largest families of sharks, comprising more than 80 species. Seven species of requiem sharks are recorded from Chesapeake Bay waters.

KEY TO THE SPECIES OF REQUIEM SHARKS IN CHESAPEAKE BAY

1a. Base of second dorsal fin at least three-fourths as long as base of first dorsal fin; dorsal fins nearly equal in size. . . . . **lemon shark,** *Negaprion brevirostris* (p. 283)

1b. Base of second dorsal fin considerably shorter than base of first dorsal fin. **2**

2a. Spiracle present. . . . . **tiger shark,** *Galeocerdo cuvier* (p. 283)

2b. Spiracle absent **3**

3a. Origin of second dorsal fin well dorsoposterior to origin of anal fin; posterior margin of anal fin straight or weakly concave . . . . **Atlantic sharpnose shark,** *Rhizoprionodon terraenovae* (p. 29)

3b. Origin of second dorsal fin typically nearly perpendicular to origin of anal fin; posterior margin of anal fin deeply concave or deeply notched **4**

4a. Midline of back between dorsal fins with low but distinct ridge of skin. **5**

4b. Midline of back between dorsal fins smooth, without ridge of skin **6**

5a. First dorsal fin very high and nearly triangular; origin of first dorsal fin far anterior, perpendicular to insertion of pectoral fin. . . . .**sandbar shark,** *Carcharhinus plumbeus* (p. 30)

5b. First dorsal fin moderate in height, with a broadly arched anterior margin; origin of first dorsal fin perpendicular to free rear tips of pectoral fin . . . . **dusky shark,** *Carcharhinus obscurus* (p. 31)

6a. Snout short and broadly rounded; fins without black tips . . **bull shark,** *Carcharhinus leucas* (p. 32)

6b. Snout long and pointed; fins with black tips . . . . . . **blacktip shark,** *Carcharhinus limbatus* (p. 283)

Atlantic sharpnose shark
Rhizoprionodon terraenovae (Richardson, 1836)

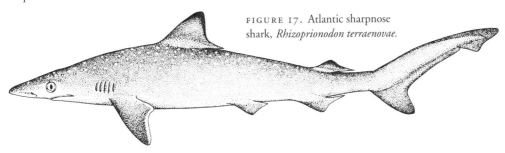

FIGURE 17. Atlantic sharpnose shark, *Rhizoprionodon terraenovae.*

KEY FEATURES   Precaudal pit present; spiracle absent; origin of second dorsal fin well posterior to origin of anal fin; posterior margin of anal fin straight or weakly concave.

OTHER CHARACTERISTICS   Body slender and fusiform; snout long and depressed, its length equal to or greater than width of mouth; snout tip narrowly rounded; teeth strongly oblique, with edges smooth (in juveniles) to finely serrate (in adults); first dorsal fin high, with gently rounded apex; origin of first dorsal fin typically perpendicular or dorsoanterior to inner posterior margin of pectoral fin; second dorsal fin low; anal fin higher than second dorsal fin; posterior margin of pectoral fin slightly concave. Brown or grayish brown dorsally; whitish ventrally; posterior edge of pectoral fin white or cream-colored; tip of dorsal fin often dusky; pale spots present in large individuals. Maximum adult size at least 1.1 m TL (3.6 ft).

GEOGRAPHIC DISTRIBUTION   Found in the western Atlantic from New Brunswick to Florida, including the Gulf of Mexico.

ECOLOGY   Atlantic sharpnose sharks are rare visitors in the lower Chesapeake Bay from their more common coastal habitats. Although primarily a coastal species, these sharks have been found in offshore waters at depths to at least 280 m (919 ft). Juveniles often occur in the surf zone off sandy beaches. Atlantic sharpnose sharks feed on a wide variety of invertebrates and small fishes. Development is viviparous; females produce litters of one to seven young that are pupped in estuaries south of Cape Hatteras from May to June. Mature males predominate in Virginia waters.

FISHING INTEREST   Landed mainly with longlines where used as food.

LITERATURE   Hildebrand and Schroeder 1928:49; Musick 1972; Compagno 1984b.

Sandbar shark
Carcharhinus plumbeus (Nardo, 1827)

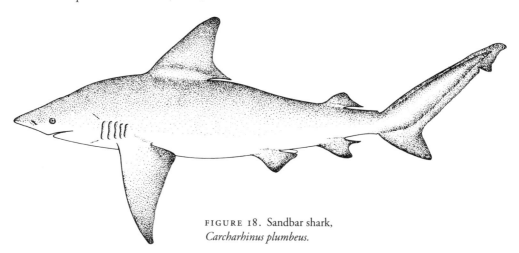

FIGURE 18. Sandbar shark, *Carcharhinus plumbeus.*

KEY FEATURES   Precaudal pit present; spiracle absent; narrow dermal ridge present between dorsal fins; teeth in upper jaw strongly serrate; first dorsal fin very high and nearly triangular, its height as much as 18% of total length; origin of first dorsal fin perpendicular or slightly dorsoanterior to rear end of pectoral fin insertion.

OTHER CHARACTERISTICS   Body stout; snout short and broadly rounded; second dorsal fin and anal fin about equal in height; origin of second dorsal fin about perpendicular to origin of anal fin; pectoral fin large and broad, with narrowly pointed or rounded tip. Grayish dorsally; venter white. Maximum adult size 2.2–2.5 m TL (7–8 ft) for females, 1.8 m TL (6 ft) for males.

GEOGRAPHIC DISTRIBUTION   Reported from coastal areas of all tropical and warm-temperate oceans and seas. In the western Atlantic this species ranges from Massachusetts to southern Brazil.

ECOLOGY   The sandbar shark is a seasonal visitor to Chesapeake Bay in summer and fall, and juveniles are common to abundant. The bay is used as a pupping ground by females and is probably one of the most important nursery grounds on the east coast of the United States for this species. The sandbar shark is typically found over muddy or sandy bottoms from intertidal zones to waters 200 m (655 ft) deep or more. Primarily a bottom feeder, this species typically preys on bottom fishes, other sharks, rays, and invertebrates. In the bay, sandbar sharks prey heavily on blue crabs. Development is viviparous. Females live as long as 21 years; males, 15 years. In the Northern Hemisphere, sandbar sharks are known to migrate south in the winter and north in the summer.

FISHING INTEREST   Caught mainly by longlines but also with gill nets and by anglers using rod and reel. The sandbar shark has been the most important commercial shark species along the east coast of the United States since the 1940s. Its meat is used for human consumption, its fins are used for soup, and the liver is extracted for oil. Presently the species has been reduced by overfishing to about 20% of its former abundance. Among all species of large sharks caught by anglers on the east coast of the United States, the sandbar shark ranks second in number caught, and in Maryland and Virginia it ranks first.

LITERATURE   Hildebrand and Schroeder 1928:48; Musick 1972; Ellis 1975; Medved and Marshall 1981; Compagno 1984b; Casey et al. 1985; Musick et al. 1993.

Dusky shark
Carcharhinus obscurus (Lesueur, 1817)

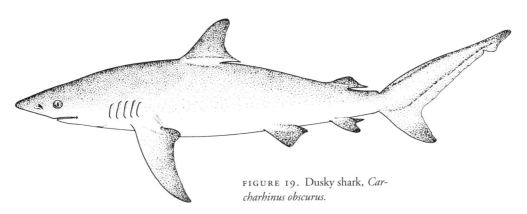

FIGURE 19. Dusky shark, *Carcharhinus obscurus.*

KEY FEATURES   Precaudal pit present; spiracle absent; dermal ridge present between dorsal fins; first dorsal fin of moderate size, with rounded apex; origin of first dorsal fin perpendicular to or somewhat dorsoanterior to posterior tips of pectoral fin.

OTHER CHARACTERISTICS   Body slender to moderately stout; snout short, its length greater than or equal to distance between nostrils; second dorsal fin and anal fin of similar size; origin of second dorsal fin about perpendicular to anal fin origin; pectoral fin falcate, with pointed tip. Bluish gray to dull gray dorsally; whitish ventrally; fin tips dusky. Maximum adult size 3.6 m TL (12 ft).

GEOGRAPHIC DISTRIBUTION   Reported from coastal areas of all tropical and warm-temperate oceans. In the western Atlantic, this species ranges from Massachusetts to southern Brazil, including the Gulf of Mexico and the Caribbean Sea.

ECOLOGY   Although formerly common along the coast, the dusky shark is now only an infrequent visitor to the lower Chesapeake Bay during the summer months. The shoals on the seaside of the Virginia Barrier Islands serve as pupping grounds for this species. Along the western Atlantic coast, the dusky shark exhibits northward migrations in the summer, retreating south when waters cool. This species ranges from the surf zone to far offshore and from the surface to about 400 m (1,300 ft) in depth. It does not normally enter estuaries; hence it is not encountered in the bay as often as the sandbar shark. Dusky sharks eat a wide variety of bony fishes, as well as rays and other sharks; they also eat crustaceans, mollusks, and sea stars. Dusky sharks are viviparous, with their litter size numbering from 3 to 14.

FISHING INTEREST   Caught with handlines and nets where abundant, and utilized for human consumption. An important recreational species, the dusky shark has been severely overfished, so that stocks are now greatly depleted.

LITERATURE   Musick 1972; Fischer 1978; Compagno 1984b.

Bull shark
Carcharhinus leucas (Valenciennes, 1841)

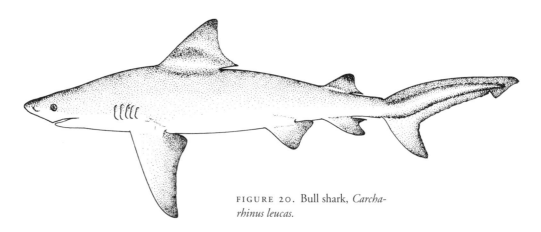

FIGURE 20. Bull shark, *Carcharhinus leucas.*

KEY FEATURES   Precaudal pit present; spiracle absent; dermal ridge absent between dorsal fins; teeth in upper jaw strongly serrate; snout broadly rounded and extremely short, its length less than width of mouth.

OTHER CHARACTERISTICS   Body stout; upper jaw teeth broad and triangular; first dorsal fin large and broadly triangular, with sharply rounded apex; origin of first dorsal fin perpendicular or just dorsoposterior to pectoral fin insertion; second dorsal fin and anal fin about equal in height; origin of second dorsal fin just dorsoanterior to origin of anal fin; pectoral fin large and broad. Grayish dorsally; white ventrally; tips of fins dusky. Maximum adult size less than 3.4 m TL (11 ft).

GEOGRAPHIC DISTRIBUTION   Reported from coastal areas in all tropical and subtropical waters, extending from New York to Brazil in the western Atlantic. Bull sharks are known to frequent brackish waters as well as low-salinity rivers and lakes. They are known from Lake Nicaragua, as well as from 1,000 miles upriver in the Amazon and Mississippi rivers.

ECOLOGY   Bull sharks are occasional visitors to Chesapeake Bay during the summer months and have been recorded from as far north in the bay as the Patuxent River. This species preys upon a wide variety of bony fishes, as well as on rays and other sharks; it also eats crustaceans, turtles, and mammals. Development is viviparous.

FISHING INTEREST   Where common, landed with longlines and with hook and line for human consumption. Bull sharks are popular in some areas among anglers but are not recognized as a game fish by the International Game Fishing Association.

ADDITIONAL REMARKS   Several attacks on humans have been attributed to the bull shark. Because of its habits, this species is frequently in proximity to humans, making attacks all the more possible. The bull shark is considered one of the three shark species that are most dangerous (the tiger shark and the white shark, *Carcharodon carcharias,* are the other two).

LITERATURE   Musick 1972; Ellis 1975; Compagno 1984b.

Smoothhounds
FAMILY TRIAKIDAE

Smoothhounds are small to medium-sized sharks that inhabit warm and temperate coastal areas. Triakids are typically shallow-water bottom dwellers, but some family members are known from considerable depths (2,000 m, or 1.2 mi). Smoothhounds feed on bottom fishes, crustaceans, and mollusks. Development is ovoviviparous or viviparous. This large family of sharks comprises 9 genera and 34 species. One species is found in Chesapeake Bay waters.

Smooth dogfish
Mustelus canis (Mitchell, 1815)

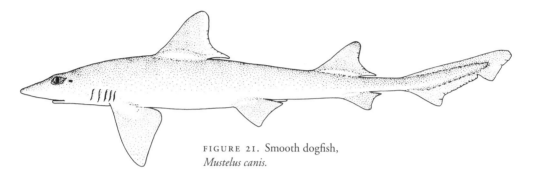

FIGURE 21. Smooth dogfish, *Mustelus canis.*

KEY FEATURES   First dorsal fin higher than second dorsal fin; both dorsal fins with rounded apex; pelvic fin origin almost midway between origins of pectoral fin and anal fin; origin of anal fin perpendicular to midpoint of second dorsal fin; teeth small and numerous, forming pavementlike appearance.

OTHER CHARACTERISTICS   Body elongate and slender; head narrow and depressed; snout tapering, its length greater than width of mouth; internasal space broad; eye large; pupil elongate posteriorly; pectoral fin somewhat broad, with rounded tip. Uniformly grayish dorsally; venter pale; able to change color with change in substrate (one of only a few sharks able to do so). Maximum adult size 1.5 m TL (5 ft).

GEOGRAPHIC DISTRIBUTION   Found only in the coastal areas of the western Atlantic but apparently absent from much of Brazil; known from Massachusetts to Venezuela and from southern Brazil to Argentina.

ECOLOGY   The smooth dogfish is a common to abundant seasonal visitor in summer and fall to the lower Chesapeake Bay, extending as far north as the mouth of the Patuxent River. Typically found in waters less than 18 m (59 ft) deep over mud or sand bottoms, the smooth dogfish is an active swimmer and bottom feeder, preying primarily on large crustaceans such as crabs. It also eats small fishes, squids, and bottom-dwelling invertebrates. Smooth dogfish swim in packs or schools; this habit may be the basis for the use of the term "dogfish." Development is viviparous. Pupping occurs in seaside coastal waters in Virginia in April and May; juveniles are found in the lower bay throughout the summer.

FISHING INTEREST   Caught incidentally by anglers and commercial fisheries. Smooth dogfish are landed primarily by longline and bottom trawl, occasionally in large numbers. They are not considered a food fish in the United States but are highly esteemed in Europe.

LITERATURE   Hildebrand and Schroeder 1928:47; Musick 1972; Ellis 1975; Compagno 1984b; Manooch 1984.

Dogfish Sharks
ORDER SQUALIFORMES

The order of dogfish sharks contains two families, one of which occurs in Chesapeake Bay.

Dogfish Sharks
FAMILY SQUALIDAE

Fishes of the family Squalidae are typically small to medium-sized sharks that are most diverse in deep water (≥50 m, or ≥164 ft). Dogfish sharks lack an anal fin, and most species have spines preceding each dorsal fin. The dorsal fins are moderately small to very small. Prey items include bony fishes, other sharks, and invertebrates. Development is aplacental viviparous; the developing pups depend entirely on yolk reserves, and no placenta is formed. The family comprises 73 species in 17 genera, with 1 genus and species recorded from Chesapeake Bay waters.

Spiny dogfish
Squalus acanthias Linnaeus, 1758

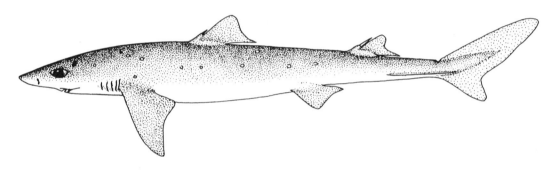

FIGURE 22. Spiny dogfish,
Squalus acanthias.

KEY FEATURES   Spine on first dorsal fin dorsoposterior to free rear tip of pectoral fin; small roundish white or pale spots typically present laterally.

OTHER CHARACTERISTICS   Body moderately slender, with depressed head and pointed snout; first dorsal fin small and preceded by exposed spine; second dorsal fin smaller than first, but with larger spine; pectoral fin moderate in size, free posteriorly, and with concave edge; pelvic fin small and closer to base of second dorsal fin than to base of first dorsal fin. Grayish or brownish dorsally; venter pale. Maximum adult size about 1.1 m TL (3.6 ft).

GEOGRAPHIC DISTRIBUTION   Inhabiting temperate coastal waters of all seas and oceans. In the northwestern Atlantic, this species is most abundant from Newfoundland to Georgia.

ECOLOGY   The spiny dogfish is common in the lower Chesapeake Bay (south of the mouth of the Potomac River) from late fall to early spring. This species is benthic in habit, typically in depths of 10–200 m (33–656 ft). It is a sluggish swimmer that often travels in large schools. During the summer months, this species is absent from bay waters and is presumably offshore in deeper water. The spiny dogfish is a voracious feeder, primarily on fishes and, to a lesser extent, on squids and benthic invertebrates. Females are reported to release their young inshore between November and January. Litter size ranges from 1 to 15, and full-term pups are approximately 30 cm TL (1 ft). Spiny dogfish grow slowly and are long-lived. Some females reach 110 m TL

(3.6 ft), 6.5 kg (143 lb), and at least 40 years of age; some males reach 90 cm TL (3.0 ft), 2.8 kg (62 lb), and at least 35 years of age.
FISHING INTEREST   Commonly caught by recreational anglers and, where abundant, of con-siderable commercial interest to bottom trawlers.
LITERATURE   Hildebrand and Schroeder 1928:52; Jensen 1966; Musick 1972; McEachran 1982; Compagno 1984a; Whitehead et al. 1984; Nammack et al. 1985.

Angel Sharks
ORDER SQUATINIFORMES

The order of angel sharks contains one family, which occurs in Chesapeake Bay.

Angel Sharks
FAMILY SQUATINIDAE

Angel sharks are highly depressed, raylike sharks that bury themselves in mud or sand. These bizarrely shaped sharks, thought to be intermediate between sharks and rays, have greatly enlarged pectoral fins, much like those of rays and skates (batoids). However, the pectoral fins of angel sharks do not attach to the head, whereas in batoids the pectoral fins are fused to the side of the head. Additionally, the gill openings of angel sharks are partially lateral, whereas in batoids the gill openings are ventral. Angel sharks feed on a variety of small fishes and invertebrates. Development is ovoviviparous. The family comprises 1 genus and 13 species, of which 1 species is recorded from Chesapeake Bay waters.

Atlantic angel shark
Squatina dumeril Lesueur, 1818

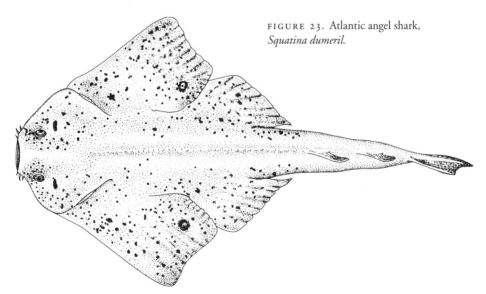

FIGURE 23. Atlantic angel shark, *Squatina dumeril.*

KEY FEATURES   Head and body greatly de-pressed, with distinct neck; pectoral fin greatly en-larged and triangular; anal fin absent; lower lobe of caudal fin slightly longer than upper lobe.

OTHER CHARACTERISTICS   Mouth and nostrils at anterior margin of head; mouth broad and traplike; teeth small and sharp; dorsal fins small and about equal in size; pelvic fin triangular and extending laterally. Grayish yellow dorsally; venter pale; abdomen, throat, and ventral fins with reddish spots. Maximum adult size about 1.5 m TL (5 ft).

GEOGRAPHIC DISTRIBUTION   Found from Massachusetts to Florida, throughout the Gulf of Mexico and the Caribbean to Venezuela.

ECOLOGY   The Atlantic angel shark is a seasonal visitor to Chesapeake Bay, in summer and fall. It is known occasionally from the lower bay and rarely from the upper bay. It probably overwinters in deep water offshore, where it is known from depths greater than 1,000 m (0.6 mi). A benthic burrower, the Atlantic angel shark feeds on bottom fishes, crustaceans, and mollusks. It is also known by the common name "sand devil," because of its propensity to bite careless anglers.

FISHING INTEREST   Of no commercial or recreational value. This species is infrequently caught by rod and reel and in bottom trawls.

LITERATURE   Hildebrand and Schroeder 1928:54; Musick 1972; Ellis 1975; Compagno 1984a.

Sawfishes
ORDER PRISTIFORMES

The order of sawfishes comprises a single family, which occurs in Chesapeake Bay.

Sawfishes
FAMILY PRISTIDAE

Although sawfishes are related to rays and skates, they have a sharklike appearance. The body of sawfishes is only slightly depressed, the pectoral fins are not unusually large, and the tail is not distinctly separated from the body. However, like rays and skates, sawfishes have a dorsoventrally flattened head, with the gill slits located ventrally. Sawfishes are found in shallow coastal waters, including estuaries, and are known to enter freshwater. The saw of sawfishes is used for slashing schools of fish and for rooting about in bottom sediments. Development is ovoviviparous. The family, distributed worldwide in tropical and subtropical seas, comprises 2 genera and 6–10 species, with 1 species known from Chesapeake Bay waters.

Smalltooth sawfish
Pristis pectinata Latham, 1794

KEY FEATURES   Snout extremely elongate, with double-edged saw blade; body sharklike in profile; caudal fin without definite lower lobe.

OTHER CHARACTERISTICS   Head and body dorsoventrally flattened; 24–32 teeth present on each side of saw; head small; spiracle well posterior to eye; eye slightly larger than spiracle; nostrils well anterior to mouth; mouth with 10–12 rows of minute teeth; dorsal fins with rounded tips and about equal in size; caudal fin triangular, with ventroposterior edge projecting only slightly; low keel present on either side of caudal fin; anal fin absent; pelvic fin origin ventroposterior to first dorsal fin; pectoral fin about twice the size of pelvic fin and originating near posterior part of head. Body uniformly dusky; grayish brown dorsally; white or grayish white ventrally. Maximum adult size about 6 m TL (20 ft).

GEOGRAPHIC DISTRIBUTION   Found on both sides of the Atlantic Ocean (and maybe the southwestern Indian Ocean). In the western Atlantic, the smalltooth sawfish is found from New York to Brazil, including the Gulf of Mexico and the Caribbean Sea.

ECOLOGY   This species inhabits the sandy or muddy bottoms of shallow coastal waters (<1 to 10 m, or <3 to 33 ft, deep). It is often encountered in bays, estuaries, and river mouths, lying

FISHING INTEREST   Of no commercial or recreational value in the region. Anglers have reported catching the smalltooth sawfish with a baited hook. This species is incidentally caught

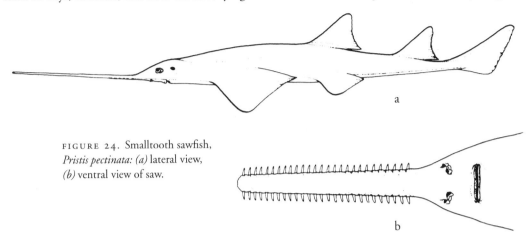

FIGURE 24. Smalltooth sawfish, *Pristis pectinata:* (a) lateral view, (b) ventral view of saw.

in the deeper holes and frequenting brackish water as often as full seawater. The smalltooth sawfish is known to ascend freshwaters. It feeds on bottom-dwelling animals by stirring up the sediment with its saw and by slashing small schooling fishes such as mullets and herrings. Gravid females reportedly carry as many as 20 embryos, which require a year of gestation.

by trawlers and net fisheries and is considered a nuisance because the saw can damage the net when the fish is entangled.

LITERATURE   Hildebrand and Schroeder 1928:55; Bigelow and Schroeder 1953b; Musick 1972; Fischer et al. 1981.

Skates

ORDER RAJIFORMES

The order of skates comprises four families, of which only one occurs in Chesapeake Bay.

Skates

FAMILY RAJIDAE

Skates are cartilaginous fishes with a flattened body and broadly rounded, winglike pectoral fins that form a somewhat circular or rhomboidal disk. Skates possess a slender, barbless tail that is longer than the width of the disk. Two small dorsal fins are located near the tip of the tail. The caudal fin is rudimentary. The mouth is located on the ventral surface of the head, with teeth that are rounded in juveniles and females and strongly conical in mature males. The eyes are situated dorsally. Small thorns are usually located along the dorsal midline, with scattered patches of thorns on the dorsal surface of the pectoral fins. Skates are found in all oceans to depths of 2,000 m (1.2 mi) but are less common in shallow waters. Skates are bottom dwellers and bury themselves partly in the bottom. Because their mouth is located on the underside, they must pounce on their prey before consuming it. Development is oviparous; the developing egg is encapsulated in an amber to black leathery case, which is frequently found washed up on the beach. There are 7 genera and 230 species of skates worldwide, with 4 species recorded from Chesapeake Bay waters.

KEY TO THE SPECIES OF SKATES IN CHESAPEAKE BAY

1a. Large thorny scales absent along middorsal zone of disk; ventral surface of disk marked with dusky dots and dashes. . . . . **barndoor skate, *Raja laevis*** (p. 38)

1b. One or more rows of thorny scales present along middorsal zone of disk; ventral surface of disk not marked with dusky dots and dashes **2**

2a. Snout acutely pointed; dorsal surface of disk with distinctive dusky bars. . . . . **clearnose skate, *Raja eglanteria*** (p. 39)

2b. Snout bluntly rounded or only slightly pointed; dorsal surface of disk with small dusky spots. **3**

3a. Several large ocellar spots typically present on dorsal surface of disk; 80 or more series of teeth present in upper jaw . . . . **winter skate, *Raja ocellata*** (p. 40)

3b. Ocellar spots typically absent on dorsal surface of disk; 70 or fewer series of teeth present in upper jaw . . . . **little skate, *Raja erinacea*** (p. 41)

Barndoor skate
Raja laevis Mitchill, 1817

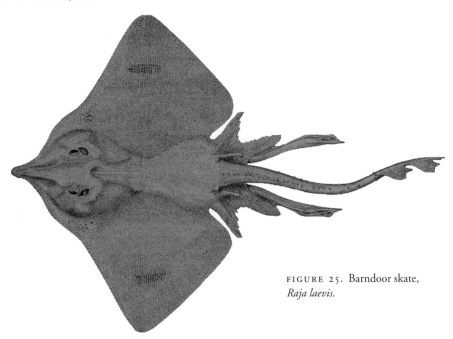

FIGURE 25. Barndoor skate, *Raja laevis*.

KEY FEATURES   Large thorns absent on dorsal midline of disk; snout acutely pointed; pectoral fin triangular (line from tip of pectoral fin to tip of snout does not intersect disk).

OTHER CHARACTERISTICS   Disk wider than long, its lateralmost margins more angular than rounded; eye small; mouth large; first and second dorsal fins similar in size and shape but first dorsal fin higher than second; both dorsal fins located near tip of tail; 3 rows of prickles present on tail; caudal fin represented by dermal fold extending over tip of tail; posterior tip of pelvic fin abruptly rounded. Dorsal surface brownish, with many dusky spots of unequal size; black pigment present around sensory pores of head and body; ventral surface whitish. Maximum adult size 1.5 m TL (5 ft).

GEOGRAPHIC DISTRIBUTION   Occurring coastally from Newfoundland to North Carolina.

ECOLOGY   The barndoor skate is a rare visitor to the lower Chesapeake Bay in winter to springtime. Barndoor skate are found on sand, mud, or gravel bottoms from inshore waters to depths as great as 470 m (1,550 ft) and are more likely to be found in deeper water during the warmer months. They feed mainly on large crustaceans such as crabs, lobsters, and shrimps but also eat a variety of fishes, squids, and worms. Egg cases are laid in winter and are produced throughout the range of the species. The young hatch in late spring to summer.

FISHING INTEREST   Of no commercial or recreational importance in the Chesapeake Bay area. This species is occasionally caught in pound nets in the lower bay but is not utilized for food. The barndoor skate is reported to bite a baited hook readily, but because of its cold-weather occurrence in the bay, bay anglers are unlikely to hook one.

LITERATURE   Hildebrand and Schroeder 1928:59; Bigelow and Schroeder 1953b; Musick 1972; Smith 1985.

Clearnose skate
Raja eglanteria Bosc, 1802
PLATE 2

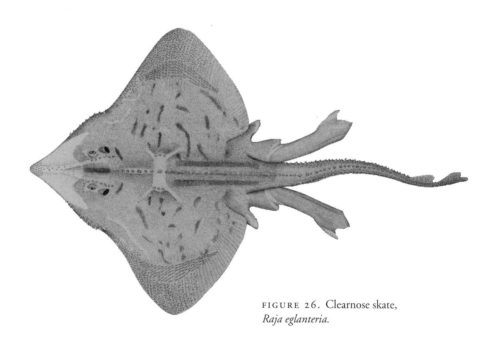

FIGURE 26. Clearnose skate, *Raja eglanteria.*

KEY FEATURES   Snout acutely pointed; area on either side of snout semitransparent; dorsal surface of pectoral fin with distinctive, elongate dusky brown to black spots and bars.

OTHER CHARACTERISTICS   Disk rhomboidal and broader than long; lateral tip of pectoral fin acutely rounded; dorsal fins equal in size and located near tip of tail; caudal fin represented by dermal fold extending over tip of tail; continuous row of thorns present from first dorsal fin to head; 3 rows of thorns present on tail; tail length about 50% of total length. Pale brown dorsally; venter white. Maximum adult size 79 cm TL (2.6 ft).

GEOGRAPHIC DISTRIBUTION   Inhabiting coastal areas from Massachusetts to Texas.

ECOLOGY   Clearnose skate are abundant seasonal visitors to the lower Chesapeake Bay during summer and fall. In autumn they leave embayments and shallow areas to move offshore and southward. They feed mainly at night on decapod crustaceans, bivalves, polychaetes, squids, and bony fishes.

FISHING INTEREST   Considered a nuisance by both commercial fisheries and anglers. The clearnose skate is caught incidentally with bottom trawls, with pound nets, and by rod and reel.

LITERATURE   Hildebrand and Schroeder 1928:58; Musick 1972; McEachran and Musick 1975; Fischer 1978; McEachran 1982; Manooch 1984.

Winter skate
Raja ocellata Mitchill, 1814

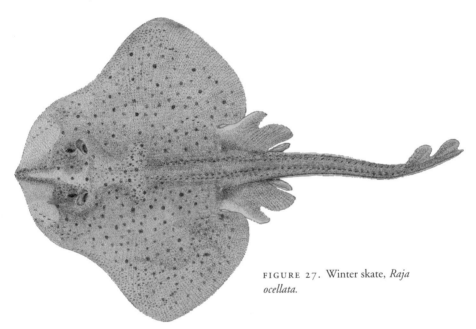

FIGURE 27. Winter skate, *Raja ocellata.*

KEY FEATURES   Thorns present along dorsal midline in juveniles, absent in adults; disk more rounded than angular; snout more blunt than pointed; typically 1–4 dusky ocellar spots present, edged with white and located near inner posterior margin of pectoral fin in most individuals; upper jaw with at least 80 series of teeth (typically 90–100) in adults.

OTHER CHARACTERISTICS   Disk only slightly broader than long; anterior margin of pectoral fin with scattered thorns; first and second dorsal fins prickly and of approximately equal shape and size; caudal fin represented by dermal fold extending over tip of tail; pelvic fin long, with deep notch. Dorsal surface brownish; whitish ventrally; rounded black spots present on pectoral fin. Maximum adult size 1 m TL (3.3 ft).

GEOGRAPHIC DISTRIBUTION   Found from the Gulf of St. Lawrence to North Carolina.

ECOLOGY   The winter skate is an occasional winter to springtime visitor to the southern Chesapeake Bay. Winter skate are found on sand or gravel bottoms from inshore waters to depths as great as 120 m (400 ft) and are more likely to be found in deeper water during the warmer months. They feed mainly on crabs but also eat a variety of fishes, shrimps, mollusks, and worms. Egg cases are produced throughout most of the range of the species throughout the year but in greater numbers from summer to autumn.

FISHING INTEREST   Of no commercial or recreational interest in the Chesapeake Bay area.

Winter skate are occasionally collected by pound nets in the lower bay during the early spring but are not utilized for food.

LITERATURE   Hildebrand and Schroeder 1928:56; Bigelow and Schroeder 1953b; Musick 1972; McEachran and Musick 1975; McEachran and Martin 1977.

Little skate
Raja erinacea (Mitchill, 1825)

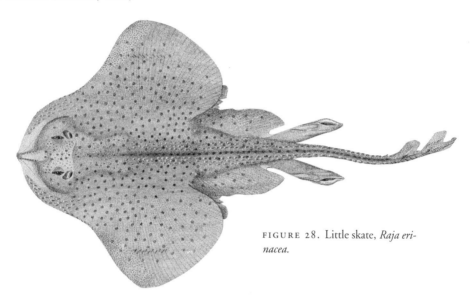

FIGURE 28. Little skate, *Raja eri-nacea.*

KEY FEATURES   Lateralmost margins of disk more rounded than angular; snout more blunt than pointed; middorsal thorns absent in adults, except immediately posterior to interorbital region; dorsal surface of disk with small dusky spots; upper jaw with 70 or fewer series of teeth (typically 55 or fewer).

OTHER CHARACTERISTICS   Disk only slightly wider than long; dorsal fins equal in size and located near tip of tail; caudal fin represented by dermal fold extending over tip of tail; triangular patch of thorns present posterior to eye; 2 or 3 rows of thorns present on either side of dorsal midline and extending onto tail. Grayish to dusky brown dorsally; venter grayish white. Maximum adult size 53 cm disk width (1.7 ft).

GEOGRAPHIC DISTRIBUTION   Occurring from the Gulf of St. Lawrence to Cape Hatteras but most abundant from Georges Bank to Delaware Bay.

ECOLOGY   The little skate is an occasional visitor to the lower Chesapeake Bay in winter and spring. Common in shallow waters along the coast, it has also been collected at depths greater than 150 m (500 ft). It feeds on bottom-dwelling organisms such as crabs, shrimps, polychaetes, sea squirts, mollusks, squids, and bony fishes.

FISHING INTEREST   Caught incidentally with bottom trawls and by rod and reel.

LITERATURE   Hildebrand and Schroeder 1928:60; Musick 1972; McEachran et al. 1976; Waring 1984; Robins et al. 1986.

Rays and Mantas
ORDER MYLIOBATIFORMES

The order of rays and mantas comprises seven families, of which five occur in Chesapeake Bay.

KEY TO THE FAMILIES OF RAYS AND MANTAS IN CHESAPEAKE BAY

1a. Eyes and spiracles located on top of head; fusion of pectoral fins (disk wings) to body continuous along sides of head and extending to tip of snout **2**

1b. Eyes and spiracles located on sides of head; fusion of pectoral fins (disk wings) to body extending only to a point just posterior to eyes **3**

2a. Disk much wider than long . . . . **butterfly rays—Gymnuridae** (p. 42)

2b. Disk width less than 1.5 times the length. . . . . **stingrays—Dasyatidae** (p. 44)

3a. Mouth extending across anterior margin of head; thin, narrow finlike structure (cephalic fin) projecting anteriorly from each side of head . . . . **mantas—Mobulidae** (p. 49)

3b. Mouth inferior; short snoutlike projection (subrostral lobe of pectoral fin), consisting of 1 or 2 lobes, extending anteriorly from underside of head **4**

4a. Snoutlike projection with only 1 lobe; white spots present on dorsal surface of disk . . . . **eagle rays—Myliobatidae** (p. 50)

4b. Snoutlike projection with 2 lobes; white spots absent on dorsal surface of disk . . . . **cownose rays—Rhinopteridae** (p. 51)

Butterfly Rays
FAMILY GYMNURIDAE

In butterfly rays the disk is much wider than it is long. The tail is slender and much shorter than the disk length. The tail may or may not possess a serrated spine. These rays have no caudal fin, and all western Atlantic representatives of the family also lack a dorsal fin. The skin is smooth. Butterfly rays eat fishes, crustaceans, and mollusks. Development is viviparous. The family contains 2 genera and 12 species, of which 2 species are recorded from Chesapeake Bay waters.

KEY TO THE SPECIES OF BUTTERFLY RAYS IN CHESAPEAKE BAY

1a. Typically 1 or 2 serrated spines present on tail, and long tentacle present at each spiracle. . . . . **spiny butterfly ray, Gymnura altavela** (p. 42)

1b. Tail spines and spiracular tentacles always absent . . . . **smooth butterfly ray, Gymnura micrura** (p. 43)

Spiny butterfly ray
Gymnura altavela (Linnaeus, 1758)

KEY FEATURES   Disk much wider than long; tail pointed and short, with 1 or 2 long, serrated poisonous spines at base; distinct single long tentacle present at inner posterior corner of each spiracle; pelvic fin narrow.

OTHER CHARACTERISTICS   Body strongly depressed, with broad lateral edges of disk narrowly angled; teeth small and pointed, in pavementlike pattern; skin smooth, without thorns or denticles. Dusky brown to coffee brown dorsally, with grayish or reddish cast; venter white; tail sometimes slightly paler than disk and having alternating crossbars; pale spots and blotches often present dorsally. Maximum adult size 2 m disk width (6.6 ft).

GEOGRAPHIC DISTRIBUTION   Known from both the eastern and western Atlantic

ECOLOGY   The spiny butterfly ray is a seasonal visitor to the lower Chesapeake Bay from May to November. It inhabits mainly soft-bottom inshore waters but is also found to 60 m (200 ft) deep. It feeds on many different bottom-dwelling animals, but its diet consists primarily of fishes and squids.

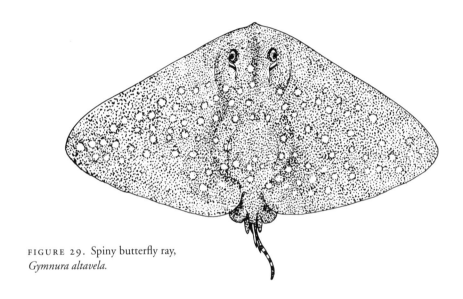

FIGURE 29. Spiny butterfly ray, *Gymnura altavela.*

coasts. In the western Atlantic, the range of this species is from Cape Cod to Uruguay. This species is most abundant in the tropical latitudes but is not common anywhere.

FISHING INTEREST   Caught as bycatch in trawls and pound nets but not utilized for human consumption in the Chesapeake Bay area.

LITERATURE   Musick 1972; Fischer et al. 1981.

Smooth butterfly ray
Gymnura micrura (Schneider, 1801)

KEY FEATURES   Disk much wider than long; tail pointed and short, without spine; tentacle-like lobe absent on posterior of spiracle; pelvic fin narrow.

OTHER CHARACTERISTICS   Body strongly depressed, with broad lateral edges of disk sharply angled; teeth small and pointed, in pavementlike pattern; skin smooth, without thorns or denticles. Gray, brown, pale green, or purple dorsally; venter white; tail sometimes slightly paler

than disk and having 3 or 4 dusky bars; pale spots and vermiculated streaks present on dorsal surface, giving marbled appearance. Maximum adult size 1.2 m disk width (4 ft).

GEOGRAPHIC DISTRIBUTION   Known from both the eastern and western Atlantic coasts. In the western Atlantic, this species ranges from Cape Cod to Brazil, including the Gulf of Mexico.

ECOLOGY   The smooth butterfly ray is a seasonal visitor to the lower Chesapeake Bay from May to November. It inhabits sandy or muddy bottoms in tropical to warm-temperate waters

FISHING INTEREST   Caught as bycatch in trawls and pound nets but not utilized for human consumption in the Chesapeake Bay area.

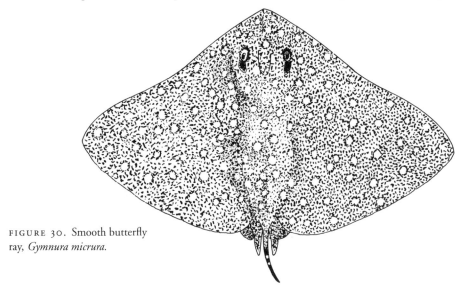

FIGURE 30. Smooth butterfly ray, *Gymnura micrura.*

from the shoreline to depths of 55 m (180 ft). Its food consists primarily of crustaceans and clams.

LITERATURE   Hildebrand and Schroeder 1928:67; Musick 1972; Fischer 1978; Fischer et al. 1981; McEachran 1982; Robins et al. 1986.

Stingrays
FAMILY DASYATIDAE

Stingrays are flattened fishes with a disk that ranges from rhomboidal to circular. The tail is slender and whiplike, possessing one or several serrated venomous spines. The glandular tissue that secretes the venom is situated in grooves near the spine tip. Stingrays can deliver painful and serious wounds to the hands and feet of unsuspecting human swimmers and careless anglers. The pectoral fins are continuous along the sides of the head, and dorsal and caudal fins are absent. Most stingrays are found in marine waters, but some are strictly freshwater. Stingrays feed on crustaceans, mollusks, polychaetes, and bony fishes. Development in stingrays is viviparous, but there is no placenta-like connection between female and young. The young are nourished by glandular secretions from the inner walls of the uterus. There are 5 genera and more than 60 species in this family, of which 1 genus and 4 species are recorded from Chesapeake Bay waters.

KEY TO THE SPECIES OF STINGRAYS IN CHESAPEAKE BAY

1a. Lateral corners of disk wings narrowly rounded or abruptly angled **2**
1b. Lateral corners of disk wings broadly and evenly rounded **3**
2a. Finlike fold of skin along underside of tail about as wide as height of tail; dorsal surface of tail with single ridge or keel posterior to spine; sides of tail without thorns . . . . **southern stingray, *Dasyatis americana*** (p. 45)
2b. Finlike fold of skin along underside of tail only about half as wide as height of tail; dorsal surface of tail without ridge or keel; in large individuals, sides of tail with thorns . . . . **roughtail stingray, *Dasyatis centroura*** (p. 46)

3a. Distance from eye to tip of snout considerably longer than distance between spiracles; front outline of disk wings concave near tip of snout . . . . **Atlantic stingray, *Dasyatis sabina*** (p. 47)

3b. Distance from eye to tip of snout shorter than distance between spiracles; front outline of disk wings weakly convex near tip of snout . . . . **bluntnose stingray, *Dasyatis say*** (p. 48)

Southern stingray
Dasyatis americana Hildebrand and Schroeder, 1928

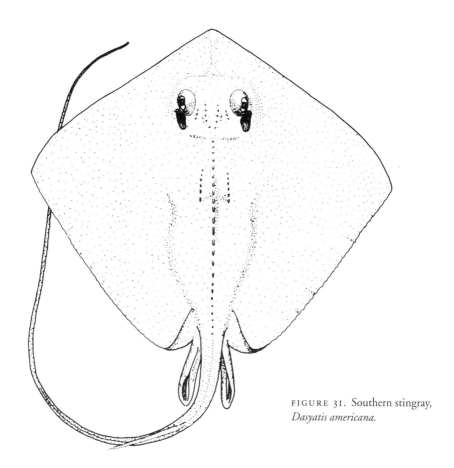

FIGURE 31. Southern stingray, *Dasyatis americana*.

KEY FEATURES   Finlike fold of skin along underside of tail about as wide as height of tail; dorsal surface of tail with single ridge or keel posterior to spine; lateral and posterior corners of disk abruptly rounded or acutely angled; small round pale spot situated posteriorly in interorbital region.

OTHER CHARACTERISTICS   Snout barely projecting; disk wider than long; median row of tubercles along midline from nuchal region to base of tail; tail slender and much longer than disk width; usually 1 (sometimes several or none) long, serrated venomous spine present at base of tail. Dorsal surface of disk pale brown, gray, or olive; venter white, with gray or brown margins; dorsal longitudinal ridge and ventral fold of tail dusky brown to black. Maximum adult size 3 m TL (10 ft).

GEOGRAPHIC DISTRIBUTION   Found in the western Atlantic from New Jersey to Florida, coastally throughout the Gulf of Mexico and the Caribbean Sea, southward to southern Brazil. The original description of the species is based on specimens from Crisfield, Maryland.

ECOLOGY   The southern stingray is a summer visitor to Chesapeake Bay that is rarely encountered in the upper bay (as far north as Tilghman Island) and is occasionally reported from the lower bay. It inhabits shallow water, burrowing into muddy or sandy bottoms. The southern stingray reproduces in late spring and summer and then migrates toward the tropics in the winter months. This species feeds primarily on bottom-dwelling invertebrates such as bivalves and worms but also preys on decapod crustaceans and small fishes. The southern stingray possesses powerful grinding teeth that enable it to crush even the toughest shells.

FISHING INTEREST   Caught mainly with trammel nets, with bottom longlines, and occasionally by rod and reel but not utilized for human consumption in the Chesapeake Bay area.

LITERATURE   Hildebrand and Schroeder 1928:64; Musick 1972; Fischer 1978; McEachran 1982; Manooch 1984.

Roughtail stingray
Dasyatis centroura (Mitchill, 1815)

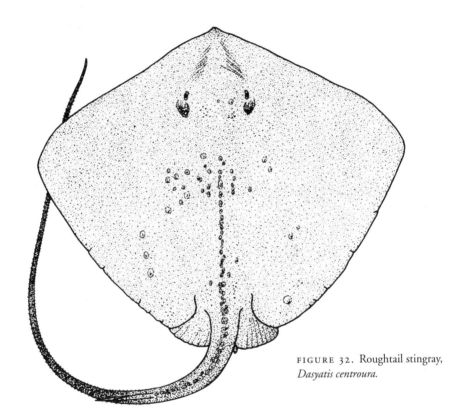

FIGURE 32. Roughtail stingray, *Dasyatis centroura.*

KEY FEATURES   Lateral and posterior corners of disk abruptly rounded or acutely angled; dorsal longitudinal ridge on tail very short, only as long as spine and situated beneath it; width of ventral tail fold about one-third the height of tail; dorsal surface of tail posterior to spine and entire sides of tail rough with thorns.

OTHER CHARACTERISTICS   Tip of snout not projecting; disk wider than long; teeth blunt and small, arranged in pavementlike pattern of about 45 rows; tail about 1.5–2 times the length of disk and bearing 1 or more strong serrated spines; irregular row of many tubercular thorns present along midline of back to tail spine; additional thorns scattered on head and inner parts of disk wings. Dorsal surface of disk uniform dusky olive brown or brown; pale ventrally; tail posterior to spine, as well as ventral fold, sometimes blackish. Maximum adult size 3 m TL (10 ft).

GEOGRAPHIC DISTRIBUTION   Known from both the eastern and western Atlantic coasts. In the western Atlantic, this species ranges from Cape Cod to Texas. It is common in mid-Atlantic coastal waters in summer. In the winter months it is found south of Cape Hatteras.

ECOLOGY   The roughtail stingray is a warm-water demersal species that undergoes summer migrations to higher latitudes. As a result of such migrations, it occasionally enters Chesapeake Bay. Roughtail stingrays typically occur in shallow coastal waters but have been reported to depths as great as 300 m (980 ft). Soft-bottom benthic invertebrates such as crustaceans, mollusks, and worms are major components of the roughtail stingray's diet.

FISHING INTEREST   Caught mainly with trammel nets, with bottom longlines, and occasionally by rod and reel.

LITERATURE   Hildebrand and Schroeder 1928:64; Musick 1972; Fischer et al. 1981.

Atlantic stingray
Dasyatis sabina (Lesueur, 1824)

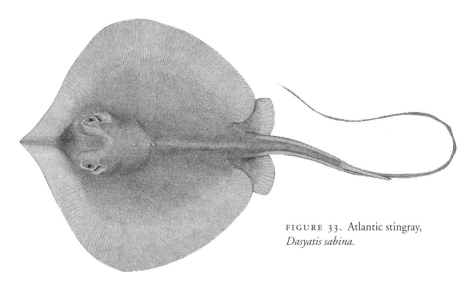

FIGURE 33. Atlantic stingray, *Dasyatis sabina.*

KEY FEATURES   Dermal fold of tail on ventral surface larger than dermal fold on dorsal surface; dermal folds of tail brown or yellow; disk narrow, its length about equal to its width; front outline of disk wings concave near tip of snout.

OTHER CHARACTERISTICS   Snout pointed; lateral corners of disk broadly rounded; teeth arranged in pavementlike pattern; large individuals with middorsal row of compressed spines extending to tail; tail long and slender, depressed anteriorly, round and whiplike posteriorly; 1 or 2 long, serrated venomous spines present on tail; pelvic fin extending well beyond disk margins. Dorsal surface brownish middorsally, paler later-ally; venter white. Maximum adult size 37 cm disk width (1.2 ft).

GEOGRAPHIC DISTRIBUTION   Found coastally from Chesapeake Bay to Mexico.

ECOLOGY   The Atlantic stingray is a subtropical seasonal visitor to the lower Chesapeake Bay during summer and fall, usually not penetrating farther north than the York River. It feeds primarily on crustaceans, but it has a larger mouth than other rays and also can eat fishes, squids, and mollusks. Usually occurring less than 25 m (80 ft) deep in shallow inshore areas on sandy or silty substrates, Atlantic stingrays can tolerate a broad salinity range and will enter freshwater.

Thus they are essentially euryhaline, and their movements are random except for migration to and from offshore areas in spring and fall. Parturition occurs in July and August. In the Gulf of Mexico a second (or replacement) spine becomes evident in late May; individuals with such spines continue to exhibit both spines until August, when individuals with a single spine become more prevalent. A similar sequence may occur in the Chesapeake Bay region.

FISHING INTEREST   Collected in seines, as well as by rod and reel.

LITERATURE   Hildebrand and Schroeder 1928:67; Musick 1972; Robins et al. 1986; Teaf and Lewis 1987; Snelson et al. 1988.

Bluntnose stingray
Dasyatis say (Lesueur, 1817)

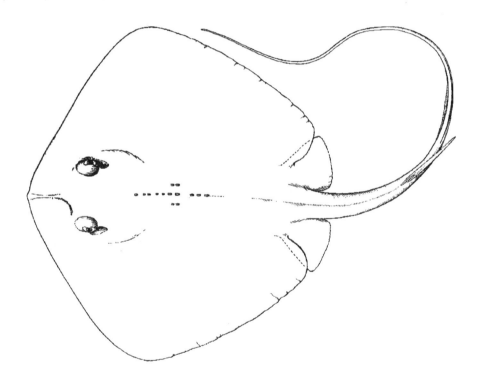

FIGURE 34. Bluntnose stingray,
Dasyatis say.

KEY FEATURES   Dermal folds of tail of equal size and blackish; disk wider than long; front outline of disk wings weakly convex near tip of snout.

OTHER CHARACTERISTICS   Snout barely projecting; lateral corners of disk broadly rounded; teeth arranged in pavementlike pattern; large individuals with middorsal row of blunt thorns; tail long and slender, depressed anteriorly, round and whiplike posteriorly; 1 or 2 long, serrated venomous spines present on tail; pelvic fin broadly rounded posteriorly and just barely extending beyond disk margins. Grayish or brownish dorsally; venter white. Maximum adult size 90 cm disk width (3 ft).

GEOGRAPHIC DISTRIBUTION   Found in

the western Atlantic from Long Island to Florida, coastally throughout the northern Gulf of Mexico, southward to Brazil.

ECOLOGY   The bluntnose stingray is a subtropical seasonal visitor to Chesapeake Bay during summer and fall. During late September through early October, this species is occasionally abundant in the lower bay. Both adults and juveniles frequent estuaries and surf zones. Like the Atlantic stingray, the bluntnose stingray feeds primarily on crustaceans.

FISHING INTEREST   Collected in pound nets and seines, as well as by rod and reel.

LITERATURE   Hildebrand and Schroeder 1928:66; Musick 1972; Benson 1982; Robins et al. 1986.

Mantas
FAMILY MOBULIDAE

Mantas are very large stingrays whose disk width can exceed 6 m (20 ft). Mantas are often observed swimming or basking at the water's surface. Like bullnose and cownose rays, mantas are highly migratory, and swimming is accomplished by vertical undulations of the pectoral fins. The anterior margins of the pectoral fins form hornlike appendages (cephalic fins), one anterior to each eye, which create a funnellike effect and give mantas an unusually shaped head. Development is viviparous. The family contains 10 species in 2 genera, with 1 species recorded from Chesapeake Bay.

Manta
Manta birostris (Walbaum, 1792)

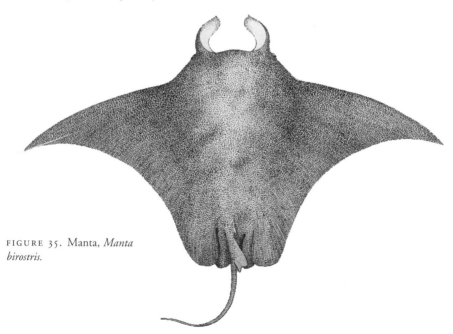

FIGURE 35. Manta, *Manta birostris.*

KEY FEATURES   Two large cephalic fins projecting anteriorly; mouth wide and terminal; tail whiplike, shorter than length of body, and spineless.

OTHER CHARACTERISTICS   Head distinct from disk; disk wider than long; lateral tips of disk acutely rounded; eyes and spiracles situated on sides of head; teeth minute, in many series;

papillae absent in mouth; caudal fin absent; small dorsal fin present on base of tail. Gray, dusky brown, or black dorsally; venter grayish white; whitish shoulder patches present on some individuals. Maximum adult size 6.7 m disk width (22 ft).

GEOGRAPHIC DISTRIBUTION   Found worldwide in tropical waters. In the western Atlantic, this species ranges from southern New England to Brazil, including the Gulf of Mexico.

ECOLOGY   The manta is a rare visitor to the lower Chesapeake Bay during the summer months but is common offshore. During the winter months, mantas disperse offshore and to the south. Mantas are usually observed swimming or basking at the water's surface but may also rest on the bottom. Mantas are filter feeders, and as they swim, they ingest small fishes and crustaceans. The frequent association of mantas with dolphins, birds, and other elasmobranchs (fishes in the same subclass as mantas) may indicate a feeding aggregation on a common prey. Mantas often breach.

FISHING INTEREST   None in the Chesapeake Bay region. Where common, mantas are occasionally landed with gill nets and harpoons. The wings are marketed for human consumption.

LITERATURE   Hildebrand and Schroeder 1928:71; Musick 1972; McEachran 1982; Robins et al. 1986; Notarbartolo-di-Sciara and Hillyear 1989.

Eagle Rays
FAMILY MYLIOBATIDAE

Eagle rays are strong long-distance travelers and are frequently observed swimming gracefully in the water column. Swimming is accomplished by lateral undulations of the muscular pectoral fins. The head of eagle rays is distinct from the disk, and the pectoral fins join ventrally to the snout, forming a subrostral lobe. The eyes and spiracles are on the sides of the head. The tail is longer than the disk width and is distally filamentous. No caudal fin is present, but a small dorsal fin is located on the base of the tail just anterior to a serrated spine (if present). Teeth are fused into grinding plates. Development is viviparous. The family comprises 22 species in 4 genera, with 2 species recorded from Chesapeake Bay waters.

KEY TO THE SPECIES OF EAGLE RAYS IN CHESAPEAKE BAY

1a. One series of large teeth present in each jaw. . . . . **spotted eagle ray, *Aetobatis narinari*** (p. 284)

1b. More than 1 (typically 7–9) series of teeth present in each jaw . . . .
. . . . **bullnose ray, *Myliobatis freminvillei*** (p. 50)

Bullnose ray
Myliobatis freminvillei Lesueur, 1824

KEY FEATURES   Anterior portions of pectoral fins forming single projecting subrostral lobe; floor of mouth with 5 or 6 papillae; teeth green.

OTHER CHARACTERISTICS   Head conspicuous, distinct from disk; disk much wider than long; lateral tip of pectoral fin acutely angled; small dorsal fin present on tail just posterior to pelvic fin margin; tail whiplike, without longitudinal folds or ridges; snout projecting; teeth flattened into pavementlike pattern; 1 or 2 long, serrated spines present just posterior to dorsal fin; juveniles with smooth dorsal surface; adults with low thorns on dorsal surface posterior to head; adult males with single thorn on orbit. Grayish, reddish brown, or dark brown dorsally, with diffuse white spots; venter white. Maximum adult size 86 cm disk width (3 ft).

GEOGRAPHIC DISTRIBUTION   Found in the western Atlantic from Cape Cod to Florida, coastally in the northern Gulf of Mexico, southward to Brazil.

ECOLOGY   The bullnose ray is a seasonal visitor that is common during summer and fall in the lower Chesapeake Bay and rare in the upper

Hatteras. Bullnose rays have been known to leap out of the water. They use their pectoral fins to dig for crustaceans and mollusks.

FISHING INTEREST   None in the Chesapeake Bay region. The bullnose ray is caught as bycatch with longlines and by pound and trammel nets.

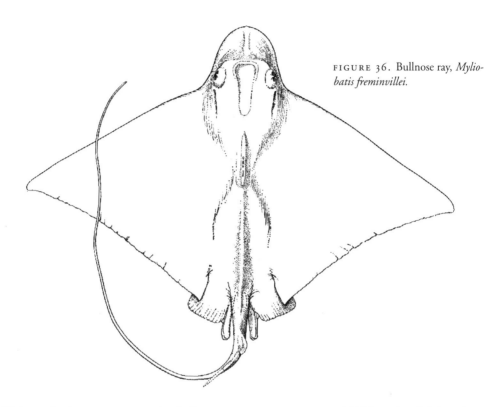

FIGURE 36. Bullnose ray, *Myliobatis freminvillei.*

bay. This species is most common in shallow estuaries, 10 m (33 ft) or less in depth. It travels northward during the summer, when it pups in shallow bays, and it winters to the south of Cape

LITERATURE   Hildebrand and Schroeder 1928:69; Musick 1972; Fischer 1978; McEachran 1982.

Cownose Rays
FAMILY RHINOPTERIDAE

The family of cownose rays is represented by a single genus *(Rhinoptera)*. Like the bullnose ray, cownose rays are strong long-distance travelers. Mass migrations of cownose rays are occasionally reported. Like the bullnose ray, cownose rays have a head that is distinct from the disk. However, the snout of cownose rays does not project as far, and the pectoral fins are separated anteriorly to form two distinct lobes ventral to the tip of the snout. The eyes and spiracles are on the sides of the head. The tail is longer than the disk width and is distally filamentous. No caudal fin is present, but a small dorsal fin is present on the base of the tail just anterior to one or two serrated spines. The teeth are fused into grinding plates. The genus *Rhinoptera* contains 10 species worldwide, with 1 species known from Chesapeake Bay.

Cownose ray
Rhinoptera bonasus (Mitchill, 1815)

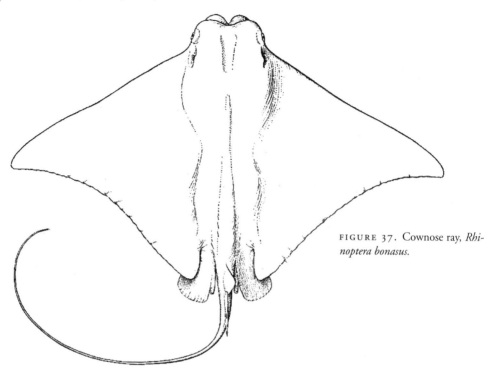

FIGURE 37. Cownose ray, *Rhinoptera bonasus.*

KEY FEATURES   Anterior portions of pectoral fins forming projecting subrostral lobe that is medially incised, thus forming 2 basally connected lobes; floor of mouth without papillae.

OTHER CHARACTERISTICS   Head conspicuous, distinct from disk; lateral tip of pectoral fin acutely angled; small dorsal fin present on tail just anteromedial to posterior pelvic fin margin; tail whiplike, without longitudinal folds or ridges; teeth flattened into pavementlike pattern; 1 or 2 long, serrated spines just posterior to dorsal fin; snout broad and emarginate. Brownish dorsally; venter pale. Maximum adult size 1 m disk width (3.3 ft).

GEOGRAPHIC DISTRIBUTION   Found in the western Atlantic from Massachusetts to the northern coast of South America, including the Gulf of Mexico.

ECOLOGY   Cownose rays are abundant in Chesapeake Bay from May to October, extending as far north as Tilghman Island. Large numbers of this species migrate north in spring. Massive schools have been aerially sighted in near-surface waters close to the Chesapeake Bay mouth; one such school was estimated to contain 5 million individuals. Cownose rays in the bay school by sex and age. Pupping occurs in the bay in early summer, and mating occurs in late summer. In autumn, cownose rays migrate offshore and southward. Although they are frequently encountered swimming at the surface, they feed on benthic shellfishes that are uncovered with the rays' pectoral fins and crushed between the tooth plates.

FISHING INTEREST   None in the Chesapeake Bay region. Cownose rays are caught incidentally in commercial fisheries and by anglers. This species is landed primarily by pound nets and occasionally by rod and reel, otter trawl, and longline. Oyster and clam growers have attributed substantial losses to cownose ray predation.

LITERATURE   Hildebrand and Schroeder 1928:71; Fischer 1978; McEachran 1982; Manooch 1984; Smith and Merriner 1987; Blaylock 1989.

Sturgeons
ORDER ACIPENSERIFORMES

The order of sturgeons contains two families, of which one occurs in Chesapeake Bay.

Sturgeons
FAMILY ACIPENSERIDAE

Sturgeons are large freshwater or anadromous fishes of north temperate regions. Although unrelated to sharks, sturgeons possess many sharklike structures and features, such as a heterocercal tail, a spiral valve intestine, a ventral protrusible mouth, and a mostly cartilaginous skeleton. A row of four barbels, which extends across most of the width of the snout, is situated midway between the mouth and the tip of the snout. The head is covered by bony plates, and the body has five rows of bony keeled scutes, with small bony scales between the scute rows. Sturgeons are excellent food fishes, and their eggs are commercially important as caviar. They spawn in the spring, migrating upstream to deposit great numbers of eggs over hard substrates. Sturgeons are modern relicts of fishes that were dominant during Paleozoic times and are represented today by only 24 species in 4 genera, with 2 species known to inhabit Chesapeake Bay waters.

KEY TO THE SPECIES OF STURGEONS IN CHESAPEAKE BAY

The head shape and the relative snout length change drastically with age in sturgeons. Because of allometric growth, the snout becomes relatively shorter and blunter. Consequently, key characters based on snout length as a proportion of total length are of little use and have frequently led to misidentifications. In particular, Atlantic sturgeon (*Acipenser oxyrhynchus*) of moderate size (approximately 1 m TL, or 3.3 ft) may be misidentified as shortnose sturgeon (*A. brevirostrum*).

1a. Mouth small, with width inside lips usually less than 62% (43–66%) of interorbital width; bony scutes present between anal fin and midlateral scutes. . . . . **Atlantic sturgeon,** *Acipenser oxyrhynchus* (p. 53)
1b. Mouth large, with width inside lips greater than 62% (63–81%) of interorbital width; bony scutes absent between anal fin and midlateral scutes . . . . **shortnose sturgeon,** *Acipenser brevirostrum* (p. 54)

Atlantic sturgeon
Acipenser oxyrhynchus Mitchill, 1814

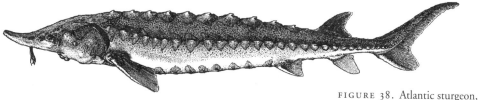

FIGURE 38. Atlantic sturgeon,
Acipenser oxyrhynchus.

KEY FEATURES   Snout relatively long and pointed; mouth small (usually <62% of interorbital width); large dermal scutes present in 5 major rows; double row of scutes present along dorsal midline posterior to dorsal fin; scutes present between anal fin base and lateral scute row; double row of scutes present along ventral midline anterior to anal fin; dorsal scutes numbering 7–13 (typically 9 or 10), lateral scutes 24–35 (typically 28 or 29), and ventral scutes 8–11 (typically 9 or 10); scutes sharp and close together in juveniles, separate and lower in profile in adults; gill rakers numbering 15–27; dorsal fin with 30–46 rays; anal fin with 23–27 rays (typically 24–26); head 26.5–27.6% of fork length; interorbital width 22.4–28.4% of head length (typically 26%).

OTHER CHARACTERISTICS   Spiracle present; 4 long, unfringed barbels present anterior to mouth; mouth protrusible; teeth absent in adults; dorsal fin located posteriorly; pelvic fin insertion ventroanterior to dorsal fin; pectoral fin insertion near ventral edge of gill cover; anal fin insertion approximately perpendicular to midpoint of dorsal fin; intestine pale (visible upon dissection). Dorsum bluish black to tan, with crests of dorsal scutes contrastingly pale; side brown, sometimes with pinkish cast; venter white; pectoral and pelvic fins and lower caudal lobe gray, with white anterior edge; anal fin white; dorsal fin and upper caudal lobe dark gray, with white margins. Maximum adult size 4.3 m TL (14 ft), with weight of more than 270 kg (>600 lb).

GEOGRAPHIC DISTRIBUTION   Recorded along the western Atlantic coast from Ungava Bay, Quebec, to the Gulf of Mexico.

ECOLOGY   Adult Atlantic sturgeon are anadromous and move through Chesapeake Bay during their spawning runs in April and May on their way into the tributaries. They also use the tidal tributaries as a nursery. At one time, spawning probably occurred in all large tributaries of the bay, but Atlantic sturgeon are rare in the bay today. There is recent evidence of limited spawning in the James and York rivers. The eggs of this species are large and numerous, with individual fecundity estimated at 800,000 to 3.76 million eggs. There is no evidence of nest building; the sticky eggs are apparently scattered over the bottom, where they become attached. Females move downstream after spawning, whereas males remain until the water temperature drops in autumn. Juveniles may spend several years in fresh or brackish water before moving into coastal waters, but juveniles tagged in the Hudson River have been taken occasionally in Chesapeake Bay. While at sea, Atlantic sturgeon appear to remain close to the coast. Atlantic sturgeon are long-lived; the largest adults have been estimated to attain age 60. In the mid-Atlantic, they reach sexual maturity at 7–12 years of age, with males maturing earlier than females. This species is typically a bottom dweller, feeding on benthic organisms such as mollusks, insects, and crustaceans. It roots along the bottom with its snout and sucks up bottom materials with its protrusible mouth.

FISHING INTEREST   Considered an excellent food fish. The roe of this species is a source of high-quality caviar. Sturgeons have been so reduced by overfishing, pollution, and dam construction that directed fisheries are active only in New York and Canada. In Chesapeake Bay the landings of Atlantic sturgeon peaked in 1890 at 329,000 kg (726,036 lb), after which the fishery rapidly declined and landings fell to 74,000 kg (162,570 lb) in 1904 and only 10,400 kg (22,898 lb) in 1920. In 1938 a law was passed in Virginia prohibiting removal of sturgeons less than 4 ft long from the waters of the state, and in 1974 it became "unlawful to take or catch and retain possession of any sturgeon fish" in Virginia. Hatchery rearing, careful management, and conservation efforts are being directed at reviving both population numbers and the industry. No sport fishery for the Atlantic sturgeon exists.

LITERATURE   Hildebrand and Schroeder 1928:72; Vladykov and Greeley 1963; Musick 1972; Eddy and Underhill 1978; Fischer 1978; Jenkins and Musick 1979; Van Den Avyle 1984; Smith 1985; Robins et al. 1986; Gilbert 1989; Musick et al. 1994.

Shortnose sturgeon
Acipenser brevirostrum Lesueur, 1818

KEY FEATURES   Snout short and blunt; mouth large (>62% of interorbital width); scutes absent along dorsal midline posterior to dorsal fin; scutes absent between anal fin base and lateral scute row; single row of scutes present along ventral midline posterior to anal fin; dorsal scutes numbering 7–13, lateral scutes 21–35, and ventral scutes 6–11; space between dorsal and lateral rows of scutes containing many rows of minute scales; gill rakers numbering 22–32; dorsal fin with 38–42 rays; anal fin with 18–24 rays.

tion currently exists. Adult shortnose sturgeon are anadromous and migrate above the fall line to spawn in swift water over rocky substrates from

FIGURE 39. Shortnose sturgeon, *Acipenser brevirostrum.*

OTHER CHARACTERISTICS   Spiracle present; 4 long, unfringed barbels anterior to mouth; mouth protrusible; teeth absent in adults; dorsal fin located posteriorly; insertion of pelvic fin ventroanterior to dorsal fin; pectoral fin insertion near ventral edge of gill cover; anal fin insertion approximately perpendicular to midpoint of dorsal fin; intestine dusky (visible upon dissection). Coloration closely similar to that of the Atlantic sturgeon, differing primarily in presence of dusky pigment in anal fin of shortnose sturgeon. Maximum adult size 1.4 m TL (4.6 ft). The shortnose sturgeon is the smallest sturgeon.

GEOGRAPHIC DISTRIBUTION   Recorded along the western Atlantic coast from St. John River, New Brunswick, to St. Johns River, Florida.

ECOLOGY   The shortnose sturgeon lives in freshwater and in low-salinity estuaries but occasionally ventures to the mouths of estuaries and the nearby coast. Historical collections of the shortnose sturgeon indicate that it once was found in the Potomac and Susquehanna rivers and may have occurred in the other major Chesapeake Bay tributaries as well. Recently it has been taken in the upper bay in the lower Susquehanna. However, it is possible that the fish that have been collected there entered the upper bay via the Chesapeake and Delaware canal from the Delaware River, where a well-documented popula-

February to April. Fecundity ranges from 27,000 to 208,000 eggs per female. Individuals grow slowly, and maturity is attained in males at 3–5 years and in females at 6–7 years. Shortnose sturgeon can live 30–40 years, with 1 female reported to have reached 67 years of age. Juveniles feed primarily on benthic crustaceans and insects; adults additionally prey on mollusks. Shortnose sturgeon reportedly feed mostly at night.

FISHING INTEREST   Classified as an endangered species by the U.S. Fish and Wildlife Service. Populations of the shortnose sturgeon have been decimated by damming and pollution of their spawning tributaries and probably by overfishing incidental to the Atlantic sturgeon fishery. Because of its endangered status, the shortnose sturgeon is protected throughout its range and cannot be legally caught for commercial or recreational purposes. Some populations are showing signs of recovery as water quality has improved. Installation of fish ladders or elimination of old dams, along with reintroduction of hatchery-reared fish, could promote the future recovery of the species in the Chesapeake system.

LITERATURE   Hildebrand and Schroeder 1928:76; Vladykov and Greeley 1963; Musick 1972; Gorham and McAllister 1974; Eddy and Underhill 1978; Fischer 1978; Dadswell et al. 1984; Gilbert 1989; Musick et al. 1994.

Gars

ORDER LEPISOSTEIFORMES

The order of gars contains a single family, of which one species occurs in Chesapeake Bay.

Gars

FAMILY LEPISOSTEIDAE

Gars are cylindrical, elongate fishes with a long, beaklike snout and large fanglike teeth. Gars retain several primitive characteristics, including encasement of the body in armorlike rhomboidal scales (ganoid scales) and a modified heterocercal caudal fin that is rounded but asymmetrical. Gars have a vascularized air bladder connected by a duct to the pharynx, thereby allowing respiration, when necessary, by air gulping. As facultative air breathers, gars can inhabit sluggish or stagnant waters low in oxygen. This family comprises seven species in two genera, of which a single species is recorded from Chesapeake Bay waters. Gars are unrelated to the needlefishes, of the family Belonidae, which gars resemble in head and body shape.

Longnose gar
Lepisosteus osseus (Linnaeus, 1758)

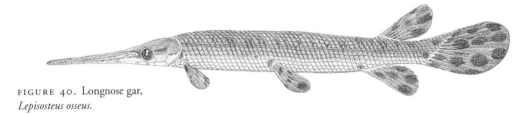

FIGURE 40. Longnose gar, *Lepisosteus osseus.*

KEY FEATURES   Snout beaklike, long, and slender; 1 row of fanglike teeth present on lower jaw, and 2 rows on upper jaw; caudal fin modified heterocercal; body scales rhomboidal and of heavy bone; dorsal and anal fins short-based, inserting just anterior to caudal fin.

OTHER CHARACTERISTICS   Body large, elongate, cylindrical, and slightly compressed posteriorly; eye small; nostrils anterior, at tip of snout; pectoral and pelvic fins low on body; pelvic fin located at approximate midbody. Appearance of coloration variable, depending on clarity and color of water; typically olive gray dorsally; venter pale or silvery; black spots sometimes present on dorsal fins, anal fins, and side; young with broad dusky brown midlateral stripe from snout to caudal base; pattern in young more highly contrasting than in older individuals. Maximum adult size 1.8 m TL (6 ft), with females tending to be somewhat larger than males.

GEOGRAPHIC DISTRIBUTION   Occurring in fresh and brackish waters from Quebec to northern Mexico.

ECOLOGY   Longnose gar are probably present in all major tributaries to Chesapeake Bay. Adults are frequently found in brackish water, especially during the winter months. Groups of adults often lie motionless near the surface, sometimes in poorly oxygenated water. In summer, when oxygen levels are at their lowest, longnose gar rise to the surface to gulp air. Spawning in the Chesapeake Bay region occurs in shallow freshwaters during May and June. The eggs are dark green and purportedly toxic to warm-blooded vertebrates. Larvae have an adhesive organ on the ventral surface of the upper jaw tip by which they attach to submerged objects above the bottom. The longnose gar is a voracious, lie-in-wait predator whose diet includes a variety of fishes and crustaceans. Once the quarry has been secured with a sideways sweep of the long jaws, it is swallowed headfirst.

FISHING INTEREST   Usually considered to be "rough" fish of no food or recreational value. Most anglers view longnose gar as competing for game and food species and damaging to fishing gear. When caught, longnose gar are often thrown on the shore to die. The world record is an individual from Texas of 1.8 m TL (6 ft) and weighing 23 kg (50 lb).

LITERATURE   Hildebrand and Schroeder 1928:77; Suttkus 1963; Musick 1972; Eddy and Underhill 1978; Fischer 1978; Jones et al. 1978; Manooch 1984; Smith 1985; Jenkins and Burkhead 1994.

Bowfins
ORDER AMIIFORMES

The order of bowfins comprises a single family that includes only a single extant species.

Bowfins
FAMILY AMIIDAE

The family Amiidae is primitive, dating to the Triassic period (about 210–245 million years ago). The bowfin retains many primitive features, including a gular plate between the two halves of the lower jaw, and an abbreviate heterocercal (hemicercal) tail. The bowfin is carnivorous, with a large mouth and strong teeth on a well-armored head. It typically inhabits swampy backwaters of rivers and lakes but occasionally is found in saline waters of 5‰ or greater. The single species, *Amia calva,* is restricted to the freshwaters of eastern and central North America.

Bowfin
Amia calva Linnaeus, 1766

FIGURE 41. Bowfin, *Amia calva.*

KEY FEATURES   Caudal fin hemicercal; dorsal fin low and long-based, originating well anterior to midbody and nearly reaching caudal fin; bony gular plate present on underside of head between halves of lower jaw; body covered with cycloid scales.

OTHER CHARACTERISTICS   Body cylindrical; head naked; mouth large; nostrils anterior, tubular, and overhanging mouth; anal fin short-based and higher than dorsal fin; pelvic fin short and located just anterior to midbody; pectoral fin low on body and rounded. Dorsum and flanks dark brown to olive green, forming reticulated pattern that continues onto caudal fin; belly yellow or cream; head with 2 or 3 dusky stripes radiating from posterior margin of eye; upper base of caudal fin with dusky spot surrounded by orange or yellow (an ocellus) in males, inconspicuous in females; dorsal fin with 2 dusky bands. Maximum adult size 1 m TL (3.3 ft).

GEOGRAPHIC DISTRIBUTION   Distributed throughout the eastern half of the United States and into Ontario. The coastal distribution is from Connecticut to Texas.

ECOLOGY   The bowfin, also known as the grindle, inhabits sluggish, swampy rivers and shallow lakes. It is more common in the Chesapeake Bay tributaries of Virginia than in the tributaries of Maryland; in Maryland the bowfin is known from fewer than a dozen localities. Like gars, the bowfin is able to gulp surface air, which is forced into the air bladder through a duct connected to the pharynx. This ability enables it to survive in waters that are periodically oxygen depleted. Spawning occurs from April to June. Males construct and guard saucer-shaped nests. After the young leave the nest, they form schools but are still guarded by the male. The young possess an attachment organ on their snout that enables them to adhere to the nest or to other objects. The schools break up when the young attain about 10 cm TL (4 in). Bowfins are primarily piscivorous but will eat almost anything that they can fit into their mouth, including crustaceans, mollusks, and insects.

FISHING INTEREST   Little valued for food and considered a nuisance by most anglers. Bowfins will take hooks or lures intended for bass and can damage nets. However, they are tenacious fighters and provide good sport on light tackle. The all-tackle record is a fish from South Carolina that weighed 9.8 kg (21.7 lb).

LITERATURE   Mansueti and Hardy 1967; Musick 1972; Jones et al. 1978; Lee et al. 1981; Fritzsche 1982; Manooch 1984; Smith 1985; Jenkins and Burkhead 1994.

Bonefishes
ORDER ALBULIFORMES

The order of bonefishes contains a single family, which occurs in Chesapeake Bay.

Bonefishes
FAMILY ALBULIDAE

Bonefishes are elongate, fusiform fishes with a conical snout and a subterminal mouth. Like their relatives, the ladyfish and the tarpon, bonefishes begin life as leptocephalus larvae and possess a gular plate. However, the gular plate of bonefishes is rudimentary and easily overlooked. Bonefishes are sought by many anglers but are of little value as a food fish because of the numerous small bones in the flesh. Bonefishes are shallow-water, nearshore inhabitants that forage on sandy or muddy bottoms for worms, mollusks, and small fishes. The family, distributed worldwide in tropical waters, comprises two genera and five species, one of which is recorded from Chesapeake Bay.

Bonefish
Albula vulpes (Linnaeus, 1758)

KEY FEATURES   Snout conical, terminating anterior to lower jaw; mouth inferior; scales small.

OTHER CHARACTERISTICS   Body elongate, not strongly compressed; scales numbering 65–71 in lateral series; single dorsal fin elevated anteriorly at approximate midpoint of body; dorsal fin with 17–19 rays; caudal fin broadly forked; anal fin with 8 or 9 rays and terminating near caudal peduncle; pelvic fin small and abdominal, originating posterior to midbody; pectoral fin low on body, pointed, and with 15–17 rays. Blue or green dorsally, with narrow dusky stripes; side and venter silvery; dusky blotch present on dorsal portion of pectoral fin base. Maximum adult size 1 m TL (3.3 ft).

GEOGRAPHIC DISTRIBUTION   Known from both the eastern and western Atlantic. In

so shallow that their dorsal and caudal fins break the surface. They feed on worms, mollusks, and crustaceans that are picked (or "grubbed") from mud and sand bottoms. Bonefish spawn offshore,

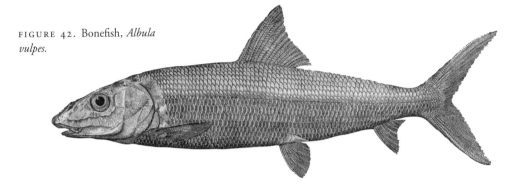

FIGURE 42. Bonefish, *Albula vulpes.*

the western Atlantic, the bonefish is known from the Bay of Fundy to Florida, throughout the Gulf of Mexico and the Caribbean Sea, southward to Brazil.

ECOLOGY   The bonefish is a rare visitor during late summer to the lower Chesapeake Bay. It frequents shallow inshore waters, including bays and estuaries. Bonefish sometimes feed in water

and the leptocephalus larvae migrate inshore to nursery areas.

FISHING INTEREST   Highly esteemed as a sport fish and caught almost exclusively by recreational anglers in the western Atlantic.

LITERATURE   Massmann 1957; Musick 1972; Fischer 1978; Jones et al. 1978; Fischer et al. 1981.

Tarpons and Tenpounders
ORDER ELOPIFORMES

The order of tarpons and tenpounders contains two families, both of which occur in Chesapeake Bay.

KEY TO THE FAMILIES OF TARPONS AND TENPOUNDERS IN CHESAPEAKE BAY

1a. Last ray of dorsal fin forming elongate filament; mouth superior, with lower jaw projecting; scales large, numbering 40–48 along lateral line; body laterally compressed. . . . . . **tarpons—Megalopidae** (p. 59)
1b. Last ray of dorsal fin not elongate; mouth terminal; scales small, usually numbering more than 100 along lateral line; body not greatly compressed . . . . **tenpounders—Elopidae** (p. 60)

Tarpons
FAMILY MEGALOPIDAE

Tarpons are marine fishes that often enter freshwater; they typically live near open ocean. Young tarpons are often found in estuaries and mangrove swamps. The air bladder of tarpons is located next to the skull, a trait unique among the elopiforms. The air bladder is highly vascularized and connected to the pharynx by a duct, allowing tarpons to supplement gill respiration by air breathing. Breathing is accomplished by periodically gulping air at the surface while exhibiting a rolling behavior similar to that of porpoises.

The family contains only two species, one found in the Indo-Pacific region and the other in the Atlantic Ocean.

Tarpon
Megalops atlanticus Valenciennes, 1847

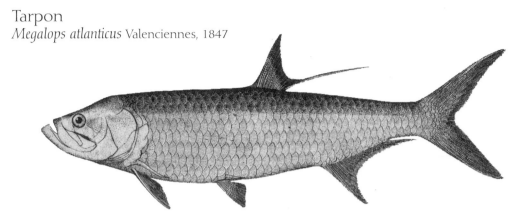

FIGURE 43. Tarpon, *Megalops atlanticus.*

KEY FEATURES   Last ray of dorsal fin forming elongate filament; mouth superior, with lower jaw projecting; scales large, numbering 40–48 along lateral line; base of anal fin longer than base of dorsal fin.

OTHER CHARACTERISTICS   Body moderately deep and strongly compressed; gular plate present; single dorsal fin at approximate midpoint of body, dorsoposterior to origin of pelvic fin; pectoral and pelvic fins with elongate axial scale; caudal fin broadly forked. Uniformly silvery blue dorsally; silver laterally and ventrally, with pale pectoral and pelvic fins. Maximum adult size 2.5 m TL (8.2 ft).

GEOGRAPHIC DISTRIBUTION   Known from both coasts of the Atlantic. In the western Atlantic, this species is known from Nova Scotia (rare north of Virginia) to Florida, throughout the Gulf of Mexico and the Caribbean to Brazil.

ECOLOGY   The tarpon is a rare summer visitor to Chesapeake Bay that has been recorded as far north in the bay as Anne Arundel County, Maryland. Tarpon are more commonly encoun-tered on the seaside of the bay's Eastern Shore in the tidal passes between the barrier islands. A coastal species, the tarpon is seldom encountered more than a few miles offshore and frequently penetrates freshwaters. Adult tarpon are active predators on fishes and crabs. Spawning apparently occurs in more southerly offshore waters over an extended period from May to September. Postmetamorphic young are found in tidal ponds and channels in mangrove forests in Florida.

FISHING INTEREST   Renowned throughout range as a game fish. Because of its prodigious head-shaking leaps when hooked, along with its hard, bony mouth, the tarpon is most frequently the victor in contests with anglers. The flesh is coarse and unpalatable to American taste but is said to be highly esteemed along the Central American coast.

LITERATURE   Hildebrand and Schroeder 1928:80; Hildebrand 1963b; Musick 1972; Fischer 1978; Jones et al. 1978; Fritzsche 1982; Manooch 1984; Smith 1989c.

Tenpounders
FAMILY ELOPIDAE

Members of the tenpounder family are elongate, fusiform fishes that possess a gular plate between the halves of the lower jaw and numerous (27–35) branchiostegal rays. These silvery fishes are typically marine, but several species may enter freshwater for short distances. Like other members of this order, and like eels and bonefishes, elopids begin life as compressed, transparent, ribbonlike larvae (leptocephali). Elopiform leptocephali differ from eel leptocephali in that the former have a forked caudal fin. The family _____ one genus and six species, which are distributed in tropical and subtropical oceans. One species _____ led from Chesapeake Bay.

h

_____saurus Linnaeus, 1766

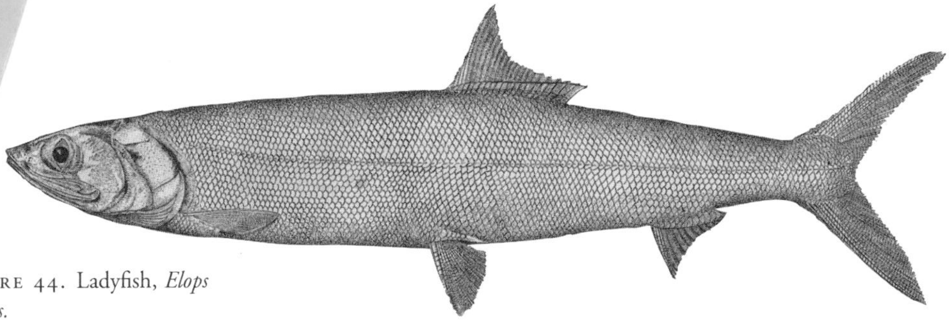

FIGURE 44. Ladyfish, *Elops saurus.*

KEY FEATURES   Dorsal fin without elongate terminal ray; gular plate present; dorsal and anal fins depressible into sheath of scales; adipose eyelid present; mouth terminal; scales very small, numbering 100–120 along lateral line; base of anal fin shorter than base of dorsal fin.

OTHER CHARACTERISTICS   Body elongate, not greatly compressed; eye large; single dorsal fin located slightly dorsoposterior to origin of pelvic fin; pectoral and pelvic fins with elongate axial scale; caudal fin broadly forked. Silvery blue dorsally; silvery gray laterally, with yellowish pectoral and pelvic fins. Maximum adult size 1 m TL (3.3 ft).

GEOGRAPHIC DISTRIBUTION   Known from Massachusetts to Florida and Bermuda and throughout the Gulf of Mexico and the Caribbean to Brazil.

ECOLOGY   The ladyfish is a seasonal visitor to the lower Chesapeake Bay in spring to fall and is infrequently encountered. It has been collected as far north in the bay as the Nanticoke River (Wicomico County, Maryland). Primarily a marine species that inhabits warm coastal waters, the ladyfish is sometimes encountered offshore or up rivers to nearly freshwater. The adults are reported to form schools. In more southerly waters, ladyfish are believed to spawn offshore in late summer and fall. No spawning is known to occur north of Cape Hatteras. However, metamorphic larvae have been taken in May through July in low-salinity waters of the lower James River. The diet of ladyfish is mainly crustaceans and small fishes.

FISHING INTEREST   Highly prized by anglers in the more tropical areas of its range, where it is more abundant, because of its ability to skip along the surface and leap out of the water when hooked. The ladyfish is not valued as food, and there is no commercial fishery.

LITERATURE   Hildebrand and Schroeder 1928:78; Hildebrand 1963b; Musick 1972; Govoni and Merriner 1978; Fischer 1978; Jones et al. 1978; Fritzsche 1982; Manooch 1984; Smith 1985; Smith 1989c; Nelson 1994.

Eels

ORDER ANGUILLIFORMES

The order of eels comprises 15 families, 3 of which occur in Chesapeake Bay. All larval eels begin life as transparent, highly compressed, ribbonlike larvae (leptocephali). Anguilliform leptocephali differ from elopiform leptocephali in that the former do not have a forked caudal fin.

KEY TO THE FAMILIES OF EELS IN CHESAPEAKE BAY

1a. Tip of tail naked, sharp, and pointed; posterior nostril with wide flaring margin and located on upper lip. . . . . **snake eels—Ophichthidae** . . . . (1 species recorded from Chesapeake Bay: speckled worm eel, *Myrophis punctatus,* p. 284)

1b. Tip of tail fringed with fin rays; posterior nostril with or without slightly raised rim and located above upper lip on a horizontal through lower margin of eye or higher **2**

2a. Origin of dorsal fin markedly dorsoposterior to tip of pectoral fin; lower jaw projecting slightly anterior to upper jaw; small embedded scales present . . . . **freshwater eels—Anguillidae** (p. 62)

2b. Origin of dorsal fin perpendicular or slightly dorsoanterior to tip of pectoral fin; upper jaw projecting slightly anterior to lower jaw; scales absent. . . . . **conger eels—Congridae** (p. 63)

Freshwater Eels

FAMILY ANGUILLIDAE

Anguillids are catadromous, leaving their freshwater habitat and migrating to the ocean to spawn. Anguillid leptocephali are approximately 60 mm (2.4 in) in total length when they arrive in coastal waters, where they metamorphose into a stage with a more eellike appearance (the glass eel stage). In the estuary, glass eels become pigmented and are then called elvers. Within a few months, elvers enter the yellow eel stage, which persists until sexual maturity. This family occurs in all seas except the eastern Pacific and South Atlantic and is represented by a single genus and approximately 15 species. In Chesapeake Bay, only 1 species is present.

American eel
Anguilla rostrata (Lesueur, 1817)
PLATE 3

FIGURE 45. American eel,
Anguilla rostrata.

KEY FEATURES   Tip of tail fringed with fin rays; posterior nostril anterior to eye; body covered with small elliptical scales embedded in skin; lower jaw projecting slightly anterior to upper jaw; origin of dorsal fin markedly dorsoposterior to tip of pectoral fin; teeth minute.

OTHER CHARACTERISTICS   Body long, slender, and serpentine, cylindrical anteriorly and compressed posteriorly; anterior nostril at end of short tube; dorsal, caudal, and anal fins continuous; pectoral fin well developed; pelvic fin absent. Uniformly greenish brown to yellowish brown dorsally; whitish gray ventrally; reproductively mature individuals with gray back, pure white belly, and silvery bronze sheen on flanks. Maximum adult size 1.5 m TL (5 ft) for females, 61 cm TL (2 ft) for males.

GEOGRAPHIC DISTRIBUTION   Present in brackish waters and their freshwater tributaries along the Atlantic coast of North America, throughout the Gulf of Mexico and the Caribbean, and along the east coast of Central America to Venezuela. The American eel also occurs inland in the St. Lawrence Seaway and the Great Lakes.

ECOLOGY   The American eel is an abundant resident of all tributaries to Chesapeake Bay. American eels spend most of their life in the yellow eel phase, in which they are nocturnally active omnivores, feeding on insects, mollusks, crustaceans, worms, and other fishes. Residence time in fresh and brackish waters as yellow eels is at least 5 years, with some individuals reported to be 20 years old when beginning their reproductive migration. Sexual maturation is delayed until just prior to the reproductive migration and involves profound changes that include the cessation of feeding, enlargement of the eyes and pectoral fins, a change in the visual pigments, and a shift in body color pattern. All of these changes adapt the eel to an oceanic existence. Reproductive migration occurs in autumn, with adults descending streams and rivers to begin their journey to an area north of the Bahamas (the Sargasso Sea), where spawning is believed to start in January. (*Anguilla anguilla,* the European counterpart of the American eel, also spawns in the Sargasso Sea.) Migrating freshwater eels may move through deep grass and shallow ditches. Downstream movements most commonly occur at night. Adult American eels purportedly die after spawning. Leptocephalus larvae of American eels drift in ocean currents for about 9–12 months before entering coastal waters. There, at about 60 mm (2.4 in) in total length, they metamorphose into the transparent glass eel stage. The glass eels move into the estuary, primarily in the fall along the Atlantic coast, where they become pigmented and are known as elvers. Some elvers remain in the estuary, but others migrate varying distances upstream, some for several hundred kilometers. Elvers are tenacious in their upstream migration and frequently overcome seemingly impassable obstacles such as spillways, dams, falls, and rapids.

FISHING INTEREST   Landed most often by fyke nets and eelpots, although also caught by anglers on hook and line. In the Chesapeake Bay area, most American eels are collected in pots and support an extensive fishery. Dockside value in 1990 averaged $1.60/lb ($0.73/kg). Some are consumed locally, but a larger demand for American eels exists in both Europe and east Asia, so most are exported. A commercial catch of more than 318,000 kg (700,000 lb) was reported by both Maryland and Virginia in 1981. Commercial catches have declined considerably since then. In 1990, for instance, the commercial catch was 54,000 kg (118,000 lb) for Maryland and 136,000 kg (299,000 lb) for Virginia. The declining catch of the American eel may indicate is overexploitation of the stock or may reflect market conditions.

LITERATURE   Hildebrand and Schroeder 1928:112; Musick 1972; Eddy and Underhill 1978; Fischer 1978; Hardy 1978a; Manooch 1984; Smith 1985; Jones et al. 1988; Smith 1989a.

Conger Eels
FAMILY CONGRIDAE

Congrids are scaleless eels with a long dorsal fin (longer than that of anguillids). Conger eels occur from shallow water to great depths and live in various habitats. However, they frequently occur over sandy bottoms near grass beds and reefs. Some congrids are burrow dwellers, and others inhabit coral reefs. Congrids are a diverse group, comprising 38 genera and 100 species. A single species is reported from Chesapeake Bay waters.

Conger eel
Conger oceanicus (Mitchill, 1814)

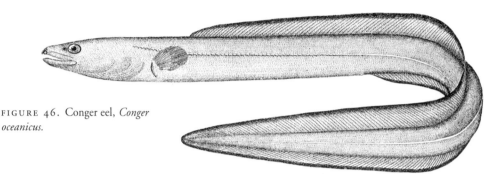

FIGURE 46. Conger eel, *Conger oceanicus.*

KEY FEATURES   Tip of tail fringed with fin rays; dorsal fin origin perpendicular or slightly dorsoanterior to tip of pectoral fin; 2 rows of small teeth present in lower jaw; posterior nostril located near eye; scales absent on body; upper jaw projecting slightly anterior to lower jaw.

OTHER CHARACTERISTICS   Body elongate and cylindrical, tapering posteriorly; dorsal, caudal, and anal fins continuous; pectoral fin well developed; pelvic fin absent. Grayish dorsally; whitish ventrally; black margin present on continuous fin. Maximum adult size 2.2 m TL (7.2 ft) for females, 76 cm TL (2.5 ft) for males.

GEOGRAPHIC DISTRIBUTION   Inhabiting coastal waters in the western Atlantic from Massachusetts to Florida and from Florida to Texas in the Gulf of Mexico. One specimen from near Yucatán is also known.

ECOLOGY   The conger eel is an occasional visitor to the lower Chesapeake Bay and is known to extend as far north as Worcester County, Maryland, and the Potomac River. Spawning apparently occurs from autumn to early winter in offshore oceanic waters, probably in the Sargasso Sea (as with *Anguilla* species, such as the American eel). The conger eel leptocephalus reaches a maximum size of about 16 cm (6.3 in). Adults are known from shallow waters to depths of nearly 600 m (1,969 ft). The conger eel is reported to associate with tilefish *(Lopholatilus chamaeleonticeps)* burrows offshore. Conger eels are nocturnal predators that primarily eat fishes, but they also prey on crustaceans and mollusks.

FISHING INTEREST   Caught frequently by rod and reel and occasionally by bottom trawl and traps. Conger eels are of no commercial importance in the Chesapeake Bay region today but were marketed fresh and salted in years past.

LITERATURE   Hildebrand and Schroeder 1928:116; Musick 1972; Fischer 1978; Hardy 1978a; Able et al. 1982; Manooch 1984; Smith 1985; Hood et al. 1988; Smith 1989b; McCleave and Miller 1994; Nelson 1994.

Anchovies and Herrings
ORDER CLUPEIFORMES

The order of anchovies and herrings contains four families, of which two occur in Chesapeake Bay.

KEY TO THE FAMILIES OF ANCHOVIES AND HERRINGS IN CHESAPEAKE BAY

1a. Mouth inferior and large, with maxilla extending well posterior to posterior margin of eye; midline of belly forming sharp angle or rounded; scutes absent . . . . **anchovies—Engraulidae** (p. 65)

1b. Mouth terminal and small, with maxilla not extending posterior to posterior margin of eye; midline of belly forming sharp saw-toothed angle composed of median row of scutes; abdominal scutes absent but 1 pelvic scute present . . . . **herrings—Clupeidae** (p. 67)

Anchovies
FAMILY ENGRAULIDAE

Anchovies have a large mouth that easily distinguishes them from herrings and silversides, which they resemble. Anchovies are small fusiform fishes with round, piglike snouts and underslung lower jaws. The dorsal and anal fins lack spines, and no lateral line is present. Anchovies are primarily marine fishes, but some species frequent brackish water and others are confined to freshwater. They are typically schooling fishes and, as such, form a sizable fishery in certain parts of the world. The family comprises about 14 genera and 139 species that are distributed worldwide. One genus and 2 species occur in Chesapeake Bay waters.

KEY TO THE SPECIES OF ANCHOVIES IN CHESAPEAKE BAY

1a. Origin of anal fin perpendicular to anterior portion or midportion of dorsal fin; anal fin with 23–31 rays . . . . **bay anchovy, Anchoa mitchilli** (p. 65)

1b. Origin of anal fin perpendicular to posterior portion of dorsal fin; anal fin with 18–24 rays . . . . **striped anchovy, Anchoa hepsetus** (p. 66)

Bay anchovy
Anchoa mitchilli (Valenciennes, 1848)

KEY FEATURES Snout short and blunt; origin of anal fin perpendicular to anterior portion or midportion of dorsal fin; anal fin with 23–31 rays; pectoral fin with 11–14 rays.

OTHER CHARACTERISTICS Body elongate fusiform and moderately compressed; belly moderately keeled; mouth large and inferior; maxilla long and sharply pointed posteriorly, with posterior end reaching nearly to margin of opercle; teeth small, pointed, and present in both jaws; gill rakers long and slender, numbering 19–25 on lower limb of first arch; scales cycloid; dorsal fin origin nearer to caudal fin than to snout; caudal fin forked; pectoral fin inserted low on body. Body greenish in life, with blue reflections dorsal to narrow silvery longitudinal stripe that is prominent from opercle to base of caudal fin, but not as prominent as in the striped anchovy. Maximum adult size about 10 cm SL (4 in).

GEOGRAPHIC DISTRIBUTION Known from the Gulf of Maine to Florida and throughout the Gulf of Mexico. The bay anchovy is most abundant in estuarine waters.

ECOLOGY The bay anchovy is abundant throughout Chesapeake Bay and the lower reaches of its tributaries in salinities of 1–33‰.

During the winter months the bay anchovy resides in deep water of the bay, but during the warmer months it is common along shorelines. The bay anchovy is a schooling species that feeds

monly encountered fish in Chesapeake Bay, and it is an important food resource for other fishes. FISHING INTEREST   Caught by seines and bottom trawls. Though not of direct commercial

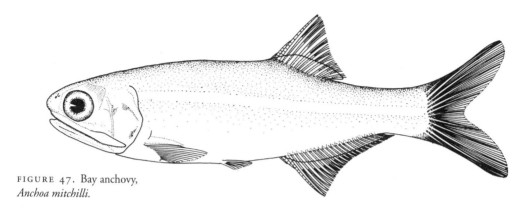

FIGURE 47. Bay anchovy,
Anchoa mitchilli.

on zooplankton. In Chesapeake Bay, spawning takes place at night over a broad range of salinities during a spawning season that extends from late April through late September, with a peak in July. Spawning typically occurs in estuaries where water temperatures are at least 12°C (54°F) and salinities are greater than 10‰. The bay anchovy is both the most abundant and the most com-

importance in Chesapeake Bay, the bay anchovy is of considerable indirect value as a forage resource.
LITERATURE   Hildebrand and Schroeder 1928:109; Hildebrand 1963c; Musick 1972; Fischer 1978; Jones et al. 1978; Olney 1983; Whitehead et al. 1985; Robins et al. 1986; Morton 1989; Luo and Musick 1991.

Striped anchovy
Anchoa hepsetus (Linnaeus, 1758)

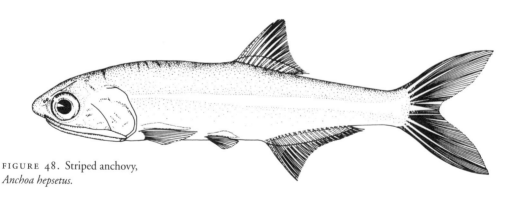

FIGURE 48. Striped anchovy,
Anchoa hepsetus.

KEY FEATURES   Snout prominent and pointed; origin of anal fin perpendicular to posterior portion of dorsal fin; anal fin with 18–24 rays (typically 21–23); pectoral fin with 15–18 rays (typically 16 or 17).

OTHER CHARACTERISTICS   Body elongate fusiform and slightly compressed; belly not sharply keeled; mouth large and inferior; maxilla long and sharply pointed posteriorly, with posterior end reaching to or nearly to margin of opercle; teeth small, sharply pointed, and present in both jaws; gill rakers long and slender, numbering 21–25 on lower limb of first arch; scales cycloid; dorsal fin origin nearer to caudal fin than to snout; caudal fin forked; pectoral fin inserted low on body. In life, bluish green dorsally; pale gray laterally, with broad, bright silver longitudinal stripe extending from opercle to base of caudal fin. Maximum adult size 15 cm SL (6 in).

GEOGRAPHIC DISTRIBUTION   Ranging from Massachusetts to Florida, throughout the Gulf of Mexico and the Caribbean, to Uruguay.

ECOLOGY   The striped anchovy is present from spring through autumn throughout Chesapeake Bay. This species is not nearly as abundant as the bay anchovy and is only occasionally encountered in the upper bay. Although tolerant of a wide range of salinities, the striped anchovy does not enter freshwater. It is most abundant in water temperatures of 20°–30°C (68°–86°F) and probably leaves the bay during the winter months to dwell in deeper waters (up to 70 m, or 230 ft, deep). The spawning season is similar to that of the bay anchovy; however, the eggs of the striped anchovy are most abundant near the bay mouth, and spawning appears limited within the bay. Like the bay anchovy, the striped anchovy is a schooling species that feeds primarily on zooplankton.

FISHING INTEREST   Frequently collected with the bay anchovy in seines and bottom trawls. The striped anchovy is not of direct commercial importance in the Chesapeake Bay region but is of considerable value indirectly as a food source for other fishes and wading birds.

LITERATURE   Hildebrand and Schroeder 1928:110; Hildebrand 1963c; Musick 1972; Fischer 1978; Jones et al. 1978; Benson 1982; Smith 1985; Whitehead et al. 1985.

Herrings
FAMILY CLUPEIDAE

Clupeids are typically marine fishes found in the coastal waters of all seas. The biology and ecology of clupeids are varied: some species live permanently in freshwater, some enter freshwater to feed or to spawn, some are filter feeders on plankton, and some are fish eaters. Many clupeid species aggregate in large schools that form the basis of important fisheries. Most clupeids are small, mostly silvery fishes that possess a series of scutes along the belly. Their bodies are strongly to moderately compressed fusiform in shape. All fins lack spines. The single dorsal fin is short-based and located near the midpoint of the body, and the caudal fin is deeply forked. Scales are cycloid, and no lateral line is present. The family comprises 180 species in 56 genera, of which 6 genera and 10 species are known from Chesapeake Bay.

KEY TO THE SPECIES OF HERRINGS IN CHESAPEAKE BAY

The color of the peritoneum is usually but not always visible without dissection.

1a. Abdominal scutes absent; 1 pelvic scute present . . . . **round herring,** *Etrumeus teres* (p. 68)
1b. Abdominal scutes and 1 pelvic scute present **2**

2a. Last ray of dorsal fin long and filamentous **3**
2b. Last ray of dorsal fin not long and filamentous **5**

3a. Predorsal midline without scales; gill rakers numbering more than 180 . . . . **4**
3b. Predorsal midline with scales; gill rakers numbering fewer than 120 . . . .
. . . . **Atlantic thread herring,** *Opisthonema oglinum* (p. 69)

4a. Upper jaw with distinct median notch (Figure 49); more than 50 scales present in lateral series; upper jaw slightly projecting; anal fin typically with 29–35 rays; prepelvic scutes typically numbering 18 or more . . . . **gizzard shad, *Dorosoma cepedianum*** (p. 70)

4b. Upper jaw without distinct median notch (Figure 50); fewer than 50 scales present in lateral series; upper jaw not projecting (mouth terminal); anal fin typically with 20–25 rays; prepelvic scutes typically numbering fewer than 18 . . . . **threadfin shad, *Dorosoma petenense*** (p. 71)

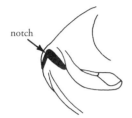

FIGURE 49. Upper jaw with median notch.

FIGURE 50. Upper jaw without median notch.

5a. Predorsal scales on either side of midline enlarged; pelvic fin with 7 rays . . . . **Atlantic menhaden, *Brevoortia tyrannus*** (p. 72)

5b. Predorsal scales on either side of midline not enlarged; pelvic fin typically with 9 rays **6**

6a. Body depth 20–26% of standard length; dark spot absent just behind opercle . . . . **Atlantic herring, *Clupea harengus*** (p. 73)

6b. Body depth 30–37% of standard length; dark spot present just behind opercle, sometimes followed by series of smaller spots **7**

7a. Eye diameter usually less than greatest cheek depth **8**

7b. Eye diameter usually equal to or greater than greatest cheek depth **9**

8a. Gill rakers on lower limb of first arch numbering 59–76; teeth absent in jaws of fish of greater than 15 cm SL (6 in); tongue with pigment in medial area; peritoneum pale to silvery . . . . **American shad, *Alosa sapidissima*** (p. 74)

8b. Gill rakers on lower limb of first arch numbering 18–23; minute teeth present in jaws of fish at all sizes; tongue without pigment in medial area; peritoneum grayish, peppered with black . . . . **hickory shad, *Alosa mediocris*** (p. 75)

9a. Gill rakers on lower limb of first arch usually numbering 39–41; eye diameter greater than snout length; dorsum grayish green; peritoneum pale, with dusky dots . . . . . **alewife, *Alosa pseudoharengus*** (p. 76)

9b. Gill rakers on lower limb of first arch usually numbering 44–50; eye diameter less than or equal to snout length; dorsum deep bluish green; peritoneum black to dusky . . . . **blueback herring, *Alosa aestivalis*** (p. 78)

Round herring
Etrumeus teres (DeKay, 1842)

KEY FEATURES   Belly rounded; no scutes present except 1 ventral scute deeply embedded around pelvic fin.

OTHER CHARACTERISTICS   Body elongate and not very compressed; snout long and rounded; mouth large; minute teeth present on jaws, vomer, and tongue; branchiostegal rays numbering 14 or 15; dorsal fin origin nearer to snout than to caudal fin; dorsal fin with 17–20 rays; caudal fin deeply forked; anal fin low on body, with 10–12 rays; pelvic fin originating posterior to midbody, with 8 rays; pectoral fin low on body, with 14–16 rays; pectoral and pelvic fins with prominent axillary scale. Greenish olive dorsally, shading to silvery on side and venter. Maximum adult size 38 cm TL (15 in), commonly to 18 cm TL (7 in).

GEOGRAPHIC DISTRIBUTION Known from the western Atlantic, western Indian, and

to the lower Chesapeake Bay during the late spring and summer months. This pelagic, schooling species moves offshore and south in winter. It is typically regarded as a warmwater fish, but little is known about its biology.

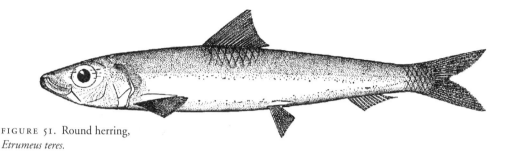

FIGURE 51. Round herring, *Etrumeus teres.*

western and eastern Pacific oceans. In the western Atlantic, the round herring is known from the Bay of Fundy to Florida, in portions of the Gulf of Mexico and the Caribbean Sea, and southward to northern South America.

ECOLOGY Although common along the coast, the round herring is a rare to occasional visitor

FISHING INTEREST Of no commercial or recreational interest. The round herring is occasionally collected with seines as bycatch.

LITERATURE Massmann 1960; Hildebrand 1963a; Musick 1972; Smith 1985; Whitehead 1985.

Atlantic thread herring
Opisthonema oglinum (Lesueur, 1817)

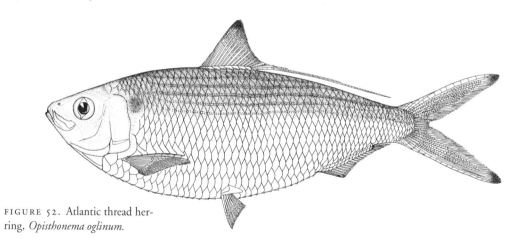

FIGURE 52. Atlantic thread herring, *Opisthonema oglinum.*

KEY FEATURES Last ray of dorsal fin filamentous; predorsal midline with scales; pelvic fin with 8 rays; upper jaw without median notch.

OTHER CHARACTERISTICS Body moderately deep, compressed fusiform; abdomen compressed, with 32–36 sharp median scutes; mouth

terminal; teeth absent on jaws; gill rakers long and slender, increasing in number with age to 80–100 on lower limb of first arch and fewer than 120 total; scales large, numbering 42–50 in lateral series; dorsal fin with 17–21 rays; anal fin low on body, with long base and 20–25 rays; pelvic fin insertion perpendicular to middle of dorsal fin base. Dorsum blue green, typically with prominent dark shoulder spot and often with several dusky horizontal stripes; ventral half of body silvery; dorsal and caudal fins usually tipped with black. Maximum adult size 30 cm SL (12 in).

GEOGRAPHIC DISTRIBUTION   Known from Maine to Florida, throughout the Gulf of Mexico and the Caribbean, to Brazil.

ECOLOGY   A summer visitor that is most abundant in the lower Chesapeake Bay, the Atlantic thread herring is a pelagic schooling species that frequents waters less than 50 m (164 ft) deep. Adult and juvenile Atlantic thread herring form schools near the surface, often with other clupeids. Spawning occurs in the nearshore coastal waters of North Carolina in early summer. This species is primarily a filter feeder on zooplankton but is also reported to eat crabs, shrimps, and small fishes.

FISHING INTEREST   Caught with seines and cast nets but of no recreational or commercial interest in Chesapeake Bay.

LITERATURE   Hildebrand and Schroeder 1928:101; Hildebrand 1963a; Musick 1972; Fischer 1978; Jones et al. 1978; Benson 1982; Whitehead et al. 1985.

Gizzard shad
Dorosoma cepedianum (Lesueur, 1818)
PLATE 4

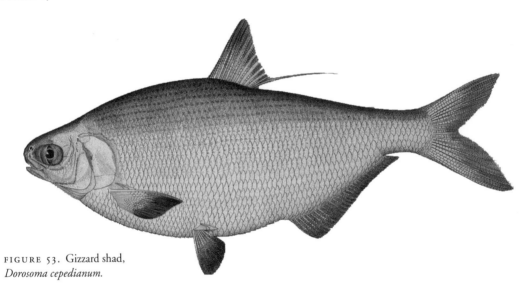

FIGURE 53. Gizzard shad, *Dorosoma cepedianum.*

KEY FEATURES   Last ray of dorsal fin filamentous; upper jaw with deep median notch; scales small, numbering 52–70 in lateral series; predorsal midline without scales; upper jaw slightly projecting and bluntly rounded; prepelvic scutes numbering 17–20 (typically 18 or more).

OTHER CHARACTERISTICS   Body deep, compressed fusiform; abdomen compressed, with 27–32 sharp scutes on midline; mouth small and inferior; jaw teeth absent in adults; gill rakers long and slender, numbering 300 or more on first arch; dorsal fin with 10–15 rays; anal fin with very long base and 25–37 rays (typically 29–35); pelvic fin with 7–10 rays and inserting slightly ventroanterior to origin of dorsal fin. Metallic blue dorsally; silver laterally, with 6–8 dusky longitudinal stripes on flanks; whitish ventrally; dusky shoulder spot present in young, becoming obscure to absent in adults. Maximum adult size 50 cm SL (20 in).

GEOGRAPHIC DISTRIBUTION   Occurring in the Mississippi and Atlantic drainages and the

Great Lakes, except Lake Superior. This species is known from all tributaries to the Gulf of Mexico as far south as northern Mexico.

ECOLOGY   The gizzard shad is a common to abundant species in all the freshwaters of tributaries to Chesapeake Bay. However, it is common in more saline bay waters only in autumn and winter, when it is taken in deeper waters near the mouths of tributaries. Gizzard shad can tolerate salinities as great as 22‰. Warm, fertile, shallow bodies of water with soft mud bottoms, high turbidity, and relatively few predators are ideal for these shad, because they have a high reproductive capacity and a rapid growth rate and they utilize plankton directly and efficiently. Such habitats often become overpopulated with this species to the exclusion of more desirable species. In addition to using soft-bottom habitats, gizzard shad are also found over mud, sand, gravel, and vegetated flats. Spawning occurs in quiet, fresh waters during late spring and early summer in the Chesapeake Bay region. This species displays no obvi-

ous spawning migration patterns, except that fish in brackish water return to freshwater. Spawning activity is associated with rapidly rising water levels and temperature; a water temperature of about 16°C (61°F) apparently provides the stimulus for spawning. Spawning activity is greatest in early evening and just after dark. Gizzard shad are filter feeders on microscopic algae and crustaceans; they also pick through mud and detritus on the bottom.

FISHING INTEREST   Of no recreational value except as a limited forage resource for other species. This species is caught incidentally with other fishes by commercial fisheries that use nets. The catch is mainly used as feed, fertilizer, or baitfish.

LITERATURE   Hildebrand and Schroeder 1928:106; Miller 1950, 1963; Musick 1972; Jones et al. 1978; Manooch 1984; Smith 1985; Whitehead et al. 1985; Williamson and Nelson 1985; Jenkins and Burkhead 1994.

Threadfin shad
Dorosoma petenense (Günther, 1867)

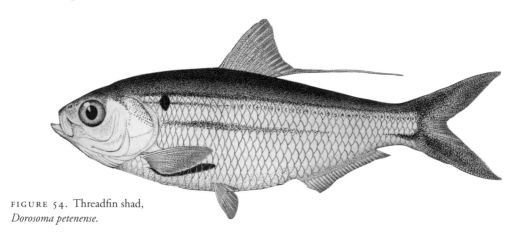

FIGURE 54. Threadfin shad,
Dorosoma petenense.

KEY FEATURES   Last ray of dorsal fin filamentous; upper jaw without distinct deep median notch; scales relatively large, numbering 41–48 in lateral series; predorsal midline without scales; mouth small and terminal; prepelvic scutes numbering 15–18 (typically 17 or fewer).

OTHER CHARACTERISTICS   Body moderately deep, compressed fusiform; abdomen com-

pressed, with 23–29 sharp scutes on midline; head moderate in size; jaw teeth absent; gill rakers long and numerous, increasing with age to more than 300 on first arch; dorsal fin with 11–14 rays; anal fin with short base and 17–27 rays (typically 20–25); pelvic fin with 7 or 8 rays and inserting perpendicular to origin of dorsal fin. Dorsum bluish black to dusky olive; bright silver laterally and ventrally; prominent dusky shoulder spot present; several dusky longitudinal stripes typically present on flanks; dorsal and caudal fins yellowish brown basally. Maximum adult size 22 cm SL (9 in).

GEOGRAPHIC DISTRIBUTION   Native to North America, originally occurring in the drainage systems of the Mississippi River and Gulf of Mexico. The threadfin shad was introduced and/or transplanted into various river systems throughout the United States, including Hawaii. In the Chesapeake Bay region, the threadfin shad was introduced into the James and Rappahannock rivers. Populations of threadfin shad are now established in the Western Shore drainage systems of the lower bay.

ECOLOGY   The threadfin shad is now com-monly encountered along the Western Shore of the lower Chesapeake Bay and has also been collected in the Nanticoke and Northeast rivers on the Eastern Shore. Although typically found in freshwater, adult threadfin shad can tolerate salinities up to 30‰. This species spawns twice a year—in spring and autumn—in freshwaters over vegetation or near submerged structure. The threadfin shad is a pelagic, schooling species that feeds primarily by filtering unicellular algae and small crustaceans with its gill rakers.

FISHING INTEREST   Of no commercial or recreational importance except as forage for larger fishes.

LITERATURE   Miller 1950, 1963; Musick 1972; Jones et al. 1978; Whitehead et al. 1985; Jenkins and Burkhead 1994.

Atlantic menhaden
Brevoortia tyrannus (Latrobe, 1802)

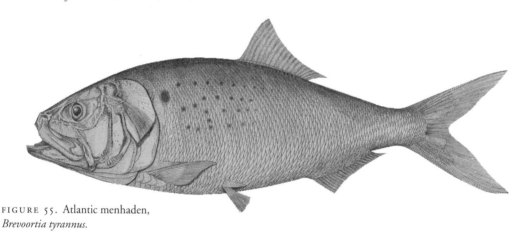

FIGURE 55. Atlantic menhaden, *Brevoortia tyrannus.*

KEY FEATURES   Predorsal scales on either side of midline enlarged; pelvic fin with 7 rays; upper jaw with deep median notch; last ray of dorsal fin not filamentous.

OTHER CHARACTERISTICS   Body moderately deep, compressed fusiform; abdomen compressed, with 30–35 sharp scutes on midline; head large and compressed; snout blunt; mouth terminal; jaw teeth absent in adults; gill rakers extremely long and slender, numbering about 160 on lower limb of first arch in adults; dorsal fin with 18–22 rays; anal fin with long base and 18–24 rays; pelvic fin insertion slightly ventroposterior to origin of dorsal fin; peritoneum black. Dorsum green to bluish; brassy laterally; black shoulder spot present posterior to gill opening, and variable number of smaller spots present on flank. Maximum adult size 38 cm SL (15 in).

GEOGRAPHIC DISTRIBUTION   Occurring in coastal waters of the western Atlantic from Nova Scotia to Florida.

ECOLOGY   Atlantic menhaden are common to abundant in all salinities throughout Chesapeake Bay in spring, summer, and autumn. They retreat to deeper, more southerly waters during the winter months, although juveniles may overwinter in the bay in some years. Atlantic menhaden are stratified along the coast in summer, with younger fish found in the Chesapeake Bay region and to the south and older fish distributed to the north. By December, most of the adult population north of the bay has moved to waters off the North Carolina coast. During March and early April, the adults regroup and migrate northward. Spawning in this region occurs in the spring (March–May) and again in the fall (September–October) in shelf waters off the bay. Larvae of 10–34 mm TL (0.4–1.3 in) appear in the bay in large numbers in May and June, with a smaller influx in November. The larvae move into the brackish waters and freshwaters, which they utilize as nursery areas, and metamorphose into juveniles. The juveniles grow rapidly through the summer and reach 40–185 mm SL (1.6–7.3 in) by fall. The young of the year leave the estuary in late fall and migrate southward in dense schools. Summer die-offs of large numbers of Atlantic menhaden are common in Chesapeake Bay, mostly associated with low-dissolved-oxygen events. A large crustacean parasite is commonly found in the mouth of the Atlantic menhaden; thus, this fish is also known as the bugfish. The Atlantic menhaden is also called bunker and fatback, names that refer to this species in the well-nourished state. A schooling, pelagic species, Atlantic menhaden are filter feeders on both phytoplankton and zooplankton.

FISHING INTEREST   Of major commercial importance as a source of fish oil, fertilizer, and fish meal. More pounds of menhaden are landed each year than of any other fish in the United States. They are taken by a variety of gear, but purse seines and pound nets are responsible for most of the catch. In recent years the fishery focus has shifted from more northerly waters to the younger and smaller fish in the Chesapeake Bay region. The bay catch in Virginia waters exceeded 227 million kilograms (more than 500 million pounds) in 1972, mostly taken by purse seines. Catch data for Virginia is incomplete after 1976. In Maryland, where purse seines are prohibited, the bay catch is primarily by pound nets and peaked at 4.9 million kilograms (10.7 million pounds) in 1981.

LITERATURE   Hildebrand and Schroeder 1928:102; Hildebrand 1963a; Reintjes 1969; Musick 1972; Jones et al. 1978; Manooch 1984; Smith 1985; Whitehead et al. 1985; Ahrenholz et al. 1987; Ahrenholz 1991.

Atlantic herring
Clupea harengus Linnaeus, 1758
PLATE 5

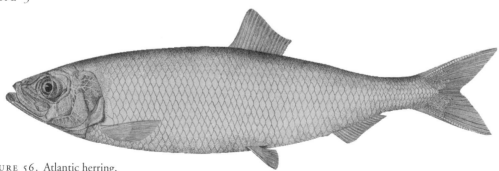

FIGURE 56. Atlantic herring,
Clupea harengus.

KEY FEATURES   Body elongate, its depth 20–26% of standard length; dusky spot absent behind opercle; upper jaw without median notch; last ray of dorsal fin not filamentous; pelvic fin with 9 rays (rarely 8 or 10).

OTHER CHARACTERISTICS   Body compressed fusiform; abdomen rounded, its scutes without prominent keel; mouth terminal; teeth absent in jaws but present on vomer; gill rakers long and slender, increasing in number with age to approximately 40 on lower limb of first arch; scales moderate in size and easily lost; origin of dorsal fin slightly posterior to midbody; dorsal fin with 18 rays; anal fin with 17 rays; pelvic fin inserting perpendicular to middle of dorsal fin base. Dorsum greenish or bluish; ventral half of body silvery. Maximum adult size 40 cm SL (1.3 ft), typically 20–25 cm (8–10 in).

GEOGRAPHIC DISTRIBUTION   Known from both coasts of the North Atlantic. In the western Atlantic, the range is from southern Greenland to South Carolina.

ECOLOGY   Atlantic herring are found in Chesapeake Bay during winter and spring and extend as far north as the Susquehanna flats, but they are more abundant in the lower bay. In general, the Atlantic herring is a pelagic, schooling species that frequents waters less than 200 m (660 ft) deep. The spawning season varies by population, with at least one population spawning during any given month of the year. Spawning occurs from shallow to deep waters (1–200 m, or 3.3–660 ft), but not in bay waters. The dense egg masses are deposited on the bottom. Atlantic herring are filter feeders on plankton.

FISHING INTEREST   Of only marginal commercial value in the Chesapeake Bay region, because of lack of abundance. However, the Atlantic herring is one of the most important, as well as one of the most abundant, food fishes in the world and is heavily exploited in the eastern North Atlantic. It is of no recreational interest.

LITERATURE   Hildebrand and Schroeder 1928:81; Musick 1972; Smith 1985; Whitehead et al. 1985.

American shad
Alosa sapidissima (Wilson, 1811)
PLATE 6

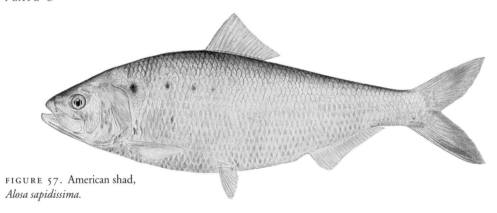

FIGURE 57. American shad,
Alosa sapidissima.

KEY FEATURES   Upper jaw with deep median notch; last ray of dorsal fin not filamentous; gill rakers on lower limb of first arch numbering 59–76; tongue with pigment in medial area; eye diameter usually less than cheek depth; jaw teeth absent in fish of greater than 15 cm SL (5.9 in); peritoneum pale to silvery.

OTHER CHARACTERISTICS   Body compressed fusiform; abdomen compressed, with 34–39 sharp scutes on midline; predorsal scales not enlarged; lateral scale rows numbering 52–64; dorsal fin small, with 15–20 rays, its origin nearer to snout than to caudal fin; anal fin with 17–23 rays and longer than dorsal fin; pelvic fin typically with 9 rays (rarely 8 or 10) and originating slightly ventroposterior to origin of dorsal fin; caudal fin deeply forked. Metallic green dorsally; silver laterally; dusky shoulder spot present, sometimes followed by smaller, paler spots. Maximum adult size 60 cm SL (2 ft).

GEOGRAPHIC DISTRIBUTION   Indigenous to the western Atlantic coast from the St. Lawrence River to Florida. The American shad was introduced to the Pacific coast of North America and in Asia on the Kamchatka Peninsula.

ECOLOGY   The American shad is an anadromous species that spends most of its adult life at sea in large schools. This species undertakes extensive ocean migrations, and fish from all Atlantic coastal rivers spend the summer and fall in the Gulf of Maine. Both juveniles and adults overwinter in deeper offshore waters. American shad enter Chesapeake Bay from January to June at ages 4–6 to spawn over fresh to low-salinity flats in the tributaries (occurring as far north as the Susquehanna River). Most American shad apparently return to their natal stream to spawn. The spawning migration is timed to correspond to favorable river water temperatures. Spawning occurs in both tidal and nontidal freshwaters. Shad usually migrate far enough upstream that the eggs drift downstream and hatch before reaching saltwater. The American shad has a relatively high fecundity of 100,000–600,000 eggs per female. After spawning, adults either die or return to the sea. Female American shad may live as long as 10 years; however, repeat spawners are apparently rare in Chesapeake Bay waters. While at sea, American shad feed on plankton, small crustaceans, and small fishes, but when migrating upriver, they do not feed. Young of the year remain in fresh to brackish water, feeding on copepods and insect larvae until early fall before entering the sea. Some juveniles, however, overwinter in deep holes near the bay mouth.

FISHING INTEREST   Valued for both meat and roe since colonial times. From the mid-1800s to the early 1900s, the American shad fishery was the largest fishery in Chesapeake Bay, with annual catches that reached 7.7 million kilograms (17 million pounds) around 1900. The fishery has been in decline over the past 75 years,

and the catch has rarely reached 454,000 kg (1 million pounds) in the past decade. The long decline seems primarily the result of overfishing and habitat degradation in spawning areas. The stocks are in such poor condition that in 1980 a moratorium on the taking of American shad was implemented in Maryland waters (with the exception of the Potomac River and coastal waters). Measures to boost the American shad population include releasing hatchery-reared fishes and fitting dams and blockages on rivers with fish passages to allow American shad to reach historical spawning areas. Presently, the largest local American shad fishery is along the Atlantic coast of Virginia. The fishery employs a variety of gear, but the bulk of the commercial catch is taken with gill nets. There are no reliable data on the recreational catch, but it is believed to be sizable. American shad are commonly taken recreationally with dip nets or by angling with artificial lures and flies when the fish are migrating to their spawning grounds.

LITERATURE   Hildebrand and Schroeder 1928:93; Hildebrand 1963a; Musick 1972; Chittenden 1975, 1976; Fischer 1978; Jones et al. 1978; Manooch 1984; MacKenzie et al. 1985; Smith 1985; Whitehead et al. 1985; Atlantic States Marine Fisheries Commission 1988; Virginia Marine Resources Commission 1990; Jenkins and Burkhead 1994.

Hickory shad
Alosa mediocris (Mitchill, 1814)
PLATE 7

KEY FEATURES   Upper jaw with deep median notch; last ray of dorsal fin not filamentous; gill rakers on lower limb of first arch numbering 18–23; tongue without pigment in medial area; eye diameter usually less than cheek depth; lower jaw projecting; jaws with minute teeth in fish at all sizes, but teeth of upper jaw typically reduced in size and number compared with those of lower jaw; predorsal scales not enlarged; peritoneum grayish, peppered with black.

OTHER CHARACTERISTICS   Body compressed fusiform; abdomen compressed, with 33–38 sharp scutes on midline; lateral scale rows numbering 45–57; dorsal fin small, its outer margin straight or slightly concave and its origin

equidistant from tip of snout and base of last ray of anal fin; anal fin lower and longer than dorsal fin, with 19–23 rays; pelvic fin small, with 9 rays and inserting about equidistant from base of pectoral and anal fins. Greenish gray dorsally; silver laterally; dusky shoulder spot present, followed by several obscure dusky spots; faint dusky spots present at base of scales dorsal to midline and forming longitudinal lines. Maximum adult size 60 cm SL (2 ft).

GEOGRAPHIC DISTRIBUTION   Occurring from the Bay of Fundy to Florida.

ECOLOGY   The hickory shad is an anadromous species that enters Chesapeake Bay waters during the spring to spawn. Spawning takes place in tidal freshwater during May and early June, and spawning grounds extend as far north in the bay as the Susquehanna River. A less pronounced autumn spawning run also occurs. Spawning apparently occurs between dusk and midnight. Information on the ecology of the hickory shad is limited. Adults apparently leave the bay soon

21,300 kg (47,000 lb) in Maryland and 49,000 kg (108,000 lb) in Virginia. A dramatic decline in catches began in the mid-1970s, and the annual commercial landings in the bay dropped to less than 900 kg (about 2,000 lb) by the late 1980s. The decline in landings is partially attributable to a moratorium on commercial fishing

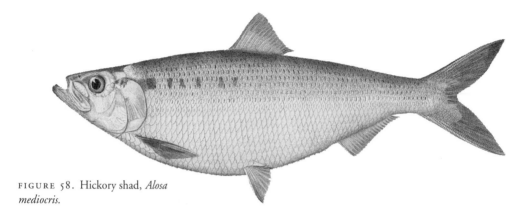

FIGURE 58. Hickory shad, *Alosa mediocris.*

after spawning. Juveniles leave the nursery grounds in summer but may remain in estuarine waters until autumn before migrating to the sea. The hickory shad is more piscivorous than other local shad, feeding on small fishes as well as on squids, crustaceans, and fish eggs.

FISHING INTEREST   Of minor commercial importance in Chesapeake Bay and usually taken in gear set for other species, such as gill nets and pound nets. Catches in the bay have never been large, and since the 1960s have not exceeded

for hickory shad in Maryland and a general decline in fishing efforts in the bay for all shad species. Recreational anglers in the vicinity of the spawning grounds use artificial lures and shad darts, with some success, to catch this species.

LITERATURE   Hildebrand and Schroeder 1928:83; Hildebrand 1963a; Musick 1972; Jones et al. 1978; Manooch 1984; Smith 1985; Whitehead et al. 1985; Atlantic States Marine Fisheries Commission 1988; Jenkins and Burkhead 1994.

Alewife
Alosa pseudoharengus (Wilson, 1811)
PLATE 8

KEY FEATURES   Upper jaw with deep median notch; last ray of dorsal fin not filamentous; gill rakers on lower limb of first arch increasing in number with age to 38–52 in adults (most frequently 39–41); eye diameter greater than snout length; lower jaw projecting; jaws with minute teeth in fish at all sizes; predorsal scales not enlarged; dorsum metallic grayish green; peritoneum pale, with dusky dots.

OTHER CHARACTERISTICS   Body compressed fusiform; abdomen compressed, with

30–36 sharp scutes on midline; dorsal fin with 15–19 rays, its outer margin slightly concave and its origin slightly nearer to tip of snout than to posterior tip of anal fin; anal fin lower and slightly longer than dorsal fin, with 15–21 rays; pelvic fin typically with 9 rays (rarely 7, 8, or 10) and inserting about midway between base of pectoral fin and origin of anal fin. Side silvery; dusky shoulder spot present in fish of greater than 10 cm TL (3.9 in). Maximum adult size 38 cm SL (15 in).

GEOGRAPHIC DISTRIBUTION   Occurring in riverine, estuarine, and western Atlantic coastal waters from Newfoundland to northern South Carolina. Reports of the alewife in Florida waters are questionable. The Great Lakes and Finger Lakes contain landlocked populations of the species.

ECOLOGY   The alewife, also called river herring, is an anadromous species that enters Chesapeake Bay in the spring to spawn. Spawning peaks in late March and April and occurs in large rivers, small streams, and ponds, including barrier beach ponds. Spawning sites are typically shallow (usually less than 1 m, or 3.3 ft, in depth), with sluggish water flow. Young alewives

valuable in Chesapeake Bay. The bulk of the catch has been by pound nets, although gill nets, haul seines, and fyke nets have also been employed. The catch in Maryland peaked in the 1930s, with catches exceeding 3.6 million kilograms (8 million pounds) annually. The Maryland fishery has been in steady decline since the mid-1950s, and since the early 1980s, catches have rarely exceeded 91,000 kg (200,000 lb). Virginia waters have typically supplied the bulk of the bay catch of river herring, with catches in the late 1960s often exceeding 13.6 million kilograms (30 million pounds). In the 1970s the Virginia fishery also declined sharply, to annual

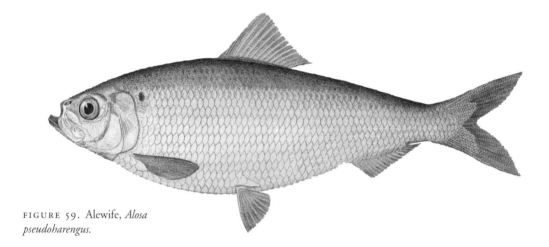

FIGURE 59. Alewife, *Alosa pseudoharengus.*

remain in fresh or brackish waters through the summer before migrating to the sea in early fall, although some individuals apparently overwinter in the bay. More typically, both adults and juveniles overwinter in deeper water offshore. Alewives feed on diatoms, copepods, ostracods, shrimps, amphipods, insects, small fishes, squids, and fish eggs. Alewives frequently school together with blueback herring.

FISHING INTEREST   Difficult to distinguish from blueback herring. Catches frequently comprise both species. Although some fishermen can distinguish between alewives and blueback herring, most fishermen simply refer to both species collectively as river herring. Both species are included in the following account of the fishery, because catch records also rarely distinguish between the two. Historically, the commercial fishery for river herring has been one of the most

catches of less than 227,000 kg (500,000 lb) by the mid-1980s. Degradation and destruction of the spawning habitat, as well as restriction of the spawning migration by dams, have been major contributors to the decline of these stocks. Large catches of alewives and blueback herring by the offshore fishing fleet in the late 1960s and early 1970s may also have contributed to the subsequent decline. River herring have supported an extensive recreational fishery that uses dip nets as well as rod and reel during the spring spawning run, but like the commercial fishery, the recreational fishery has been reduced in recent years.

LITERATURE   Hildebrand and Schroeder 1928:89; Hildebrand 1963a; Musick 1972; Jones et al. 1978; Manooch 1984; Smith 1985; Whitehead et al. 1985; Atlantic States Marine Fisheries Commission 1988; Bozeman and Van Den Avyle 1989; Jenkins and Burkhead 1994.

Blueback herring
Alosa aestivalis (Mitchill, 1814)

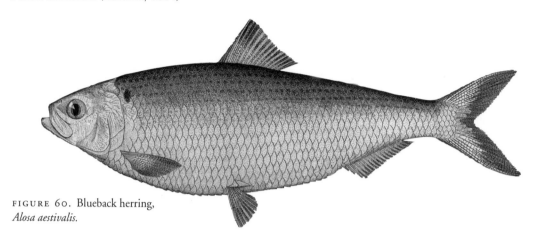

FIGURE 60. Blueback herring,
Alosa aestivalis.

KEY FEATURES   Upper jaw with deep median notch; last ray of dorsal fin not filamentous; predorsal scales not enlarged; gill rakers on lower limb of first arch increasing with age, to 38–52 in adults (most frequently 44–50); eye diameter less than or equal to snout length; lower jaw projecting; jaws with minute teeth in fish at all sizes; dorsum deep bluish green; peritoneum black to dusky.

OTHER CHARACTERISTICS   Body compressed fusiform; abdomen compressed, with 31–37 sharp scutes along midline; dorsal fin with 15–20 rays, its margin concave and its origin nearer to tip of snout than from base of caudal fin; anal fin lower and longer than dorsal fin, with 16–21 rays; pelvic fin with 9 rays and originating equidistant from base of pectoral fin and from origin of anal fin. Side silvery; dorsolateral scales with distinct dusky lines in adults; 1 dusky spot present on shoulder. Maximum adult size 38 cm SL (15 in).

GEOGRAPHIC DISTRIBUTION   Occurring in riverine, estuarine, and western Atlantic coastal waters from Nova Scotia to Florida, but most common in southern portion of range.

ECOLOGY   The blueback herring, also called river herring, is similar to its close relative, the alewife, in ecology and life history (see the species account for the alewife, page 77). The blueback herring differs from the alewife by spawning later in the spring (April and May) and by preferring to spawn in swift-flowing, deeper stretches of rivers and streams. Brackish and tidal areas are rarely used by blueback herring for spawning. Blueback herring make repeat spawning runs and return to the same river to spawn.

FISHING INTEREST   See the species account for the alewife, page 77.

LITERATURE   Hildebrand and Schroeder 1928:85; Musick 1972; Fischer 1978; Manooch 1984; Smith 1985; Whitehead et al. 1985; Bozeman and Van Den Avyle 1989; Jenkins and Burkhead 1994.

Lizardfishes

ORDER AULOPIFORMES

The order of lizardfishes contains 12 families, of which 1 occurs in Chesapeake Bay.

Lizardfishes

FAMILY SYNODONTIDAE

Lizardfishes are slender, cylindrical fishes with spineless dorsal and anal fins and a small adipose fin. The mouth is large, containing numerous slender, sharp teeth on the jaws and tongue. The pointed head and bands of pointed teeth of these fishes give them a reptilian appearance. They are voracious, lie-in-wait predators that can dart quickly to capture small fishes. Lizardfishes are typically shallow-water bottom dwellers. The family comprises 4 genera and 34 species, with 1 species known from Chesapeake Bay waters.

Inshore lizardfish
Synodus foetens (Linnaeus, 1766)

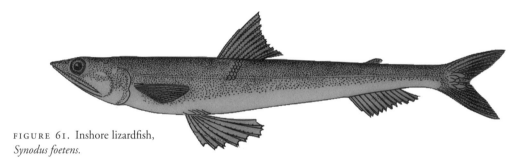

FIGURE 61. Inshore lizardfish, *Synodus foetens.*

KEY FEATURES   Single dorsal fin with only soft rays; small adipose fin present; mouth large, with slender sharp teeth on jaws and tongue; scales cycloid; modified elongate scales extending onto caudal fin; pelvic fin larger than pectoral fin.

OTHER CHARACTERISTICS   Body elongate and cylindrical; head depressed; snout pointed; dorsal fin high; anal fin low and long; pectoral fin small; caudal fin forked. Greenish brown dorsally; whitish laterally and ventrally; side and belly may be variously blotched or spotted; apparently able to assume various patterns, depending upon conditions of background and light. Maximum adult size 40 cm SL (16 in).

GEOGRAPHIC DISTRIBUTION   Occurring coastally from Massachusetts to Brazil.

ECOLOGY   The inshore lizardfish, an occasional to common seasonal visitor to Chesapeake Bay, is encountered during summer and autumn and extends as far north as Annapolis (the Western Shore) and the Chester River (the Eastern Shore) in the upper bay. It is found on both shallow and deep sand flats among vegetation, in the tidal portions of large rivers, and in deep channels. It is probably more common over mud than over shell bottoms. Inshore lizardfish are known to partially bury themselves in sandy or muddy substrates in order to conceal themselves from unsuspecting prey. Despite its common name, the inshore lizardfish has been collected from depths as great as 100 m (330 ft).

FISHING INTEREST   Incidentally caught by rod and reel and by bottom trawls and not valued as a food fish.

LITERATURE   Hildebrand and Schroeder 1928:130; Anderson et al. 1966; Musick 1972; Jones et al. 1978; Manooch 1984; Smith 1985; Nelson 1994.

Suckers and Minnows
ORDER CYPRINIFORMES

The large order of suckers and minnows comprises more than 3,000 species of primarily freshwater fishes within its 6 families. Two families (Catostomidae and Cyprinidae), however, have representatives that are known to occasionally penetrate into Chesapeake Bay tidal waters with salinities of 5‰ or greater.

KEY TO THE FAMILIES OF SUCKERS AND MINNOWS IN CHESAPEAKE BAY

1a. Mouth inferior; lips fleshy .... **suckers—Catostomidae** (p. 80)
1b. Mouth terminal or subterminal; lips not fleshy .... **carps and minnows—Cyprinidae** (p. 83)

Suckers
FAMILY CATOSTOMIDAE

Suckers are close relatives of the carps and minnows; they all share an unusual bony connection between the swim bladder and the ear called the Weberian apparatus. (Characins, of the family Characidae, and catfishes also have a Weberian apparatus.) Suckers have a toothless mouth and possess comblike or molariform teeth on the pharyngeal bones of the throat; these pharyngeal teeth are correlated with the bottom-feeding habits of suckers. Suckers patrol along river and stream bottoms, "slurping up" bottom-dwelling organisms with their inferior mouths. Suckers are a numerous and varied group in North America but are also represented in Asia by 2 species. The family comprises 13 genera and approximately 75 species. Although suckers are primarily found in freshwater, 3 species are known from brackish waters (with salinities >5‰) of Chesapeake Bay.

KEY TO THE SPECIES OF SUCKERS IN CHESAPEAKE BAY

1a. Dorsal fin with more than 23 rays .... **quillback, *Carpiodes cyprinus*** (p. 80)
1b. Dorsal fin with fewer than 19 rays **2**

2a. More than 50 scales present in lateral line .... **white sucker, *Catostomus commersoni*** (p. 81)
2b. Fewer than 50 scales present in lateral line...
.... **shorthead redhorse, *Moxostoma macrolepidotum*** (p. 82)

Quillback
Carpiodes cyprinus (Lesueur, 1817)

KEY FEATURES   Dorsal fin sickle-shaped (anterior rays long, posterior rays short), with 24–33 fin rays; scales in lateral line numbering 35–40. OTHER CHARACTERISTICS   Body deep and compressed; dorsal profile arched anteriorly; snout rounded; mouth inferior; lateral line complete; dorsal fin falcate, long-based, and originating nearer to tip of snout than to base of caudal fin; caudal fin forked; anal fin short-based, with nearly concave posterior margin; pelvic fin origin equidistant from snout tip and caudal fin base;

pectoral fin low on body and about equal in size to pelvic fin; pelvic axillary scale undeveloped. Silvery to yellowish brown dorsally, shading to milky white ventrally; ventral fins gray or orangish, with white leading edge. Maximum adult size 66 cm TL (26 in), commonly to 38 cm TL (15 in). GEOGRAPHIC DISTRIBUTION   Known from southern Canada and the central and eastern United States, extending as far south as the Gulf coast.

ECOLOGY   Quillback are found in the larger tributaries to Chesapeake Bay (Susquehanna, Potomac, and James river systems) and are more

July in riffle areas. Quillback are reported to feed on insects and other bottom invertebrates. They can attain 10 years of age.

FIGURE 62. Quillback, *Carpiodes cyprinus*.

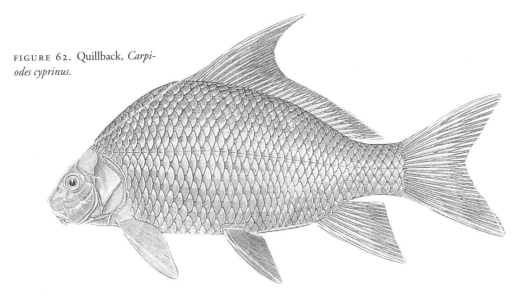

commonly encountered in quiet waters. They occasionally penetrate into bay waters with salinities of 5‰ or greater and can tolerate salinities as great as 11‰. Little is known about the life history of quillback. Spawning occurs from April to

FISHING INTEREST   Of no commercial value and only of little recreational interest.
LITERATURE   Vanicek 1961; Musick 1972; Pflieger 1975; Jones et al. 1978; Smith 1985; Jenkins and Burkhead 1994.

White sucker
Catostomus commersoni (Lacepède, 1803)
PLATE 9

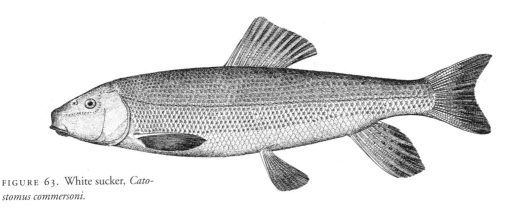

FIGURE 63. White sucker, *Catostomus commersoni*.

KEY FEATURES   Lateral line complete and continuous; scales small, numbering 55–85 in lateral series.

OTHER CHARACTERISTICS   Body elongate, little compressed; head little deeper than broad; snout conical or rounded; mouth inferior;

lips papillose; lower lip larger than upper lip; scales decreasing in size anteriorly; dorsal fin about as long as high, with outer margin nearly straight, with 10–14 rays, and originating nearer to tip of snout than to base of caudal fin; caudal fin moderately forked; anal fin with 6–8 rays (typically 7); base of anal fin shorter than base of dorsal fin; anal fin higher than dorsal fin and originating about equidistant from pelvic fin base and caudal fin base; pelvic fin short, inserting perpendicular to midpoint of dorsal fin; pelvic axillary scale distinct; pectoral fin low on body. Gray, olive, bluish green, or brassy brown dorsally; pale ventrally; dorsal and caudal fins dusky; other fins pale orange; breeding males with rosy lateral band and dusky blotches, as well as prominent tubercles on anal rays. Maximum adult size 64 cm TL (25 in).

GEOGRAPHIC DISTRIBUTION   Native throughout much of North America east of the Rocky Mountains. On the Atlantic coast, the white sucker ranges from Nova Scotia to Georgia.

ECOLOGY   Found in all tributaries to Chesapeake Bay throughout the year, the white sucker occurs in nearly every kind of habitat from shallow creeks to large lakes. It will penetrate into brackish water during the winter months and has been collected in bay waters with salinities of 5‰ or greater. In order to spawn, white suckers ascend creeks in spring, when water temperatures reach 10°C (50°F). Spawning occurs in riffles or swiftly flowing water over gravel. White suckers feed on insects and worms.

FISHING INTEREST   Of no commercial interest in the Chesapeake Bay region. Only rarely do anglers target the white sucker, even though it will readily take a baited hook. The white sucker is very often snagged and gigged in the Midwest. Its maximum weight is 2.3 kg (5 lb).

LITERATURE   Hildebrand and Schroeder 1928:119; Musick 1972; Pflieger 1975; Twomey et al. 1984; Smith 1985; Jenkins and Burkhead 1994.

Shorthead redhorse
Moxostoma macrolepidotum (Lesueur, 1817)

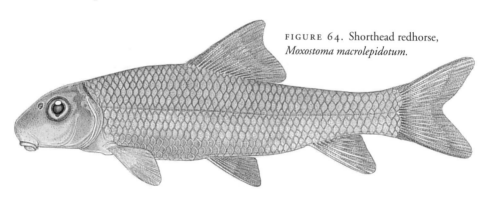

FIGURE 64. Shorthead redhorse, *Moxostoma macrolepidotum.*

KEY FEATURES   Scales large, numbering 39–48 in lateral series; dorsal fin with 10–15 rays (typically 12 or 13).

OTHER CHARACTERISTICS   Body elongate; dorsal profile slightly arched anteriorly; snout rounded; mouth inferior; lower lip plicate (ribbed) anteriorly and papillose posteriorly; posterior margin of lower lip almost straight; lateral line complete and straight; scales with dusky crescents on bases; origin of dorsal fin nearer to snout than to base of caudal fin; outer margin of dorsal fin concave; caudal fin forked, with lobes rounded and approximately equal in size; anal fin with rounded edges and 6–8 rays (typically 7); pelvic fin with 9 or 10 rays and located at midbody; pelvic axillary scale distinct; pectoral fin low on body and about equal in size to pelvic fin. Brassy to olive brown dorsally; venter white; ventral fins orange or red; dorsal and caudal fins reddish. Maximum adult size 61 cm TL (25 in), commonly to 46 cm TL (18 in).

GEOGRAPHIC DISTRIBUTION   Known from southern Canada and central and eastern United States, extending as far south as Oklahoma and northern Alabama. Along the Atlantic coast, shorthead redhorses range from the St. Lawrence River to South Carolina.

ECOLOGY   In the Chesapeake Bay region, the shorthead redhorse typically inhabits moderately large, swift-flowing rivers with silt-free bottoms. It occasionally penetrates into bay waters with salinities of 5‰ or greater; its maximum reported salinity tolerance is 8‰. Bottom-dwelling insects compose the primary diet. Shorthead redhorses spawn as groups in riffle areas of streams during spring. This species can attain 9 years of age or more.

FISHING INTEREST   Not targeted by either commercial or recreational fisheries in the Chesapeake Bay region.

LITERATURE   Musick 1972; Pflieger 1975; Jones et al. 1978; Smith 1985; Jenkins and Burkhead 1994.

Carps and Minnows
FAMILY CYPRINIDAE

Widely distributed throughout North America, Africa, Europe, and Asia, the cyprinids compose the largest family of freshwater fishes in the world. Most members of the family are small (2.5–15 cm, or 1–6 in), but a few grow much larger. The common carp, for example, may reach a length of 1.2 m (4 ft) and exceed 23 kg (50 lb), whereas the largest of the North American minnows, the Colorado squawfish (*Ptychocheilus lucius*), occasionally reaches 1.8 m (6 ft) in length. Minnows have a single dorsal fin, pelvic fins located near the midbody, and pectoral fins situated low on the body. All minnow species lack teeth on their jaws, and none has an adipose fin. The small size and great abundance of minnows make them valuable as forage for many piscivorous fishes. In the Chesapeake Bay region, only the common carp, which was introduced from Europe in the mid-1800s, is considered a food fish. However, many species are utilized as bait, and several minnow species are propagated by a thriving bait industry. Cyprinids display a wide variety of food habits that include herbivory, piscivory, planktivory, insectivory, and omnivory. The breeding males of many minnows are brightly colored and have small wartlike structures (breeding tubercles) on their heads and fins that function in stimulating females and in aggressively maintaining spawning sites and position. Of the more than 40 species of cyprinids that occur in the Chesapeake Bay drainage basin, the following 7 species occasionally move into low-salinity bay waters from their more typical freshwater habitats.

KEY TO THE SPECIES OF CARPS AND MINNOWS IN CHESAPEAKE BAY

1a. First ray of dorsal and anal fins hardened and spinelike; dorsal fin with more than 12 rays **2**

1b. First ray of dorsal and anal fins not hardened and spinelike; dorsal fin with fewer than 12 rays **3**

2a. Two barbels present on each side of upper jaw .... **common carp, *Cyprinus carpio*** (p. 84)

2b. Barbels absent on jaws .... **goldfish, *Carassius auratus*** (p. 85)

3a. Anal fin with 10 or more rays; ventral midline between pelvic and anal fins forming keel .... **golden shiner, *Notemigonus crysoleucas*** (p. 86)

3b. Anal fin typically with 10 or fewer rays; ventral midline between pelvic and anal fins not forming keel **4**

4a. Peritoneum black and visible through belly; intestine very long and coiled (visible upon dissection) .... **eastern silvery minnow, *Hybognathus regius*** (p. 87)

4b. Peritoneum typically silvery or speckled, sometimes visible through belly; intestine not very long and coiled (sometimes visible without dissection) **5**

5a. Posterior interradial membranes of dorsal fin with dusky pigment .... **spotfin shiner, *Cyprinella spiloptera*** (p. 87)

5b. Posterior interradial membranes of dorsal fin without dusky pigment **6**

6a. Black longitudinal stripe extending from opercle to caudal fin . . . .
. . . . **spottail shiner,** *Notropis hudsonius* (p. 88)

6b. Black longitudinal stripe extending from snout to caudal fin . . . .
. . . . **bridle shiner,** *Notropis bifrenatus* (p. 89)

Common carp
Cyprinus carpio Linnaeus, 1758

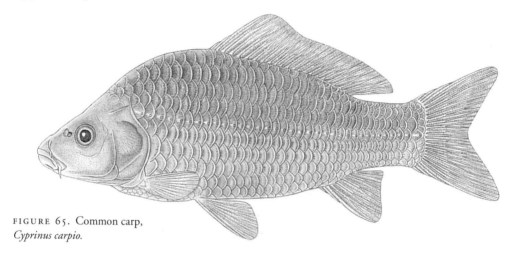

FIGURE 65. Common carp,
Cyprinus carpio.

KEY FEATURES   First ray of dorsal and anal fins hardened and spinelike; 2 barbels present on each side of upper jaw; lateral line with 32–41 scales (except in the common carp varieties "mirror carp," which have very few scales, and "leather carp," which have no scales); dorsal fin with 15–23 rays (typically more than 18).

OTHER CHARACTERISTICS   Body elongate and robust; back elevated; head small; snout blunt; mouth subterminal; scales large; base of dorsal fin long; caudal fin forked; anal fin with 6 rays; pelvic fin originating near midbody. Golden or brassy dorsally, shading to silver ventrally. Maximum adult size 1.2 m TL (4 ft).

GEOGRAPHIC DISTRIBUTION   Native to Europe and Asia but widely introduced in North America. The common carp is firmly established throughout the United States, including Hawaii.

ECOLOGY   Common carp were introduced to the Chesapeake Bay region in 1877. Populations are now well established in all major tributaries to the bay and are known to travel downstream to enter the main stem of the bay. Although able to tolerate salinities as great as 17‰, common carp are most abundant in quiet freshwaters that support large quantities of aquatic vegetation. Common carp are omnivorous but principally feed on plants. They root about the bottom, churning up sediment as they feed on plant and animal matter. Some experts assert that the decline in numbers of some native freshwater fishes can be attributed to the common carp, which alters the habitat of streams, lakes, and rivers by uprooting vegetation. Spawning begins in late spring, when water temperature reaches 17°C (63°F), and extends into August. Spawning common carp crowd and splash in shallow water. The female deposits the adhesive eggs in vegetation, where they adhere in clumps. Common carp and goldfish are known to hybridize. Carp are known to exceed 40 years of age; however, most reach age 20 or less.

FISHING INTEREST   Of some recreational value in the Chesapeake Bay region. The common carp is highly esteemed by some people as a food fish and commercially important in other regions. The world record is a fish from Virginia that weighed 26 kg (57 lb).

LITERATURE   Hildebrand and Schroeder 1928:121; Musick 1972; Eddy and Underhill 1978; Jones et al. 1978; Smith 1979; Manooch 1984; Smith 1985; Page and Burr 1991; Jenkins and Burkhead 1994.

Goldfish
Carassius auratus (Linnaeus, 1758)
PLATE 10

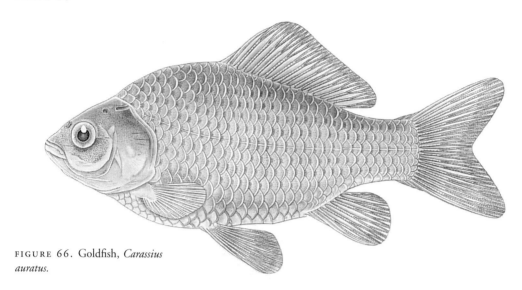

FIGURE 66. Goldfish, *Carassius auratus.*

KEY FEATURES   First ray of dorsal and anal fins hardened and spinelike; barbels absent on jaws; lateral line with 25–34 scales; dorsal fin typically with 14–21 rays.

OTHER CHARACTERISTICS   Body short and robust; back elevated; head short; snout blunt; mouth inferior; scales large; base of dorsal fin long; caudal fin forked; anal fin with 6 rays and rounded margin; pelvic fin originating anterior to midbody. Variable in color; body reddish orange, pink, gray, or black; most wild individuals olive, brassy, or dusky gray; spots and blotches sometimes present. Maximum adult size 48 cm TL (1.6 ft).

GEOGRAPHIC DISTRIBUTION   Native to Asia and introduced in Europe and North America. The goldfish is firmly established throughout the United States, including Hawaii.

ECOLOGY   Goldfish were introduced to the Chesapeake Bay region during the late 1800s. Populations are now well established in all tributaries to the bay and are known to travel downstream to enter the main stem of the bay. Although able to tolerate salinities of 7–8‰ (with some reports indicating tolerance to at least 17‰), goldfish are most abundant in quiet freshwaters that support large quantities of submerged aquatic vegetation. Goldfish are omnivorous but principally feed on phytoplankton and bottom-dwelling organisms such as insects, worms, and mollusks. Spawning season for goldfish extends from late March to mid-August, when water temperatures reach 16°C (61°F). Prolific spawners, female goldfish produce many thousands of eggs that are deposited in vegetation near shorelines. Goldfish and common carp are known to hybridize.

FISHING INTEREST   Of no recreational value but used commercially as a baitfish (known as the Baltimore minnow in the baitfish trade). Goldfish have been collected in pound nets near the Chesapeake Bay mouth.

LITERATURE   Musick 1972; Eddy and Underhill 1978; Jones et al. 1978; Smith 1979; Smith 1985; Page and Burr 1991; Jenkins and Burkhead 1994.

Golden shiner
Notemigonus crysoleucas (Mitchill, 1814)
PLATE 11

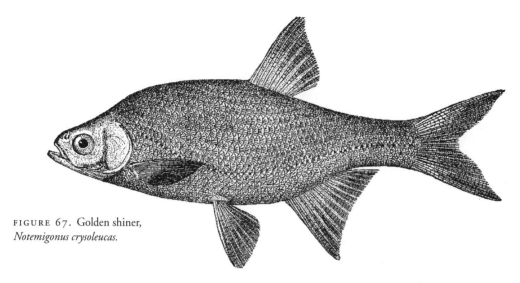

FIGURE 67. Golden shiner,
Notemigonus crysoleucas.

KEY FEATURES   Ventral midline between pelvic and anal fins forming keel; dorsal fin with 7–9 rays (typically 8); anal fin with 8–19 rays (typically 10–15); first ray of dorsal and anal fins not hardened and spinelike; lateral line curving ventrally near midbody; mouth small, terminal, and oblique.

OTHER CHARACTERISTICS   Body elongate and compressed; back elevated; head short; snout blunt; lateral line with 39–57 scales; caudal fin forked; anal fin with falcate margin; pelvic fin originating near midbody. Metallic blue green dorsally; silvery on side, with dusky midlateral stripe; in darkly stained waters, appearing brassy gold on side; ventral fins sometimes yellowish. Maximum adult size 31 cm TL (1 ft), with weight of 680 g (1.5 lb).

GEOGRAPHIC DISTRIBUTION   Native to lakes, streams, and rivers of eastern and central North America from Quebec and Manitoba to Florida and Mexico. The golden shiner, because of its use as a baitfish, has been widely introduced in North America, including west of the Rocky Mountains.

ECOLOGY   Common to abundant in all tributaries to Chesapeake Bay, the golden shiner is occasionally collected in waters with salinities greater than 5‰ and has been collected in bay waters of 17‰ salinity. It occupies a variety of habitats, from clear ponds and lakes to sluggish streams and rivers and darkly stained swamp waters. It can tolerate low oxygen levels, high turbidity, and high temperature. Usually found in midwater or near surface waters in small, loosely aggregated schools, golden shiners are omnivorous but principally feed on plankton, insects, and mollusks. Spawning season for the golden shiner begins when water temperatures reach 15°C (59°F) and typically extends from April to August (or later). Female golden shiners are broadcast spawners whose eggs adhere to vegetation and debris.

FISHING INTEREST   Of considerable value as a baitfish for basses and catfishes and widely propagated for that purpose. Large individuals propagated in ponds by the aquaculture industry are sold as "wild shiners" and are especially effective for creeling trophy largemouth bass associated with submerged and surface aquatic vegetation.

LITERATURE   Hildebrand and Schroeder 1928:123; Musick 1972; Pflieger 1975; Eddy and Underhill 1978; Jones et al. 1978; Manooch 1984; Smith 1985; Page and Burr 1991; Jenkins and Burkhead 1994.

Eastern silvery minnow
Hybognathus regius Girard, 1856

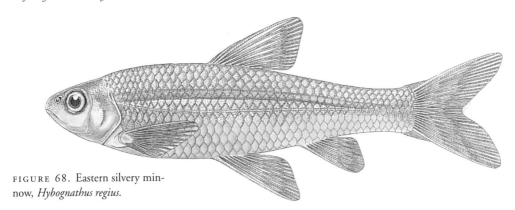

FIGURE 68. Eastern silvery minnow, *Hybognathus regius.*

KEY FEATURES   Peritoneum black and visible through belly; intestine very long and coiled; dorsal fin with 7–10 rays (typically 8); anal fin with 8 or 9 rays (typically 8).

OTHER CHARACTERISTICS   Body slender and compressed; head long; mouth subterminal, with lower jaw crescentic; lateral line complete, slightly decurved anteriorly, and with 31–45 scales; dorsal fin short-based and originating much nearer to tip of snout than to base of caudal fin; caudal fin moderately forked; anal fin similar to dorsal fin in shape and size; origin of pelvic fin perpendicular to origin of dorsal fin. Greenish or olive dorsally; silver laterally; pale ventrally; dusky midlateral stripe present. Maximum adult size 15 cm TL (5.9 in).

GEOGRAPHIC DISTRIBUTION   Found in Atlantic coast drainages from the St. Lawrence Basin to Florida.

ECOLOGY   Abundant in all tributaries to Chesapeake Bay, the eastern silvery minnow is occasionally collected in waters with salinities greater than 5‰ and has been collected in bay waters with a salinity of 14‰. The eastern silvery minnow lives over silty or sandy bottoms in lakes, large streams, pools, and backwaters. It lives in schools near the bottom, often in association with other minnows and shiners. When feeding, the eastern silvery minnow stirs up bottom sediments, primarily eating plants and algae. Spawning occurs from April to mid-May; females deposit nonadhesive eggs over silty bottoms. Vigorous vibrations during spawning often stir up the bottom and muddy the water. This species can live as long as 3 years.

FISHING INTEREST   Of no direct commercial or recreational interest. Indirectly, the eastern silvery minnow is of considerable value as a forage species for larger fishes.

LITERATURE   Hildebrand and Schroeder 1928:124; Musick 1972; Pflieger 1975; Eddy and Underhill 1978; Jones et al. 1978; Smith 1985; Page and Burr 1991; Jenkins and Burkhead 1994.

Spotfin shiner
Cyprinella spiloptera (Cope, 1868)

KEY FEATURES   Posterior interradial membranes of dorsal fin with dusky pigment; prominent narrow dusky stripe on side of caudal peduncle; scales appearing diamond-shaped; anal fin with 7–9 rays (typically 8).

OTHER CHARACTERISTICS   Body slender and compressed; head small; snout conical; mouth terminal and oblique; lateral line complete, with 35–41 scales; dorsal fin short-based, with 7–10 rays (typically 8), and originating near midbody; caudal fin moderately forked; anal fin similar to dorsal fin in shape; origin of pelvic fin slightly ventroanterior to origin of dorsal fin. Silvery blue dorsally, shading to white or pale ventrally; distinct dusky stripe present along dorsal midline; large juveniles and adults with dusky or black blotch on posterior 2 or 3 membranes of dorsal fin; posterior lateral stripe silvery in life, dusky in death. Maximum adult size 11 cm TL (4.5 in), typically 6–9 cm TL (2.5–3.5 in).

GEOGRAPHIC DISTRIBUTION   Native to central and eastern North America. The spotfin

rivers. It lives in schools in midwater, often in association with other shiners. Spotfin shiners are omnivorous but feed principally on insects. Spawning season for the spotfin shiner is from mid-June to mid-August. Eggs are deposited in crevices of rocks and logs and are defended by males.

FISHING INTEREST   Of no direct commercial or recreational interest. Indirectly, the spotfin

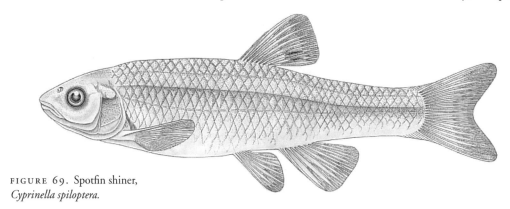

FIGURE 69. Spotfin shiner, *Cyprinella spiloptera.*

shiner is found along the Atlantic coast from the Hudson River to the Potomac drainage.

ECOLOGY   Found in large tributaries to Chesapeake Bay, the spotfin shiner is occasionally collected in waters with salinities greater than 5‰ but is typically found in lakes and in large creeks and

shiner is of considerable value as a forage species for larger fishes.

LITERATURE   Musick 1972; Pflieger 1975; Eddy and Underhill 1978; Smith 1985; Page and Burr 1991; Jenkins and Burkhead 1994.

Spottail shiner
Notropis hudsonius (Clinton, 1824)

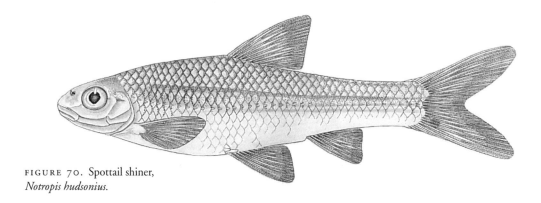

FIGURE 70. Spottail shiner, *Notropis hudsonius.*

KEY FEATURES   Distinct black longitudinal stripe present along dorsal midline, typically ending at large black spot at base of tail (spot some-

times faint or absent in large adults and in specimens from Potomac drainage); dorsal fin with 7–10 rays; anal fin with 7–9 rays (typically 8).

OTHER CHARACTERISTICS   Body slender and slightly compressed; head moderate-sized; snout conical; mouth subterminal and oblique; lateral line complete, with 36–42 scales; dorsal fin short-based and originating nearer to tip of snout than to base of caudal fin; caudal fin forked; anal fin similar to dorsal fin in shape; origin of pelvic fin slightly ventroposterior to origin of dorsal fin. Greenish or olive yellow dorsally; silver laterally; silvery white or pale ventrally. Maximum adult size 15 cm TL (6 in).

GEOGRAPHIC DISTRIBUTION   Native to central and eastern North America. Along the Atlantic coast, the spottail shiner is known from the St. Lawrence River to Georgia.

ECOLOGY   Abundant in all tributaries to Chesapeake Bay, the spottail shiner is occasionally collected in waters with salinities greater than 5‰

and has been collected in bay waters of 12‰ salinity. This species is typically found in quiet shallow waters with a firm bottom. It lives in schools in midwater, often in association with other shiners. The spottail shiner is omnivorous but principally feeds on insects, crustaceans, plants, and algae. Spawning season for this species is from May to late August. Spottail shiners can live as long as 4 years.

FISHING INTEREST   Of no direct commercial or recreational interest. Indirectly, the spottail shiner is of considerable value as a forage species for larger fishes.

LITERATURE   Hildebrand and Schroeder 1928:125; Musick 1972; Pflieger 1975; Eddy and Underhill 1978; Jones et al. 1978; Smith 1985; Page and Burr 1991; Jenkins and Burkhead 1994.

Bridle shiner
Notropis bifrenatus (Cope, 1869)

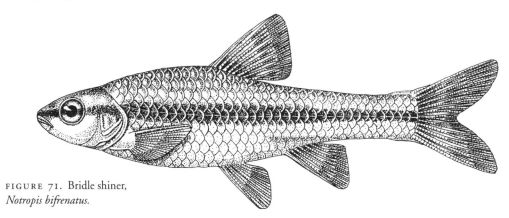

FIGURE 71. Bridle shiner, *Notropis bifrenatus.*

KEY FEATURES   Prominent black longitudinal stripe extending from tip of snout (not including lower jaw) to caudal fin; prominent spot absent at caudal fin base; dorsal fin with 7 or 8 rays (typically 8); anal fin with 7 rays.

OTHER CHARACTERISTICS   Body slightly compressed; snout blunt; mouth very oblique; lateral line typically incomplete, with 31–37 scales; dorsal fin short-based and originating nearer to tip of snout than to base of caudal fin; caudal fin moderately forked; anal fin with slightly concave margin; origin of pelvic fin almost perpendicular to origin of dorsal fin; pectoral fin long and situated low on body. Yellowish green dorsally; silver

white ventrally. Maximum adult size 60 mm TL (2.4 in).

GEOGRAPHIC DISTRIBUTION   Known only along the Atlantic coast from Maine to South Carolina.

ECOLOGY   Although uncommon, the bridle shiner inhabits most tributaries to Chesapeake Bay, extending as far north as Havre de Grace, Maryland, and frequents sluggish waters. Some of the Virginia populations of the bridle shiner have been extirpated. The species is sometimes collected in brackish waters of 5‰ or greater salinity and has been reported to tolerate salinities as high as 12‰. The bridle shiner is most often found over grassy bottoms. Small crustaceans and insects compose much of its diet. From May to July, spawning occurs, with the eggs adhering to bottom vegetation.

FISHING INTEREST   Of no direct commercial or recreational interest.

LITERATURE   Hildebrand and Schroeder 1928:126; Musick 1972; Jones et al. 1978; Smith 1985; Jenkins and Burkhead 1994.

Catfishes
ORDER SILURIFORMES

The large and diverse order of catfishes comprises 33 families, of which 2 occur in Chesapeake Bay.

KEY TO THE FAMILIES OF CATFISHES IN CHESAPEAKE BAY

1a. Four pairs of barbels present around mouth . . . .**bullhead catfishes—Ictaluridae** (p. 90)
1b. Two or 3 pairs of barbels present around mouth . . . . **sea catfishes—Ariidae** (p. 96)

Bullhead Catfishes
FAMILY ICTALURIDAE

Species of the family Ictaluridae are found only in North American freshwaters. Bullhead catfishes are diverse in form, but all lack scales and possess an adipose fin as well as a single stout, often serrated spine in the dorsal and pectoral fins. There are four pairs of barbels ("whiskers"—hence the common name "catfishes") around the mouth, two on the chin, one at the angle of the mouth, and one at the posterior nostril. The family is often divided into three groups: catfishes, bullheads, and madtoms. Unlike catfishes and bullheads, madtoms are small secretive fishes that are rarely seen in nature and seldom exceed 13 cm (5 in) in total length. Members of this family are most active at night. They have numerous external taste buds, many of which are located on the barbels. Consequently, bullhead catfishes can taste something by touching it with their barbels. Ictalurids are summer spawners that lay their eggs in cavities or nests constructed by the parents. Parental care of the eggs and young is common. The larger species of catfishes, especially the channel catfish, are important commercial and sport fishes. The family comprises 6 genera and about 40 species, 4 of which are occasionally collected in Chesapeake Bay waters with salinities greater than 5‰.

KEY TO THE SPECIES OF BULLHEAD CATFISHES IN CHESAPEAKE BAY

1a. Tail distinctly forked **2**
1b. Tail rounded, truncate, or slightly emarginate but not forked. **4**

2a. Anal fin typically with fewer than 26 rays; tail moderately forked . . . .
. . . . **white catfish, *Ameiurus catus*** (p. 91)
2b. Anal fin typically with 26 or more rays; tail deeply forked **3**

3a. Outer margin of anal fin rounded; anal fin with fewer than 30 rays; body typically with dusky spots . . . .
. . . . **channel catfish, *Ictalurus punctatus*** (p. 92)
3b. Outer margin of anal fin straight; anal fin typically with 30 or more rays; body without dusky spots . . . .
. . . . **blue catfish, *Ictalurus furcatus*** (p. 93)

4a. Lower jaw strongly projecting beyond upper jaw; snout greatly flattened . . . .
. . . . **flathead catfish, *Pylodictis olivaris*** (p. 94)

4b. Lower jaw not projecting beyond upper jaw; snout not greatly flattened **5**

5a. Chin barbels whitish; anal fin with 24–28 rays; caudal fin margin straight or nearly so . . . .
. . . . **yellow bullhead, *Ameiurus natalis*** (p. 94)

5b. Chin barbels grayish or blackish; anal fin typically with 24 or fewer rays; caudal fin margin slightly
notched . . . . **brown bullhead, *Ameiurus nebulosus*** (p. 95)

White catfish
Ameiurus catus (Linnaeus, 1758)

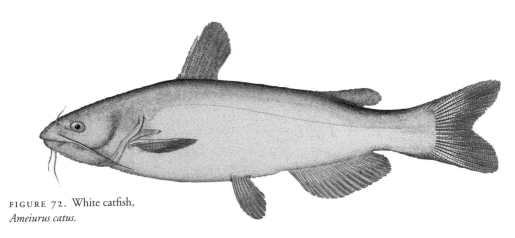

FIGURE 72. White catfish,
Ameiurus catus.

KEY FEATURES   Tail moderately forked; spots absent on body; anal fin with 21–26 rays (typically 22–24).

OTHER CHARACTERISTICS   Body robust, compressed posteriorly; head depressed and broad; snout and mouth very broad; teeth small and in villiform bands; dorsal fin short-based, with 1 spine and 5–7 soft rays; adipose fin located perpendicular to middle of anal fin base; caudal fin lobes rounded; margin of anal fin rounded; pelvic fin inserting nearer to caudal fin than to tip of snout; pectoral spines stout and strongly serrated. Gray to bluish gray dorsally; whitish ventrally; chin barbels pale; other barbels dusky. Maximum adult size 60 cm TL (2 ft), typically to 30–33 cm TL (12–13 in). This species is often confused with the channel catfish (*Ictalurus punctatus*); however, the white catfish rarely exceeds 2.7 kg (6 lb), whereas channel catfish reach 34 kg (75 lb).

GEOGRAPHIC DISTRIBUTION   Native to Atlantic coast drainages from New York to Florida, including the Gulf coast of Florida. The white catfish has been introduced into the Mid-west and along the west coast of the United States.

ECOLOGY   The white catfish is common to abundant in all Chesapeake Bay tributaries and is often encountered in waters of 5‰ salinity or greater. It has been collected in waters with salinities as high as 16‰. The white catfish occurs in lakes, rivers, ponds, and streams as well as in estuarine waters. Spawning occurs in early summer, when water temperatures reach 20°–22°C (68°–72°F). Eggs are laid in a large, saucer-shaped nest constructed by the spawning pair; the eggs and young are guarded by one or both parents. This species feeds on a wide variety of fishes, insects, and crustaceans. White catfish can live as long as 11 years.

FISHING INTEREST   Along with other catfishes, forming an important commercial and recreational fishery in the tributaries of Chesapeake Bay. White catfish, channel catfish, and brown bullheads all contribute to the fishery, but the three species are not distinguished in available fishery statistics. The commercial fishery primarily utilizes fish pots, fyke nets, pound nets, and haul seines, but sizable catches also come from gill nets and hook and line. Through the 1980s, the fishery grew and commercial landings averaged about 907,500 kg (2 million pounds) per year, with approximately 60% of the catch taken in Virginia and 40% in Maryland. Catfishes are also popular target species of recreational anglers; however, no reliable catch data exist.

LITERATURE   Hildebrand and Schroeder 1928:129; Musick 1972; Pflieger 1975; Jones et al. 1978; Smith 1979; Manooch 1984; Smith 1985; Jones et al. 1988; Page and Burr 1991; Jenkins and Burkhead 1994.

Channel catfish
Ictalurus punctatus (Rafinesque, 1818)

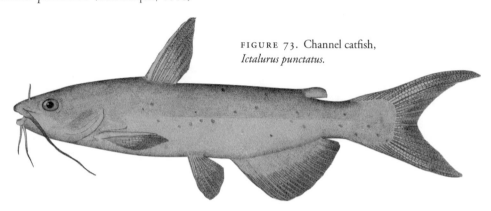

FIGURE 73. Channel catfish, *Ictalurus punctatus.*

KEY FEATURES   Tail deeply forked; body sprinkled with black or dusky spots in juveniles and small adults; anal fin with 23–32 rays (typically 26 or 27).

OTHER CHARACTERISTICS   Body slender, compressed posteriorly; head depressed; snout and mouth very broad; teeth very small and in patches; dorsal fin short-based, with 1 spine and 6 soft rays; adipose fin located perpendicular to latter third of anal fin base; caudal fin lobes mostly straight; margin of anal fin rounded; origin of pelvic fin nearer to tip of snout than to caudal fin base; pectoral spines stout and strongly serrated. Blue or gray to greenish gray dorsally; whitish ventrally; chin barbels white to dusky. Maximum adult size 1 m TL (3.3 ft), typically less than 60 cm TL (2 ft).

GEOGRAPHIC DISTRIBUTION   Native to central North America from southern Canada and the Great Lakes to the Gulf of Mexico and the southeastern United States. The channel catfish has been widely introduced elsewhere, including Hawaii.

ECOLOGY   The channel catfish was introduced into the mid-Atlantic region and now is common in all tributaries of Chesapeake Bay. It has been collected in waters with salinities as great as 18‰ and is often encountered in waters of 5‰ salinity or greater. Although the channel catfish occurs in lakes and ponds, it is more often encountered in large streams or rivers. Adult channel catfish occupy deep pools in and around logs and other cover. Juveniles occur in faster-moving, shallower waters. Spawning occurs in late spring, when water temperatures reach 24°C (75°F) or higher. The eggs are laid in a nest, and one or both parents guard the eggs and young. Channel catfish feed on a wide variety of insects and other bottom-dwelling arthropods, and fishes are also included in their diet. Channel catfish can live as long as 14 years, with some reported to exceed age 25.

FISHING INTEREST   See discussion for the white catfish, page 91. The channel catfish is one of the most important commercial fishes in the Mississippi River and is the basis of a major aquaculture industry in the southern United States. Channel catfish are also targeted by anglers. The sportfishing record is a specimen from Georgia that weighed 14.5 kg (32 lb) from Georgia.

LITERATURE   Musick 1972; Pflieger 1975; Eddy and Underhill 1978; Jones et al. 1978; Smith 1979; Manooch 1984; Smith 1985; Page and Burr 1991; Jenkins and Burkhead 1994.

Blue catfish
Ictalurus furcatus (Lesueur, 1840)

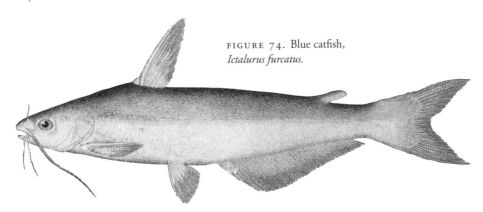

FIGURE 74. Blue catfish, *Ictalurus furcatus.*

KEY FEATURES   Tail deeply forked; body without dusky spots in fish at all sizes; anal fin with 27–38 rays (typically 30–36); distal margin of anal fin straight.

OTHER CHARACTERISTICS   Body typically slender (large adults sometimes robust), compressed posteriorly; head depressed; snout and mouth very broad; teeth small and in villiform bands; profile from tip of snout to dorsal fin steeply sloping; dorsal fin short-based, with 1 spine and 6 soft rays; adipose fin perpendicular to latter third of anal fin base; caudal fin lobes mostly straight; pelvic fin inserting nearer to tip of snout than to caudal fin base; pectoral spines stout and strongly serrated. Bluish silver dorsally; silvery white ventrally. Maximum adult size 1.7 m TL (5.5 ft), typically less than 60 cm TL (2 ft). An individual of 1 m TL (3.3 ft) can weigh more than 23 kg (50 lb). In the 1800s there were reports of blue catfish that exceeded 68 kg (150 lb).

GEOGRAPHIC DISTRIBUTION   Native to large rivers in central North America. The blue catfish has been introduced in the Chesapeake Bay region.

ECOLOGY   The blue catfish is occasionally encountered in the brackish waters (salinity less than 12‰) of Chesapeake Bay tributaries but is principally an inhabitant of the main channels and backwaters of medium-sized to large rivers. Spawning occurs from April to June, and the nest, constructed by the parents, is cared for until the young hatch. The blue catfish is a carnivorous bottom feeder that eats a variety of prey, including fishes, insects, crayfishes, clams, and mussels. Individuals are reported to reach at least 10 years of age.

FISHING INTEREST   Highly valued as a food fish, because of large size and firm, well-flavored flesh. The tidal portions of the James and Rappahannock rivers support an ample directed sport fishery for blue catfish, and commercial fisheries probably catch them as well. In the central United States, this species is much sought after by anglers. The world record is a fish from South Dakota that weighed 44 kg (97 lb).

LITERATURE   Pflieger 1975; Smith 1979; Jenkins and Burkhead 1994.

Flathead catfish
Pylodictis olivaris (Rafinesque, 1818)
PLATE 12

FIGURE 75. Flathead catfish,
Pylodictis olivaris.

KEY FEATURES   Posterior margin of caudal
fin slightly notched but not forked; lower jaw
strongly projecting beyond upper jaw; snout
greatly flattened.
OTHER CHARACTERISTICS   Body slender
or robust, compressed posteriorly; head strongly
flattened; snout and mouth very broad; teeth
small; premaxillary band of teeth present, with
posteriorly projecting extension on each side; dorsal fin short-based, with 1 spine and 6 soft rays;
adipose fin large, perpendicular to anal fin base;
caudal fin rounded; anal fin with 14–17 rays and
rounded margin; pelvic fin inserting nearer to
caudal fin than to tip of snout; pectoral spines
stout and strongly serrated. Dorsal and lateral surfaces pale yellow to pale brown, mottled with
brown or black; pale yellow or creamy white ventrally. Maximum adult size 1.4 m TL (4.6 ft),
with weights exceeding 55 kg (120 lb).
GEOGRAPHIC DISTRIBUTION   Native to
the central United States and Mexico and introduced elsewhere, including the Chesapeake Bay
region.
ECOLOGY   Flathead catfish are uncommonly
encountered in the brackish waters of Chesapeake

Bay tributaries. They live alone in deep holes and
channels of large and medium-sized rivers and
are most abundant in large rivers. Often these
habitats have submerged logs or undercut banks
that afford cover. Flathead catfish inhabit both
clear and turbid waters and are found more often
over hard bottoms than over silty bottoms. The
young live in riffles of rivers, frequently under
rocks. Adults move at night from deeper water or
cover to riffles and shallows in order to feed. Juveniles feed almost exclusively on aquatic insects,
whereas adults (>50 cm, or >20 in, SL) prey on
fishes and crayfishes. Spawning peaks during June
and July in Virginia. Nests are saucer-shaped depressions excavated by the parents. Individuals
may live for almost 20 years.
FISHING INTEREST   Taken only occasionally in the Chesapeake watershed (the tidal portion of the James River, for instance). In the
Midwest the flathead catfish is an important commercial fish and is taken by anglers in large
streams and reservoirs. Many flathead catfish are
caught on trotlines.
LITERATURE   Pflieger 1975; Smith 1979; Lee
and Terrell 1987; Jenkins and Burkhead 1994.

Yellow bullhead
Ameiurus natalis (Lesueur, 1819)
PLATE 13

KEY FEATURES   Chin barbels uniformly whitish; caudal fin margin nearly straight, not
notched; gill rakers numbering 12–18 (typically
13–16); anal fin with 24–28 rays.

OTHER CHARACTERISTICS   Body moderately slender, compressed posteriorly; head depressed; snout and mouth very broad; teeth very
small and in patches; all barbels dusky except

those on chin; dorsal fin short-based, with 1 spine and 6 or 7 soft rays; adipose fin perpendicular to latter third of anal fin base; dorsal and ventral margins of caudal fin rounded; margin of anal fin rounded; pelvic fin inserting only slightly nearer to tip of snout than to caudal fin base;

sionally encountered in waters with salinities greater than 5‰. Spawning occurs in May and June, with eggs deposited in a nest that may be in vegetation or out in the open. The male guards the eggs and young. This species feeds on a wide variety of insects and other bottom-

FIGURE 76. Yellow bullhead, *Ameiurus natalis.*

pectoral spines stout and moderately serrated. Brownish to slate gray dorsally; yellowish white ventrally; fins dusky; anal fin frequently with dark stripe. Maximum adult size 60 cm TL (2 ft), typically less than 30 cm TL (1 ft).

GEOGRAPHIC DISTRIBUTION   Native to central and eastern North America, from Minnesota and the Great Lakes to the Gulf of Mexico and the Atlantic Coast.

ECOLOGY   The yellow bullhead is probably found in all of the tributaries of Chesapeake Bay. It prefers shallow, vegetated, slow-flowing streams but also inhabits ponds and lakes. It is only occa-

dwelling organisms, such as mollusks and crustaceans. The yellow bullhead can live as long as 7 years.

FISHING INTEREST   Of no commercial importance and of minor recreational importance in the Chesapeake Bay region. The yellow bullhead is caught mainly with traps and nets and by bottom fishing with hook and line.

LITERATURE   Musick 1972; Pflieger 1975; Eddy and Underhill 1978; Jones et al. 1978; Smith 1979; Manooch 1984; Smith 1985; Page and Burr 1991; Jenkins and Burkhead 1994.

Brown bullhead
Ameiurus nebulosus (Lesueur, 1819)
PLATE 14

KEY FEATURES   Chin barbels grayish or blackish; caudal fin margin slightly notched; gill rakers typically numbering 13–15; anal fin with 18–24 rays.

OTHER CHARACTERISTICS   Body stout, compressed posteriorly; head depressed; snout and mouth very broad; teeth small and in patches; dorsal fin short-based, with 1 spine and 6 or 7 soft rays; adipose fin perpendicular to latter third of anal fin base; dorsal and ventral margins of caudal fin rounded; margin of anal fin rounded; pelvic fin inserting about equidistant

from tip of snout and caudal fin base; pectoral spines stout and strongly serrated. Olive to blackish dorsally; yellowish white ventrally; heavily mottled or marbled laterally; all barbels and fins dusky. Maximum adult size 53 cm TL (1.75 ft), with adults typically less than 30 cm TL (1 ft).

GEOGRAPHIC DISTRIBUTION   Native to central and eastern North America, from southern Canada and the Great Lakes to Florida and Texas.

ECOLOGY   The brown bullhead is found in all tributaries of Chesapeake Bay, including ponds, lakes, and slow-flowing streams. Because it tolerates salinities as great as 20‰, it is more commonly encountered than the yellow bullhead in

as mollusks and crustaceans. The brown bullhead can live as long as 7 years, with some individuals reported to attain 10 years.

FIGURE 77. Brown bullhead, *Ameiurus nebulosus*.

brackish waters. Spawning occurs from April to June, with the eggs deposited in a nest made under an overhang, a log, or a rock. The eggs and young are guarded by both the male and the female. This species feeds on a wide variety of insects and other bottom-dwelling organisms, such

FISHING INTEREST   See under discussion for the white catfish, page 91.

LITERATURE   Musick 1972; Pflieger 1975; Eddy and Underhill 1978; Smith 1979; Manooch 1984; Smith 1985; Page and Burr 1991; Jenkins and Burkhead 1994.

Sea Catfishes
FAMILY ARIIDAE

Sea catfishes occur in marine, brackish, and freshwaters of warm-temperate and tropical regions. Ariids are mostly confined to the coastlines of the continent and continental islands. They may be locally abundant in the turbid waters of certain habitats, particularly large river estuaries and mangrove-lined lagoons. In common with the bullhead catfishes, sea catfishes possess naked skin, an adipose fin, a forked caudal fin, and a single pungent spine in the dorsal and pectoral fins. Sea catfishes differ from bullhead catfishes by having two or three pairs of barbels around the mouth. The sharp spines of sea catfishes can produce painful puncture wounds. Some marine species attain lengths of 1 m (3.3 ft) or more. There are 20 genera and approximately 120 species of ariids, 2 of which are known from Chesapeake Bay.

KEY TO THE SPECIES OF SEA CATFISHES IN CHESAPEAKE BAY

1a. Four barbels present on head (1 pair on chin); dorsal and pectoral fins with elongate and ribbonlike filament . . . . **gafftopsail catfish, *Bagre marinus*** (p. 96)
1b. Six barbels present on head (2 pairs on chin); dorsal and pectoral fins without elongate filament . . . . **hardhead catfish, *Arius felis*** (p. 284)

Gafftopsail catfish
Bagre marinus (Mitchill, 1815)

KEY FEATURES   Two pairs of well-developed and elongate barbels present around mouth, 1 pair on upper jaw and 1 pair on lower jaw; barbels on upper jaw noticeably flattened; long filaments on dorsal and pectoral fins reaching nearly to or beyond anal fin.

OTHER CHARACTERISTICS   Body robust, depressed anteriorly and compressed posteriorly; head and snout broad; teeth small and in patches; filament on dorsal fin frequently reaching to adipose fin; adipose fin small, originating perpendicular to midpoint of anal fin; caudal fin deeply forked, with upper lobe slightly longer than lower lobe; anal fin with concave margin; pelvic fin inserting about halfway between tip of snout and caudal fin base; filament on pectoral fin reaching nearly to anal fin origin. Bluish gray to dusky brown dorsally; silver laterally, with a

early May to June. The male holds the large fertilized eggs in its mouth for up to 2 months, until they hatch; the male ceases feeding during the incubation period. Gafftopsail catfish are opportunistic feeders over mud and sand bottoms and eat invertebrates and small fishes.

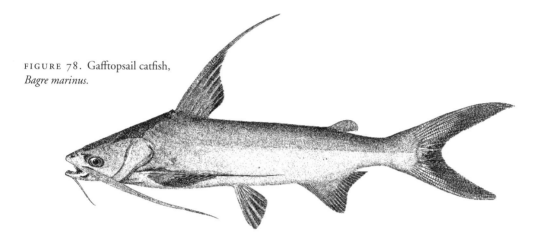

FIGURE 78. Gafftopsail catfish, *Bagre marinus*.

white venter. Maximum adult size 60 cm TL (2 ft).

GEOGRAPHIC DISTRIBUTION   Occurring in the western Atlantic from Cape Cod to Brazil, including the Gulf of Mexico and the Caribbean Sea.

ECOLOGY   The gafftopsail catfish is a rare summer visitor to Chesapeake Bay and reaches as far north as the Potomac River. It is a predominantly marine species that enters estuaries and sometimes freshwater. Spawning occurs from

FISHING INTEREST   Where plentiful, caught incidentally with longlines (large individuals), bottom trawls, shore seines, cast nets, and hook and line. Gafftopsail catfish are not valued as food, and there is no commercial fishery for the species in this country. The gafftopsail is generally considered a nuisance.

LITERATURE   Hildebrand and Schroeder 1928:127; Musick 1972; Fischer 1978; Jones et al. 1978; Muncy and Wingo 1983; Robins et al. 1986; Nelson 1994.

Salmon, Trouts, and Pickerels
ORDER SALMONIFORMES

The order of salmon, trouts, and pickerels comprises 15 families, 3 of which are known from Chesapeake Bay.

KEY TO THE FAMILIES OF SALMON, TROUTS, AND PICKERELS IN CHESAPEAKE BAY

1a. Dorsal fin near midbody; adipose fin present . . . .**trouts—Salmonidae** (p. 98)
1b. Dorsal fin far posterior on body; adipose fin absent **2**

2a. Caudal fin rounded . . . . **mudminnows—Umbridae** (p. 102)
2b. Caudal fin moderately forked . . . . **pikes—Esocidae** (p. 103)

Trouts
FAMILY SALMONIDAE

The family Salmonidae includes salmon, chars, graylings, whitefishes, and trouts—all fishes typically found in cold-temperate waters. All members of this family possess an adipose fin. These medium-sized to large fishes constitute major commercial and recreational fisheries; some species are important components of the aquaculture industry. Some members of this family are confined to freshwater; others are anadromous, entering rivers and streams to spawn. Some species of salmon make long and arduous migrations from the ocean to their natal stream (stream of their birth) to spawn, and when spawning is complete, they expire. Navigation for such migrations is assisted in part by olfactory cues that are imprinted soon after hatching. The species of salmonid fishes are plastic in their physical characteristics and readily develop into distinctive ecotypes in response to localized conditions. In the past, many of these ecotypes have been considered as full species and named accordingly, thus creating considerable confusion in the scientific nomenclature of this family. The salmonids, restricted to the Northern Hemisphere, comprise 11 genera and more than 65 species, 5 of which are recorded from Chesapeake Bay.

KEY TO THE SPECIES OF TROUTS IN CHESAPEAKE BAY

1a. Anal fin with 13–19 rays (excluding small splintlike rays at front of fin) . . . .
. . . . **coho salmon, *Oncorhynchus kisutch*** (p. 284)
1b. Anal fin with 7–12 rays **2**

2a. Spots on side pale; more than 190 scales present along lateral line . . . .
. . . . **brook trout, *Salvelinus fontinalis*** (p. 98)
2b. Spots on side blackish; fewer than 180 scales present along lateral line **3**

3a. Head and body heavily spotted with black and/or red **4**
3b. Head and body with only a few scattered black spots . . . . **Atlantic salmon, *Salmo salar*** (p. 99)

4a. Caudal fin with spots usually restricted to dorsalmost portion of upper lobe; dorsal fin with 12–16 rays
. . . . **brown trout, *Salmo trutta*** (p. 100)
4b. Entire caudal fin with spots; dorsal fin with 10–12 rays . . . .
. . . . **rainbow trout, *Oncorhynchus mykiss*** (p. 101)

Brook trout
Salvelinus fontinalis (Mitchill, 1814)

KEY FEATURES   Side with numerous pale spots of various sizes and shapes; scales very small and numbering more than 190 in lateral series; pectoral, pelvic, and anal fins with white leading edge followed by black streak and with rest of fin yellow, orange, or red; pale wormlike markings present on dorsal surface.

OTHER CHARACTERISTICS   Body typically fusiform; snout rounded; head scaleless; mouth moderately oblique and large; dorsal fin with 11–15 rays and nearly straight margin; adipose fin present; caudal fin more truncate in adults than in juveniles; anal fin with 9–12 rays and concave margin; origin of pelvic fin slightly dorsoposterior to dorsal fin origin; pelvic axillary scale well developed; pectoral fin low on body. Dorsum olive; lower side with yellowish and red spots; caudal and dorsal fins with rows of black or dusky spots; breeding males with red or orange belly; females pale or yellow ventrally. Maximum adult size 60 cm TL (2 ft).

GEOGRAPHIC DISTRIBUTION   Native to eastern Canada and the northern United States, from Iowa to Long Island; also indigenous to higher elevations of the Appalachian Mountains as far south as Georgia. The brook trout has been introduced in many other areas of the United States, including the Chesapeake Bay region.

ECOLOGY   Brook trout typically inhabit the colder, swifter, less fertile headwater regions of rivers and streams and are also found in cool-water

Brook trout feed on a variety of aquatic animals, including insects, tadpoles, snakes, salamanders, and fishes. Spawning occurs in the autumn over gravel bottoms.

FISHING INTEREST   Of special interest to fly fishers and considered to be of fine flavor, but

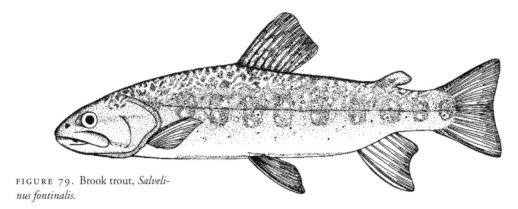

FIGURE 79. Brook trout, *Salvelinus fontinalis*.

lakes. They are intolerant of water temperatures greater than 24°C (75°F) and consequently are maintained on the Chesapeake coastal plain only by restocking. Anadromous populations of brook trout are known as far southward as Long Island, and individuals have been collected in Chesapeake Bay waters of 5‰ or greater salinity.

of no commercial importance. The world-record brook trout is a fish from Ontario that weighed 6.6 kg (14.5 lb).

LITERATURE   Dymond 1963; Musick 1972; Smith 1985; Raleigh et al. 1986; Jenkins and Burkhead 1994.

Atlantic salmon
Salmo salar Linnaeus, 1758

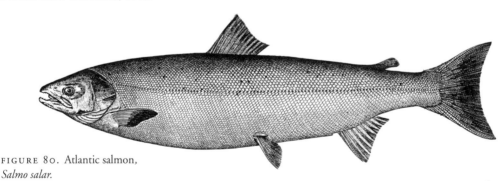

FIGURE 80. Atlantic salmon, *Salmo salar*.

KEY FEATURES   Black spots small, few in number, and mostly restricted to head and body; caudal fin with shallow to deep fork and few or no black spots.

OTHER CHARACTERISTICS   Body elongate, somewhat compressed laterally, and deepest at dorsal fin origin or slightly posterior to dorsal

fin; head length about equal to or slightly less than body depth; eye moderate in size; snout rounded; mouth terminal, large, and extending to rear of eye; well-developed teeth present on upper and lower jaws; teeth present on vomer, palatines, and tongue; dorsal fin located at midbody and with 10–12 rays; adipose fin usually unspotted and without black border; anal fin with 8–11 rays; pelvic fin slightly smaller than pectoral fin; pectoral fin low on body. Coloration variable with age, environment, and life stage; adults olive brown to green dorsally and silvery laterally and ventrally; large fish with scattered X-shaped marks on dorsum and head; pectoral and caudal fins blackish; spawning fish sometimes with orange or orange red lateral blotches and overall darker coloration. Typical adult size 46–76 cm SL (1.5–2.5 ft).

GEOGRAPHIC DISTRIBUTION   Found on both sides of the Atlantic. In the western Atlantic, the Atlantic salmon is found from northern Quebec and Newfoundland to the Connecticut River. Spawning runs probably do not occur south of the Connecticut River, but individuals stray southward at least as far as the mouth of Chesapeake Bay.

ECOLOGY   Only a few records of Atlantic salmon in Chesapeake Bay are known, and those are from near the bay mouth. Atlantic salmon are anadromous, living and feeding primarily at sea and returning to the freshwater stream of their birth only to spawn. While at sea, they roam widely, but usually close to shore; they move into rivers in the spring and summer, although they do not spawn until October or November. Landlocked populations move into streams in early fall. The female excavates a nesting depression (redd) by fanning with her caudal fin. After spawning, she moves upstream and fans more gravel, which is carried downstream by the current and covers the eggs. Spawning is repeated until the female has deposited all of her eggs; then the spawners move downstream to a deep pool to rest for a few weeks before moving back to the lake or ocean. The eggs hatch in April, and the young salmon spend 2–3 years in streams before moving into larger bodies of water. Unlike Pacific salmon species, which die after one spawning, the Atlantic salmon may live to spawn several times, although few individuals live more than 9 years. In streams, young Atlantic salmon feed mostly on aquatic insects, with terrestrial insects contributing to the diet especially in late summer and fall. In the ocean, this species feeds on small fishes and crustaceans.

FISHING INTEREST   Rated one of the best sport fishes. Atlantic salmon are hard fighters and high jumpers and are considered a prestigious game fish by many anglers. The rod and reel record for Atlantic salmon is an individual caught in Norway in 1928 that weighed 79 kg (174 lb). Because of low population levels of wild stocks, angling for the Atlantic salmon is now largely restricted by law to fly-fishing only. In the Northeast an important commercial fishery for Atlantic salmon existed for more than a century before collapsing because of declining stocks. Atlantic salmon were once so abundant in some rivers of New England that they were speared during their spawning run and used for fertilizer. In 1992 the entire spawning run of Atlantic salmon for all New England rivers combined consisted of fewer than 3,000 fish. Because of the low population numbers, this species has been considered for endangered status. Degraded water quality and barriers to migration continue to minimize progress in the efforts to restore wild Atlantic salmon stocks. However, a thriving New England aquaculture industry based on pen-reared Atlantic salmon has developed in the 1980s and 1990s. In 1992 this industry harvested 6.1 million kilograms (13.5 million pounds) of Atlantic salmon, and in Maine the cultured Atlantic salmon fishery was second only to the lobster fishery in value.

LITERATURE   Musick 1972; Scott and Crossman 1973; Danie et al. 1984; Smith 1985.

Brown trout
Salmo trutta Linnaeus, 1758

KEY FEATURES   Head and body with numerous dusky or black spots and some scattered red spots along side; caudal fin without spots or with few spots usually confined to dorsalmost lobe; dorsal fin with 12–16 rays.

OTHER CHARACTERISTICS   Body ovate and compressed; snout rounded; mouth terminal; well-developed teeth present on jaws, vomer, palatines, and tongue; eye large; dorsal fin with nearly straight margin and located near midbody;

adipose fin present; caudal fin slightly forked in adults, truncate in others; anal fin with 10–12 rays, smaller than dorsal fin, and perpendicular to adipose fin; pelvic fin originating perpendicular to posterior part of dorsal fin; pelvic axillary scale well developed; pectoral fin low on body. Olive brown dorsally; lower side and belly yellow-

can be maintained in coastal streams of the Chesapeake Bay region only by annual restocking. The brown trout is frequently found near cover and is more secretive than the rainbow trout. The brown trout feeds on aquatic insects, snails, amphipods, crayfishes, and fishes. It is typically a stream spawner, and spawning occurs in fall or

FIGURE 81. Brown trout, *Salmo trutta.*

ish or white. Maximum adult size about 1 m TL (3.3 ft).

GEOGRAPHIC DISTRIBUTION   Indigenous to Europe and west Asia. The brown trout was introduced to North America in the 1880s and has been stocked in many countries around the world.

ECOLOGY   Brown trout have been stocked in both streams and lakes in the Chesapeake Bay region, and they sometimes penetrate into waters of 5‰ or greater salinity. Brown trout typically occupy the deeper, lower-velocity, warmer, and more fertile downstream regions of rivers and streams. Water temperatures greater than 27°C (81°F) are lethal to brown trout, so the species

early winter. In some parts of its range, anadromous populations are known. Anadromous brown trout have been reported to live to age 18, whereas brown trout restricted to freshwater have lived as long as 13 years.

FISHING INTEREST   Highly prized by anglers. Brown trout are considered more difficult to catch than rainbow trout and thus are more challenging to anglers. The American record for brown trout is a fish caught in Arkansas in 1988 that weighed 18 kg (39.5 lb) .

LITERATURE   Musick 1972; Smith 1979; Smith 1985; Raleigh et al. 1986; Jenkins and Burkhead 1994.

Rainbow trout
Oncorhynchus mykiss (Walbaum, 1792)

KEY FEATURES   Head, body, and entire caudal fin heavily spotted with black; dorsal fin with 10–12 rays.

OTHER CHARACTERISTICS   Body elongate, ovate, and deepest anterior to dorsal fin; head small; snout rounded; mouth terminal, oblique, and extending to rear of eye; teeth present on jaws, vomer, palatines, and tongue; eye large; dorsal fin with slightly concave margin and located at midbody, originating slightly dorso-anterior to pelvic fin; adipose fin present; caudal fin emarginate to slightly forked, with slightly

rounded lobes, and covered with radiating rows of black spots; anal fin with 8–12 rays; pelvic fin smaller than pectoral fin and with convex margins; pectoral fin low on body. Olive to blue green dorsally; side and venter whitish gray or yellow; side with pink or rose-colored stripe; dorsal and adipose fins with black spots. Typical adult size 25–40 cm TL (10–16 in); lake-run individuals or sea-run individuals (steelheads) are larger.

GEOGRAPHIC DISTRIBUTION   Originally found west of the Rocky Mountains from Baja California to Alaska. The rainbow trout has been widely introduced elsewhere in North America, Europe, Asia, South America, New Zealand, and Australia.

ECOLOGY   During the mid-1800s the rainbow trout was introduced into some Maryland tribu-

winter to spring. The female creates a nest by fanning the bottom with her tail, which displaces gravel. After fertilization, the male joins the female in the nest, and the eggs are covered. The maximum age of rainbow trout is 8 years. They

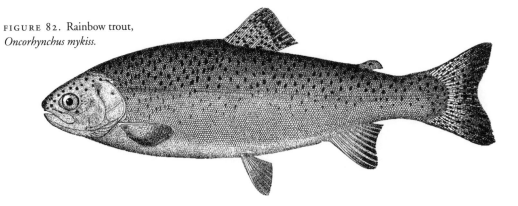

FIGURE 82. Rainbow trout, *Oncorhynchus mykiss*.

taries to Chesapeake Bay. Rainbow trout are intolerant of water temperatures greater than 21°C (70°F), so annual stocking is necessary to maintain the population. They occur in small creeks to large streams with gravelly or rocky bottoms. They also occur in lakes but must have access to streams in order to reproduce. Some rainbow trout are anadromous and spend much of their life at sea. Sea-run rainbow trout are commonly called steelheads. Rainbow trout spawn in late

feed on aquatic insects, crustaceans, and small fishes. At sea, steelheads feed on squids and fishes.

FISHING INTEREST   Much sought after by fly fishers. The all-tackle record for rainbow trout is a fish from Alaska that weighed 19 kg (42 lb).

LITERATURE   Musick 1972; Scott and Crossman 1973; Smith 1985; Jenkins and Burkhead 1994.

Mudminnows
FAMILY UMBRIDAE

Members of the mudminnow family are small to medium-sized fishes that inhabit slow-moving waters and swamps of the temperate and arctic Northern Hemisphere. In members of this group, both the anal and dorsal fins are located posteriorly on the body. The common name for the family is derived from the habit these fishes have of burying themselves in the bottom substrate, typically mud. Some mudminnows are reported to be resistant to freezing and able to overwinter in shallow, frozen water bodies. The swim bladder serves as an accessory breathing organ in some members of the family, allowing them to survive drought conditions by burrowing in thick detritus or soft ooze. Because of their hardiness, mudminnows are commonly used as baitfish. The family comprises only three genera and six species, one of which is known from Chesapeake Bay tributaries.

Eastern mudminnow
Umbra pygmaea (DeKay, 1842)

KEY FEATURES   Ten or more longitudinal dusky lines present on side; pelvic fin originating at midbody; dorsal fin originating posteriorly; origin of anal fin ventroposterior to origin of dorsal fin; caudal fin rounded.

OTHER CHARACTERISTICS   Body elongate and robust; snout rounded; mouth small; gill rakers well developed; lateral line absent; scales in lateral series numbering 30–34; dorsal fin spineless, low, rounded posteriorly, and with 13–15 rays; anal fin low, rounded posteriorly, and with 6–8 soft rays; pelvic fin short-based; pectoral fin broadly rounded. Dusky brown dorsally; pale brown laterally and ventrally; lateral stripes brownish and separated by pale lines; black bar present on caudal peduncle. Maximum adult size 130 mm TL (5 in), commonly to 75 mm (3 in) or less.

in waters of 5‰ or greater salinity; the highest recorded salinity tolerance for this species is 12‰. Of the four species of mudminnows found in North America, the eastern mudminnow is the most tolerant of warmer waters and is found farther south than any of the others. It feeds on aquatic insects and small crustaceans. In the Chesapeake Bay region, spawning

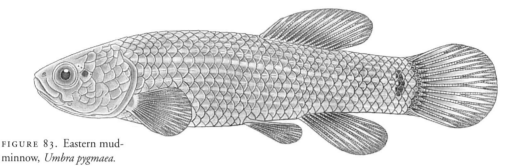

FIGURE 83. Eastern mudminnow, *Umbra pygmaea*.

GEOGRAPHIC DISTRIBUTION   Limited to the eastern coastal plain of the United States from southern New York to Florida, including the Gulf coast of Florida.

ECOLOGY   The eastern mudminnow inhabits swamps and sluggish waterways and is found in all tributaries of Chesapeake Bay. It is typically found in freshwaters but is occasionally collected

occurs in late March and April when water temperatures reach 10°–15°C (50°–59°F).

FISHING INTEREST   Of no recreational value, because of small size, except indirectly as food for larger fishes and as bait.

LITERATURE   Musick 1972; Eddy and Underhill 1978; Smith 1985; Jenkins and Burkhead 1994.

Pikes

FAMILY ESOCIDAE

Members of the pike family are characterized by long, cylindrical bodies and prominent jaws that are shaped like a duck's bill and armed with numerous fanglike teeth. The dorsal and anal fins are situated posteriorly on the body near the caudal fin. Pikes and pickerels are widely distributed in freshwaters in much of North America, and pikes are also found in Asia and Europe. They are highly predaceous, feeding on fishes and any other living prey small enough to seize. The members of this family spawn in the spring, scattering their eggs at random in shallow water, where they are fertilized and left to develop without parental care. Esocids grow very rapidly, and some species, such as the muskellunge *(Esox masquinongy)*, reach a large size. The larger species are popular game fishes. The family, comprising five species all belonging to the genus *Esox,* is represented by two species in low-salinity (5‰ or lower) Chesapeake Bay waters.

KEY TO THE SPECIES OF PIKES IN CHESAPEAKE BAY

1a. Branchiostegal rays numbering 16 or fewer (typically 12–14); snout length contained more than 8 times in total length; suborbital bar with slight ventroposterior slant; side with 20–36 wavy vertical bars....................................**redfin pickerel, *Esox americanus americanus*** (p. 104)

1b. Branchiostegal rays numbering 14 or more; snout length contained less than 7 times in total length; suborbital bar vertical; side with reticulated (chainlike) pattern in specimens of greater than 30 cm SL (12 in)...**chain pickerel, *Esox niger*** (p. 105)

Redfin pickerel
Esox americanus americanus Gmelin, 1788

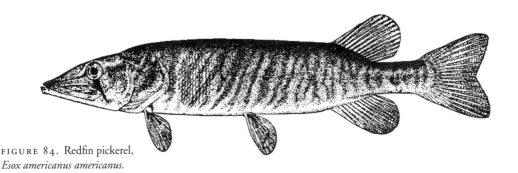

FIGURE 84. Redfin pickerel,
Esox americanus americanus.

KEY FEATURES   Branchiostegal rays numbering 11–16 (typically 12–14); snout shorter than
in the chain pickerel, its length contained 8.7
times in total length, or about 3 times in head
length; suborbital bar with slight ventroposterior
slant; side with 20–36 wavy vertical bars.

OTHER CHARACTERISTICS   Body elon-
gate, almost circular in cross section, and deepest
near middle; snout long, depressed, and broad;
mouth large and nearly horizontal; lower jaw
projecting slightly beyond upper jaw; teeth present on jaws, vomer, palatines, and tongue; cheek
fully scaled; lateral line complete; scales small and
numbering fewer than 120 in lateral series; dorsal
and anal fins located posteriorly on body near
caudal fin; caudal fin forked; pelvic fin originating near midpoint of body; pectoral fin low on
body. Olivaceous to blackish dorsally; venter pale
to amber; all fins with red margins, except dorsal
fin. Maximum adult size 37 cm TL (1.2 ft).

GEOGRAPHIC DISTRIBUTION   Known
from the St. Lawrence Seaway southward along
the Atlantic coast to northern Florida.

ECOLOGY   The redfin pickerel is common in
many tributaries of Chesapeake Bay. Although
more often encountered in freshwaters, redfin
pickerel can tolerate salinities up to 10‰. Typical habitats for this species are quiet, heavily vegetated waters in ponds, drainage canals, streams,
and small lakes. Redfin pickerel often occur with

chain pickerel; in ponds the chain pickerel is usually more abundant than the redfin pickerel,
whereas in small streams the opposite is true.
The life history of the redfin pickerel is similar
in many respects to that of the chain pickerel. In
the Chesapeake Bay region, redfin pickerel spawn
in February and March at water temperatures of
4°–10°C (39°–50°F). Eggs are scattered in shallow water near and on vegetation. As redfin pickerel grow, their diet changes from invertebrates to
fishes; they are diurnal feeders. Redfin pickerel
can reach 7–8 years of age.

FISHING INTEREST   Not commercially important. The redfin pickerel is not regarded as a
sport fish, because of its small size, but it readily
strikes at lures and live bait.

ADDITIONAL REMARKS   Two subspecies of
E. americanus are recognized: *E. a. americanus*
(the redfin pickerel, described here) and *E. a. ver-
miculatus* (the grass pickerel). The grass pickerel
is found in the drainages of the Gulf of Mexico
and the Mississippi River. Intergrading populations of the two subspecies occur in Florida,
Georgia, Alabama, and Louisiana.

LITERATURE   Hildebrand and Schroeder
1928:134; Dick 1964; Musick 1972; Eddy and
Underhill 1978; Jones et al. 1978; Smith 1985;
Page and Burr 1991; Jenkins and Burkhead
1994.

Chain pickerel
Esox niger Lesueur, 1818

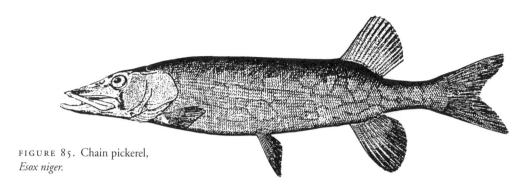

FIGURE 85. Chain pickerel,
Esox niger.

KEY FEATURES   Branchiostegal rays numbering 14–17; snout longer than in the redfin pickerel, its length contained less than 7 times in total length, about 2.5 times in head length; suborbital bar vertical; side with reticulated (chainlike) pattern in specimens of greater than 30.5 cm SL (12 in).

OTHER CHARACTERISTICS   Body slender, somewhat compressed, and deepest near middle; snout long, depressed, and broad; mouth large and nearly horizontal; lower jaw projecting beyond upper jaw; teeth prominent and present on jaws, vomer, palatines, and tongue; cheek fully scaled; lateral line complete; scales small and numbering more than 110 in lateral series; dorsal and anal fins located posteriorly on body near caudal fin; caudal fin forked; pelvic fin originating near midpoint of body; pectoral fin low on body. Greenish dorsally; pale ventrally. Maximum adult size 1 m TL (3.3 ft), typically 35–50 cm TL (14–20 in).

GEOGRAPHIC DISTRIBUTION   Known from the St. Lawrence Seaway southward along the Atlantic coast to Florida, along the Gulf Coast to Texas, and in the Mississippi Valley to Missouri and Kentucky.

ECOLOGY   The chain pickerel is common in all tributaries of Chesapeake Bay. Although more often encountered in freshwaters, chain pickerel can tolerate salinities up to 22‰. They are typically found in weedy backwaters and pools of streams and rivers, as well as in ponds and lakes. The chain pickerel spawns in early spring when water temperatures reach 10°C (50°F). Eggs are laid in mats or strings that adhere to submerged vegetation. Chain pickerel are visual predators and are primarily active during the day. Individuals larger than 15 cm TL (6 in) feed on other fishes and crayfishes. This species' ambush style of hunting requires cover, usually sought in the form of aquatic plants, tree stumps, and fallen logs. Chain pickerel can live as long as 10 years.

FISHING INTEREST   Popular as a game fish. Angling for chain pickerel presents difficulties, as they are typically found in waters clogged with weeds and brush. The angling record is a fish from Georgia that measured 79 cm TL (31 in). In the early part of the twentieth century, the chain pickerel was commercially harvested in Chesapeake Bay waters with a variety of nets.

LITERATURE   Hildebrand and Schroeder 1928:132; Dick 1964; Musick 1972; Eddy and Underhill 1978; Jones et al. 1978; Smith 1985; Page and Burr 1991; Jenkins and Burkhead 1994.

Toadfishes

ORDER BATRACHOIDIFORMES

The toadfish order comprises a single family, the Batrachoididae.

Toadfishes

FAMILY BATRACHOIDIDAE

Toadfishes are sluggish demersal predators that feed primarily on crustaceans and mollusks. They possess a large mouth and strong jaws and thus are sometimes called oyster crackers. Toadfishes are frequently described as ugly or grotesque because of their bulging eyes, fleshy "whiskers," and broad, flat heads. Many toadfish species are capable of sound production, one use of which is by males to attract females to nests. The family comprises 19 genera and approximately 69 species, of which 1 species is known from Chesapeake Bay.

Oyster toadfish
Opsanus tau (Linnaeus, 1766)
PLATE 15

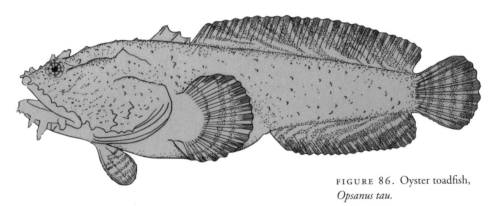

FIGURE 86. Oyster toadfish,
Opsanus tau.

KEY FEATURES   Body robust and compressed posteriorly; head depressed; eye large and "toad-like"; fleshy flaps present on cheeks and jaws; mouth very broad, with strong blunt teeth on jaws, vomer, and palatines; opercle with 2 partly concealed spines; skin scaleless, smooth, and slimy; axil of pectoral fin with large blind pouch.
OTHER CHARACTERISTICS   Snout short and broad; dorsal fins separate; first dorsal fin with 3 short spines enveloped in skin; second dorsal fin long and of uniform height; caudal fin rounded; anal fin long; pelvic fin jugular; pectoral fin broad, with concentric brown bands. Skin pale or yellowish brown; body mottled with dusky brown oblique bars that extend onto fins; head with dusky brown reticulations. Maximum adult size 38 cm TL (1.25 ft).

GEOGRAPHIC DISTRIBUTION   Found in the western Atlantic from Maine to the West Indies.
ECOLOGY   The oyster toadfish is an abundant year-round resident that is found throughout Chesapeake Bay on mud, rock, sand, and oyster shell bottoms and is most common in lower and middle portions of estuaries. The oyster toadfish is renowned for its vocalizations, which are accomplished by rapid contractions of striated muscles attached to the walls of the air bladder. Although both sexes can produce a grunting sound, only the male can produce the "boat whistle" sound that apparently attracts females to the nest site. The spawning season is protracted, extending from April to October. Large shells or, frequently, old cans and jars are utilized as nest

sites, where the very large, adhesive eggs (5 mm, or 0.2 in, in diameter) are guarded by the male. After depositing her eggs, the female oyster toadfish moves to deeper water. This species is omnivorous but principally preys on crustaceans, most frequently on small crabs.

FISHING INTEREST   Of no commercial or sportfishing value but caught with bottom trawls and seines as well as by rod and reel. The oyster toadfish is edible but, because of its appearance,

is rarely eaten. Most anglers consider it a nuisance because its powerful and potentially dangerous jaws make hook removal and handling difficult. It makes a grunting sound when caught and can survive for extended periods out of water.

LITERATURE   Hildebrand and Schroeder 1928:337; Schwartz and Dutcher 1963; Musick 1972; Schwartz 1974; Fine 1975; Martin and Drewry 1978; Manooch 1984; Nelson 1994.

Clingfishes
ORDER GOBIESOCIFORMES

The order of clingfishes comprises a single family, the Gobiesocidae.

Clingfishes
FAMILY GOBIESOCIDAE

Clingfishes are typically small, inconspicuous, demersal fishes possessing a ventral sucking disk formed from highly modified pelvic fins. The sucking disk enables these fishes to cling to rocks, shells, or other objects. Clingfishes are usually found in shallow water or intertidal zones. Most are marine, but a few freshwater representatives are known from Central America. The family comprises 36 genera and about 120 species distributed worldwide. One species is known from Chesapeake Bay waters.

Skilletfish
Gobiesox strumosus Cope, 1870

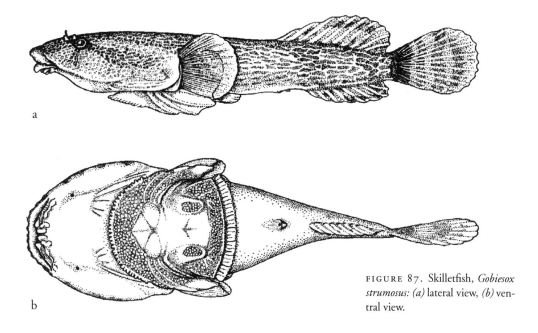

a

b

FIGURE 87. Skilletfish, *Gobiesox strumosus: (a)* lateral view, *(b)* ventral view.

KEY FEATURES   Head broadly rounded and flattened; body compressed posteriorly and without scales; sucking disk large; single dorsal fin present, originating posterior to midbody.

OTHER CHARACTERISTICS   Mouth inferior, with strong teeth in both jaws; eye small; opercle with sharp spine; dorsal and anal fins long-based and without spines; dorsal fin base slightly longer than anal fin base; caudal fin rounded. Variable pattern present on dusky to pale gray background; some individuals with pale crossbars. Maximum adult size 75 mm SL (3 in).

GEOGRAPHIC DISTRIBUTION   Found from New Jersey to Florida, throughout the northern Gulf of Mexico, and southward to Brazil.

ECOLOGY   The skilletfish is a year-round resident in Chesapeake Bay, extending as far north as the Magothy River (Anne Arundel County, Maryland). It is common to abundant throughout its range in the bay and is typically found on oyster bars and in eelgrass beds. During the warmer months the skilletfish is found closer to shore, and in the winter it retreats to deeper water. Spawning occurs in empty oyster shells from April through August. The skilletfish feeds primarily on small crustaceans and polychaete worms.

FISHING INTEREST   Of no interest but occasionally collected in seines. The skilletfish readily adapts to the aquarium, where it typically adheres to the glass.

LITERATURE   Hildebrand and Schroeder 1928:339; Musick 1972; Martin and Drewry 1978; Robins et al. 1986; Briggs 1993; Nelson 1994.

Goosefishes
ORDER LOPHIIFORMES

The order of goosefishes comprises 18 families, of which 3 are known from Chesapeake Bay.

KEY TO THE FAMILIES OF GOOSEFISHES IN CHESAPEAKE BAY

1a. Body dorsoventrally flattened **2**

1b. Body robust, globose, and not dorsoventrally flattened . . . . **frogfishes—Antennariidae**
. . . . (1 species reported from Chesapeake Bay: sargassumfish, *Histrio histrio,* p. 285)

2a. Three slender dorsal fin spines present on head; first dorsal fin modified into fishing lure with fleshy appendage at tip; mouth very large and wide . . . . **goosefishes—Lophiidae** (p. 108)

2b. Slender dorsal fin spines absent on head; fishing lure (esca) small, located in small depression between snout and mouth; mouth not large . . . . **batfishes—Ogcocephalidae**
. . . . . . (1 species reported from Chesapeake Bay waters: longnose batfish, *Ogcocephalus corniger,* p. 285)

Goosefishes
FAMILY LOPHIIDAE

Goosefishes are marine, bottom-dwelling fishes with very broad, depressed heads and enormous mouths. The jaws bear numerous long, sharp teeth. The first impression is that the fish is mostly head and that the head is mostly mouth—hence the colloquial name "allmouth" has been given to goosefishes in some regions. As in most other families of this order (Lophiiformes), goosefishes possess cephalic dorsal fin spines. The three dorsal spines located on the head are unconnected by membrane, and the anteriormost, situated near the tip of the snout, has its terminus modified into an angling apparatus that bears a fleshy appendage, the esca. The first spine is quite mobile and can be angled forward such that the esca is dangled in front of the mouth. The esca is wiggled like a bait to lure fishes or other prey near to the large mouth, where the prey is engulfed. The family comprises 4 genera and 25 species, 1 of which is known from Chesapeake Bay waters.

Goosefish
Lophius americanus Valenciennes, 1837

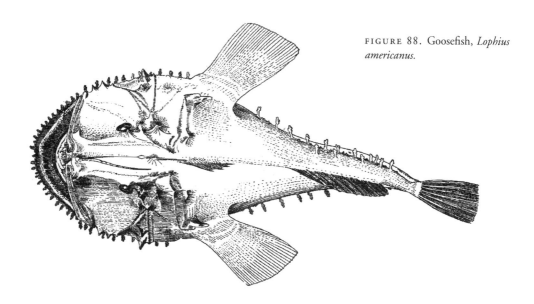

FIGURE 88. Goosefish, *Lophius americanus.*

KEY FEATURES   Head and anterior part of body much depressed and very broad; posterior portion of body tapering; mouth superior and exceedingly wide; lower jaw projecting beyond upper jaw; jaws with long, sharp, depressible teeth; head with 3 long, slender spines, and anteriormost spine with esca; gill openings via channel that exits in pectoral fin axil.

OTHER CHARACTERISTICS   Head as wide as long, and longer than body; eye small; skin smooth and without scales; lower jaw fringed with short dermal flaps, and similar flaps present laterally on body; dorsal fins separate; postcephalic dorsal fin spines connected by black membrane; pelvic fin slightly ventroanterior to pectoral fin; pectoral fin very broad and armlike; spines present anterior to pectoral fin base; anal fin short-based. Dusky brown dorsally; pale tan ventrally; ventral surface of pectoral fin blackish distally. Maximum adult size 1.2 m TL (4 ft).

GEOGRAPHIC DISTRIBUTION   Found from the northern Gulf of St. Lawrence to northern Florida.

ECOLOGY   The goosefish is an occasional visitor to the lower Chesapeake Bay from late fall to early spring. It is most abundant in waters with temperatures of 3°–11°C (37°–52°F); thus it occurs in the lower bay only during the colder months. The goosefish inhabits sand, mud, and broken shell bottoms from a few centimeters to more than 800 m (2,300 ft) in depth. Spawning occurs primarily during May and June, with females extruding a gelatinous mass of purplish brown eggs that floats as a broad mat on the surface. Aided by its fishing appendage, the goosefish is a voracious lie-in-wait benthic predator of other fishes. Goosefish have been reported to take prey nearly one-half their size, as well as to capture waterbirds at the surface. Male goosefish can live to 9 years, and females to 11 years.

FISHING INTEREST   A valuable and tasty species, mostly landed as bycatch and marketed in the Chesapeake Bay area as "monkfish." Goosefish are caught primarily with trawls and only rarely by rod and reel.

LITERATURE   Hildebrand and Schroeder 1928:352; Musick 1972; Fischer 1978; Caruso 1981, 1983; Manooch 1984; Smith 1985; Eschmeyer 1990; Armstrong et al. 1992.

Cods and Hakes
ORDER GADIFORMES

The order of cods and hakes comprises 10 families, 2 of which are known from Chesapeake Bay.

KEY TO THE FAMILIES OF CODS AND HAKES IN CHESAPEAKE BAY

FIGURE 89. V-shaped ridge on dorsal surface of head.

1a. Chin barbel present in all juveniles and most adults; V-shaped ridge absent on dorsal surface of head . . . . **cods—Gadidae** (p. 110)

1b. Chin barbel absent at all life stages; V-shaped ridge present on dorsal surface of head (Figure 89) . . . . **silver hakes—Merlucciidae** (p. 114)

Cods
FAMILY GADIDAE

The family Gadidae comprises a commercially important group of marine fishes, including cods, haddock, hakes, whiting, and pollock. Although the family is thought of as marine, several gadid species enter or live in freshwater. The members of this family are characterized by a long, soft dorsal fin that in some species may be divided into two or three parts. Most gadids bear a single barbel on the chin and possess pelvic fins that are located jugularly. Adult gadids live on or near the bottom, whereas juveniles are pelagic. Depth distribution ranges from seasonal occurrence in estuaries for some species to more than 1,000 m (3,200 ft) for others. The family is most abundant in temperate waters of both the Northern and Southern hemispheres and comprises 20 genera and approximately 60 species. Three genera and 5 species are known from Chesapeake Bay waters.

KEY TO THE SPECIES OF CODS IN CHESAPEAKE BAY

1a. Lower jaw projecting beyond upper jaw; chin barbel absent or tiny (present only in juvenile pollock) . . . . **pollock, *Pollachius virens*** (p. 111)

1b. Upper jaw projecting beyond lower jaw; chin barbel present and obvious 2

2a. Three dorsal fins and 2 anal fins present; caudal fin truncate or nearly so . . . . **Atlantic cod, *Gadus morhua*** (p. 112)

2b. Two dorsal fins and 1 anal fin present; caudal fin rounded 3

3a. First dorsal fin without elongate filament . . . . **spotted hake,** *Urophycis regia* (p. 113)
3b. First dorsal fin with elongate filament **4**

4a. Lateral scale rows numbering 95–120; 3 gill rakers present on upper limb of first arch; scales between lateral line and first dorsal fin base numbering about 7–10 . . . . . **red hake,** *Urophycis chuss* (p. 113)
4b. Lateral scale rows numbering about 120–150; 2 gill rakers present on upper limb of first arch; scales between lateral line and first dorsal fin base numbering about 11–13 . . . . **white hake,** *Urophycis tenuis* (p. 285)

Pollock
Pollachius virens (Linnaeus, 1758)
PLATE 16

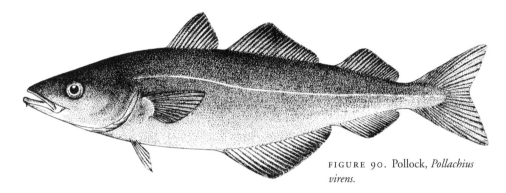

FIGURE 90. Pollock, *Pollachius virens.*

KEY FEATURES   Lower jaw projecting beyond upper jaw; 3 dorsal fins present; 2 anal fins present; first anal fin long, with base one-half or more as long as preanal distance; pelvic fin rays short; caudal fin moderately forked.

OTHER CHARACTERISTICS   Body rather elongate and compressed, tapering posteriorly; head conical; teeth small and pointed; tiny barbel present at tip of lower jaw in juveniles, absent in adults; scales small and cycloid; dorsal and anal fins separate from caudal fin; pelvic fin small, inserting slightly ventroanterior to pectoral fin. Dusky green dorsally; silvery gray ventrally; caudal and dorsal fins dusky green. Maximum adult size 1.2 m TL (4 ft).

GEOGRAPHIC DISTRIBUTION   Occurring along both coasts of the northern Atlantic. In the western Atlantic, the pollock is found from the Gulf of St. Lawrence to North Carolina.

ECOLOGY   The pollock is a rare to occasional visitor to the lower Chesapeake Bay in late winter and early spring. An active swimmer, the pollock occupies any and all levels between the surface and the bottom, occurring in inshore and offshore waters to about 200 m (660 ft) deep. Migrations to coastal waters in spring and to deeper waters in winter are known to occur. Spawning takes place in offshore waters from New England to New Jersey from September to March; estimates of egg production are as high as 4 million per female. The pollock is a voracious predator; juveniles feed primarily on small crustaceans, whereas adults prey predominantly on fishes, including herrings, pouts, and sand lances. The maximum age for pollock is 25 years.

FISHING INTEREST   In New England, commercially valuable and caught primarily with trawls. The pollock is also a popular target species of anglers. Although not abundant in the Chesapeake Bay area, the pollock is occasionally collected in pound nets.

LITERATURE   Hildebrand and Schroeder 1928:155; Musick 1972; Smith 1985; Morse et al. 1987; Cohen et al. 1990; DuBuit 1991.

Atlantic cod
Gadus morhua Linnaeus, 1758

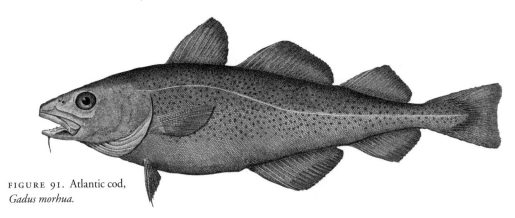

FIGURE 91. Atlantic cod,
Gadus morhua.

KEY FEATURES   Three dorsal fins and 2 anal fins present; first anal fin short, with base less than one-half as long as preanal distance; pelvic fin rays short, with 1 slightly elongate; small barbel at tip of lower jaw well developed; upper jaw and snout projecting.

OTHER CHARACTERISTICS   Body elongate and slightly compressed, tapering posteriorly; head conical; teeth small, pointed, and in bands on jaws and vomer; scales very small and cycloid; first dorsal fin the highest, with convex distal margin; second and third dorsal fins tapering posteriorly, with distal margins nearly straight; caudal fin truncate or slightly emarginate; first anal fin longer than base of second anal fin; pelvic fin small, inserting slightly ventroanterior to pectoral fin; first ray of pelvic fin filamentous. Dusky spots present dorsolaterally on pale green or red background; lateral line pale to white. Maximum adult size 2 m SL (6.6 ft), with most not exceeding 1 m TL (3.3 ft).

GEOGRAPHIC DISTRIBUTION   Occurring along both coasts of the northern Atlantic. In the western Atlantic, the Atlantic cod is found from Newfoundland to North Carolina.

ECOLOGY   The Atlantic cod is a rare to occasional visitor to the lower Chesapeake Bay in late winter and early spring. Typically a bottom-dwelling fish, it will rise in the water column to feed or spawn. It lives in almost every salinity, from nearly freshwater to full seawater, and in a wide range of temperatures, from nearly 0° to 20°C (nearly 32° to 68°F). The Atlantic cod usually occupies continental shelf areas 150–200 m (500–650 ft) deep but is occasionally found from the shoreline to depths greater than 600 m (2,000 ft). Dense schools of this species form during the day, then disband at night. Western Atlantic cod in the southernmost part of their range migrate north in the late summer and autumn because of increased water temperature and then migrate back in early winter. Atlantic cod spawn offshore from November to April; estimates of egg production are as high as 5 million for a 10-kg (22-lb) female. The Atlantic cod is a voracious and omnivorous predator. Juveniles feed primarily on invertebrates such as crabs, clams, brittle stars, and worms, and adults prey predominantly on fishes, including herrings and sand lances. The maximum age for Atlantic cod is about 20 years.

FISHING INTEREST   Among the most valuable of fishes. The Atlantic cod is referred to as "beef of the sea." This species is landed primarily by trawls and accounts for nearly 30% of the world's total groundfish catch. Atlantic cod are also caught by recreational anglers; the all-tackle record is 45 kg (99 lb). Not abundant in the Chesapeake Bay region, Atlantic cod are occasionally collected in pound nets.

LITERATURE   Hildebrand and Schroeder 1928:156; Musick 1972; Smith 1985; Whitehead et al. 1986a; Morse et al. 1987; Cohen et al. 1990.

Spotted hake
Urophycis regia (Walbaum, 1792)

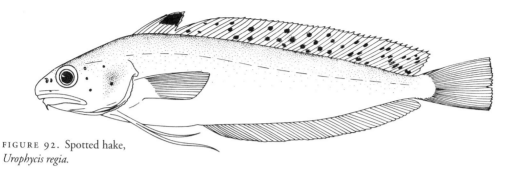

FIGURE 92. Spotted hake,
Urophycis regia.

KEY FEATURES   First dorsal fin without fila-mentous ray; oblique scale rows numbering 85–100.

OTHER CHARACTERISTICS   Body elongate and compressed; head small and slightly de-pressed; mouth large; upper jaw projecting; scales small and cycloid; 2 dorsal fins present and of about equal height; second dorsal fin long-based; caudal fin slightly rounded to truncate; anal fin low and long-based; pectoral fin long; barbel pres-ent at tip of lower jaw; 2 pelvic fin rays present, joined at base and filamentous. Body pale brown, with whitish venter; second dorsal fin with black spots; first dorsal fin with black blotch and white margin; lateral line black but interrupted by se-ries of white spots; pelvic fin white; series of dusky spots present on head. Maximum adult size about 41 cm TL (1.3 ft).

GEOGRAPHIC DISTRIBUTION   Found from southern New England to Florida and in the northeastern Gulf of Mexico. Juvenile spotted hakes are occasionally found as far north as Nova Scotia.

ECOLOGY   The spotted hake is a seasonal visi-tor to Chesapeake Bay. Juveniles are common in the lower bay from March to June and are only occasionally found in the upper bay, extending as far north as the Gunpowder River. Spotted hakes are occasionally caught near the bay mouth at times other than from March to June. This spe-cies is typically associated with objects on the bot-tom. Juveniles spend part of their life in estuaries such as Chesapeake Bay, migrating to deeper wa-ter offshore (as deep as 400 m, or 1,300 ft) once bay waters reach 25°C (77°F). Young spotted hakes are unable to tolerate salinities of less than 7‰. Spawning occurs outside of the bay from late summer to winter. This species feeds primar-ily on crustaceans but also eats fishes and squids.

FISHING INTEREST   Of limited commercial value. The spotted hake is collected with bottom trawls and also by rod and reel.

LITERATURE   Hildebrand and Schroeder 1928:160; Barans 1969, 1972; Musick 1972; Fischer 1978; Hardy 1978a; Smith 1985; Cohen et al. 1990; Comyns and Grant 1993.

Red hake
Urophycis chuss (Walbaum, 1792)

KEY FEATURES   Third ray of first dorsal fin produced and filamentous; oblique scale rows numbering 95–120; 3 gill rakers present on dor-sal part of gill arch.

OTHER CHARACTERISTICS   Body elon-gate, compressed; head small and slightly de-pressed; mouth large; upper jaw projecting; scales small and cycloid; 2 dorsal fins present and of about equal height; second dorsal fin long-based; caudal fin rounded; anal fin low and long-based; pectoral fin long; barbel present at tip of lower jaw; 2 pelvic fin rays present, joined at base and filamentous. Reddish to olive brown dorsally; sil-very ventrolaterally; venter white, gray, or yellow-ish; dusky blotch present on opercle. Maximum adult size about 52 cm TL (1.7 ft).

GEOGRAPHIC DISTRIBUTION   In both the eastern and the western Atlantic. Along the western Atlantic coast, the red hake is found from Nova Scotia to North Carolina.

low waters. As waters warm during the summer, it migrates to deeper water offshore (as deep as 550 m, or 1,800 ft) and stays offshore until the following spring. Spawning occurs off southern

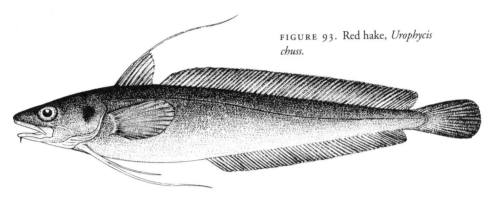

FIGURE 93. Red hake, *Urophycis chuss.*

ECOLOGY   A seasonal visitor to Chesapeake Bay, the red hake is sometimes common in the lower bay during late winter and spring and is occasionally found in the upper bay, extending as far north as the Patuxent River. Red hakes are typically found over soft mud or silt bottoms, less frequently over sand and shell, and never over rock. Juveniles are reported to inhabit the mantle cavity of sea scallops for 2 to 3 months. Juveniles live along coasts at shallow depths (4–6 m, or 13–20 ft); adults dwell in waters deeper than 35 m (115 ft). From late spring until early summer, the red hake moves from deep to shal-

New England and all around the inshore areas of the Gulf of Maine, beginning in early summer. Red hakes feed primarily on crustaceans but also eat fishes and squids.

FISHING INTEREST   Of limited commercial value. The red hake is collected with bottom trawls and also by rod and reel.

LITERATURE   Hildebrand and Schroeder 1928:159; Musick 1972, 1973, 1974; Hardy 1978a; Smith 1985; Robins et al. 1986; Whitehead et al. 1986a; Cohen et al. 1990; Luczkovich et al. 1991; Comyns and Grant 1993.

Silver Hakes
FAMILY MERLUCCIIDAE

Silver hakes, also known as whiting, lack the chin barbel of true hakes. Silver hakes are voracious predators that live in large schools, sometimes at considerable depths. They are swift, strong swimmers. Silver hakes are worldwide in distribution, with major fisheries in the eastern and western Atlantic as well as the eastern Pacific. The family comprises a single genus and 13 species, with 1 species recorded from Chesapeake Bay.

Silver hake
Merluccius bilinearis (Mitchill, 1814)
PLATE 17

KEY FEATURES   Chin barbel absent; lower jaw projecting beyond upper jaw; V-shaped ridge present on dorsal surface of head; 2 dorsal fins present, the first higher and triangular, the sec-

ond long and partially subdivided by notch; anal fin similar to second dorsal fin.

OTHER CHARACTERISTICS   Body elongate and compressed; head long; snout moderately broad; mouth large, with sharp teeth present on jaws and vomer; caudal peduncle narrow; caudal fin emarginate to truncate; pelvic fin well developed and inserting slightly ventroanterior to ori-

This species exhibits a seasonal onshore–offshore migration: spawning adults and feeding juveniles move inshore during spring, and when winter cooling occurs on the shelf, they migrate to warmer wa-

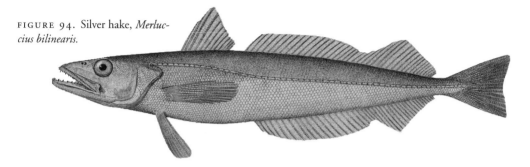

FIGURE 94. Silver hake, *Merluccius bilinearis*.

gin of pectoral fin; pectoral fin narrow and moderately long. Dusky gray or brownish dorsally; flanks and venter silvery and highly iridescent. Maximum adult size 76 cm TL (2.5 ft).

GEOGRAPHIC DISTRIBUTION   Found in the western Atlantic from Newfoundland to the Bahamas.

ECOLOGY   The silver hake is an occasional to common visitor to the lower Chesapeake Bay during autumn, winter, and spring, extending as far north as the Chester River. Silver hakes (also known as whiting) congregate in large schools on the continental shelf in depths of 55–300 m (180–985 ft) on sandy grounds, but sometimes they stray into shallower water and they can also be found in depths as great as 914 m (3,000 ft).

ters on the continental edge and slope. Spawning occurs in offshore waters. The silver hake is a voracious nocturnal predator that primarily eats fishes and amphipods.

FISHING INTEREST   A valuable commercial species in the northern part of the range and collected by trawls. The flesh of the silver hake is white, flaky, and low in fat. Merluccid hakes are worldwide in distribution, with major commercial fisheries in the eastern and western Atlantic as well as the eastern Pacific.

LITERATURE   Hildebrand and Schroeder 1928:162; Fritz 1962; Musick 1972; Fahay 1974, 1983; Hardy 1978a; Bowman 1984; Smith 1985; Morse et al. 1987; Cohen et al. 1990; Nelson 1994.

Cusk-eels
ORDER OPHIDIIFORMES

The order of cusk-eels comprises four families, one of which is known from Chesapeake Bay.

Cusk-eels
FAMILY OPHIDIIDAE

Cusk-eels are elongate, tapering fishes with long dorsal and anal fins that are continuous with the caudal fin in some species. Cusk-eels have numerous tiny scales, as well as thin pelvic fins that, when present, are located jugularly. Most species inhabit the continental shelf, but a few inhabit reefs. Cusk-eels are nocturnally active, feeding on small crustaceans and other fishes. The family occurs worldwide and comprises about 46 genera and 209 species. One species is recorded from Chesapeake Bay.

Striped cusk-eel
Ophidion marginatum (DeKay, 1842)

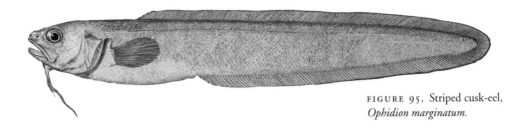

FIGURE 95. Striped cusk-eel,
Ophidion marginatum.

KEY FEATURES   Pelvic fin far anterior, ventral to eye; 2 soft rays of unequal length present in each pelvic fin; dorsal, caudal, and anal fins continuous.

OTHER CHARACTERISTICS   Body very elongate, compressed; mouth moderately large; jaws, palatines, and vomer with bands of teeth; teeth in jaws pointed; scales small and absent on head; origin of dorsal fin perpendicular to middle of pectoral fin; pectoral fin broad; late juvenile and adult males distinguished from females by presence of hump on top of head, posterior to eye and formed by hypertrophy of bone and muscles associated with sound-producing apparatus. Greenish gray dorsally; side golden; venter white; dorsal fin with distinct dusky marginal line that continues around tail to about middle of anal fin. Maximum adult size 23 cm TL (9 in).

GEOGRAPHIC DISTRIBUTION   Found in the western Atlantic from New York to Texas.

ECOLOGY   The striped cusk-eel is an occasional visitor to the lower Chesapeake Bay during spring, summer, and autumn. Little is known about the life history of this species. The air bladder, anterior vertebrae, and dorsal cranial muscles are highly modified to form a drumming apparatus, the details of which differ between the sexes. The use to which this complex sound-producing mechanism is put is not known. The striped cusk-eel is a benthic burrower that is nocturnally active and is reported to feed on small crustaceans and fishes.

FISHING INTEREST   Of no commercial or recreational value but occasionally collected by trawls.

LITERATURE   Hildebrand and Schroeder 1928:335; Courtenay 1971; Musick 1972; Smith 1985; Eschmeyer 1990; Fahay 1992; Nelson 1994.

Needlefishes and Halfbeaks
ORDER BELONIFORMES

The order of needlefishes and halfbeaks comprises five families, of which three are represented in Chesapeake Bay.

KEY TO THE FAMILIES OF NEEDLEFISHES AND HALFBEAKS IN CHESAPEAKE BAY

1a. Pectoral fin normal; both jaws produced to form needlelike beak . . . **needlefishes—Belonidae** (p. 117)
1b. Pectoral fin exceedingly long, forming "wing," or if pectoral fin normal, lower jaw considerably produced but upper jaw normal **2**

2a. Lower jaw produced; upper jaw normal; pectoral fin not winglike . . . .
. . . . **halfbeaks—Hemiramphidae** (p. 119)

2b. Upper and lower jaws normal (not needlelike) and of approximately equal size; lower jaw slightly
produced, if at all; pectoral fin exceedingly long and winglike . . . . **flyingfishes—Exocoetidae**
. . . . (1 species reported from Chesapeake Bay: Atlantic flyingfish, *Cypselurus melanurus*, p. 285)

Needlefishes
FAMILY BELONIDAE

Needlefishes have extremely slender, silvery bodies that are shaded a dusky blue or green dorsally. Both
jaws are produced into a pointed beak and are armed with needlelike teeth. The dorsal and anal fins are
located posteriorly, and the pelvic fins are abdominal. All fins lack spines, and the bones are green.
Surface-dwelling predators of small fishes, needlefishes catch their prey sideways in their beaks. Needlefishes can leap or skip across the surface at high speed, especially at night when attracted by light, and
people have been injured when struck or impaled by them. Most species are marine, but a few occur in
freshwater. The family comprises 10 genera and 32 species, distributed worldwide in warm-temperate and
tropical waters. Four species are recorded from Chesapeake Bay.

KEY TO THE SPECIES OF NEEDLEFISHES IN CHESAPEAKE BAY

1a. Body strongly compressed; side with series of vertical bars; pectoral fin falcate; anal fin with 24–28
rays . . . . **flat needlefish, *Ablennes hians*** (p. 117)

1b. Body roundish in cross section; side without vertical bars; pectoral fin not falcate; anal fin with 16–23
rays **2**

2a. Dorsal fin with 14–17 rays; lateral keel absent on caudal peduncle; caudal fin with concave margin,
not deeply forked . . . . **Atlantic needlefish, *Strongylura marina*** (p. 118)

2b. Dorsal fin with 21–26 rays; lateral keel present on caudal peduncle; caudal fin deeply forked **3**

3a. Dorsal fin with 21–23 rays (typically 22 or 23); anal fin with 18–22 rays (typically 20 or 21) . . . .
. . . . **houndfish, *Tylosurus crocodilus*** (p. 119)

3b. Dorsal fin with 23–26 rays (typically 24); anal fin with 20–24 rays (typically 21 or 22) . . . .
. . . . **agujon, *Tylosurus acus*** (p. 286)

Flat needlefish
Ablennes hians (Valenciennes, 1846)

KEY FEATURES   Body elongate and laterally
compressed; anal fin with 24–28 rays (usually 26
or 27); pectoral fin falcate; 12–14 dusky vertical
bars present on body.

OTHER CHARACTERISTICS   Snout very
long and slender; mouth large, with sharply
pointed teeth; caudal fin broadly forked; lateral
keel absent on caudal peduncle; dorsal fin origin
more posterior than anal fin origin. Body greenish, with suffusion of bright bluish green dorsally; bright silvery ventrally; side with dusky

stripe in addition to vertical bars; fins greenish;
margins of pectoral and dorsal fins dusky; caudal
fin margin pale. Maximum adult size 83 cm SL
(2.7 ft).

GEOGRAPHIC DISTRIBUTION   Occurring
worldwide. In the western Atlantic, the flat needlefish is found from Massachusetts to Florida,
throughout the Gulf of Mexico and the Caribbean, southward to Brazil.

ECOLOGY   From late spring to early autumn,
the flat needlefish is a rare to occasional visitor to

the lower Chesapeake Bay, reaching as far north as the Potomac River. Little is known about the life history of this species. The flat needlefish is primarily pelagic and is more common offshore

gill nets or by casting and trolling artificial lures at the surface.

LITERATURE   Hildebrand and Schroeder 1928:150; Berry and Rivas 1962; Musick 1972;

FIGURE 96. Flat needlefish, *Ablennes hians.*

than inshore. It feeds chiefly on fishes and is thought to spawn during the spring.

FISHING INTEREST   None. Flat needlefish are occasionally collected as bycatch in seines and

Fischer 1978; Hardy 1978a; Fahay 1983; Collette et al. 1984.

Atlantic needlefish
Strongylura marina (Walbaum, 1792)

FIGURE 97. Atlantic needlefish, *Strongylura marina.*

KEY FEATURES   Body roundish in cross section; side without vertical bars; pectoral fin not falcate; anal fin with 16–20 rays; dorsal fin with 14–17 rays; lateral keel absent on caudal peduncle; caudal fin with concave margin.

OTHER CHARACTERISTICS   Body slender, not compressed; caudal peduncle depressed; head long and flattened dorsally; jaws produced into long, slender beak; jaw teeth sharply pointed; dorsal fin origin more posterior than anal fin origin; anal fin base longer than dorsal fin base; pelvic fin inserting posterior to midpoint of body. Greenish dorsally; side silvery, with narrow bluish stripe extending from pectoral fin to caudal fin base; venter white. Maximum adult size 64 cm SL (2 ft).

GEOGRAPHIC DISTRIBUTION   Inhabiting coastal waters from Massachusetts to Texas and along the eastern coastline of Central and South America to Brazil; apparently absent from the West Indies.

ECOLOGY   The Atlantic needlefish is found throughout Chesapeake Bay during the summer and fall, reaching as far north as the Susquehanna River. It is known to ascend rivers and enter freshwater. Its habit of swimming near the surface and being attracted to lighted piers and bridges makes the Atlantic needlefish a conspicuous fish. This species apparently spawns inshore in bays and estuaries during May and June. Young Atlantic needlefish as small as 5 cm (2 in) are frequently found in the summer in grass beds and along marsh margins from the Chesapeake Bay mouth to the Patuxent River. Female Atlantic needlefish possess only a single ovary and release demersal, filamentous eggs. This species feeds primarily on fishes, catching prey sideways in its jaws and then turning the prey in order to swallow it (much as fish-eating birds do).

FISHING INTEREST   None. Atlantic needlefish are occasionally collected as bycatch in seines and gill nets or by casting and trolling artificial lures at the surface.

LITERATURE   Hildebrand and Schroeder 1928:148; Berry and Rivas 1962; Musick 1972; Fischer 1978; Hardy 1978a; Fahay 1983; Collette et al. 1984; Manooch 1984; Smith 1985.

Houndfish
Tylosurus crocodilus (Peron and Lesueur, 1821)

FIGURE 98. Houndfish, *Tylosurus crocodilus.*

KEY FEATURES   Body roundish in cross section; side without vertical bars; pectoral fin not falcate; anal fin with 18–22 rays; dorsal fin with 21–23 rays; small black lateral keel present on caudal peduncle; caudal fin deeply forked, with ventral lobe much longer than dorsal lobe.

OTHER CHARACTERISTICS   Body very elongate; caudal peduncle depressed; head long and flattened dorsally; jaws produced into long, slender beak; jaw teeth sharply pointed; dorsal fin origin approximately perpendicular to anal fin origin; anal fin base shorter than dorsal fin base; pelvic fin inserting posterior to midpoint of body. Dusky bluish green dorsally; silvery white ventrally, with narrow bluish stripe extending from pectoral fin to caudal fin base; scales and bones greenish. Maximum adult size 1.0 m SL (3.3 ft).

GEOGRAPHIC DISTRIBUTION   Occurring worldwide. In the western Atlantic, the houndfish is found from Chesapeake Bay to Florida, throughout the Gulf of Mexico and the Caribbean, southward to Brazil.

ECOLOGY   The houndfish is primarily a coastal species that occasionally visits Chesapeake Bay in late spring and summer, extending as far north in the bay as the lower Susquehanna River Basin. Little is known about the life history of this species. It feeds primarily on fishes.

FISHING INTEREST   None. Houndfish are occasionally collected as bycatch in seines and gill nets or by casting and trolling artificial lures at the surface.

LITERATURE   Hildebrand and Schroeder 1928:149; Berry and Rivas 1962; Musick 1972; Fischer 1978; Hardy 1978a; Fahay 1983; Collette et al. 1984.

Halfbeaks
FAMILY HEMIRAMPHIDAE

Halfbeaks are slender, active, surface-dwelling fishes. With few exceptions, the lower jaw of halfbeaks is significantly longer than the upper jaw and forms a flattened spike that lacks prominent teeth and is often tipped in red or orange. Like flyingfishes, at least one species of halfbeak is capable of gliding through the air on outstretched pectoral fins. Most halfbeaks are marine, but a few inhabit freshwater. Halfbeaks are omnivorous, feeding on floating bits of algae and sea grasses, zooplankton, and small fishes. The family is distributed worldwide in warm-temperate and tropical waters. Of the 12 genera and 80 species in the family, 2 species are known from Chesapeake Bay.

KEY TO THE SPECIES OF HALFBEAKS IN CHESAPEAKE BAY

1a. Dorsal fin origin markedly more anterior than anal fin origin; origin of pelvic fin closer to base of caudal fin than to opercle; caudal fin deeply forked, with ventral lobe almost twice as long as dorsal lobe . . . . **ballyhoo,** *Hemiramphus brasiliensis* (p. 120)

1b. Dorsal fin origin perpendicular to or only slightly more anterior than anal fin origin; origin of pelvic fin about midway between opercle and base of caudal fin; caudal fin moderately forked, with lobes nearly equal in length . . . . **American halfbeak,** *Hyporhamphus meeki* (p. 120)

Ballyhoo
Hemiramphus brasiliensis (Linnaeus, 1758)

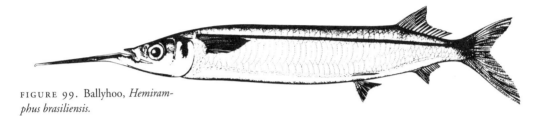

FIGURE 99. Ballyhoo, *Hemiramphus brasiliensis.*

KEY FEATURES   Dorsal fin origin markedly more anterior than anal fin origin; pelvic fin nearer to caudal fin than to opercle; caudal fin deeply forked, with long ventral lobe; upper jaw without teeth.

OTHER CHARACTERISTICS   Body elongate and compressed; dorsal and anal fins located posteriorly; dorsal fin with 12–15 rays; anal fin with 11–15 rays; ventral fins small. Dusky bluish green dorsally; silvery laterally; lower jaw black, with red tip; dorsal lobe of caudal fin yellowish orange. Maximum adult size 35 cm SL (1 ft).

GEOGRAPHIC DISTRIBUTION   Inhabiting both the eastern and the western Atlantic. In the western Atlantic, the ballyhoo occurs from Massa- chusetts to Florida, throughout the Gulf of Mexico and the Caribbean, southward to Brazil.

ECOLOGY   The ballyhoo is a rare tropical visitor to the lower Chesapeake Bay. This inshore schooling species is attracted to lights at night and is reported to feed on sea grasses and small fishes.

FISHING INTEREST   None in Chesapeake Bay but utilized as both a food fish and a bait- fish where abundant. Ballyhoos are collected by seines and dip nets.

LITERATURE   Hildebrand and Schroeder 1928:153; Musick 1972; Fischer 1978; Fahay 1983; Collette et al. 1984.

American halfbeak
Hyporhamphus meeki Banford and Collette, 1993

KEY FEATURES   Dorsal fin origin perpendicu- lar to or only slightly more anterior than anal fin origin; pelvic fin located about midway between caudal fin and opercle; caudal fin moderately forked, with lobes nearly equal in length; upper jaw with teeth.

OTHER CHARACTERISTICS   Body elongate and compressed; dorsal and anal fins located pos- teriorly; dorsal fin with 12–17 rays (typically 14 or 15); anal fin with 14–18 rays (typically 15– 17); bases of dorsal and anal fins covered with scales. Tannish green dorsally; silvery laterally; fleshy tip of lower jaw red. Maximum adult size 18 cm SL (7 in).

GEOGRAPHIC DISTRIBUTION   Found in the western Atlantic from Massachusetts to Florida and throughout the Gulf of Mexico to Yucatán.

ECOLOGY   The American halfbeak is a sea- sonal visitor in the lower Chesapeake Bay during summer and autumn, extending as far north as

the Patuxent River. It is an inshore schooling species that is typically found over sandy, vegetated
bottoms. This species is attracted to lights at
night but is a quick and agile swimmer that is

FISHING INTEREST   None in Chesapeake
Bay but utilized as a baitfish where abundant.
American halfbeaks are collected by seines and
dip nets.

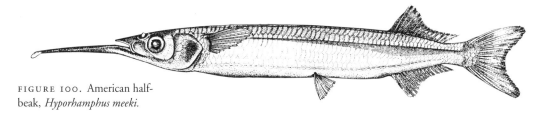

FIGURE 100. American halfbeak, *Hyporhamphus meeki.*

difficult to capture with a dip net. Spawning occurs in the Chesapeake Bay region during the
summer, and the eggs have been found attached
by their adhesive filaments to floating eelgrass
blades. American halfbeaks are reported to feed
on algae and small organisms.

LITERATURE   Hildebrand and Schroeder
1928:152; Musick 1972; Fischer 1978; Hardy
1978a; Fahay 1983; Olney and Boehlert 1988;
Banford and Collette 1993.

Killifishes and Livebearers
ORDER CYPRINODONTIFORMES

The order of killifishes and livebearers comprises five families, two of which are represented in Chesapeake Bay.

KEY TO THE FAMILIES OF KILLIFISHES AND LIVEBEARERS IN CHESAPEAKE BAY

1a. Third anal fin ray branched; anal fin of males not modified . . . **killifishes—Cyprinodontidae** (p. 121)
1b. Third anal fin ray unbranched; anal fin of males modified to form intromittent organ . . . .
. . . . **livebearers—Poeciliidae** (p. 129)

Killifishes
FAMILY CYPRINODONTIDAE

Killifishes are typically small and slender, with the single dorsal fin located posterior to the midpoint of
the body. The caudal fin margin is rounded or squared, and the pelvic fins are small and abdominal in
position. Killifishes lack a lateral line, and the dorsal surface of the head is flattened. Killifishes have
adapted to a variety of habitats and conditions, including extremes of heat and salinity. They are primarily freshwater fishes, although a few species occur in brackish or coastal marine habitats. Several groups
are brightly colored. Sexual dimorphism is usually manifested in size and coloration differences. The
fishes spawn in pairs, usually among aquatic vegetation. Eggs are demersal and are attached to plants by
means of adhesive threads. Some species build nests that are guarded by the male parent. The family contains about 50 genera and more than 300 species distributed on all continents except Australia. Three genera and 7 species are known from Chesapeake Bay.

KEY TO THE SPECIES OF KILLIFISHES IN CHESAPEAKE BAY

1a. Body deep, with greatest depth about one-half of standard length; teeth wedge-shaped and incisor-like, with 3 cusps (points); humeral scale (modified scale dorsoposterior to gill opening) very large (Figure 101) . . . . **sheepshead minnow,** *Cyprinodon variegatus* (p. 122)

1b. Body more elongate, with greatest depth one-third or less of standard length; teeth conical or pointed; humeral scale typically small or absent **2**

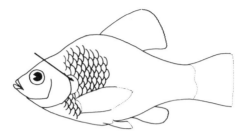

FIGURE 101. Humeral scale of sheepshead minnow.

2a. Teeth in single row; longitudinal scale rows numbering fewer than 30 . . . . **rainwater killifish,** *Lucania parva* (p. 123)

2b. Teeth in more than 1 row, with outer row sometimes large and inner row or rows sometimes small; longitudinal scale rows numbering more than 30 . . . . **3**

3a. Longitudinal scale rows usually numbering more than 40 . . . . **banded killifish,** *Fundulus diaphanus* (p. 124)

3b. Longitudinal scale rows numbering 31–39 . . . . **4**

4a. Dorsal fin with 8 or 9 rays (usually 8); anal fin base longer than dorsal fin base; gill opening restricted, with dorsal end opposite or slightly dorsal to dorsalmost edge of pectoral fin base . . . . **spotfin killifish,** *Fundulus luciae* (p. 125)

4b. Dorsal fin with 10–15 rays; anal fin base shorter than dorsal fin base; gill opening not restricted, with dorsal end markedly dorsal to pectoral fin base near posterodorsal corner of opercle **5**

5a. Snout long, pointed, and about twice as long as eye diameter in lateral view; dorsal fin with 13–15 rays; adult females with several irregular longitudinal stripes . . . . **striped killifish,** *Fundulus majalis* (p. 126)

5b. Snout short, rounded, and about equal in length to eye diameter in lateral view; dorsal fin with 10–12 rays; adult females without longitudinal stripes but sometimes with vertical bars **6**

6a. Anal fin with 9–11 rays (usually 10); dorsal fin origin perpendicular to anal fin origin; both sexes usually with ocellus or 1 or 2 black blotches on last few dorsal fin rays; pouch (oviduct) on first anal fin ray in females absent or, when present, extending less than one-fifth the ray length . . . . **marsh killifish,** *Fundulus confluentus* (p. 127)

6b. Anal fin with 10–12 rays (usually 11); dorsal fin origin more anterior than anal fin origin; females without ocellus or blotches on dorsal fin; pouch (oviduct) on first anal fin ray in females extending more than one-fifth the ray length . . . . **mummichog,** *Fundulus heteroclitus* (p. 128)

Sheepshead minnow
Cyprinodon variegatus Lacepède, 1803

KEY FEATURES   Body short and deep, with greatest depth about one-half of standard length; predorsal area elevated; dorsal fin origin more anterior than anal fin origin; teeth in single series, incisor-like, and tricuspid; humeral scale very large.

OTHER CHARACTERISTICS   Body robust anteriorly, compressed posteriorly; longitudinal scale rows numbering 24–27; dorsal fin with 11 or 12 rays; caudal fin truncate; anal fin base slightly smaller than dorsal fin, with 10 or 11 rays; pectoral fin rounded. Coloration varying with gender and breeding condition. Females

quents shallow flats, marshes, and tidal ponds during the summer months and retreats to channels or burrows into the silt in marsh ponds in the winter. This species is often found over a substrate of thick mud and detritus. It is a hardy species that has been found from freshwater to waters with salinities exceeding 90‰. This killi-

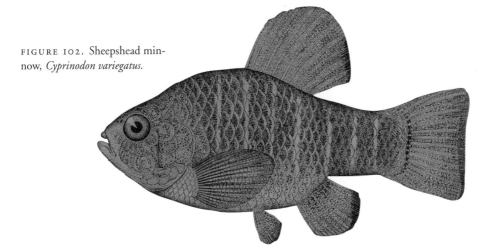

FIGURE 102. Sheepshead minnow, *Cyprinodon variegatus*.

brassy on back and side, with dusky lateral blotches usually forming bars low on side; rear of dorsal fin with ocellus; caudal fin greenish, with dusky bar at base; anal and pelvic fins yellowish; pectoral fin orangish. Males olivaceous, suffused with iridescent blue dorsally; venter bright orange during breeding season; dorsal fin blackish, with orange margin; caudal fin olivaceous, with dusky bar at base and black margin; anal, pelvic, and pectoral fins orange, with dusky margins. Maximum adult size 7.6 cm TL (3 in), with males larger than females.

GEOGRAPHIC DISTRIBUTION   Found in freshwaters and brackish waters from Cape Cod to Mexico.

ECOLOGY   The sheepshead minnow is abundant throughout Chesapeake Bay, where it fre-

fish travels in large schools, swimming near the shoreline and entering marshes during high tide. Spawning occurs throughout the spring and summer in shallows near the shoreline. The diet of the sheepshead minnow is primarily plant detritus, with small numbers of crustaceans. The intestine is very long, commensurate with the herbivorous habits of this species.

FISHING INTEREST   None, but occasionally used as bait and of considerable indirect value as forage for other fishes and wading birds. The sheepshead minnow is collected by seines.

LITERATURE   Hildebrand and Schroeder 1928:135; Raney et al. 1953; Martin 1972; Musick 1972; Baer 1974; Able 1976; Hardy 1978a; Smith 1985; Brill 1991.

Rainwater killifish
Lucania parva (Baird and Girard, 1855)

KEY FEATURES   Teeth pointed, in single irregular series; longitudinal scale rows numbering 25 or 26; body short and compressed.

OTHER CHARACTERISTICS   Dorsal fin with 11 or 12 rays and with origin more anterior

than anal fin origin; anal fin with 10 or 11 rays and smaller than dorsal fin; caudal fin slightly rounded; pectoral fin small and slightly rounded. Olivaceous dorsally; pale ventrally, with scale margins outlined in dusky pigment; dorsal, caudal, and pectoral fins greenish; coloration of males and females similar in most respects, except males with dusky margins on dorsal and anal fins and dusky spot on anterior base of dorsal fin; during spawning season, anal and pelvic fins reddish in males, with dusky leading edge. Maximum adult size 5.8 cm SL (2.3 in).

erate both freshwater and seawater, and during the summer it is abundant in all brackish-water habitats where vegetation is present. During the winter it burrows into the bottom silt in low-salinity tidal ponds. Rainwater killifish travel in schools and are often found in association with *Gambusia* and *Fundulus* species. Spawning occurs

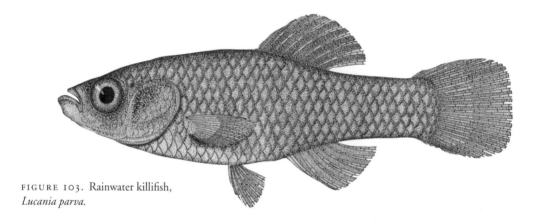

FIGURE 103. Rainwater killifish, *Lucania parva.*

GEOGRAPHIC DISTRIBUTION   Found in brackish and coastal waters from Cape Cod to Mexico. The rainwater killifish has been introduced into several waterways in California and Utah.

ECOLOGY   The rainwater killifish is found in Chesapeake Bay as far north as the Chester River and is a year-round resident. Although most often found in brackish waters, this species will tol-

from April through July. The rainwater killifish feeds primarily on small crustaceans.

FISHING INTEREST   None, but of considerable value indirectly as a food source for other fishes and wading birds. The rainwater killifish is most often collected by seining.

LITERATURE   Hildebrand and Schroeder 1928:136; Musick 1972; Able 1976; Hardy 1978a; Smith 1985; Brill 1991.

Banded killifish
Fundulus diaphanus (Lesueur, 1817)

FIGURE 104. Banded killifish, *Fundulus diaphanus.*

KEY FEATURES   Longitudinal scale rows numbering 35–52; side with 12–20 dusky bars; caudal fin margin truncate to concave.

OTHER CHARACTERISTICS   Body elongate and compressed; teeth in bands in each jaw; dorsal fin long, with 10–15 rays (typically 13 or

14), and with origin more anterior than anal fin origin; anal fin with 9–13 rays (typically 10 or 11) and slightly smaller than dorsal fin; pectoral fin rounded. Coloration varying with gender. Females olive dorsally and silvery white laterally, with white venter; bars greenish; dorsal, caudal, and pectoral fins yellow; other fins translucent. Males olive green dorsally; venter white; bars silvery; caudal and dorsal fins dusky; anal and pectoral fins yellowish; pelvic fin mostly white. Maximum adult size 11 cm TL (4.5 in).

GEOGRAPHIC DISTRIBUTION   Occurring from the upper Mississippi Valley and the Great Lakes to Quebec, southward to South Carolina.

ECOLOGY   The banded killifish is a common to abundant resident of fresh and estuarine waters in all of Chesapeake Bay's tributaries. It oc-

curs over a variety of bottom types and prefers low-salinity waters. It is therefore more likely to be found in freshwaters than are other members of the genus. This species has never been reported from areas with salinities exceeding 20‰ and only rarely from areas exceeding 5‰. Spawning occurs from April to September. This killifish feeds primarily on small crustaceans, small mollusks, and worms.

FISHING INTEREST   None, but of considerable value indirectly as a food source for other fishes and wading birds. The banded killifish is most often collected by seining.

LITERATURE   Hildebrand and Schroeder 1928:143; Musick 1972; Eddy and Underhill 1978; Hardy 1978a; Smith 1985; Weisberg 1986; Jenkins and Burkhead 1994.

Spotfin killifish
Fundulus luciae (Baird, 1855)

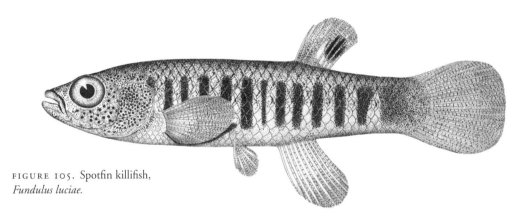

FIGURE 105. Spotfin killifish, *Fundulus luciae.*

KEY FEATURES   Dorsal fin with 8 or 9 rays (usually 8); anal fin base longer than dorsal fin base; gill opening restricted, with dorsal end opposite or slightly dorsal to dorsalmost edge of pectoral fin base; dorsal fin origin slightly more posterior than anal fin origin.

OTHER CHARACTERISTICS   Body elongate and compressed; longitudinal scale rows numbering 34–36; teeth pointed and in bands in each jaw; caudal fin slightly rounded; anal fin with 10 rays; pelvic fin small to tiny. Coloration varying with gender and breeding condition; both sexes greenish gray, with pale venter and yellowish brown fins. Males as follows during breeding season: 11–14 dusky bars present; black ocellus pres-

ent on posterior rays of dorsal fin; olive green dorsally, golden ventrolaterally, and whitish orange ventrally, with orange, pinkish, or pale brown fins. Maximum adult size 5 cm TL (2 in). This is the smallest species of *Fundulus.*

GEOGRAPHIC DISTRIBUTION   Inhabiting intertidal marshes from Massachusetts to Georgia.

ECOLOGY   The spotfin killifish is rarely encountered, probably because of its small size and preferred habitat. In the Chesapeake Bay area it is a permanent resident in tidal rivulets and puddles in the upper reaches of intertidal marshes. This killifish is a hardy species that tolerates a wide range of salinities, temperatures, and oxygen levels. It is omnivorous and feeds on plant detritus, diatoms, and a variety of small crustaceans, insects, and worms. Spawning occurs from April to October.

FISHING INTEREST   None, but of considerable value indirectly as a food source for other

fishes and wading birds. The spotfin killifish is most often collected by seining.

LITERATURE   Hildebrand and Schroeder 1928:144; Musick 1972; Byrne 1978; Hardy 1978a; Smith 1985; Brill 1991.

Striped killifish
Fundulus majalis (Walbaum, 1792)
PLATE 18

FIGURE 106. Striped killifish, *Fundulus majalis: (a)* male, *(b)* female.

KEY FEATURES   Snout long, pointed, and about twice as long as eye diameter in lateral view; dorsal fin with 13–15 rays; adult females with several irregular longitudinal stripes; adult males with vertical bars.

OTHER CHARACTERISTICS   Body slender and compressed; teeth pointed and in bands in each jaw; longitudinal scale rows numbering 31–38; dorsal fin long-based, especially in males, and with origin more anterior than anal fin origin; caudal fin truncate or slightly rounded; anal fin with 11 or 12 rays; pectoral fin rounded. Coloration varying with gender. Females olive dorsally, with white venter, and typically with 2 or 3 irregular black longitudinal stripes laterally and several black vertical bars near caudal fin. Males olive dorsally and yellowish on side and belly,

with 15–20 black vertical bars; anal, pelvic, and pectoral fins pale yellow; other fins dusky; dorsal fin with black spot posteriorly. Maximum adult size 20 cm TL (8 in), with females attaining larger sizes than males. This is the largest of the killifishes of Chesapeake Bay.

GEOGRAPHIC DISTRIBUTION   Inhabiting coastal waters and river mouths from New Hampshire to Florida.

ECOLOGY   The striped killifish is an abundant permanent resident of the entire Chesapeake Bay and is found in tidal creeks, sand flats, and grass beds. Striped killifish prefer higher salinities and rarely, if ever, enter freshwater. The striped killifish is often found in large schools swimming in shallow waters, sometimes in depths of only a few inches. Striped killifish tend to occur over sandy sediments more often than do other local killifishes and are reported to burrow in mud during the coldest months. They spawn in still, shallow water close to shore from April to September. Females have been reported to bury their eggs actively. This killifish feeds primarily on polychaete worms, small crustaceans, small mollusks, and insects.

FISHING INTEREST   None, but used as bait and of considerable indirect value as forage for other fishes and wading birds. The striped killifish is collected by seines and minnow traps.

LITERATURE   Hildebrand and Schroeder 1928:140; Musick 1972; Baer 1974; Able 1976; Hardy 1978a; Abraham 1985; Smith 1985.

Marsh killifish
Fundulus confluentus Goode and Bean, 1879

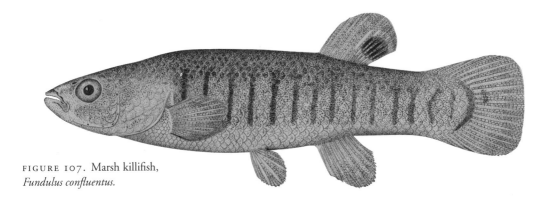

FIGURE 107. Marsh killifish, *Fundulus confluentus.*

KEY FEATURES   Anal fin with 9–11 rays (usually 10); dorsal fin origin perpendicular to anal fin origin; both sexes usually with ocellus or 1 or 2 black blotches on last few dorsal fin rays; pouch (oviduct) on first anal fin ray in females absent or, when present, extending less than one-fifth the ray length.

OTHER CHARACTERISTICS   Body slender and compressed; longitudinal scale rows numbering 34–36; teeth small and in bands in each jaw; caudal fin slightly rounded; anal fin approximately same size as dorsal fin and larger in males than in females; pelvic fin small. Coloration varying geographically and with sex and breeding condition. Females brownish olive dorsally, with slightly greenish venter and dusky yellow brown fins; approximately 13 blackish crossbars present laterally; scattered black spots present on body; large black ocellus usually present on rear of dorsal fin. Males dusky green dorsally and with pale venter; side with whitish spots and 12–20 whitish or silvery vertical bars; black ocellus usually present posteriorly on dorsal fin; caudal and anal fins slightly dusky; other fins translucent. Maximum adult size 6 cm TL (2.5 in).

GEOGRAPHIC DISTRIBUTION   Inhabiting coastal waters from Lynnhaven Bay, Virginia, to Corpus Christi, Texas.

ECOLOGY   The marsh killifish is a resident of Chesapeake Bay that inhabits muddy marshes and grass flats. It is reported to associate with the mummichog. Spawning in Chesapeake Bay waters occurs during April and May, whereas the spawning season is extended in more southerly waters. The marsh killifish is omnivorous and feeds on small fishes, insects, small crustaceans, plants, annelid worms, and mollusks. Recent attempts to find this species in Chesapeake Bay have been unsuccessful. The only well-documented population, in Lynnhaven Bay, may have been extirpated.

FISHING INTEREST   None, but of considerable indirect value as forage other fishes and wading birds. The marsh killifish is collected by seines and minnow traps.

LITERATURE   Hildebrand and Schroeder 1928:141; Harrington and Harrington 1972; Musick 1972; Hardy 1978a.

Mummichog
Fundulus heteroclitus (Linnaeus, 1766)

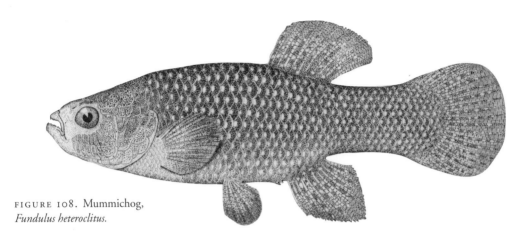

FIGURE 108. Mummichog,
Fundulus heteroclitus.

KEY FEATURES   Anal fin with 10–12 rays (usually 11); dorsal fin origin more anterior than anal fin origin; females without ocellus or blotches in dorsal fin; pouch (oviduct) on first anal fin ray in females extending more than one-fifth the ray length.

OTHER CHARACTERISTICS   Body robust anteriorly and compressed posteriorly; teeth pointed and in bands in each jaw; dorsal fin long-based, especially in males, and with 11 or 12 rays; caudal fin broadly rounded; longitudinal scale rows numbering 31–38; anal fin rays longer than dorsal fin rays; pelvic fin small; pectoral fin broad and rounded. Coloration varying with sex. Females brownish green dorsally and with pale venter; 12–15 dusky vertical bars typically present; dorsal and anal fins with greenish tinge. Males green or olive dorsally, silver laterally, and yellowish ventrally, with about 15 silvery vertical bars and numerous white or yellowish spots; anal, pelvic, and pectoral fins yellow; other fins dusky, with yellow margins; dorsal fin often with black spot posteriorly; males in breeding phase more brightly colored, with blue dorsum, pearly spots, and bright bars. Maximum adult size 12 cm TL (4.7 in), with females attaining larger sizes than males.

GEOGRAPHIC DISTRIBUTION   Found in coastal waters and rivers from Labrador to Mexico.

ECOLOGY   The mummichog is an abundant permanent resident of the entire Chesapeake Bay. It is found in muddy marshes, channels, and grass flats. During the colder months it may burrow in bottom silt or retreat to deeper waters. This species has been observed to swim under the ice of small tributaries near their outflow to large tidal rivers. Mummichog schools may number in the hundreds of individuals. The name "mummichog" is derived from a local Native American term that means "going in crowds." The mummichog is rarely taken in full seawater and is more frequently found in freshwater than is the striped killifish, although the habitats of these two species overlap. Mummichog spawning occurs from April to August in fresh, brackish, and salt water. Eggs are laid in empty mollusk shells or on dead vegetation. Most mummichogs attain sexual maturity during their second year and live for a total of 3 years. The mummichog can tolerate high temperatures, up to 34°C (93°F) at 14‰ salinity. Mummichogs feed on a wide variety of items, including small crustaceans, small mollusks, worms, insects, plants, algae, and other fishes. In Massachusetts, they are known to prey heavily on young soft-shell clams. They have been widely introduced for the control of mosquito larvae.

FISHING INTEREST   Often sold as live bait and also of considerable indirect value as forage for other fishes and wading birds. Mummichogs are collected by seines and minnow traps.

LITERATURE   Chidester 1920; Hildebrand and Schroeder 1928:138; Musick 1972; Baer 1974; Able and Castagna 1975; Hardy 1978a; Kelso 1979; Abraham 1985; Smith 1985.

Livebearers
FAMILY POECILIIDAE

The livebearers are small fishes similar in overall appearance to the killifishes, and like them, livebearers lack a lateral line. Their mode of reproduction distinguishes poeciliids from killifishes and most other fishes, in that female livebearers give birth to live young—hence the common name. Internal fertilization is accomplished by means of an intromittent organ in the male called the gonopodium, which is formed by the modification of the first three to five rays of the anal fin. Livebearers are lowland species indigenous to fresh and brackish waters of Central America, much of South America, and parts of the central and southern United States. Livebearers include such popular hobbyist species as guppies. The popularity of poeciliids in the aquarium trade has led to the introduction and establishment of many populations of a variety of species in North America and Hawaii. The family comprises 22 genera and 140 species, of which 1 species is resident to Chesapeake Bay.

Eastern mosquitofish
Gambusia holbrooki Girard, 1859

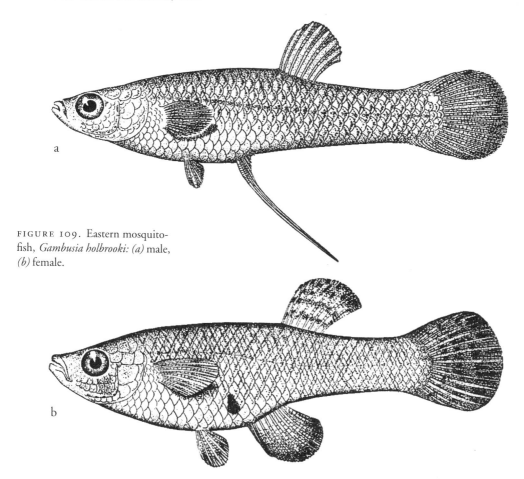

FIGURE 109. Eastern mosquito-fish, *Gambusia holbrooki: (a)* male, *(b)* female.

KEY FEATURES   Third ray of anal fin un-branched; in males, first 3–5 rays of anal fin modified as intromittent organ; caudal fin rounded.

OTHER CHARACTERISTICS   Body moderately robust; head short and depressed; snout short and broad; mouth superior; teeth small, pointed, and in bands; longitudinal scale rows numbering 26–32; dorsal fin small and with origin more posterior than anal fin origin; dorsal fin with 7–9 rays; anal fin similar to dorsal fin in females; anal fin with 8–10 rays; pelvic fin small and rounded; pectoral fin larger than pelvic fin and also rounded. Olivaceous dorsally; grayish laterally; venter pale; dusky blotch ventral to eye typically present; dusky spots sometimes present on dorsal and caudal fins; swollen belly of pregnant females marked by dark lateral blotch. Maximum adult size 6.3 cm TL (2.5 in), with females larger than males.

GEOGRAPHIC DISTRIBUTION   Occurring in freshwaters and brackish coastal waters from New Jersey to Florida, throughout the northern Gulf of Mexico, and from the Mississippi Valley northward to Illinois. The eastern mosquitofish has been introduced into California, Hawaii, and many countries outside the United States for mosquito control.

ECOLOGY   The eastern mosquitofish is abundant throughout Chesapeake Bay in tidal pools and streams, dwelling near the surface. This species overwinters in silt beds of low salinity or freshwaters. Like other members in the family, the mosquitofish is viviparous, producing well-developed larvae 8–10 mm (0.3–0.4 in) in length. Young are born from mid-April to September, with females capable of producing more than one brood per season. Livebearers feed on insects and insect larvae, other animals, and plant material. This mosquitofish is an effective eradicator of mosquito larvae and, for this reason, was distributed widely by humans to control mosquitoes and their diseases.

FISHING INTEREST   None, but of considerable indirect value as forage for other fishes and wading birds and for mosquito control. The eastern mosquitofish is collected by seines and dip nets.

LITERATURE   Hildebrand and Schroeder 1928:145; Musick 1972; Eddy and Underhill 1978; Fischer 1978; Hardy 1978a; Jenkins and Burkhead 1994.

Silversides
ORDER ATHERINIFORMES

The order of silversides comprises two families, one of which is represented in Chesapeake Bay.

Silversides
FAMILY ATHERINIDAE

Silversides are typically shallow-water fishes that frequent tidal salt marshes, sea grass meadows, and shore zones. Some species inhabit freshwater. Silversides lack a lateral line and possess a broad, silvery midlateral band. Their very small mouth distinguishes them from anchovies, which they superficially resemble. Atherinids are schooling fishes that feed on zooplankton and are ecologically valuable as forage for other fishes. One of the better-known atherinids is the California grunion (*Leuresthes tenuis*), whose spawning corresponds with the lunar cycle and takes place at night on the beaches of southern California. The family is distributed worldwide, comprising 25 genera and 165 species. Two genera and 3 species inhabit Chesapeake Bay.

KEY TO THE SPECIES OF SILVERSIDES IN CHESAPEAKE BAY

1a. Scales rough, with posterior margins fringed; bases of dorsal and anal fins with large deciduous scales . . . . **rough silverside,** *Membras martinica* (p. 131)

1b. Scales smooth, with posterior margins unfringed; bases of dorsal and anal fins without scales **2**

2a. Origin of spinous dorsal fin posterior to a vertical through anus; lateral scales numbering 43–55; segmented anal fin rays numbering 19–29 (typically 23–25) . . . .
. . . .**Atlantic silverside, *Menidia menidia*** (p. 131)

2b. Origin of spinous dorsal fin dorsoanterior to anus; lateral scales numbering 36–42; segmented anal fin rays numbering 13–19 (typically 16) . . . .**inland silverside, *Menidia beryllina*** (p. 132)

Rough silverside
Membras martinica (Valenciennes, 1835)

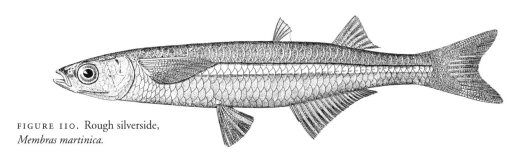

FIGURE 110. Rough silverside, *Membras martinica.*

KEY FEATURES   Scales with fringed posterior margins; bases of dorsal and anal fins with sheath of large deciduous scales.

OTHER CHARACTERISTICS   Body elongate and moderately compressed; caudal peduncle strongly compressed; top of head flattened; mouth small, oblique, and strongly protractile; jaw teeth small, pointed, and in narrow bands; scales firm and rough to the touch; first dorsal fin small, with origin slightly dorsoanterior to origin of anal fin; origin of second dorsal fin perpendicular to posterior half of anal fin; caudal fin moderately forked; anal fin long-based; pelvic fin small, inserting nearer to tip of snout than to base of caudal fin; pectoral fin pointed and located near midline. Translucent blue to green dorsally; side and belly silvery, with broad, intensely silver lateral stripe bounded dorsally by black line. Maximum adult size 10 cm TL (4 in).

GEOGRAPHIC DISTRIBUTION   Inhabiting coastal areas from New York to Mexico.

ECOLOGY   Although rarely encountered in winter, the rough silverside is a year-round resident that inhabits shallow grass flats and open water throughout Chesapeake Bay. Unlike other bay silversides, the rough silverside is not a marsh species and is usually found along exposed shorelines and beaches over a firm bottom. This species typically schools near the surface, from shallow flats to water 3–15 m (10–49 ft) deep. The rough silverside feeds primarily on copepods and other planktonic crustaceans. The spawning period is from May to early August. The eggs are attached to submerged vegetation on sand flats.

FISHING INTEREST   None in Chesapeake Bay, but of considerable indirect value as forage for other fishes. The rough silverside is collected most often by seines.

LITERATURE   Hildebrand and Schroeder 1928:191; Musick 1972; Martin and Drewry 1978; Smith 1985.

Atlantic silverside
Menidia menidia (Linnaeus, 1766)

KEY FEATURES   Scales with smooth margins; bases of dorsal and anal fins without large scales; origin of spinous dorsal fin dorsoposterior to anus; lateral scales numbering 43–55; segmented anal fin rays numbering 19–29 (typically 23–25).

OTHER CHARACTERISTICS   Body variable, from very slender to moderately deep and compressed; caudal peduncle long; snout pointed; mouth small and oblique; teeth in bands and pointed; first dorsal fin with 3–7 spines; origin of second dorsal fin perpendicular to middle of anal fin; caudal fin moderately forked; anal fin long-based; pelvic fin small; pectoral fin pointed. Translucent green dorsally; silvery white ventrally, with bright silver midlateral stripe. Maximum adult size 12.7 cm SL (5 in).

spawning activity usually occurs at a new or full moon, followed by spawning peaks at 2-week intervals. Spawning occurs from March to July in the intertidal zone or shallow estuarine waters, with the eggs attached by means of adhesive filaments to vegetation. The Atlantic silverside usu-

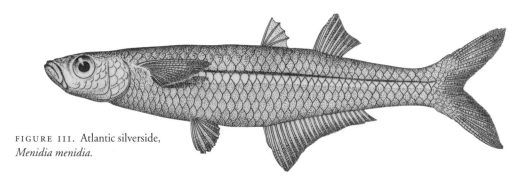

FIGURE 111. Atlantic silverside, *Menidia menidia.*

GEOGRAPHIC DISTRIBUTION   Inhabiting coastal areas from Nova Scotia to Florida.
ECOLOGY   The Atlantic silverside is the most common and abundant of the silversides in Chesapeake Bay, as well as one of the most abundant fishes in the bay. It is often the most abundant species encountered in the shore zone and is an important forage item for striped bass and bluefish. The Atlantic silverside prefers higher-salinity habitats than the inland silverside. It inhabits tidal creeks and grass flats during the summer but migrates to deeper water in the winter, with some individuals traveling as far as the waters of the inner continental shelf. The Atlantic silverside is one of more than 50 species known to have lunar-related spawning cycles. Spawning occurs strictly during daylight hours in large schools and coincides with high tide. The first

ally travels and spawns in schools of a few dozen to several hundred fish. The primary food of this species is crustaceans. When nearshore, this silverside feeds high in the water column on copepods; when in deeper water in winter, it feeds closer to the bottom, primarily on mysid shrimps. Feeding schools are opportunistic omnivores that follow the tidal ebb and flow along shorelines.
FISHING INTEREST   None, but of considerable indirect value as forage for other fishes and wading birds. The Atlantic silverside is collected most often by seines.
LITERATURE   Hildebrand and Schroeder 1928:187; Bayliff 1950; Musick 1972; Martin and Drewry 1978; Middaugh 1981; Conover and Murawski 1982; Fay et al. 1983; Smith 1985; Warkentine and Rachlin 1989.

Inland silverside
Menidia beryllina (Cope, 1866)

KEY FEATURES   Scales with smooth margins; origin of spinous dorsal fin dorsoanterior to anus; lateral scales numbering 36–42; segmented anal fin rays numbering 13–19 (typically 16).
OTHER CHARACTERISTICS   Body slender and moderately compressed; caudal peduncle long; snout pointed; mouth small, terminal, and strongly oblique; teeth small, pointed, and in narrow bands; first dorsal fin with 4 or 5 spines; origin of second dorsal fin slightly dorsoanterior to

middle of anal fin; anal fin moderately long-based; caudal fin forked; pelvic fin small. Waxy greenish dorsally; silvery white ventrally, with midlateral silver stripe. Maximum adult size 7.5 cm TL (3 in).
GEOGRAPHIC DISTRIBUTION   Inhabiting coastal areas from Massachusetts to Mexico. Freshwater populations of inland silversides have also been established in lacustrine systems in South Carolina, Florida, Texas, and California.

ECOLOGY   The inland silverside is an abundant year-round resident of Chesapeake Bay, inhabiting tidal creeks and grass flats in the summer but retreating to deeper water in the winter. This species typically prefers lower salinities, although it may be

schools and primarily locates its prey by sight. It feeds predominantly on crustaceans such as copepods and mysids.

FISHING INTEREST   None, but of considerable indirect value as forage for other fishes and

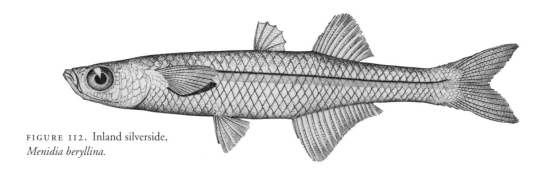

FIGURE 112. Inland silverside,
Menidia beryllina.

found seasonally along the entire salinity gradient and has become established in wholly freshwater systems. Spawning occurs in the bay from April to September in fresh or brackish shallow waters containing submerged aquatic vegetation. The inland silverside is a daytime predator that forms dense

wading birds. The inland silverside is collected most often by seines.

LITERATURE   Hildebrand and Schroeder 1928:189; Musick 1972; Martin and Drewry 1978; Smith 1985; Weinstein 1986.

Squirrelfishes
ORDER BERYCIFORMES

The order of squirrelfishes comprises 12 families, 1 of which occurs in Chesapeake Bay.

Squirrelfishes
FAMILY HOLOCENTRIDAE

Squirrelfishes are relatively deep-bodied fishes with large eyes and mouths, small teeth, large scales, and stout spines in the dorsal and anal fins. All species have four spines in the anal fin, and one spine and seven soft rays in the pelvic fins. Typically reddish in color, most holocentrid species inhabit shallow-water coral reefs. Members of this family are nocturnal, foraging in and around reefs for crustaceans, worms, or small fishes. During the day squirrelfishes can be found hiding under rocks and ledges of reefs. The family, comprising 8 genera and 65 species, is found in all tropical seas. One species is known from Chesapeake Bay.

Squirrelfish
Holocentrus adscensionis (Osbeck, 1765)
PLATE 19

KEY FEATURES   Preopercle with long, strong spine; dorsal fin with 11 spines in anterior portion and none in elongate posterior portion.

OTHER CHARACTERISTICS   Body moderately compressed and slender; upper jaw long; pored scales in lateral line numbering 46–51; spinous portion of dorsal fin long-based; posterior (soft) portion of dorsal fin with 14–16 soft rays; caudal fin deeply forked; anal fin with 4 spines and 10 soft rays; pelvic fin large; pectoral fin moderate-sized to large. Body reddish on dorsum and side, with alternating red (or pink) and

ECOLOGY   The squirrelfish is a rare visitor to the lower Chesapeake Bay in late summer. In more southern waters it inhabits shallow coral reefs and offshore rocky reefs in depths exceeding 100 m (330 ft). Squirrelfish confine themselves to reef crevices during the day and emerge at

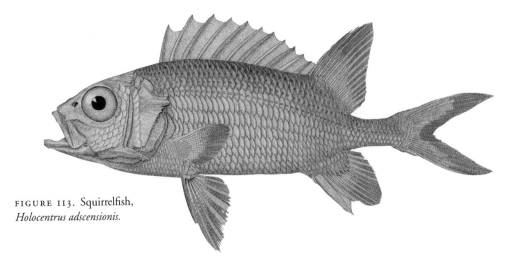

FIGURE 113. Squirrelfish, *Holocentrus adscensionis.*

white stripes; venter white; pelvic, anal, and caudal fins with white on leading edge; membranes between dorsal spines reddish anteriorly and greenish posteriorly. Maximum adult size 61 cm TL (2 ft).

GEOGRAPHIC DISTRIBUTION   In the western Atlantic, known from Virginia to Florida and throughout the Gulf of Mexico and the Caribbean to Brazil. The squirrelfish is also known from islands in the tropical mid-Atlantic and West Africa.

night to feed away from the reef over sand and grass flats. They primarily prey on crabs, shrimps, and other crustaceans. Spawning has been documented as far north as North Carolina in May.

FISHING INTEREST   Infrequently caught with traps, nets, or rod and reel.

LITERATURE   Musick 1972; Fischer 1978; Manooch 1984; Nelson 1994.

Sticklebacks

ORDER GASTEROSTEIFORMES

The order Gasterosteiformes comprises four families, one of which occurs in Chesapeake Bay.

Sticklebacks

FAMILY GASTEROSTEIDAE

Sticklebacks are characterized by a series of free dorsal spines anterior to the soft dorsal fin and pelvic fins, which contain strong spines. Sticklebacks lack scales, but many species have a series of lateral scutes. The family is found only in the Northern Hemisphere, inhabiting freshwater or salt water. Several species are anadromous. Some species of sticklebacks are broadly distributed and include ecotypes that differ greatly in morphology. The spawning habits of sticklebacks are some of the most extensively studied among fishes. Typically, the male constructs a nest from grasses and fibers bound together by a threadlike kidney secretion. The nest varies from tubular to cup-shaped and may contain one or two tunnellike passageways. One or more females are then enticed into the nest to lay their eggs. The male guards and protects the eggs and young for several weeks. The adult males are highly territorial and pugnacious, attacking other males or even other fishes that intrude near their nests. Sticklebacks are relatively short-lived; most have a life span of 1–3 years. They are predators on small invertebrates and larval fishes. The family contains five genera and eight species. Two species are recorded from Chesapeake Bay.

KEY TO THE SPECIES OF STICKLEBACKS IN CHESAPEAKE BAY

1a. Vertical, elongate bony scutes present along side; typically 3 dorsal spines present .... **threespine stickleback, *Gasterosteus aculeatus*** (p. 135)
1b. Bony scutes absent along side; typically 4 dorsal spines present .... **fourspine stickleback, *Apeltes quadracus*** (p. 136)

Threespine stickleback
Gasterosteus aculeatus Linnaeus, 1758

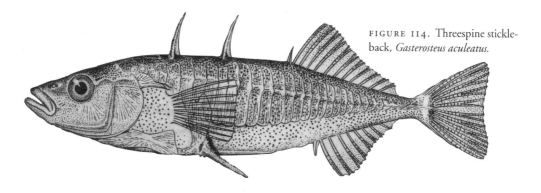

FIGURE 114. Threespine stickleback, *Gasterosteus aculeatus.*

KEY FEATURES   Few to many lateral bony plates present; typically 2 large free dorsal spines present, along with 1 smaller spine connected to soft dorsal fin; prominent lateral keel present on caudal peduncle.

OTHER CHARACTERISTICS   Body elongate and compressed; caudal peduncle slender; head long and compressed; snout pointed; mouth small and oblique; innominate bones forming lanceolate plate on belly between and posterior to pelvic fin; dorsal spines strong, the first spine inserting perpendicular to pectoral fin base, the second spine the longest, and the third spine very short and connected to soft dorsal fin; soft dorsal fin low and with 12 or 13 soft rays; caudal fin emarginate; anal fin low, with 9 soft rays, and

with very short spine preceding fin; pelvic spine serrate and long, inserting ventroposterior to pectoral fin. Dusky green dorsally; silver ventrally; numerous black speckles present on body; males with reddish belly during breeding season. Maximum adult size 10 cm SL (4 in).

GEOGRAPHIC DISTRIBUTION   Known from both the eastern and western Atlantic coasts, as well as the Pacific. In the western Atlantic, this species is known from Labrador to Chesapeake Bay.

ECOLOGY   The threespine stickleback visits Chesapeake Bay during winter and spring, extending as far north as Kent Island, and is absent from the bay the remainder of the year. In the bay area, this species is anadromous, ascending

Western Shore tributaries such as the James and York rivers to spawn. However, in the colder waters of the northern part of its range, it is strictly marine. Spawning occurs from late February to September. Egg laying occasionally occurs without nest building. This stickleback feeds on small crustaceans.

FISHING INTEREST   None.

LITERATURE   Hildebrand and Schroeder 1928:178; Musick 1972; Lagler et al. 1977; Hardy 1978a; Smith 1985; Whitehead et al. 1986a; Bakker and Sevenster 1988; Cowen et al. 1991; Jenkins and Burkhead 1994.

Fourspine stickleback
Apeltes quadracus (Mitchill, 1815)

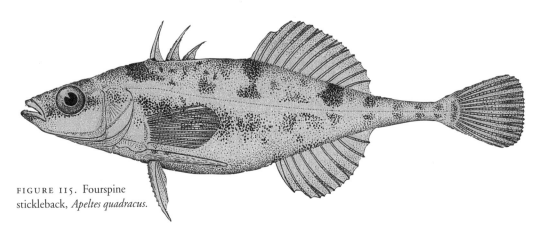

FIGURE 115. Fourspine stickleback, *Apeltes quadracus.*

KEY FEATURES   Lateral bony scutes absent; typically 3 large free dorsal spines present, along with 1 spine connected to soft dorsal fin; keel absent on caudal peduncle.

OTHER CHARACTERISTICS   Body elongate and compressed, tapering anteriorly and posteriorly; caudal peduncle slim; head long; snout pointed; mouth small and oblique; innominate bones not joined to form lanceolate plate on belly; soft dorsal fin with 10–13 soft rays; caudal fin rounded; anal fin low and with 1 spine and 8 or 9 soft rays; pelvic fin with strong serrate spines and inserting perpendicular to pectoral fin. Brownish green or black dorsally; silver ventrally; dusky mottles scattered on body. Maximum adult size 6 cm SL (2.5 in).

GEOGRAPHIC DISTRIBUTION   Occurring along the western Atlantic coast from Newfoundland to Chesapeake Bay.

ECOLOGY   The fourspine stickleback, a year-round resident of Chesapeake Bay, is abundant throughout the entire bay. During the summer it inhabits estuarine grass flats, and it retreats to deeper water in channels during winter. This species differs from other sticklebacks in that it builds a cup-shaped nest rather than a barrel-shaped one. The fish ventilates the nest by pumping water through its gill covers. A single male may build and maintain several nests simultaneously. Spawning occurs in the bay from late April to early May. The males usually have a 1-year life span, and some females may live to spawn again at age 2. The fourspine stickleback feeds primarily on planktonic crustaceans by sucking in prey with a pipetting action.

FISHING INTEREST   None. This species is collected by seines along vegetated shorelines and frequently is collected with pipefishes.

LITERATURE   Hildebrand and Schroeder 1928:180; Krueger 1961; Nelson 1968; Musick 1972; Coad and Power 1973; Smith 1985.

Pipefishes and Cornetfishes
ORDER SYNGNATHIFORMES

The order of pipefishes and cornetfishes comprises five families, two of which occur in Chesapeake Bay.

KEY TO THE FAMILIES OF PIPEFISHES AND CORNETFISHES IN CHESAPEAKE BAY

1a. Body encased in series of bony rings; caudal fin rounded or absent . . . .
. . . . **pipefishes and seahorses—Syngnathidae** (p. 137)

1b. Body not encased in bony rings; caudal fin forked, with central 2 rays forming elongate filament . . . .
. . . . **cornetfishes—Fistulariidae** (p. 140)

Pipefishes and Seahorses
FAMILY SYNGNATHIDAE

Pipefishes and seahorses typically have a long, tubular snout with a small, terminal, toothless mouth. The elongate body is encased in rings of bony plates. The gill opening is restricted to a pore in the opercular membrane. The spinous dorsal fin and pelvic fins are absent, and seahorses and some of the pipefishes have also lost the caudal fin. In seahorses the tail serves as a prehensile organ. Seahorses are unique in maintaining a vertical orientation of the body while the position of the head remains horizontal. Pipefishes and seahorses propel themselves by means of their rapidly undulating pectoral and dorsal fins. Male pipefishes and seahorses possess a ventral brood pouch, in which the eggs are fertilized and incubated after being deposited by the female. Nearly all species are small, inconspicuous bottom dwellers that feed on minute benthic and planktonic animals. The family, comprising 52 genera and 215 species, is found worldwide in tropical and warm-temperate marine waters, typically in shallow-water habitats. A few species inhabit freshwaters. Two genera and 4 species are known from Chesapeake Bay.

KEY TO THE SPECIES OF PIPEFISHES AND SEAHORSES IN CHESAPEAKE BAY

In pipefishes the first trunk ring bears the pectoral fins, and the last trunk ring surrounds the anus.

1a. Tail prehensile; caudal fin absent . . . . **lined seahorse,** *Hippocampus erectus* (p. 138)

1b. Tail not prehensile; caudal fin present **2**

2a. Trunk rings numbering 16–19 (typically 17); rings totaling 46–58 (typically 48–53); dorsal fin covering 0.25–3.0 trunk rings (typically less than 2.5); dorsal fin typically with fewer than 32 rays . . . . . .
. . . . **dusky pipefish,** *Syngnathus floridae* (p. 139)

2b. Trunk rings numbering 18–21 (typically 19 or 20); rings totaling 52–60 (typically 54–57); dorsal fin covering 1.5–6.5 trunk rings (typically more than 2.5); dorsal fin typically with more than 32 rays . . .
. . . . **3**

3a. Trunk rings numbering 19–21 (typically 20); dorsal fin covering 1.5–4.0 trunk rings (typically less than 3.5); snout depth about 10% of snout length . . . . **chain pipefish,** *Syngnathus louisianae* (p. 139)

3b. Trunk rings numbering 18–21 (typically 19); dorsal fin covering 3.75–5.0 trunk rings (typically 4.0 or more); snout depth about 20% of snout length . . .**northern pipefish,** *Syngnathus fuscus* (p. 140)

Lined seahorse
Hippocampus erectus Perry, 1810

FIGURE 116. Lined seahorse,
Hippocampus erectus.

KEY FEATURES   Tail tapered, prehensile, and without fin at tip; head shaped like horse's head and situated nearly at right angle to axis of body. OTHER CHARACTERISTICS   Dorsal fin with 16–20 rays; anal fin with 3 or 4 rays; trunk rings numbering 11; tail rings numbering 33–38; head with spines; snout slender; teeth absent; pectoral fin fan-shaped and with 14–17 rays. Overall coloration ranging from pale yellow to nearly black; dusky lines and spots present laterally,

with lines most prominent on head; dorsal fin with black spots. This species exhibits broad variation in coloration, degree of spination on the head and body, and presence and extent of dermal flaps. Maximum adult size 17 cm TL (6.7 in).

GEOGRAPHIC DISTRIBUTION   Found from Nova Scotia to Uruguay, including the Gulf of Mexico and the Caribbean Sea.

ECOLOGY   The lined seahorse is a resident of the middle-lower Chesapeake Bay, extending as far north as Calvert County, Maryland, and is occasional to common in abundance. During the summer months the lined seahorse inhabits channels and flats, and in winter it retreats to deeper waters. Both males and females have restricted home ranges, limited to only a few feet. The lined seahorse is a master of camouflage and a voracious ambush predator. It can change color in seconds to match its background and awaits potential prey items by clinging to vegetation or other holdfasts such as sponges, pilings, or ropes. Prey, such as small crustaceans, are ingested by sucking them through the long, tubular snout. Males and females often form pair bonds, and after an elaborate courtship the female deposits eggs (typically 250–300) in the male's abdominal pouch, where they are fertilized. Males protect, aerate, osmoregulate, and nourish the developing embryos for several weeks before releasing them as independent young when they reach about 6 mm TL (0.2 in).

FISHING INTEREST   None. The lined seahorse is collected by seines along vegetated shorelines and shallow-water grass flats. It can be kept in an aquarium if live food (brine shrimps or zooplankton) is provided.

LITERATURE   Hildebrand and Schroeder 1928:185; Musick 1972; Hardy 1978a; Vari 1982; Smith 1985; Vincent 1990.

Dusky pipefish
Syngnathus floridae (Jordan and Gilbert, 1882)

FIGURE 117. Dusky pipefish,
Syngnathus floridae.

KEY FEATURES   Trunk rings numbering
16–19 (typically 17); rings totaling 46–58 (typically 48–53); dorsal fin covering 0.25–3.0 trunk
rings (typically less than 2.5); dorsal fin typically
with fewer than 32 rays.

OTHER CHARACTERISTICS   Body slender;
pectoral fin with 12–16 rays; tail rings numbering 29–39; head length 1.6–2.1 times the snout
length; preorbital region broad. Body near white
to brownish, with markings mostly tan to near
black; snout typically with dusky lateral stripe;
side and dorsum of posterior tail rings usually
with characteristic pattern of irregular, narrow
brownish stripes; caudal fin brownish, often with
pale margin. The dusky pipefish has been reported to change color to match its background.
Maximum adult size 26 cm TL (10 in).

GEOGRAPHIC DISTRIBUTION   Found
from Chesapeake Bay to the Gulf of Mexico and
the Caribbean Sea as far south as Panama.

ECOLOGY   The dusky pipefish is a year-round
resident of the middle-lower Chesapeake Bay, extending as far north as Plum Point, Calvert
County, Maryland. It is abundant in shallow water (1–3 m, or 3–10 ft deep) over grass flats during the summer, and it occupies deep channels in
the winter. Males with eggs in their brood pouch
have been collected between May and October in
the bay. Males typically are sexually mature at
14–15 cm TL (5.5–5.9 in). The dusky pipefish
feeds almost exclusively on very small crustaceans.

FISHING INTEREST   None. The dusky pipefish is collected by seines in shallow-water grass
flats.

LITERATURE   Hildebrand and Schroeder
1928:183; Musick 1972; Hardy 1978a; Dawson
1982.

Chain pipefish
Syngnathus louisianae Günther, 1870

FIGURE 118. Chain pipefish, *Syngnathus louisianae.*

KEY FEATURES   Trunk rings numbering
19–21 (typically 20); dorsal fin covering 1.5–4.0
trunk rings (typically less than 3.5); snout depth
about 10% of snout length.

OTHER CHARACTERISTICS   Body slender;
dorsal fin with 33–42 rays; pectoral fin with
12–16 rays; tail rings numbering 33–38; head
length 1.5–1.9 times the snout length. Body usually near white to tan; markings variable, mostly
tan to brown; brownish stripe present on snout
laterally; body with 14 or 15 brown bands; caudal fin brownish. Maximum adult size 36 cm TL
(14 in).

GEOGRAPHIC DISTRIBUTION   Found
from New Jersey to the northern Gulf of Mexico
as far west as northern Mexico.

ECOLOGY   The chain pipefish has been infrequently reported from Chesapeake Bay and is apparently a rare summer visitor to the lower bay, extending as far north as St. Marys County, Maryland. It is most commonly found among aquatic vegetation such as eelgrass in depths of 10 m (33 ft) or less. The food of the chain pipefish is almost exclusively small crustaceans such as shrimp and amphipods.

FISHING INTEREST   None. This species is collected by seines in shallow-water grass flats.
LITERATURE   Hildebrand and Schroeder 1928:184; Musick 1972; Hardy 1978a; Dawson 1982.

Northern pipefish
Syngnathus fuscus Storer, 1839

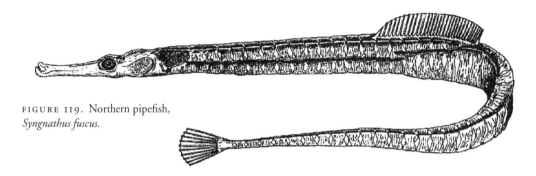

FIGURE 119. Northern pipefish, *Syngnathus fuscus.*

KEY FEATURES   Trunk rings numbering 18–21 (typically 19); dorsal fin covering 3.75–5.0 trunk rings (typically 4.0 or more); snout depth about 20% of snout length.
OTHER CHARACTERISTICS   Body slender; dorsal fin with 33–49 rays; pectoral fin with 12–15 rays; tail rings numbering 34–39; head length 1.7–2.4 times the snout length. Body usually pale tan to brown; markings variable, mostly dusky tan to brown; diagonal bar from eye to opercle; part or all of side crossed by 12 or 13 brown bands; caudal fin brownish, with narrow pale margin. Maximum adult size 28 cm TL (11 in).
GEOGRAPHIC DISTRIBUTION   Occurring from the Gulf of St. Lawrence to the east coast of Florida.

ECOLOGY   The northern pipefish is the most common pipefish in Chesapeake Bay. An abundant year-round resident throughout the bay, it inhabits shallow eelgrass beds during summer, retreating to deeper channels or the continental shelf in winter. Males with eggs in their brood pouches have been collected between April and October in the bay, with the breeding peak from May to June. Males typically are sexually mature at 9–10 cm TL (3.5–3.9 in). The northern pipefish feeds primarily on small crustaceans.
FISHING INTEREST   None. This species is collected by seines in shallow-water grass flats.
LITERATURE   Hildebrand and Schroeder 1928:182; Musick 1972; Orth and Heck 1980; Dawson 1982; Smith 1985; Lazzari and Able 1990.

Cornetfishes
FAMILY FISTULARIIDAE

Cornetfishes are characterized by a vertically flattened (depressed), elongate body and a long, whiplike tail filament produced by the middle two caudal rays. The caudal fin is forked. The mouth is small and located at the end of a tubular snout. The skin is naked. Cornetfishes are found in shallow water over grass flats and reefs or in deeper water over soft bottoms. They feed on small fishes and shrimp. Cornetfishes are marine and circumtropical. The family comprises one genus and four species, one of which is known from Chesapeake Bay.

Bluespotted cornetfish
Fistularia tabacaria Linnaeus, 1758

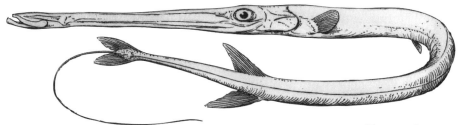

FIGURE 120. Bluespotted cornet-fish, *Fistularia tabacaria*.

KEY FEATURES   Body elongate and depressed; elongate filament emanating from middle of caudal fin; mouth located at tip of elongate snout; rows of blue spots present along back.

OTHER CHARACTERISTICS   Dorsal fin perpendicular to anal fin; dorsal and anal fins each with short base and 14–16 soft rays; pectoral fin with 15–17 rays; pelvic fin small, abdominal, and with 6 rays; body without scales. Brownish olive dorsally; pale ventrally; series of pale blue spots present from head to dorsal fin on midline of back, 1 row of blue spots present lateral to mid-dorsal row, and 2 rows of blue spots present on snout; caudal filament blue. Maximum adult size 2 m SL (7 ft).

GEOGRAPHIC DISTRIBUTION   Found in both the eastern and the western Atlantic. In the western Atlantic, the bluespotted cornetfish ranges from Cape Cod to southern Brazil, including the Gulf of Mexico and the Caribbean Sea.

ECOLOGY   The bluespotted cornetfish is a rare to occasional visitor to the lower Chesapeake Bay in late summer to early autumn. Within the bay, it frequents sea grass beds, but in tropical portions of its range it is often found on coral reefs. Little is known of the ecology or the life history of this species.

FISHING INTEREST   Of no commercial or recreational importance. The bluespotted cornetfish is collected by seines in shallow-water grass flats.

LITERATURE   Hildebrand and Schroeder 1928:186; Musick 1972; Fischer 1978; Fritzsche 1982; Smith 1985.

Searobins and Sculpins
ORDER SCORPAENIFORMES

The order of searobins and sculpins comprises 25 families, 266 genera, and an estimated 1,250 species. Four families of scorpaeniform fishes are recorded from Chesapeake Bay.

KEY TO THE FAMILIES OF SEAROBINS AND SCULPINS IN CHESAPEAKE BAY

1a. Spiny crest from nape terminating posterior to area adjacent to midbase of first dorsal fin . . . .
. . . . **flying gurnards—Dactylopteridae** (p. 142)
1b. Spiny crest from nape absent or terminating anterior to first dorsal fin **2**

2a. Ventralmost rays of pectoral fin separate and fingerlike . . . . **searobins—Triglidae** (p. 143)
2b. Pectoral fin entire, without separate rays **3**

3a. Pelvic fins modified into ventral sucking disk . . . . **lumpsuckers—Cyclopteridae** (p. 145)
3b. Pelvic fins not modified into ventral sucking disk . . . . **sculpins—Cottidae** (p. 146)

Flying Gurnards
FAMILY DACTYLOPTERIDAE

Flying gurnards superficially resemble searobins in having a large, blunt, heavily armored head that possesses spines and keels. The body is covered with scutelike keeled scales. The pectoral fins are enormous and winglike, and the lowermost rays are free from the remainder of the fin. Flying gurnards are strictly marine. They are benthic fishes found on sand bottoms, and they have the ability to "walk" along the bottom by alternately moving the pelvic fins. Despite the often repeated assertion to the contrary, flying gurnards do not "fly" above the surface; instead they use their greatly enlarged pectoral fins in underwater display. They feed on small, sand-dwelling crustaceans, mollusks, worms, and fishes. The family comprises four genera and four species and occurs throughout the tropics and warm-temperate waters. Only one species is recorded from Chesapeake Bay.

Flying gurnard
Dactylopterus volitans (Linnaeus, 1758)

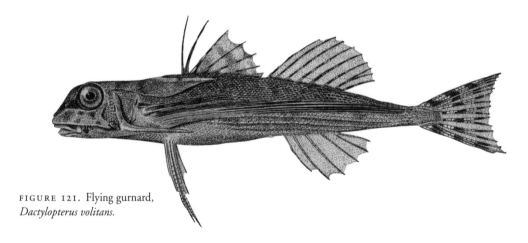

FIGURE 121. Flying gurnard,
Dactylopterus volitans.

KEY FEATURES   Head dorsally armored with heavy bony plates that extend dorsoposteriorly and terminate adjacent to midpoint of first dorsal fin base; angle of preopercle bearing long, serrated spine that extends posteriorly along pectoral fin base; pectoral fin base oriented nearly horizontally and divided into 2 sections; dorsalmost (anteriormost) section of pectoral fin short and with 6 rays; ventralmost section of pectoral fin long and broad, reaching to caudal base in adults; first 2 spines of dorsal fin separate.
OTHER CHARACTERISTICS   Body moderately elongate; head blunt; 2 dorsal fins separated by notch; first dorsal fin with 6 spines; second dorsal fin with 1 spine and 8 rays; anal fin with 6 rays; caudal fin emarginate, with 2 sharp keels on base; scales scutelike, with prominent keels; pelvic fin narrow and pointed, with 1 spine and 4 rays and with middle rays the longest. Coloration varying with surroundings, typically either brownish green or yellowish green; first dorsal fin with purplish brown bars; caudal fin with 2 or 3 wine-colored bars; pectoral fin with bright blue bars and spots. Maximum adult size 50 cm TL (20 in).
GEOGRAPHIC DISTRIBUTION   Found on both coasts of the Atlantic Ocean. In the western

Atlantic, the flying gurnard ranges from Massachusetts to Argentina, including the Gulf of Mexico and the Caribbean Sea.

ECOLOGY The flying gurnard is a rare visitor to the lower Chesapeake Bay in the late summer and fall. It is often associated with sandy or muddy bottoms, usually at depths of 10–30 m (33–100 ft) and occasionally as shallow as 2 m (7 ft). When this species is alarmed, it spreads its pectoral fins in a prominent display that may function to dissuade potential predators. The fly-

ing gurnard is primarily a bottom feeder on crabs and clams.

FISHING INTEREST Of no commercial or recreational importance. This species is landed as bycatch in trawl catches offshore.

LITERATURE Hildebrand and Schroeder 1928:316; Musick 1972; Fischer 1978; Fritzsche 1978, 1982; Fischer et al. 1981; Randall 1983; Smith 1985; Whitehead et al. 1986b; Nelson 1994.

Searobins
FAMILY TRIGLIDAE

Searobins are benthic marine fishes that inhabit continental and insular shelves to depths of about 180 m (600 ft) in all tropical and temperate seas. They are unusual in having a large bony head with many ridges and spines. Additionally, the ventralmost rays of the pectoral fins are fleshy and detached from one another (that is, unconnected by membranes), thus assuming the appearance of fingers or legs. Searobins occur on muddy or sandy bottoms and use their free pectoral rays for support and to search for food. They are well known for their sound production, which results from muscular action on the large swim bladder. Searobins feed on a variety of benthic crustaceans and fishes. The family comprises approximately 10 genera and 70 species, 4 of which are known from Chesapeake Bay.

KEY TO THE SPECIES OF SEAROBINS IN CHESAPEAKE BAY

1a. Branchiostegal membranes black or dusky; second dorsal fin with 13 or 14 rays **2**

1b. Branchiostegal membranes not black or dusky; second dorsal fin with 11 or 12 rays **3**

2a. Chest completely scaled; opercular flap naked . . . **northern searobin, *Prionotus carolinus*** (p. 143)

2b. Chest incompletely scaled; opercular flap scaled . . . . . .**leopard searobin, *Prionotus scitulus*** (p. 286)

3a. Narrow black stripe extending along lateral line from head to caudal fin, with second, incomplete stripe ventral to it; pectoral fin with numerous narrowly separated dusky stripes . . . . **striped searobin, *Prionotus evolans*** (p. 144)

3b. Black stripes on body rudimentary or absent; stripes on pectoral fin broad and widely spaced . . . . **bighead searobin, *Prionotus tribulus*** (p. 286)

Northern searobin
Prionotus carolinus (Linnaeus, 1771)
PLATE 20

KEY FEATURES Branchiostegal membranes blackish; 5 dusky saddlelike blotches present dorsally; first dorsal fin with dusky spot near outer edge of fin between fourth and sixth spines; second dorsal fin with 13 or 14 soft rays.

OTHER CHARACTERISTICS Head moderately large, depressed, and slightly broader than

deep; body moderately robust, slightly compressed posteriorly; mouth rather small; teeth in jaws in broad bands; scales small; spines on head moderately developed; dorsal fins separate; first dorsal fin with 9 or 10 spines; caudal fin margin concave; pectoral fin with 3 free rays. Grayish or reddish brown dorsally; pale ventrally; spinous dorsal fin with white horizontal band ventral to dusky spot; pectoral fin with spots on upper rays. Maximum adult size 40 cm TL (16 in).

GEOGRAPHIC DISTRIBUTION   Found along the western Atlantic coast from Nova Scotia to the east coast of Florida.

(66–200 ft). Spawning occurs from late spring into summer. The northern searobin, like the striped searobin, uses its modified pectoral rays to feel for food and also to stir up sand, weeds, and debris, thus dislodging prey items such as shrimps, crabs, squids, and small fishes.

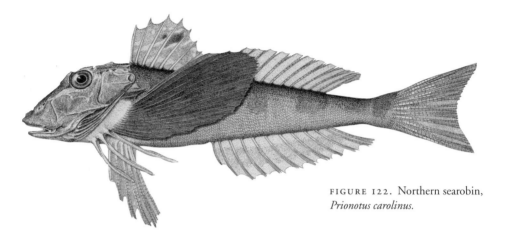

FIGURE 122. Northern searobin, *Prionotus carolinus.*

ECOLOGY   The northern searobin is the most common searobin throughout Chesapeake Bay and is abundant in the lower reaches of the bay. Like the striped searobin, the northern searobin is present in the bay from spring through early winter, retreating offshore or southward during the winter. The northern searobin inhabits sandy bottoms from shallow estuaries to the deeper waters at the edge of the continental shelf but is most commonly found at depths of 20–60 m

FISHING INTEREST   Considered a nuisance by anglers. Searobins steal bait and are unpleasant to handle. Commercial fisheries consider searobins to be trash fish when caught incidentally in trawls and pound nets.

LITERATURE   Hildebrand and Schroeder 1928:314; Musick 1972; Fischer 1978; Richards et al. 1979; Fritzsche 1982; Fahay 1983; Manooch 1984; Russell et al. 1992; Nelson 1994.

Striped searobin
Prionotus evolans (Linnaeus, 1766)

KEY FEATURES   Branchiostegal membranes pale or whitish; narrow black stripe extending along lateral line from head to caudal fin, with second, incomplete stripe ventral to it; second dorsal fin with 11 or 12 soft rays; pectoral fin brown, with numerous narrowly separated dusky stripes.

OTHER CHARACTERISTICS   Head large, depressed, and broader than deep; body moderately robust, compressed posteriorly; mouth large; teeth in jaws in broad bands; scales small; spines on head not very large; dorsal fins separate; first dorsal fin with 9–11 spines; caudal fin truncate;

pelvic fins well developed; pectoral fins large and rounded, with 3 free rays. Reddish to olive brown dorsally; pale ventrally. Maximum adult size 45 cm TL (18 in).

GEOGRAPHIC DISTRIBUTION   Occurring along the western Atlantic coast from Nova Scotia to the east coast of Florida.

ECOLOGY   The striped searobin is a temperate-subtropical species inhabiting sandy bottoms from inshore estuaries to depths of about 160 m (525 ft) but most commonly found at depths of 20–70 m (66–230 ft). It is a regular visitor to Chesapeake Bay from spring to early winter and is more common in the lower bay than in the upper. It is most often found in deep flats and channel margins. During the winter striped searobins migrate offshore and to the

FISHING INTEREST   See under discussion for the northern searobin, page 144.

LITERATURE   Hildebrand and Schroeder 1928:312; McEachran and Davis 1970; Musick

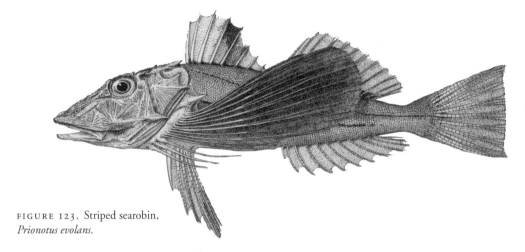

FIGURE 123. Striped searobin, *Prionotus evolans.*

south. Spawning occurs within the bay from May through early July. This species feeds primarily on crustaceans and mollusks and occasionally consumes squids and other fishes.

1972; Fischer 1978; Richards et al. 1979; Fritzsche 1982; Manooch 1984; Russell et al. 1992; Nelson 1994.

Lumpsuckers
FAMILY CYCLOPTERIDAE

Lumpsuckers are small to moderately large, mostly globose fishes distinguished by the presence of a ventral sucking disk. The skin of lumpsuckers is embedded with large horny tubercles. Adult lumpsuckers are quite sedentary, using the sucking disk to attach to rocks or other hard surfaces, often in deep water (100–400 m, or 330–1,310 ft). All species are apparently oviparous, and some are known to migrate to shallow waters to spawn. Lumpsuckers are found in cool, marine waters of the Northern Hemisphere. The family comprises 7 genera and 28 species, 1 of which is recorded from Chesapeake Bay.

Lumpfish
Cyclopterus lumpus Linnaeus, 1758

KEY FEATURES   Bony tubercles well developed on head and body; pelvic fins modified to form sucking disk; skin thick; body globose.

OTHER CHARACTERISTICS   Body deep; gill opening wide; snout short; eye small; mouth broad and terminal; teeth small and in bands; first dorsal fin with 6–8 spines and often covered by thick skin in adults; second dorsal fin with 9–11 rays; anal fin with 9–11 rays; 3 distinct rows of bony tubercles present laterally, with

many smaller tubercles scattered among them; caudal fin slightly rounded; pelvic fins modified into 6 pairs of fleshy knobs surrounded by circular flap of skin, with entire disk about as wide as head; pectoral fin long-based, with ventral edge inserting anterior to sucking disk. Coloration variable; young yellowish to greenish; adults bluish to brownish; spawning males reddish. Maximum adult size 61 cm TL (2 ft).

GEOGRAPHIC DISTRIBUTION   Occurring along both coasts of the North Atlantic. The lumpfish ranges southward along the North American coast as far as Chesapeake Bay.

ECOLOGY   Lumpfish are occasional visitors to the lower Chesapeake Bay during winter and early spring. The lumpfish is typically associated

fore settling to the bottom. Lumpfish feed on ctenophores, jellyfishes, crustaceans, polychaetes, and small fishes.

FISHING INTEREST   None in the Chesapeake Bay area but utilized as a food fish in

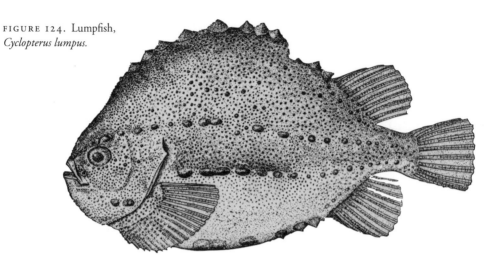

FIGURE 124. Lumpfish, *Cyclopterus lumpus.*

with rocky bottoms in waters 50–150 m (160–490 ft) deep; however, spawning individuals are often found inshore. The demersal adhesive eggs are deposited in large clumps in comparatively shallow water. Egg masses are guarded by the male and may include as many as 300,000 eggs. The young are pelagic for a short time be-

northern Europe and the Soviet Union. The flesh of this species is usually smoked, and the roe is processed and sold as lumpfish caviar.

LITERATURE   Hildebrand and Schroeder 1928:311; Musick 1972; Fritzsche 1978, 1982; Whitehead et al. 1986b.

Sculpins
FAMILY COTTIDAE

Sculpins have a depressed head that typically possesses large spines. The eyes are large and located more dorsally than laterally. The body is scaleless, or nearly so, but does have prickles. The sculpin family is primarily marine, but a number of species are restricted to freshwater. Sculpins are bottom dwellers and demersal spawners. Egg masses are deposited on the bottom and are often guarded by the male. The larvae are pelagic. Sculpins occur in rivers and along coastlines of the Northern Hemisphere as well as Australia, New Zealand, and Argentina. They feed on crustaceans, bivalves, aquatic insects, and small fishes. The family comprises approximately 67 genera and 300 species, 2 of which are known from Chesapeake Bay.

KEY TO THE SPECIES OF SCULPINS IN CHESAPEAKE BAY

1a. Dorsal fin spines numbering 10 or fewer . . . . **longhorn sculpin, *Myoxocephalus octodecemspinosus*** (p. 147)
1b. Dorsal fin spines numbering 16 or more . . . . **sea raven, *Hemitripterus americanus*** (p. 286)

Longhorn sculpin
Myoxocephalus octodecemspinosus (Mitchill, 1814)
PLATE 21

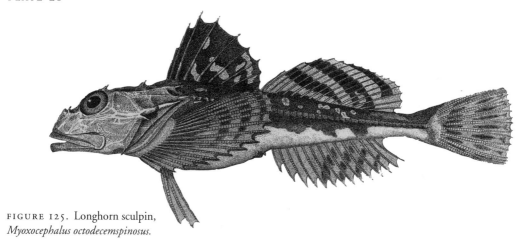

FIGURE 125. Longhorn sculpin,
Myoxocephalus octodecemspinosus.

KEY FEATURES   Dorsal fin spines numbering 7–10; dorsalmost preopercular cheek spine long, about 4 times as long as spine immediately ventral to it; cartilaginous plates present along lateral line; anal fin originating perpendicular to origin of second or third ray of second dorsal fin.

OTHER CHARACTERISTICS   Head moderately flat; 3 spines present on preopercle; second dorsal fin with 15 or 16 rays; anal fin with 14 elements; pectoral fin fanlike. Maximum adult size 46 cm TL (18 in).

GEOGRAPHIC DISTRIBUTION   Occurring from the Gulf of St. Lawrence to Chesapeake Bay.

ECOLOGY   The longhorn sculpin is a rare to occasional wintertime visitor to the lower Chesapeake Bay, entering river mouths and creeks but not freshwater. It is benthic and feeds on worms, hydroids, shrimps, crabs, mussels, and small fishes. It has been reported from depths as great as 190 m (630 ft).

FISHING INTEREST   None. However, in areas where abundant, the longhorn sculpin is known to bite on just about any bait.

LITERATURE   Bigelow and Schroeder 1953a; Musick 1972; Fritzsche 1982; Fahay 1983; Smith 1985; Robins et al. 1986.

Perchlike Fishes
ORDER PERCIFORMES

The extremely diverse order of perchlike fishes comprises more than 150 families, nearly 1,300 genera, and possibly 13,000 species. About three-quarters of all Perciformes species are marine shorefishes. Thirty-four families of perciforms are represented in Chesapeake Bay waters, and more than half of the species treated in this book belong to this order.

KEY TO THE FAMILIES OF PERCHLIKE FISHES IN CHESAPEAKE BAY

1a. Pelvic fin absent **2**
1b. Pelvic fin present **4**

2a. Body short and very deep . . . . **butterfishes—Stromateidae** (p. 153)
2b. Body elongate and not deep. **3**

3a. Caudal fin absent; body ribbonlike . . . . **snake mackerels—Trichiuridae** (p. 156)
3b. Caudal fin present; body not ribbonlike . . . . **sand lances—Ammodytidae** (p. 157)

4a. Anal fin preceded by 2 spines detached from main body of fin (Figure 126). . . . .
. . . . **jacks, in part—Carangidae** (p. 158)
4b. Anal fin spines contiguous with main body of fin **5**

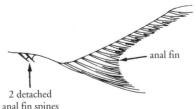

FIGURE 126. Anal fin spines of some jacks.

2 detached
anal fin spines

anal fin

5a. Three to 9 free spines present in dorsal fin (spines may be connected by membrane in Carangidae of less than 30 mm, or 1.2 in, SL) **6**
5b. Free spines absent in dorsal fin **7**

6a. Head and body strongly compressed; color predominantly silver . . . .
. . . . **jacks, in part—Carangidae** (p. 158)
6b. Head depressed; body only slightly compressed; color not predominantly silver . . . .
. . . . **cobia—Rachycentridae** (p. 176)

7a. Dorsal spines absent **8**
7b. Dorsal spines present **9**

8a. Top of head with large sucking disk (Figure 127); dorsal fin originating posteriorly . . . .
. . . . **remoras—Echeneidae** (p. 177)
8b. Sucking disk absent; dorsal fin originating on head . . . . **dolphins—Coryphaenidae** (p. 287)

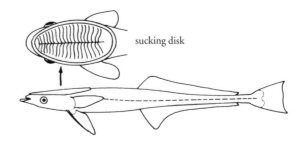

sucking disk

FIGURE 127. Sucking disk of a remora.

9a. Dorsal fin divided, or nearly divided, into distinct spinous and soft dorsal portions (Figure 128) . . . **10**
9b. Dorsal fin with continuous spinous and soft portions (Figure 129) **23**

10a. Spinous and soft dorsal fins widely separated (Figure 130) **11**
10b. Spinous and soft dorsal fins contiguous (connected basally by membrane; Figure 128) **15**

11a. Lower 4–10 rays of pectoral fin filamentous and detached . . . . **threadfins—Polynemidae** (p. 287)
11b. Pectoral fin without detached rays **12**

12a. Dorsal and anal fins followed by series of small detached finlets (Figure 130). . . . .
. . . . **mackerels, in part—Scombridae** (p. 178)
12b. Dorsal and anal fins not followed by series of small detached finlets **13**

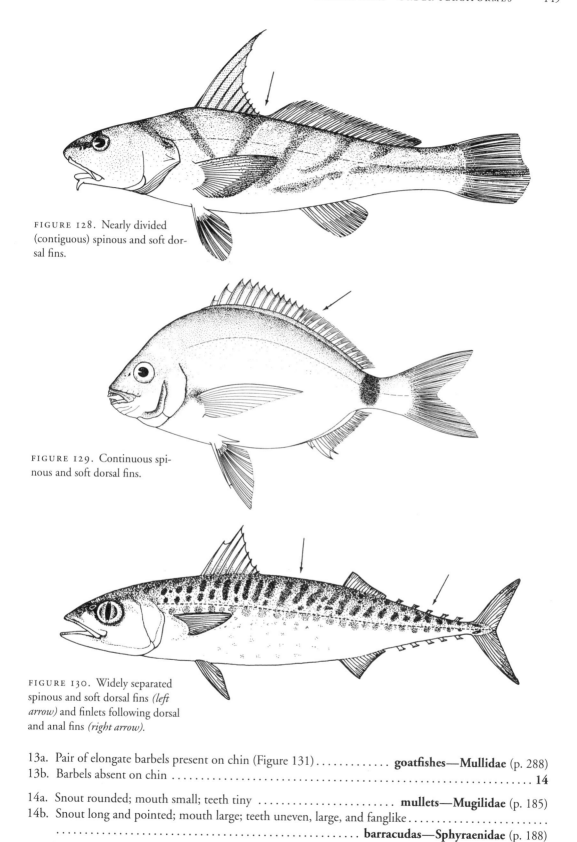

FIGURE 128. Nearly divided (contiguous) spinous and soft dorsal fins.

FIGURE 129. Continuous spinous and soft dorsal fins.

FIGURE 130. Widely separated spinous and soft dorsal fins *(left arrow)* and finlets following dorsal and anal fins *(right arrow)*.

13a. Pair of elongate barbels present on chin (Figure 131). . . . . **goatfishes—Mullidae** (p. 288)
13b. Barbels absent on chin **14**

14a. Snout rounded; mouth small; teeth tiny . . . . **mullets—Mugilidae** (p. 185)
14b. Snout long and pointed; mouth large; teeth uneven, large, and fanglike. . . . .
. . . . **barracudas—Sphyraenidae** (p. 188)

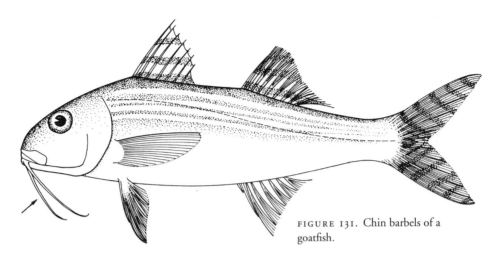

FIGURE 131. Chin barbels of a goatfish.

15a. Dorsal and anal fins followed by series of small detached finlets (Figure 130) . . . .
. . . . **mackerels, in part—Scombridae** (p. 178)
15b. Dorsal and anal fins not followed by series of small detached finlets **16**

16a. Eye located dorsally; mouth nearly vertical; lips with fringe . . . . **stargazers—Uranoscopidae** (p. 190)
16b. Eye more or less lateral; mouth not nearly vertical; lips without fringe **17**

17a. Lateral line (and scales) extending onto central caudal fin rays to posterior margin (Figure 132) . . . . .
. . . . **drums—Sciaenidae** (p. 191)
17b. Lateral line not extending onto caudal fin **18**

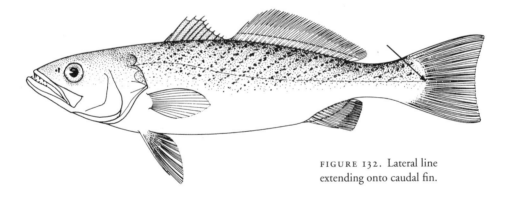

FIGURE 132. Lateral line extending onto caudal fin.

18a. Dorsal and anal soft fins covered with fine scales **19**
18b. Dorsal and anal soft fins not covered with fine scales **20**

19a. Body very deep and compressed; teeth small and in bands . . . . **spadefishes—Ephippidae** (p. 207)
19b. Body elongate and moderately compressed; teeth in outer row large and bladelike . . . .
. . . . **bluefishes—Pomatomidae** (p. 209)

20a. Pelvic fins formed into sucking disk (Figure 133) . . . . **gobies—Gobiidae** (p. 211)
20b. Pelvic fins not formed into sucking disk **21**

21a. Lateral line absent on body; gill openings ventrally restricted by connection of gill membrane to
isthmus . . . . **sleepers—Eleotridae** (p. 288)
21b. Lateral line present on body; gill openings ventrally unrestricted **22**

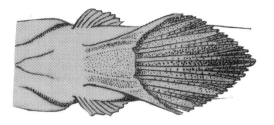

FIGURE 133. Sucking disk of a goby.

22a. Three anal spines present .... **striped basses—Moronidae** (p. 216)
22b. One or 2 anal spines present .... **perches—Percidae** (p. 220)

23a. Spines in dorsal and anal fins flexible; teeth close-set and comblike; ocular cirri usually present (Figure 134) .... **combtooth blennies—Blenniidae** (p. 222)
23b. Spines in dorsal and anal fins stiff; teeth not close-set or comblike; ocular cirri absent **24**

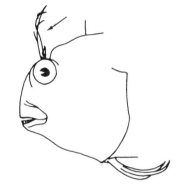

FIGURE 134. Ocular cirri of a combtooth blenny.

24a. Pelvic axillary process present (Figure 135) **25**
24b. Pelvic axillary process absent **30**

FIGURE 135. Pelvic axillary process and protrusible mouth of a mojarra.

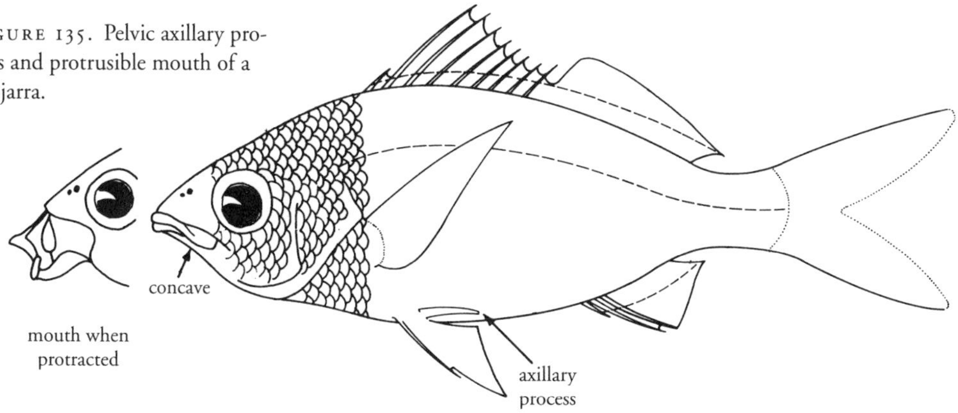

concave

mouth when protracted

axillary process

25a. Caudal fin rounded .... **butterflyfishes—Chaetodontidae** (p. 225)
25b. Caudal fin forked **26**

26a. Mouth greatly protrusible (Figure 135) .... **mojarras—Gerreidae** (p. 226)
26b. Mouth moderately protrusible **27**

27a. Posterior jaw teeth molarlike (Figure 136) . . . . **porgies—Sparidae** (p. 230)

27b. Molarlike teeth absent **28**

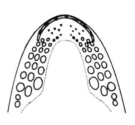

FIGURE 136. Ventral view of
upper jaw teeth of a porgy.

28a. Upper jaw with 1 or 2 pairs of greatly enlarged caninelike teeth . . **snappers—Lutjanidae** (p. 235)

28b. Upper jaw without enlarged caninelike teeth **29**

29a. Spines of dorsal fin depressible into groove of scales; soft portions of dorsal and anal fins scaled to
near margin. . . . . **sea chubs—Kyphosidae** (p. 289)

29b. Spines of dorsal fin not depressible into groove of scales; soft portions of dorsal and anal fins largely
unscaled . . . . **grunts—Haemulidae** (p. 237)

30a. Last (innermost) pelvic ray connected to body by membrane **31**

30b. Last (innermost) pelvic ray not connected to body by membrane **32**

31a. Eye very large; body predominantly red . . . . **bigeyes—Priacanthidae** (p. 239)

31b. Eye not greatly enlarged; body not predominantly red . . . . **sunfishes—Centrarchidae** (p. 241)

32a. Jaw teeth projecting (Figure 137); slitlike opening into pharynx absent posterior to last (fourth) gill arch
. . . . **33**

32b. Jaw teeth not projecting; slitlike opening into pharynx present posterior to last (fourth) gill arch
. . . . **34**

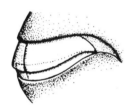

FIGURE 137. Projecting, fused
teeth of a parrotfish.

FIGURE 138. Projecting, unfused
teeth of a wrasse.

33a. Jaw teeth fused into plates (Figure 137) . . . . **parrotfishes—Scaridae** (p. 290)

33b. Jaw teeth not fused into plates; teeth usually uneven and projecting outward (Figure 138) . . . .
. . . . **wrasses—Labridae** (p. 251)

34a. Caudal fin forked . . . . **medusafishes—Centrolophidae** (p. 253)

34b. Caudal fin rounded, truncate, or emarginate **35**

35a. Opercle without 3 enlarged spines; soft lobes of dorsal and anal fins very large and rounded . . . .
. . . . **tripletails—Lobotidae** (p. 254)

35b. Opercle with 3 enlarged spines (Figure 139), with middle spine largest; soft lobes of dorsal and anal
fins only moderately large . . . . **sea basses and groupers—Serranidae** (p. 256)

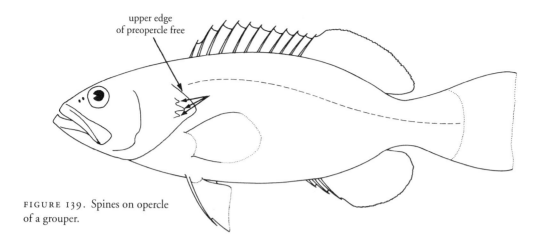

FIGURE 139. Spines on opercle
of a grouper.

Butterfishes

FAMILY STROMATEIDAE

Butterfishes are very deep-bodied and highly compressed, and adults lack pelvic fins. These small school-ing fishes are found in bays and over continental shelves. The young are often found in association with floating mats of vegetation as well as with jellyfishes, which serve as a food source for them. The flesh of butterfishes is highly esteemed. The family, found in all tropical, subtropical, and temperate waters, com-prises 3 genera and approximately 13 species. Two species are known from Chesapeake Bay.

KEY TO THE SPECIES OF BUTTERFISHES IN CHESAPEAKE BAY

1a. Dorsal and anal fins (especially anal fin) greatly elongate anteriorly, with longest rays much longer than head length; pores absent near base of dorsal fin; body depth greater than 60% of standard length . . . . **harvestfish,** *Peprilus alepidotus* (p. 153)
1b. Dorsal and anal fins slightly elongate anteriorly, with longest rays somewhat shorter than head length; series of well-developed, conspicuous pores present near base of dorsal fin; body depth less than 60% of standard length . . . . **butterfish,** *Peprilus triacanthus* (p. 154)

Harvestfish
Peprilus alepidotus (Linnaeus, 1766)

KEY FEATURES   Dorsal and anal fins greatly elongate anteriorly, with falcate margins, and with longest rays much longer than head length; pores absent near base of dorsal fin; body strongly compressed and deep, with depth about 65–70% of standard length.

OTHER CHARACTERISTICS   Head short; snout blunt; mouth small; teeth in jaws weak and in single row; eye large and surrounded by small area of adipose tissue; scales small, thin, and easily detached; dorsal and anal fins with very long and similarly shaped bases; 3 weak spines preceding dorsal and anal fins; lateral line arched, following curvature of back; caudal fin stiff and deeply forked, with both lobes longer than head; pelvic fin absent; pectoral fin narrow and longer than head. Pale blue to green dor-sally; silvery with yellowish sheen ventrally. Maxi-mum adult size 30 cm TL (1 ft).

GEOGRAPHIC DISTRIBUTION   Found along the western Atlantic coast from Maine to Uruguay, including the Gulf of Mexico and the eastern Caribbean Sea. The harvestfish is infre-quently encountered north of Chesapeake Bay.

ECOLOGY   A visitor to Chesapeake Bay from April through October, the harvestfish is common in the lower bay and occasional in the up- per bay, as far north as Annapolis and Love Point, Maryland. Harvestfish are found in large schools in inshore and offshore waters, sometimes

Presently of minor commercial importance in Chesapeake Bay. In former years, catches in the bay were much larger. In 1920, Chesapeake Bay landings were

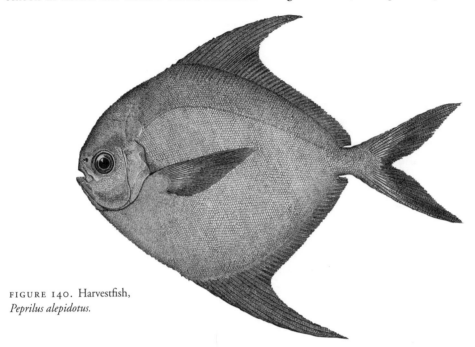

FIGURE 140. Harvestfish, *Peprilus alepidotus.*

occurring in mixed schools with butterfish. The harvestfish is a pelagic species found over sand or mud bottoms and tolerates a wide range of salini- ties (from 4‰ to full seawater). Spawning occurs offshore in spring and early summer in the Chesa- peake Bay region. Young-of-the-year harvestfish of about 25–30 mm TL (1.0–1.2 in) show up in the bay in July and August. Juveniles are often found in shallow coastal waters associated with floating vegetation and jellyfishes. Juveniles feed primarily on plankton, whereas adults feed mainly on jellyfishes, small fishes, crustaceans, and worms.

near 145,000 kg (320,000 lb), almost all from pound-net catches in Virginia waters. The 1989 and 1990 landings for the Virginia waters of the bay were 16,000 and 43,000 kg (35,000 and 94,000 lb), respectively. Catches exhibit a single peak that usually occurs in May or June. Harvest- fish are of limited recreational value because they rarely take a bait; however, they are occasionally taken in haul seines and fyke nets.
LITERATURE   Hildebrand and Schroeder 1928:210; Horn 1970; Musick 1972; Fischer 1978; Martin and Drewry 1978; Fritzsche 1982.

Butterfish
Peprilus triacanthus (Peck, 1804)
PLATE 22

KEY FEATURES   Dorsal and anal fins slightly elongate anteriorly, with longest rays somewhat shorter than head length; series of well- developed, conspicuous pores present near base of dorsal fin; body strongly compressed and mod-

erately deep, with depth about 45–55% of stan- dard length.
OTHER CHARACTERISTICS   Body moder- ately ovate; head short; snout blunt; mouth moderate-sized; teeth in jaws very small and in

single row; eye moderate-sized and surrounded by small area of adipose tissue; scales small; dorsal and anal fins with very long and similarly shaped bases; 3 weak spines preceding dorsal and anal fins; lateral line gently curving; caudal fin deeply forked; pelvic fin absent; pectoral fin longer than peake Bay region. After hatching, juveniles move from offshore surface waters to near-coastal waters, sometimes including bays and estuaries. There they often hide from predators in masses of floating seaweed or among the tentacles of jellyfish. Juveniles feed primarily on plankton,

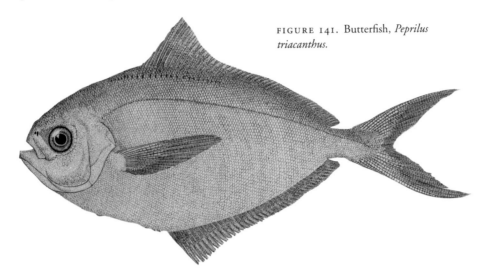

FIGURE 141. Butterfish, *Peprilus triacanthus.*

head. Pale blue to green dorsally; silvery ventrally; numerous irregular dusky spots present dorsolaterally. Maximum adult size 30 cm TL (1 ft).

GEOGRAPHIC DISTRIBUTION   Found along the western Atlantic coast from Nova Scotia to Florida and in the Gulf of Mexico.

ECOLOGY   The butterfish occurs in Chesapeake Bay from March through November and is common to abundant in the lower bay and occasional in the upper bay, extending as far north as the Patapsco River. Within the bay, butterfish move northward in the spring, first appearing in Virginia waters in March but not found above the Rappahannock River before May. All leave the bay by December and overwinter offshore in deeper water (180–210 m, or 590–690 ft). The butterfish forms large schools in inshore and offshore waters, but typically at depths shallower than the harvestfish does. Butterfish are a pelagic species, typically found over sand bottoms. They spawn offshore from May to July in the Chesa-

whereas adults feed mainly on jellyfishes, small fishes, crustaceans, and worms.

FISHING INTEREST   Presently of minor commercial importance in Chesapeake Bay. In former years, bay catches were much larger. In 1920, Chesapeake Bay landings were more than 590,000 kg (1.3 million pounds), almost all from pound-net catches in Virginia waters. The 1989 and 1990 landings for the Virginia waters of the bay were 43,000 and 9,100 kg (94,000 and 20,000 lb), respectively. Catches exhibit two peaks of abundance, the first usually occurring in April–May and the second in September–October. Butterfish are of limited recreational interest because they rarely take a bait; however, they are occasionally taken in haul seines and fyke nets.

LITERATURE   Hildebrand and Schroeder 1928:213; Horn 1970; Musick 1972; Fischer 1978; Martin and Drewry 1978; Murawski et al. 1978; Fritzsche 1982; Manooch 1984.

Snake Mackerels
FAMILY TRICHIURIDAE

Voracious predators found in tropical to warm-temperate waters, snake mackerels typically inhabit deeper waters of the continental shelf and slope, but some species are common in shallow coastal areas. The body of trichiurids is ribbonlike and usually silvery. The mouth is large and contains fanglike teeth. Pelvic fins are much reduced or absent altogether. The family, found worldwide, comprises 9 genera and 34 species, 1 of which is recorded from Chesapeake Bay.

Atlantic cutlassfish
Trichiurus lepturus Linnaeus, 1758

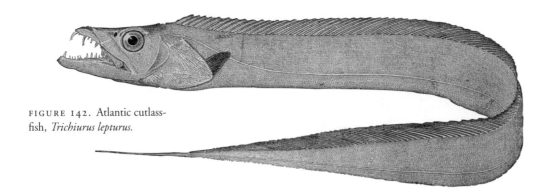

FIGURE 142. Atlantic cutlass-fish, *Trichiurus lepturus*.

KEY FEATURES   Body ribbonlike, extremely elongate, and strongly compressed, tapering to a point; caudal fin absent; pelvic fin absent; scales absent; single dorsal fin extending from head to near posterior tip of body.

OTHER CHARACTERISTICS   Head long and compressed; mouth large; teeth in jaws strong, of unequal size, and compressed; largest teeth with distinct barbs on posterior edges; lower jaw projecting and with dermal process at tip; eye large; dorsal fin extremely long; anal fin consisting of very short spines; pectoral fin small. Metallic blue in life; silvery gray in death. Maximum adult size 1.2 m SL (4 ft).

GEOGRAPHIC DISTRIBUTION   Found worldwide in tropical and temperate waters. In the western Atlantic, the Atlantic cutlassfish ranges from Cape Cod to northern Argentina, including the Caribbean Sea and the Gulf of Mexico.

ECOLOGY   The Atlantic cutlassfish is a common member of the Chesapeake Bay fish fauna from spring to autumn throughout mesohaline and polyhaline waters. It migrates offshore in au-

tumn. This species is both pelagic and bottom-living and may occur to depths of 500 m (1,640 ft) or more, but it is usually found in shallow coastal waters over muddy bottoms. Large adults typically feed near the surface during the day and spend the night near the bottom; the feeding pattern of juveniles and small adults is the opposite of that of large adults. Spawning is reported to occur offshore in the Gulf of Mexico, but little is known about spawning along the Atlantic coast. A ball (about 0.5 m, or 1.6 ft, in diameter) of intertwined Atlantic cutlassfish was observed by one of us (R.S.B.) drifting at the surface near the Chesapeake Bay mouth. This behavior may be associated with spawning. The pelagic larvae and early juveniles are carried by currents into shallow waters, sometimes into estuaries. About 40% of the fish mature at the end of their first year of life, and all are mature at 5 years. The Atlantic cutlassfish feeds on a wide range of fishes as well as on squids and shrimps.

FISHING INTEREST   Not a significant commercial or recreational resource. Cutlassfishes are eaten in some parts of their range and constitute an important fishery in East Asia. Atlantic cut-lassfish readily take a bait, and in Chesapeake Bay they are landed as bycatch in pound nets, bottom trawls, and beach seines.

LITERATURE Hildebrand and Schroeder 1928:208; Musick 1972; Fischer 1978; Fritzsche 1978; Benson 1982; Whitehead et al. 1986a; Nakamura and Parin 1993; Nelson 1994.

Sand Lances
FAMILY AMMODYTIDAE

Sand lances are schooling marine fishes that bury themselves in the bottom when threatened. They are found from the water's edge to depths as great as 150 m (490 ft). Sand lances feed on planktonic organisms and are preyed upon by many commercially important species. Members of the family are characterized by having a narrow, elongate body and a small head, with the lower jaw protruding beyond the upper jaw. The family, found in the Atlantic, Indian, and Pacific oceans, comprises 5 genera and approximately 18 species, 1 of which is recorded from Chesapeake Bay.

American sand lance
Ammodytes americanus DeKay, 1842

FIGURE 143. American sand lance, *Ammodytes americanus.*

KEY FEATURES Pelvic fin absent; body elongate; jaws without teeth; lateral plicae (oblique folds of skin on lateral surfaces) numbering 106–126.

OTHER CHARACTERISTICS Body very slender, slightly compressed; head long; snout sharply pointed; eye moderate-sized; mouth large; lower jaw projecting; scales small; lateral line straight; single dorsal fin low and spineless, originating perpendicular to pectoral fin tip and terminating near caudal fin base; anal fin similar in outline to dorsal fin, originating perpendicular to middle of dorsal fin and terminating near caudal fin base; caudal fin deeply forked; pectoral fin pointed. Olive, brown, or bluish green dorsally; side silvery; venter white. Maximum adult size 22 cm SL (9 in).

GEOGRAPHIC DISTRIBUTION Occurring coastally from Labrador to North Carolina.

ECOLOGY The American sand lance is a rare visitor to the lower Chesapeake Bay during the fall and winter. This species inhabits substrates conducive to burrowing, such as sand bottoms with crushed shells or fine-graveled bottoms. The American sand lance burrows into the substrate and settles into a resting position with its head protruding at an angle. It feeds primarily on copepods. Spawning occurs from November to May at depths of 9–21 m (30–69 ft).

FISHING INTEREST Of no commercial or recreational importance but of considerable value as a food source for other fishes.

LITERATURE Massmann 1960; Musick 1972; Fritzsche 1978; Meyer et al. 1979; Smith 1985; Nizinski et al. 1990; Pietsch and Zabetian 1990.

Jacks

FAMILY CARANGIDAE

Carangid fishes are strong-swimming, open-water predators on fishes and crustaceans. The species are diverse in body shape, but most are either short, deep, and greatly compressed or elongate fusiform and slightly compressed. Carangids are characterized by having two stout spines slightly removed from and preceding the anal fin (these spines are embedded and not externally visible in large adults of some species). Many species have adipose eyelids, and most have the posterior part (or all) of the lateral line covered by enlarged hardened scales (scutes). Jacks primarily inhabit coastal marine waters, but some, particularly the young, enter brackish estuarine waters. Worldwide, the carangids are among the most economically important food fishes and are also highly regarded by anglers. The family, found in all tropical and temperate waters, comprises approximately 32 genera and about 140 species. Nine genera and 17 species of carangids are known from Chesapeake Bay.

KEY TO THE SPECIES OF JACKS IN CHESAPEAKE BAY

1a. Body superficially naked, with scales minute and embedded **2**
1b. Body scales easily observed and present over most of body **4**

2a. Front of head rising gradually and forming smooth curve above eye; pelvic fin of adults longer than upper jaw .... **African pompano,** *Alectis ciliaris* (p. 160)
2b. Front of head slightly concave in profile, rising nearly vertically and then forming sharp angle above eye; pelvic fin of adults short, about one-fourth to one-third as long as upper jaw **3**

3a. Anterior rays of second dorsal fin and anal fin notably elongate; body depth contained 2.3–2.8 times in fork length; small juveniles with 4 or 5 faint interrupted bands on body ....
.... **lookdown,** *Selene vomer* (p. 161)
3b. Anterior rays of second dorsal fin and anal fin not notably elongate; body depth contained 1.8–2.3 times in fork length; small juveniles with black oval spot on side above straight part of lateral line...
.... **Atlantic moonfish,** *Selene setapinnis* (p. 162)

4a. Posterior part of lateral line consisting of enlarged scutes (except scutes small and restricted to caudal peduncle in Atlantic bumper, *Chloroscombrus chrysurus*); pectoral fin long, more than 90% of head length **5**
4b. Posterior part of lateral line without enlarged scutes; pectoral fin short, less than 90% of head length **11**

5a. Lower shoulder girdle margin bearing deep furrow with large papilla just above it (visible only when gill cover raised; Figure 144) .... **bigeye scad,** *Selar crumenophthalmus* (p. 163)
5b. Lower shoulder girdle margin without deep furrow and adjoining papilla **6**

FIGURE 144. Shoulder girdle of bigeye scad, showing cleithral furrow bearing large fleshy papillae.

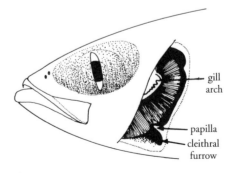

6a. Scutes covering entire length of lateral line to head (anterior scutes sometimes obscured by overgrowth of adjacent body scales) . . . . **rough scad,** *Trachurus lathami* (p. 164)

6b. Scutes present only on posterior portion of lateral line **7**

7a. Scutes very small and restricted to caudal peduncle; ventral profile more convex than dorsal profile; black blotch present on upper part of caudal peduncle . . . . **Atlantic bumper,** *Chloroscombrus chrysurus* (p. 164)

7b. Scutes prominent, extending well anterior to caudal peduncle; ventral profile not more convex than dorsal profile; black blotch absent on caudal peduncle **8**

8a. Anal fin with 16–18 rays; dorsal fin with 19–22 rays **9**

8b. Anal fin with 19–24 rays; dorsal fin with 22–28 rays **10**

9a. Dusky blotch present on lower rays of pectoral fin; chest naked except for small patch of scales anterior to pelvic fin . . . . **crevalle jack,** *Caranx hippos* (p. 165)

9b. Dusky blotch absent on lower rays of pectoral fin; chest completely covered by scales . . . . **horse-eye jack,** *Caranx latus* (p. 166)

10a. Gill rakers on lower limb of first arch numbering 25–28; dorsal fin with 22–25 rays; anal fin with 19–21 rays; upper jaw reaching dorsoventrally to middle of eye . . . . **blue runner,** *Caranx crysos* (p. 167)

10b. Gill rakers on lower limb of first arch numbering 18–21; dorsal fin with 25–28 rays; anal fin with 21–24 rays; upper jaw reaching dorsoventrally to anterior margin of eye . . . . **yellow jack,** *Caranx bartholomaei* (p. 168)

11a. Transverse groove present dorsally and ventrally on caudal peduncle just anterior to caudal fin; anal fin base decidedly shorter than base of second dorsal fin; body only slightly compressed **12**

11b. Transverse groove absent dorsally and ventrally on caudal peduncle just anterior to caudal fin; anal fin base equal to or only slightly shorter than base of second dorsal fin; body strongly compressed **15**

12a. First dorsal fin with 8 spines **13**

12b. First dorsal fin with 7 spines **14**

13a. Six dusky solid bars present on body of juveniles (less than 30 cm, or 1 ft, FL); third, fourth, and fifth dusky bars extending into soft fin membranes; tips of caudal fin white . . . . **banded rudderfish,** *Seriola zonata* (p. 169)

13b. Seven dusky irregular and broken bars present on body; third through seventh dusky bars extending into soft ray membranes of second dorsal fin and anal fin; eighth dusky bar small and situated at terminus of caudal peduncle; dusky rounded spot present on medial rays of caudal fin; caudal fin otherwise clear . . . . **lesser amberjack,** *Seriola fasciata* (p. 286)

14a. Longest ray in second dorsal fin contained about 7 times in fork length . . . . **greater amberjack,** *Seriola dumerili* (p. 170)

14b. Longest ray in second dorsal fin contained about 5 times in fork length . . . . **almaco jack,** *Seriola rivoliana* (p. 171)

15a. Snout pointed; body elongate, with greatest depth contained 3.4–3.9 times in standard length; posterior part of dorsal and anal fins with semidetached finlets; scales needlelike and partially embedded . . . . **leatherjack,** *Oligoplites saurus* (p. 172)

15b. Snout rounded; body short and deep, with greatest depth contained 1.3–2.6 times in standard length; posterior part of dorsal and anal fins without semidetached finlets; scales normal and oval-shaped . . **16**

16a. Dorsal fin with 22–27 rays; anal fin with 20–24 rays . . . . **Florida pompano,** *Trachinotus carolinus* (p. 172)

16b. Dorsal fin with 17–21 rays; anal fin with 16–19 rays **17**

17a. Body without vertical bars; longest dorsal fin rays not reaching posteriorly beyond caudal fin base . . . .
. . . . **permit, *Trachinotus falcatus*** (p. 174)
17b. Body usually with 4 narrow vertical bars that are black or silvery in life; longest dorsal fin rays reaching
posteriorly well beyond caudal fin base . . . . **palometa, *Trachinotus goodei*** (p. 175)

African pompano
Alectis ciliaris (Bloch, 1787)

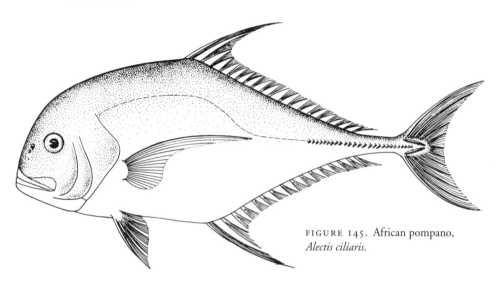

FIGURE 145. African pompano,
Alectis ciliaris.

KEY FEATURES   Spinous dorsal fin absent in fish longer than 15 cm SL (6 in); anterior rays of second dorsal fin and anal fin very long and filamentous in fish smaller than 40 cm SL (16 in) and sometimes in larger fish; posterior part of lateral line with scutes; pectoral fin falcate and longer than head; body deep; scales very small and difficult to see; pair of small lateral keels present on caudal peduncle; pelvic fin longer than upper jaw.

OTHER CHARACTERISTICS   Body compressed; snout bluntly pointed; mouth large; teeth in jaws in bands; eye moderately large and with adipose eyelid; first dorsal fin with 7 short spines that become reabsorbed and embedded with age; second dorsal fin high anteriorly and long; caudal peduncle narrow and extended; caudal fin broadly forked; anal fin similar and perpendicular to second dorsal fin; anal fin spines becoming reabsorbed and embedded with age. Body silvery blue to blue green dorsally, darkest on top of head and upper shoulder; rest of body and head silvery. Maximum adult size 90 cm FL (3 ft).

GEOGRAPHIC DISTRIBUTION   Found worldwide in tropical marine waters. In the western Atlantic, the African pompano is known from Massachusetts to Brazil, including throughout the Gulf of Mexico and the Caribbean Sea.

ECOLOGY   The African pompano is an occasional visitor to the lower Chesapeake Bay during summer and autumn but is rarely encountered in the upper bay, extending as far north as Calvert and Dorchester counties, Maryland. African pompano are strong-swimming and mostly solitary and are frequently found near the bottom, as deep as 60 m (200 ft). Juveniles and the smaller adults of this species are among the most spectacular of jacks, possessing long, delicate, trailing filamentous dorsal and anal fin rays. Juveniles are usually pelagic and drifting; their streaming fin rays may help them resemble jellyfishes and thus afford them a measure of protection from predation. The diet of African pompano consists of slow-swimming or sedentary crustaceans; small crabs and fishes are also occasionally eaten.

FISHING INTEREST   Considered a strong game fish on rod and reel. The world angling record is a fish caught in Florida that weighed 20.6 kg (45.5 lb). The African pompano is of no commercial importance in the Chesapeake Bay area but is esteemed as a food fish in regions where it is more abundant. The juveniles are sometimes taken in beach seines in the lower bay.

LITERATURE   Hildebrand and Schroeder 1928:224; McClane 1965; Musick 1972; Fischer 1978; Johnson 1978.

Lookdown
Selene vomer (Linnaeus, 1758)

FIGURE 146. Lookdown, *Selene vomer.*

KEY FEATURES   Front of head slightly concave in profile, rising nearly vertically and then forming sharp angle above eye; body short, deep, and extremely compressed; body depth contained 2.3–2.8 times in fork length; scutes very small and present only on posterior part of lateral line; body scaled except in area anterior to second dorsal fin to below curved portion of lateral line; scales very small and difficult to see; pelvic fin short, much shorter than upper jaw; anteriormost ray of second dorsal fin and of anal fin notably elongate.

OTHER CHARACTERISTICS   Head very deep; snout bluntly pointed; mouth large; teeth in jaws in narrow irregular bands; eye moderately small and without adipose eyelid; first dorsal fin with 8 spines, the second and third spines very long and filamentous in juveniles; caudal peduncle narrow; caudal fin broadly forked; anal fin similar and perpendicular to second dorsal fin; detached spines of anal fin embedded and not apparent in fish larger than about 13 cm FL (5 in); pectoral fin falcate and longer than head. Body and head silvery and golden; upper body sometimes with metallic blue sheen. Maximum adult size 40 cm FL (1.3 ft).

GEOGRAPHIC DISTRIBUTION   Known from Maine to Uruguay, including coastal areas of the Gulf of Mexico and the Caribbean Sea. The lookdown is more common south of Chesapeake Bay.

ECOLOGY   The lookdown is a common visitor to the lower Chesapeake Bay during the summer and autumn and is occasionally encountered in the upper bay, extending as far north as Calvert and Talbot counties, Maryland. This species frequents hard or sandy bottoms around pilings and bridges in shallow coastal waters, usually in small schools near the bottom. The lookdown feeds on small crustaceans, worms, and fishes.

FISHING INTEREST   Landed as commercial bycatch in trawls, seines, and pound nets. The lookdown is of minimal recreational importance.

LITERATURE   Hildebrand and Schroeder 1928:225; Musick 1972; Fischer 1978; Johnson 1978.

Atlantic moonfish
Selene setapinnis (Mitchill, 1815)

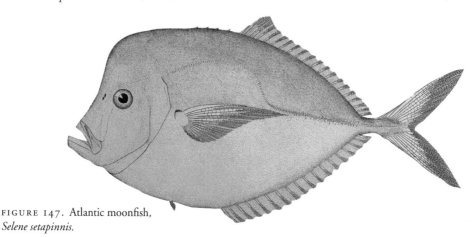

FIGURE 147. Atlantic moonfish, *Selene setapinnis.*

KEY FEATURES   Front of head slightly concave in profile, rising nearly vertically and then forming sharp angle above eye; body short, deep, and extremely compressed; body depth contained 1.8–2.3 times in fork length; scutes very small and present only on posterior part of lateral line; most of lower body scaled; scales very small and difficult to see; pelvic fin much shorter than upper jaw; anterior rays of second dorsal fin only slightly elongate.

OTHER CHARACTERISTICS   Snout bluntly pointed; mouth large; teeth in jaws in narrow irregular bands; first dorsal fin with 8 short spines; eye moderately small and with adipose eyelid developed posteriorly; caudal peduncle narrow and extended, with pair of small lateral keels; anterior

dorsal fin spines long but not filamentous in juveniles smaller than 5 cm TL (2 in); caudal fin broadly forked; anal fin similar and perpendicular to second dorsal fin; detached spines of anal fin embedded and not apparent in fish larger than about 13 cm FL (5 in); pectoral fin falcate and longer than head. Body and head silvery; upper body sometimes with metallic blue green sheen. Maximum adult size 33 cm FL (1.1 ft).

GEOGRAPHIC DISTRIBUTION   Known from Nova Scotia to Argentina, including coastal areas of the Gulf of Mexico and the Caribbean Sea. The Atlantic moonfish is not common north of Chesapeake Bay.

ECOLOGY   The Atlantic moonfish is a regular visitor to the lower Chesapeake Bay during summer and autumn but is rarely encountered in the upper bay, extending as far north as Calvert County, Maryland. It is schooling fish, usually found near the bottom in inshore waters, but it may occur to depths greater than 50 m (165 ft). Juveniles are frequently found in bays and river mouths. Atlantic moonfish feed on small crustaceans and fishes.

FISHING INTEREST   Said to be tasty, though providing little flesh. Where abundant, this species is fished commercially with trawls, seines, and pound nets. The Atlantic moonfish is of little recreational importance.

LITERATURE   Hildebrand and Schroeder 1928:226; Musick 1972; Fischer 1978; Johnson 1978; Smith 1985.

Bigeye scad
Selar crumenophthalmus (Bloch, 1793)

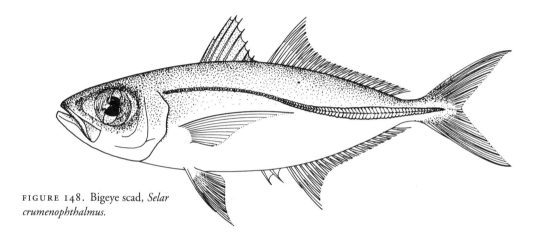

FIGURE 148. Bigeye scad, *Selar crumenophthalmus.*

KEY FEATURES   Lower shoulder girdle margin bearing deep furrow with large papilla just above it (visible only when gill cover raised); scutes present only on posterior part of lateral line; body elongate; pectoral fin falcate and about 95% of head length; eye large, with well-developed adipose eyelid.

OTHER CHARACTERISTICS   Body moderately compressed; mouth large; teeth small and recurved; upper jaw with narrow band of teeth; lower jaw with single irregular row of teeth; dorsal fins slightly separated; first dorsal fin with 8 spines; second dorsal fin high anteriorly and long; caudal peduncle narrow; caudal fin forked; anal fin similar and perpendicular to second dorsal fin. Dorsal surface of body and head metallic blue or bluish green; rest of body and head silvery or whitish; small elongate blackish spot present near upper margin of gill cover. Maximum adult size 27 cm SL (11 in).

GEOGRAPHIC DISTRIBUTION   Found worldwide in tropical and subtropical marine wa-

ters. In the western Atlantic, the bigeye scad is known from Nova Scotia to Brazil, including throughout the Gulf of Mexico and the Caribbean Sea.

ECOLOGY   Bigeye scad are occasional to common visitors to the lower Chesapeake Bay during summer and autumn but are rarely encountered in the upper bay, extending as far north as Calvert County, Maryland. They are found in small or large schools, mainly inshore, but they are known from all depths to about 170 m (560 ft). Bigeye scad feed on small shrimps and benthic invertebrates when inshore and on zooplankton and fish larvae when offshore.

FISHING INTEREST   Of no commercial or recreational importance. Bigeye scad are taken mainly as bycatch with trawls and seines and also occasionally by hook and line.

LITERATURE   Hildebrand and Schroeder 1928:217; Musick 1972; Fischer 1978; Johnson 1978.

Rough scad
Trachurus lathami Nichols, 1920

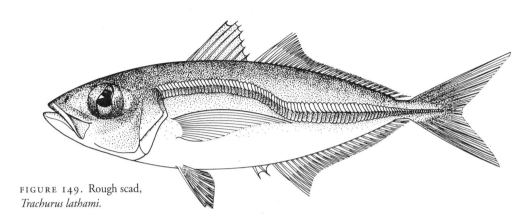

FIGURE 149. Rough scad,
Trachurus lathami.

KEY FEATURES   Enlarged scutes covering entire lateral line to head (anterior scutes sometimes obscured by overgrowth of adjacent body scales); body elongate; pectoral fin falcate and about 95% of head length; eye large, with well-developed adipose eyelid.

OTHER CHARACTERISTICS   Body slightly compressed; mouth large; teeth small and in single row in both jaws; dorsal fins slightly separated; first dorsal fin with 8 spines; second dorsal fin high anteriorly and long-based; caudal peduncle narrow; caudal fin forked; anal fin similar and perpendicular to second dorsal fin; pelvic fin small. Dorsal surface dusky, bluish, or bluish green; rest of body and head silvery to whitish; small oval blackish spot present on upper edge of gill flap. Maximum adult size 33 cm SL (1.1 ft).

GEOGRAPHIC DISTRIBUTION   Known from the Gulf of Maine to northern Argentina, including coastal areas of the Gulf of Mexico and the Caribbean Sea.

ECOLOGY   The rough scad is an occasional summer visitor to the lower Chesapeake Bay and is rare to occasional in the upper bay. This schooling species occurs from surface waters to depths of about 90 m (295 ft). Rough scad are believed to spawn offshore from April to June. Juveniles have been taken offshore associated with jellyfishes. Rough scad feed on small invertebrates.

FISHING INTEREST   Of no commercial or recreational importance. Rough scad are caught mainly as bycatch in trawls.

LITERATURE   Massmann 1960; Musick 1972; Fischer 1978; Johnson 1978.

Atlantic bumper
Chloroscombrus chrysurus (Linnaeus, 1766)

KEY FEATURES   Scutes very small and restricted to caudal peduncle; prominent black blotch present on upper part of caudal peduncle; body deep; ventral profile more convex than dorsal profile; entire body with scales; lateral keels absent on caudal peduncle; upper lobe of caudal fin typically longer than lower lobe.

OTHER CHARACTERISTICS   Body ovate and extremely compressed; snout short and pointed; mouth small; teeth in jaws in narrow bands; eye small, with slight adipose eyelid; dorsal fins only slightly separated; first dorsal fin

with 8 spines; second dorsal fin raised anteriorly and long; caudal peduncle narrow and extended; caudal fin broadly forked; anal fin similar and perpendicular to second dorsal fin; first 2 anal fin spines removed from third; pectoral fin falcate and longer than head. Body and head dusky dorsally, sometimes with metallic blue sheen; side and venter silvery; fins yellowish in life. Maximum adult size 26 cm FL (10 in).

GEOGRAPHIC DISTRIBUTION   Occurring on both sides of the Atlantic. In the western Atlantic, the Atlantic bumper is known from Massachusetts to Uruguay, including coastal areas of the Gulf of Mexico and the Caribbean Sea. A closely related species *(Chloroscombrus orqueta)* occurs in the eastern Pacific Ocean.

ECOLOGY   The Atlantic bumper is an uncommon visitor to the lower Chesapeake Bay during autumn. This species typically occurs in schools

spring and summer along the southeastern U.S. coast. Juveniles are often found offshore, occasionally in association with jellyfish.

FISHING INTEREST   Landed commercially as bycatch in trawls and seines. The Atlantic bumper is of no recreational importance but is occasionally caught on hook and line.

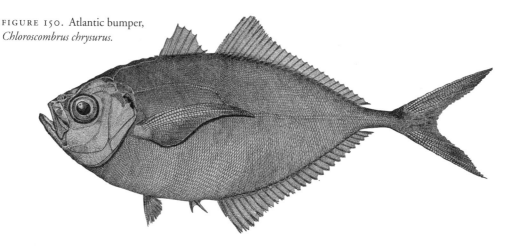

FIGURE 150. Atlantic bumper, *Chloroscombrus chrysurus.*

in shallow coastal waters but is also found offshore to depths of 90 m (295 ft). Atlantic bumpers often emit a grunting sound when out of the water. The probable spawning period is during

LITERATURE   Hildebrand and Schroeder 1928:220; Musick 1972; Fischer 1978; Johnson 1978; Tolley 1987.

Crevalle jack
Caranx hippos (Linnaeus, 1766)
PLATE 23

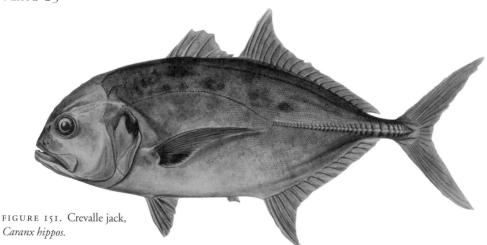

FIGURE 151. Crevalle jack, *Caranx hippos.*

KEY FEATURES   Dusky oval blotch present on lower pectoral fin rays; 23–35 prominent scutes present on posterior part of lateral line;

body deep; chest naked except for small patch of scales anterior to pelvic fin; paired lateral keels present on caudal peduncle; caudal fin lobes equally elongate; anal fin with 16 or 17 rays; dorsal fin with 19–21 rays.

OTHER CHARACTERISTICS   Body robust and compressed; head short and deep; snout bluntly pointed; mouth large; teeth in upper jaw in 2 rows; teeth in lower jaw in single row; eye large, with adipose eyelid; lateral line with strong anterior arch; first dorsal fin with 8 spines; second dorsal fin elongate anteriorly and long; caudal peduncle narrow and extended; caudal fin broadly forked; anal fin similar and perpendicular to second dorsal fin; first 2 anal fin spines removed from third; pectoral fin falcate and longer than head. Blue to bluish or bluish black dorsally; silvery white or golden on side and venter; marginal black spot present on opercle; juveniles with 5 dusky bars on body. Maximum adult size 1.0 m TL (3.3 ft).

GEOGRAPHIC DISTRIBUTION   Occurring throughout the Atlantic Ocean. In the western Atlantic, the crevalle jack is known from Nova Scotia to Uruguay, including the Gulf of Mexico and the Caribbean Sea. A closely related species (Caranx caninus) occurs in the eastern Pacific Ocean.

ECOLOGY   The crevalle jack occurs occasionally to commonly in the lower Chesapeake Bay during summer and autumn, extending as far north as Yorktown, Virginia. This species typically travels in fast-moving, moderate-sized to large schools and often enters brackish water and ascends rivers. Larger fish are usually solitary and are most often found offshore. Spawning apparently occurs offshore from March through September. Little is known of the spawning and early life history of this species, and the majority of the spawning for crevalle jacks in the western Atlantic may take place south of U.S. waters. However, young of the year of this species are fairly abundant in estuaries of the Mid-Atlantic Bight, indicating that these estuaries are used as nurseries. Like most large jacks, this species feeds primarily on fishes and a variety of invertebrates.

FISHING INTEREST   Along with other members of the genus Caranx, generally held in low esteem as a food fish in the United States, although of considerable commercial importance worldwide. The crevalle jack is landed primarily with purse seines, gill nets, and handlines and in the Chesapeake Bay area by pound nets. Anglers consider the crevalle jack a good sport fish that will put up an energetic fight when taken with light tackle. The world angling record is a fish weighing 26.0 kg (57.3 lb) that was caught off the coast of Angola in 1992.

LITERATURE   Hildebrand and Schroeder 1928:221; Berry 1959; McClane 1965; Musick 1972; Fischer 1978; Johnson 1978; Fahay 1983; Whitehead et al. 1986a.

Horse-eye jack
Caranx latus Agassiz, 1831

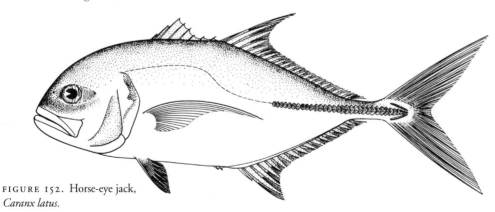

FIGURE 152. Horse-eye jack, *Caranx latus.*

KEY FEATURES   Entire body with scales; pectoral fin without dusky blotch; anal fin with 16–18 rays; dorsal fin with 19–22 rays; 32–39 prominent scutes present on posterior part of lateral line; body deep; paired lateral keels present on caudal peduncle; caudal fin lobes equally elongate.

OTHER CHARACTERISTICS   Body elongate and moderately compressed; snout bluntly pointed; mouth large; teeth in upper jaw in 2 rows; teeth in lower jaw in single row; eye large, with adipose eyelid; lateral line with strong anterior arch; first dorsal fin with 8 spines; second dorsal fin elongate anteriorly and long-based; caudal peduncle narrow and extended; caudal fin broadly forked; anal fin similar and perpendicular to second dorsal fin; first 2 anal fin spines removed from third; pectoral fin falcate and longer than head. Dusky blue to bluish gray dorsally; silvery white or golden on side and venter; juveniles with 5 dusky bars on body. Maximum adult size 80 cm TL (2.6 ft).

GEOGRAPHIC DISTRIBUTION   Known from throughout the Atlantic Ocean but not abundant on the Atlantic coast of the United States. In the western Atlantic, the horse-eye jack is known from New Jersey to Brazil, including the Gulf of Mexico and the Caribbean Sea.

ECOLOGY   The horse-eye jack is a rare visitor to the lower Chesapeake Bay during summer and autumn. What is known of the ecology of this species differs little from that of the crevalle jack. Spawning apparently occurs offshore and south of the bay from March to July.

FISHING INTEREST   See under discussion for the crevalle jack, page 166. The world angling record for horse-eye jack is a fish weighing 10.9 kg (24.0 lb) that was caught off Florida in 1987.

LITERATURE   Hildebrand and Schroeder 1928:223; Berry 1959; McClane 1965; Musick 1972; Fischer 1978; Johnson 1978; Fahay 1983; Whitehead et al. 1986a.

Blue runner
Caranx crysos (Mitchill, 1815)

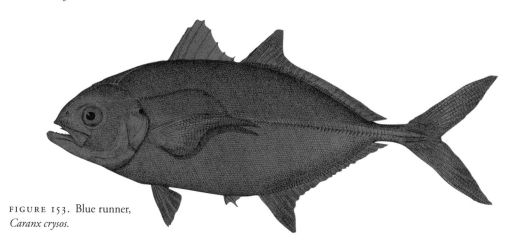

FIGURE 153. Blue runner, *Caranx crysos.*

KEY FEATURES   Anal fin with 19–21 rays; dorsal fin with 22–25 rays; gill rakers on lower limb of first arch numbering 23–28; upper jaw reaching dorsoventrally to middle of eye; 46–56 prominent scutes on posterior part of lateral line; body moderately deep; entire body with scales; paired lateral keels on caudal peduncle; caudal fin lobes equally elongate.

OTHER CHARACTERISTICS   Body elongate and moderately compressed; snout slightly pointed; mouth large; teeth in upper jaw in 2 rows; teeth in lower jaw in single row; eye moderate-sized, with adipose eyelid; first dorsal fin with 8 spines; second dorsal fin high anteriorly and long-based; caudal peduncle narrow and extended; caudal fin broadly forked; anal fin similar and perpendicular to second dorsal fin; first 2 anal fin spines removed from third; pectoral fin falcate and longer than head. Pale olive to bluish gray dorsally; silvery gray or golden on side and venter; juveniles with 7 dusky bars on body. Maximum adult size 70 cm TL (2.3 ft).

GEOGRAPHIC DISTRIBUTION   Occurring throughout the Atlantic. In the western Atlantic, the blue runner is known from Nova Scotia to southern Brazil, including the Gulf of Mexico and the Caribbean Sea. A closely related, if not the same, species *(Caranx caballus)* occurs in the eastern Pacific Ocean.

ECOLOGY   The blue runner is an occasional to common visitor to the lower Chesapeake Bay during summer and autumn and is sometimes encountered in the upper bay. It is one of the most common jacks in the western Atlantic and is found most often inshore and usually in large schools. Spawning occurs offshore and to the south of the bay from January through August, with a peak in summer. The young have been collected offshore associated with jellyfish. The blue runner feeds on fishes, crabs, and shrimps.

FISHING INTEREST   Of considerable commercial importance in regions where more abundant than in the Chesapeake Bay. In Florida the blue runner is an important commercial species and is landed primarily by haul seines and gill nets. Many blue runners are caught by anglers, and the flesh is considered of good flavor, especially if the fish is bled immediately upon landing.

LITERATURE   Hildebrand and Schroeder 1928:222; Berry 1959; McClane 1965; Musick 1972; Fischer 1978; Johnson 1978; Fahay 1983; Whitehead et al. 1986a.

Yellow jack
Caranx bartholomaei Cuvier, 1833

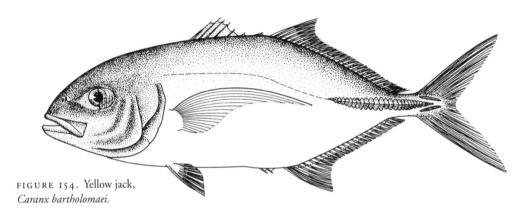

FIGURE 154. Yellow jack, *Caranx bartholomaei.*

KEY FEATURES   Anal fin with 21–24 rays; dorsal fin with 25–28 rays; gill rakers on lower limb of first arch numbering 16–21; 22–28 prominent scutes present on posterior part of lateral line; upper jaw reaching dorsoventrally to anterior margin of eye; body moderately deep; entire body with scales; paired lateral keels present on caudal peduncle; caudal fin lobes equally elongate.

OTHER CHARACTERISTICS   Body compressed and somewhat elongate; snout moderately pointed; mouth large; teeth in upper jaw in 2 rows; teeth in lower jaw in single row; eye moderately large, with adipose eyelid; first dorsal fin with 8 spines; second dorsal fin moderately high anteriorly and long-based; caudal peduncle narrow and extended; caudal fin broadly forked;

anal fin similar and perpendicular to second dorsal fin; first 2 anal fin spines removed from third; pectoral fin falcate and longer than head. Pale greenish blue dorsally; silvery gray on side and venter; juveniles with 5 dusky bars on body. Maximum adult size 1 m TL (3.3 ft).

GEOGRAPHIC DISTRIBUTION   Known from Massachusetts to Brazil, including the Gulf of Mexico and the Caribbean Sea.

ECOLOGY   The yellow jack is a very rare summer visitor to the lower Chesapeake Bay, recorded from Kiptopeke, Virginia. Yellow jacks are most common offshore, where they are solitary or in small schools. Spawning occurs offshore and south of U.S. waters from February to October. The young are found offshore in association with floating sargassum and jellyfishes. The yellow jack feeds primarily on fishes near the bottom.

FISHING INTEREST   Of no commercial importance in U.S. waters, but of some commercial value in the Caribbean. The yellow jack is landed primarily with haul seines and trawls. Anglers land yellow jacks when trolling or bottom-fishing.

LITERATURE   Berry 1959; McClane 1965; Musick 1972; Fischer 1978; Johnson 1978.

Banded rudderfish
Seriola zonata (Mitchill, 1815)
PLATE 24

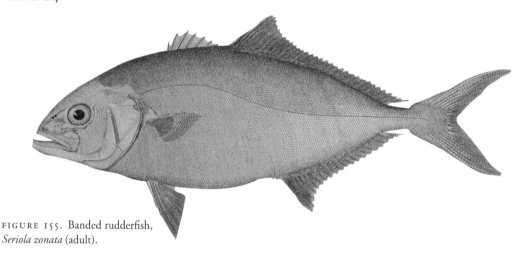

FIGURE 155. Banded rudderfish, *Seriola zonata* (adult).

KEY FEATURES   Lateral line without scutes; transverse groove present dorsally and ventrally on caudal peduncle just anterior to caudal fin; first dorsal fin with 8 spines, with last spine becoming reduced and covered with skin in fish larger than about 55 cm FL (22 in); second dorsal fin with 1 spine and 33–40 rays; anal fin much shorter than second dorsal fin, its base contained about 1.6–2.1 times in base of second dorsal fin; longest ray in second dorsal fin contained about 7 times in fork length; pectoral fin shorter than head.

OTHER CHARACTERISTICS   Body elongate, moderately deep, and slightly compressed; mouth large; teeth small and in single row in both jaws; eye small; caudal peduncle narrow and extended; caudal fin broadly forked; anal fin with 19–21 soft rays (about half as many as second dorsal fin); first 2 anal fin spines removed from third but may be skin-covered or recessed in large adults; pelvic fin larger than pectoral fin. Bluish gray dorsally; silvery white on side and venter; dusky stripe from eye to dorsal fin origin sometimes present; juveniles (to about 30 cm, or 1 ft, FL) with 6 dusky bars on body. Maximum adult size 69 cm FL (2.3 ft).

GEOGRAPHIC DISTRIBUTION   Known from Maine to Brazil, including coastal areas of the Gulf of Mexico and the Caribbean Sea.

ECOLOGY   The banded rudderfish is most common in coastal waters over the continental shelf but is an occasional visitor to the lower Chesapeake Bay during the summer. Adults are free-swimming, often near the bottom. Juveniles migrate northward along the U.S. Atlantic seaboard during the summer and are frequently found under or around jellyfishes, drifting seaweeds, or larger fishes. Spawning occurs year-round (with a possible summer hiatus) in offshore waters south of Cape Hatteras. Banded rudderfish feed on fishes and shrimps.

FISHING INTEREST   Caught incidentally by commercial fisheries and anglers. There is no directed fishery anywhere in the range of this species. Banded rudderfish are taken in traps, in pound nets, and with rod and reel by trolling or bottom-fishing.

LITERATURE   McClane 1965; Musick 1972; Fischer 1978; Johnson 1978; Fahay 1983.

Greater amberjack
Seriola dumerili (Risso, 1810)

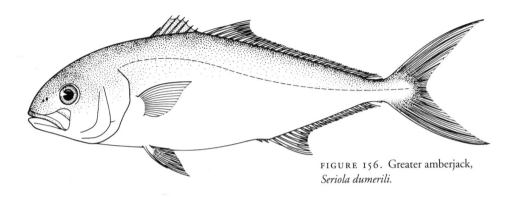

FIGURE 156. Greater amberjack,
Seriola dumerili.

KEY FEATURES   Lateral line without scutes; transverse groove present dorsally and ventrally on caudal peduncle just anterior to caudal fin; first dorsal fin with 7 spines, with last spine becoming reduced and skin-covered in fish larger than about 55 cm FL (1.8 ft); anal fin considerably shorter than second dorsal fin; anal fin base contained about 1.4–1.7 times in base of second dorsal fin; longest ray in second dorsal fin contained about 7 times in fork length; pectoral fin shorter than head.

OTHER CHARACTERISTICS   Body elongate and slightly compressed; mouth large; teeth minute and in single band in both jaws; eye small; second dorsal fin with 29–35 soft rays; anal fin with 18–22 soft rays; first 2 anal fin spines removed from third but sometimes skin-covered or recessed in large adults; pelvic fin slightly longer than pectoral fin; caudal fin broadly forked. Blue or olivaceous dorsally; silvery white laterally and ventrally; head characterized by dusky stripe originating at upper jaw and extending through eye to first dorsal fin; longitudinal amber stripe extending from eye to tail frequently present; juveniles with 6 dusky bars on body. Maximum adult size 1.5 m FL (5 ft).

GEOGRAPHIC DISTRIBUTION   Found worldwide in tropical and temperate seas, except the eastern Pacific. The western Atlantic distribution is from Nova Scotia to Brazil, including the entire Gulf of Mexico and the Caribbean Sea.

ECOLOGY   During summer, the greater amberjack is an occasional visitor to the lower Chesapeake Bay, where it concentrates around reefs, rock outcrops, and wrecks. Greater amberjacks utilize the entire water column, with juvenile fish often found in waters less than 10 m (33 ft) deep. Adult fish frequent waters of greater depths, sometimes exceeding 100 m (330 ft). Greater amberjacks spawn offshore from March through July, with a peak in May or June. The prey comprises fishes, crabs, and squids.

FISHING INTEREST   Important as a sport species along the Atlantic and Gulf coasts. Although greater amberjacks are occasionally taken by commercial fisheries using longlines, pound nets, gill nets, and trawls, most are caught by anglers. Greater amberjacks are considered an excellent fighting fish and will take live, dead, or artificial bait fished on the bottom or trolled. The world angling record is a fish weighing 70.7 kg (155.8 lb) that was caught off Bermuda in 1981. The flesh of the greater amberjack is slightly oily but has a mild and excellent flavor. In large fish the more posterior muscles, especially the muscle of the caudal peduncle, is often infested with long, thin parasitic worms. Although this parasite is not transmittable to humans, most people will want to discard the infested portion of the fish. An alternative is to remove the worms individually from the fish; they usually pull free from the raw flesh rather easily.

LITERATURE   Hildebrand and Schroeder 1928:218; McClane 1965; Musick 1972; Fischer 1978; Johnson 1978; Manooch 1984; Whitehead et al. 1986a.

Almaco jack
Seriola rivoliana Valenciennes, 1833

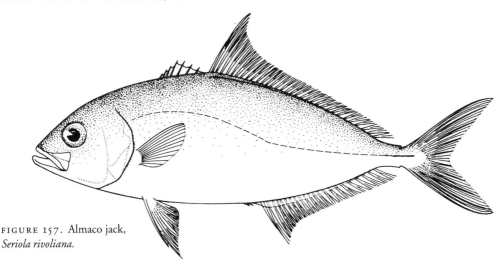

FIGURE 157. Almaco jack,
Seriola rivoliana.

KEY FEATURES   Longest ray in second dorsal fin contained about 5 times in fork length; lateral line without scutes; transverse groove present dorsally and ventrally on caudal peduncle just anterior to caudal fin; first dorsal fin with 7 spines and with last spine becoming reduced and skin-covered in fish larger than about 55 cm FL (1.8 ft); anal fin considerably shorter than dorsal fin; anal fin base contained about 1.5–1.6 times in base of second dorsal fin; pectoral fin shorter than head.

OTHER CHARACTERISTICS   Body elongate, moderately deep, and slightly compressed; mouth large; teeth minute and in single band in both jaws; eye moderately small; second dorsal fin with 27–33 soft rays; anal fin with 18–22 soft rays; first 2 anal fin spines removed from third but sometimes skin-covered or recessed in large adults; pelvic fin longer than pectoral fin; caudal fin forked. Head and body uniformly dusky brown or bluish green; pale brass or lavender laterally and ventrally; faint amber stripe extending from eye toward dorsal fin origin frequently present; juveniles with 5 irregular bars on body. Maximum adult size 97 cm FL (3.2 ft).

GEOGRAPHIC DISTRIBUTION   Circumtropical in marine waters, entering temperate waters in some areas. In the western Atlantic, the almaco jack is found from Cape Cod to Argentina, including the Gulf of Mexico and the Caribbean Sea.

ECOLOGY   The almaco jack typically frequents offshore waters and is a rare to occasional visitor during summer and autumn in the lower Chesapeake Bay. It is usually found around wrecks, buoys, and reefs. Adults occur throughout the water column. Little is known of the ecology of this species, but spawning is believed to occur offshore in spring through fall. The pelagic juveniles are found offshore under floating sargassum and debris. The almaco jack feeds mainly on fishes.

FISHING INTEREST   Occasionally taken by commercial fisheries but not the target of a directed commercial fishery. Most catches are by anglers, who consider the almaco jack to be an excellent fighting fish. This species will take live, dead, or artificial bait fished on the bottom or trolled.

LITERATURE   McClane 1965; Musick 1972; Fischer 1978; Manooch 1984; Whitehead et al. 1986a.

Leatherjack
Oligoplites saurus (Schneider, 1801)

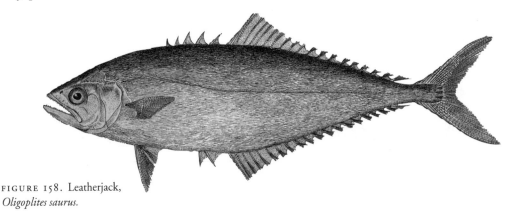

FIGURE 158. Leatherjack,
Oligoplites saurus.

KEY FEATURES   Posterior 11–15 rays of dorsal and anal fins forming semidetached finlets; scales needlelike and partially embedded; snout pointed; body compressed and elongate; greatest body depth contained 3.4–3.9 times in standard length; lateral line without scutes; pectoral fin shorter than head; transverse grooves absent on caudal peduncle.

OTHER CHARACTERISTICS   Mouth large; teeth small and in 2 rows in both jaws; eye small; first dorsal fin with 4–6 spines (typically 5); second dorsal fin high anteriorly, long-based, and with 19–21 soft rays; anal fin with 19–22 soft rays; first 2 anal fin spines removed from third; pelvic fin about equal in size to pectoral fin; caudal fin broadly forked. Bluish dorsally; silvery white laterally and ventrally; sometimes 7 or 8 irregular, broken silvery bars and white interspaces present along middle of side. Maximum adult size 30 cm FL (1 ft).

GEOGRAPHIC DISTRIBUTION   Found from Massachusetts to Brazil, including coastal areas of the entire Gulf of Mexico and Caribbean Sea. A closely related subspecies *(O. s. inornatus)* occurs in the eastern Pacific.

ECOLOGY   The leatherjack is a rare visitor to the lower Chesapeake Bay during summer and autumn. This schooling, fast-moving fish frequents inshore habitats, usually along sandy beaches and in bays and inlets. It tolerates low salinities and is found more often in turbid water than in clear water. Spawning occurs in shallow inshore waters from early spring to midsummer. Juveniles have been observed floating at the surface with tail bent and head down, suggesting a floating leaf. Leatherjacks feed on fishes and crustaceans.

FISHING INTEREST   Taken by commercial fisheries as bycatch in gill nets, seines, and trawls but reported to be of poor eating quality and not selectively fished. The leatherjack is considered an excellent fighting fish on ultralight tackle. The two detached anal fin spines of the leatherjack are purportedly connected to toxic glands, and in Florida this fish has been called the stinging jack.

LITERATURE   Hildebrand and Schroeder 1928:219; McClane 1965; Musick 1972; Smith-Vaniz and Staiger 1973; Fischer 1978; Johnson 1978.

Florida pompano
Trachinotus carolinus (Linnaeus, 1766)
PLATE 25

KEY FEATURES   Snout rounded; body short, compressed, and deep; greatest body depth contained 2–2.5 times in standard length; posterior part of dorsal and anal fins without semidetached finlets; lateral line without scutes; pectoral fin shorter than head; transverse groove absent on caudal peduncle; scales small, oval-shaped, and partially embedded; dorsal fin typically with 24 or 25 rays; anal fin typically with 21 or 22 rays. OTHER CHARACTERISTICS   Teeth small and reabsorbed by the time fish reach 20 cm FL (7.9 in); eye small; first dorsal fin with 6 spines; schools migrate north in summer along the U.S. Atlantic seaboard and are most abundant in the bay in July and August. Florida pompano are usually found in shallow waters along sandy beaches, around inlets, and in brackish-water bays, often moving with the tide. Spawning apparently oc-

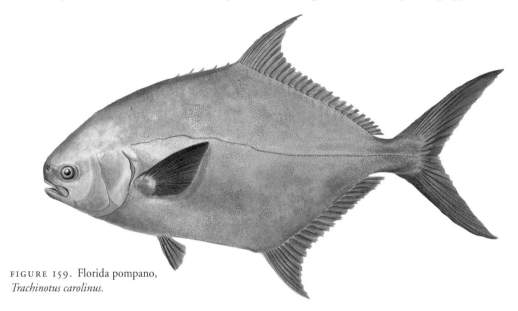

FIGURE 159. Florida pompano, *Trachinotus carolinus.*

second dorsal fin high anteriorly, with 22–27 soft rays, and with longest rays not reaching caudal fin base when appressed; anal fin base shorter than base of second dorsal fin base; anal fin with 20–24 soft rays; first 2 anal fin spines removed from third; caudal fin broadly forked; pelvic fin considerably smaller than pectoral fin. Body and head metallic green to bluish green dorsally; whitish ventrally. Maximum adult size at least 60 cm FL (2 ft), rarely reaching more than 40 cm FL (1.3 ft).
GEOGRAPHIC DISTRIBUTION   Found from Massachusetts to Brazil, including coastal areas of the entire Gulf of Mexico and Caribbean Sea. A closely related species *(Trachinotus rhodopus)* occurs in the eastern Pacific.
ECOLOGY   The Florida pompano is a common visitor to the lower and middle Chesapeake Bay during summer and autumn, extending as far north as Solomons Island. Small to large curs offshore in late spring to summer. After moving inshore, the juveniles are most abundant along low-energy beaches. Florida pompano feed on clams, shrimps, crabs, and mussels.
FISHING INTEREST   Renowned as a gourmet food item and commanding a high price per pound but of minor commercial importance in the Chesapeake Bay region. The commercial fishery, primarily employing gill nets and trammel nets, is centered along the lower west coast of Florida. This species is also held in high regard as a game fish by anglers for its fast strikes and runs. Florida pompano are caught from the surf, off piers, and in boats on shallow flats by using jigs baited with crabs or mole crabs.
LITERATURE   Hildebrand and Schroeder 1928:229; McClane 1965; Berry and Iverson 1966; Musick 1972; Fischer 1978; Johnson 1978; Manooch 1984.

Permit
Trachinotus falcatus (Linnaeus, 1758)

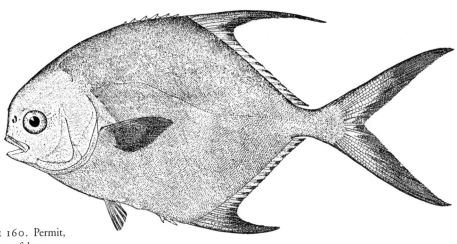

FIGURE 160. Permit,
Trachinotus falcatus.

KEY FEATURES   Snout rounded; body short and deep, with greatest depth contained 1.3–2.3 times in standard length; longest rays of dorsal and anal fins not reaching base of caudal fin; posterior part of dorsal and anal fins without semidetached finlets; scales small, oval-shaped, and partially embedded; lateral line without scutes; pectoral fin shorter than head; transverse groove absent on caudal peduncle; dorsal fin typically with 18–20 rays; anal fin typically with 17–18 rays; narrow bars absent on body.

OTHER CHARACTERISTICS   Teeth small and reabsorbed by the time fish reach 20 cm FL (7.9 in); eye small; first dorsal fin with 6 spines; anal fin base about equal in length to base of second dorsal fin; first 2 spines of anal fin removed from third; caudal fin broadly forked; pelvic fin smaller than pectoral fin. Head and body bluish gray to blue green dorsally; silvery ventrally; dusky ovoid spot present near pectoral fin in some individuals. Maximum adult size 1.1 m FL (3.5 ft).

GEOGRAPHIC DISTRIBUTION   Found from Massachusetts to Brazil, including coastal areas of the entire Gulf of Mexico and Caribbean Sea.

ECOLOGY   The permit is an occasional visitor to the lower Chesapeake Bay during summer and autumn. It is rare in the middle and upper bay, extending as far north as St. Marys County, Maryland. Permits occur from surface to bottom in shallow water and to depths greater than 35 m (115 ft). They frequent channels, holes, sandy flats, reefs, and, at times, mud bottoms. Adult permits tend to be solitary or travel in small schools, whereas juveniles can be found in large schools, especially during summer in the surf zone along sandy beaches. Juveniles can also tolerate brackish waters. Spawning probably occurs offshore in Gulf Stream waters. Adults feed primarily on mollusks, crustaceans, and small fishes.

FISHING INTEREST   Little sought in the Chesapeake Bay area because of rarity. In south Florida, where permits are abundant, they are given game fish status and form the basis of an important recreational fishery. Along with the tarpon and the bonefish, the permit is ranked among the gamest of shallow-water marine fishes. Anglers usually pursue permits on flats or along channel margins, using spinning tackle and crabs. The world angling record for the permit is a fish from Florida that was caught in 1978 and weighed 23.4 kg (51.5 lb). Permits weighing less than 4.5 kg (10 lb) are of excellent eating quality.

LITERATURE   Hildebrand and Schroeder 1928:228; McClane 1965; Musick 1972; Fischer 1978; Johnson 1978.

Palometa
Trachinotus goodei Jordan and Evermann, 1896

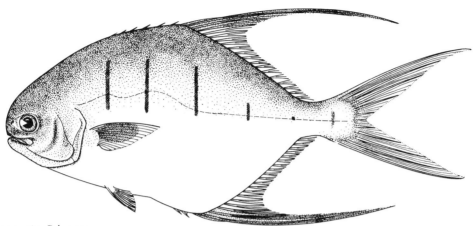

FIGURE 161. Palometa,
Trachinotus goodei.

KEY FEATURES   Longest rays of dorsal fin reaching well beyond caudal fin base; body usually with 4 narrow vertical bars; snout rounded; body short, compressed, and deep; greatest body depth contained 1.9–2.6 times in standard length; lateral line without scutes; pectoral fin shorter than head; transverse groove absent on caudal peduncle; posterior soft rays of dorsal and anal fins not forming semidetached finlets; scales small, oval-shaped, and partially embedded; dorsal fin with 19 or 20 rays; anal fin with 16–18 rays.

OTHER CHARACTERISTICS   Teeth small and present in fish at all sizes; eye small; first dorsal fin with 6 spines; caudal fin broadly forked; anal fin base about equal in length to base of second dorsal fin; first 2 anal fin spines removed from third; pelvic fin smaller than pectoral fin. Head and body bluish gray to blue green dorsally; silvery ventrally; 2 spots typically present along lateral line between head and caudal peduncle; spots and bars black or silvery in life. Maximum adult size 51 cm TL (1.7 ft).

GEOGRAPHIC DISTRIBUTION   Found from Massachusetts to Argentina, including coastal areas of the entire Gulf of Mexico and Caribbean Sea. A closely related species *(Trachinotus paitensis)* occurs in the eastern Pacific.

ECOLOGY   Palometas are rare visitors to the lower Chesapeake Bay. In the Caribbean, where they are more abundant, they form large schools in the surf zone and clear water along sandy beaches. They are also found around reefs and rocky areas and prefer high-salinity waters. On rare occasions they move into inlets and bays. Little is known of their spawning habits and early life history. Palometas feed on fishes and small invertebrates.

FISHING INTEREST   Not the target of a directed fishery in U.S. waters but occasionally taken with seines and by anglers using rod and reel.

LITERATURE   Hildebrand and Schroeder 1928:229; McClane 1965; Musick 1972; Fischer 1978; Johnson 1978.

Cobia
FAMILY RACHYCENTRIDAE

The cobia, the sole member of the family Rachycentridae, is distributed worldwide in tropical to warm-temperate coastal waters. The body is elongate and fusiform, and the head long and pointed, with a projecting lower jaw. The pectoral fin is large, and the first dorsal fin comprises seven to nine short, stout isolated spines. In general conformation and color pattern, especially when young, this species closely resembles the sharksuckers of the family Echeneidae, to which it is generally believed to be closely related. Sharksuckers differ most noticeably in having a large sucking disk located on top of the head. Cobia are known to follow sharks and large rays occasionally, a behavior typical of sharksuckers. Cobia are most frequently solitary but occasionally are found in small groups. The cobia is esteemed as a game and food fish.

Cobia
Rachycentron canadum (Linnaeus, 1766)

FIGURE 162. Cobia,
Rachycentron canadum.

KEY FEATURES   First dorsal fin comprising 7–9 (typically 8) short, stout isolated spines that fit in groove when depressed.

OTHER CHARACTERISTICS   Body elongate, somewhat fusiform, and only slightly compressed; head long, pointed, and slightly depressed; eye small; mouth large; lower jaw projecting; second dorsal fin long and elevated anteriorly; caudal peduncle nearly round; caudal fin forked in adults, with upper lobe slightly longer than lower lobe; pelvic fin thoracic in position; pectoral fin broad and pointed. Blackish dorsally; brown laterally; yellowish ventrally; side with 2 sharply defined silvery bands sandwiching broad dusky lateral stripe running from tip of snout to base of tail. Maximum adult size 2 m TL (6.6 ft).

GEOGRAPHIC DISTRIBUTION   Known from the Atlantic and Indo–West Pacific oceans. In the western Atlantic, the cobia is known from Massachusetts to Argentina, including the Gulf of Mexico and the Caribbean Sea.

ECOLOGY   The cobia is an occasional to common summer visitor in the lower Chesapeake Bay. Cobia enter the bay in late May or early June and migrate out of the bay and south by mid-October. Spawning occurs from mid-June to mid-August near the bay mouth or just offshore, where cobia form aggregations. Cobia are most often found in open water around buoys, pilings, or floating objects. They sometimes associate with sharks, rays, and pilotfish. Although cobia eat some fishes and squids, the bulk of their diet is crabs and shrimps—hence the colloquial name "crabeater" in some areas.

FISHING INTEREST   Caught incidentally by commercial fisheries throughout most of range, because of solitary habits. Commercial landings in Chesapeake Bay amounted to about 7,700 kg (17,000 lb) in 1990, with the bulk coming from pound-net and gill-net catches. The average size of commercially caught cobia in Virginia waters is 10 kg (23 lb). The cobia is highly prized by anglers and is considered an excellent eating fish and a rugged fighter that will make determined runs and leaps when hooked. Anglers in the lower bay use either live or artificial bait to fish for cobia around buoys, towers, bridges, and other open-water structures. The Chesapeake Bay (and U.S.) record for cobia is a fish taken near Mobjack Bay, Virginia, in 1980 that weighed 47.0 kg (103.5 lb).

LITERATURE   Hildebrand and Schroeder 1928:235; Joseph et al. 1964; Richards 1967; Musick 1972; Fischer 1978; Hardy 1978b; Benson 1982; Manooch 1984; Smith 1985; Whitehead et al. 1986a; Shaffer and Nakamura 1989.

Remoras
FAMILY ECHENEIDAE

Remoras are marine fishes that can attach themselves to other vertebrates by means of a sucking disk located on the flattened dorsal surface of the head. The disk is formed in part from highly modified dorsal spines. Hosts include sharks, whales, turtles, rays, swordfish, marlins, barracudas, jacks, and a variety of other large fishes. Some remora species primarily associate with a specific host, whereas others show little host preference. Remoras display three basic feeding niches: (1) predators on planktonic crustaceans and small nekton, (2) scavengers on scraps (mostly fish flesh) from the host's meal, and (3) symbionts removing parasites (mostly copepods) from the skin or gills of the host. Most remora species exhibit, at least to a limited extent, all three types of feeding. However, some species display a considerable preference for one food source over the others. The family, found in the Atlantic, Pacific, and Indian oceans, comprises four genera and eight species, with four species known from Chesapeake Bay.

KEY TO THE SPECIES OF REMORAS IN CHESAPEAKE BAY

1a. Dorsal fin and anal fin elements numbering fewer than 30; body color nearly uniform, without lateral stripes; pectoral fin rounded **2**
1b. Dorsal fin and anal fin elements numbering more than 30; body color pattern with dusky longitudinal stripe bounded above and below by whitish stripes; pectoral fin pointed. **3**

2a. Pectoral fin rays stiff. . . . . **marlinsucker, Remora osteochir** (p. 286)
2b. Pectoral fin rays soft and flexible . . . . **whalesucker, Remora australis** (p. 286)

3a. Sucking disk with 18–23 laminae (most frequently 21) . . . .
. . . . **whitefin sharksucker, Echeneis neucratoides** (p. 287)
3b. Sucking disk with 21–29 laminae (most frequently 23). . . **sharksucker, Echeneis naucrates** (p. 177)

Sharksucker
Echeneis naucrates Linnaeus, 1758

KEY FEATURES   Dorsal fin with 33–45 rays (most frequently 39); anal fin with 31–41 rays (most frequently 36); sucking disk with 21–29 laminae (most frequently 23); side with dusky longitudinal stripe bounded by white stripes; pectoral fin pointed.

OTHER CHARACTERISTICS   Body elongate and fusiform; head depressed and broad; sucking disk large; snout broad and flat; jaws broad; lower jaw projecting beyond upper jaw; teeth in jaws in broad bands; dorsal and anal fins long-based and higher anteriorly; caudal fin lanceolate in young and truncate in adults; pelvic fin long and narrow; pectoral fin pointed, high on body, and about equal in size to pelvic fin. Dusky brown dorsally; pale brown laterally; juveniles with dorsal and anal fins whitish distally; caudal fin whitish dorsally and ventrally. Maximum adult size 66 cm SL (2.2 ft).

GEOGRAPHIC DISTRIBUTION   Found worldwide in tropical and temperate seas. In the western Atlantic, the sharksucker is known from Massachusetts to Uruguay, including the Gulf of Mexico.

ECOLOGY   The sharksucker is an occasional summer visitor to the upper and lower Chesapeake Bay, reaching as far north as Annapolis. This species is the most common inshore remora in the western Atlantic. Unlike most other remoras, the sharksucker is often found free-swimming and occurs in shallow inshore waters. It will at-tach temporarily to a wide variety of hosts such as sharks, barracudas, sea turtles, and various large fishes. The sharksucker is also known to attach to ships, buoys, floating objects, and even bathers. The diet of the sharksucker appears to comprise mostly planktonic crustaceans, but some parasitic copepods are also taken.

FISHING INTEREST   Of no commercial or recreational value but occasionally caught on hook and line.

LITERATURE   Hildebrand and Schroeder 1928:329; Cressey and Lachner 1970; Musick 1972; Fischer 1978; Martin and Drewry 1978; Smith 1985; Böhlke and Chaplin 1993.

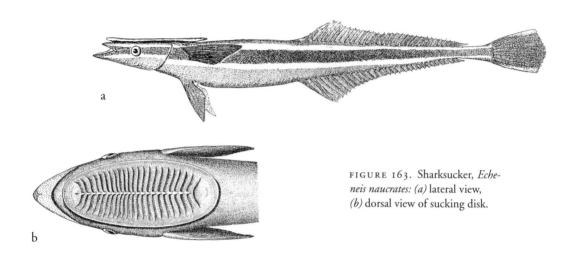

FIGURE 163. Sharksucker, *Echeneis naucrates: (a)* lateral view, *(b)* dorsal view of sucking disk.

Mackerels
FAMILY SCOMBRIDAE

Mackerels are medium-sized to large fishes that include in their numbers some of the fastest and most efficient swimmers in the ocean. Among the anatomical specializations for fast and efficient swimming are a streamlined fusiform body shape, fins that fold into grooves or depressions, a series of finlets following the dorsal and anal fins, lateral keels on the caudal peduncle, and a falcate caudal fin. All of these features reduce turbulent flow around the fish and, hence, reduce drag as it moves rapidly through the water. The scombrids are generally restricted to marine coastal and oceanic waters; however, some coastal species occasionally enter estuaries. Members of this family support some of the most important commercial and recreational fisheries throughout the tropical and temperate waters of the world. The family, comprising 15 genera and 49 species, inhabits all tropical and temperate seas. Eight species are known from Chesapeake Bay.

KEY TO THE SPECIES OF MACKERELS IN CHESAPEAKE BAY

The presence or absence of a swim bladder is determined by dissection.

1a. Dorsal fins widely separated; 2 small keels present on either side of caudal peduncle; 5 dorsal and anal finlets present **2**

1b. Dorsal fins close together; 2 small keels and 1 large median keel between them present on either side of caudal peduncle; 7–10 dorsal and anal finlets present **3**

2a. Dorsal fin spines numbering 9 or 10; dorsum with numerous oblique lines that zigzag and undulate; dusky rounded blotches present on lower side and belly; swim bladder present . . . . **chub mackerel, *Scomber japonicus* (p. 179)**

2b. Dorsal fin spines numbering 11–13; dorsum with dark, wavy, oblique to vertical bars or streaks; dusky blotches absent on lower side and belly; swim bladder absent . . . . **Atlantic mackerel, *Scomber scombrus* (p. 180)**

3a. Teeth in jaws strong, compressed, and almost triangular or knifelike; body elongate, compressed . . . **4**

3b. Teeth in jaws slender, conical, and hardly compressed; body fusiform, rounded (tuna-shaped) **6**

4a. Lateral line abruptly curving downward below second dorsal fin; side without markings; first dorsal fin with 14–16 spines; anterior third of first dorsal fin without black pigment . . . . **king mackerel, *Scomberomorus cavalla* (p. 181)**

4b. Lateral line gradually curving downward to caudal peduncle; side with brassy yellow spots; first dorsal fin with 17–19 spines; anterior third of first dorsal fin with black pigment **5**

5a. Side of body with spots only and without longitudinal stripes . . . . **Spanish mackerel, *Scomberomorus maculatus* (p. 182)**

5b. Side of body with spots and 1 or 2 longitudinal stripes . . . . . . **cero, *Scomberomorus regalis* (p. 287)**

6a. Dorsum and upper side with 7–12 oblique stripes extending below lateral line; dorsal surface of tongue without cartilaginous longitudinal ridges; first dorsal fin with 20–23 spines . . . . **Atlantic bonito, *Sarda sarda* (p. 183)**

6b. Dorsum and upper side without oblique stripes; dorsal surface of tongue with 2 cartilaginous longitudinal ridges; first dorsal fin with 9–16 spines **7**

7a. Dorsum above lateral line with wavy, dark, reticulated lines; chest ventral to pectoral fin with 4 or 5 dusky spots; posterior part of body without scales . . . . . **little tunny, *Euthynnus alletteratus* (p. 184)**

7b. Stripes, spots, and wavy lines absent from body; posterior part of body covered with very small scales . . . . **bluefin tuna, *Thunnus thynnus* (p. 287)**

Chub mackerel
Scomber japonicus Houttuyn, 1782
PLATE 26

KEY FEATURES Dorsal fin with 9 or 10 spines; 5 finlets posterior to dorsal and anal fins; dorsum with numerous oblique faint dusky lines that zigzag and undulate; belly with numerous dusky rounded blotches or wavy broken lines; dorsal fins widely separated, the distance be-tween them shorter than length of base of first dorsal fin.

OTHER CHARACTERISTICS Body elongate and rounded; head long and slender; snout pointed; teeth small and in single row in jaws; front and hind portions of eye covered by adipose eyelid; entire body covered by small scales; first dorsal fin with slender spines; caudal peduncle slender, with small keel above and below midline; caudal fin broadly forked; anal fin similar to second dorsal fin and with origin only slightly ventroposterior to origin of second dorsal fin; pelvic fin small; pectoral fin short; swim

migration brings individuals to the bay region for overwintering and spawning. There spawning occurs offshore during winter, most often at water temperatures of 15°–20°C (59°–68°F). The larvae are more common south of Cape Hatteras. The chub mackerel is an opportunistic feeder on crustaceans, small fishes, and squids.

FIGURE 164. Chub mackerel, *Scomber japonicus.*

bladder present. Steel blue dorsally; silvery yellow ventrally. Maximum adult size 50 cm FL (1.6 ft).

GEOGRAPHIC DISTRIBUTION   Inhabiting the warm and temperate waters of all oceans. In the western Atlantic, the chub mackerel is found from Nova Scotia to Argentina but is rare in the Gulf of Mexico and the Caribbean Sea.

ECOLOGY   The chub mackerel is a rare to occasional springtime visitor to the lower Chesapeake Bay. Primarily a coastal pelagic species, these fish school by size and occur from the surface to depths of 300 m (985 ft). A north–south

FISHING INTEREST   Not a target of a significant fishery in the western Atlantic. In other regions, especially the northwestern Pacific, important commercial fisheries exist for this species. The chub mackerel is primarily caught with purse seines. In the Chesapeake Bay area it is not sufficiently abundant or predictable to be of commercial or recreational importance.

LITERATURE   Hildebrand and Schroeder 1928:202; Musick 1972; Fischer 1978; Fritzsche 1978; Collette and Nauen 1983; Fahay 1983; Whitehead et al. 1986a.

Atlantic mackerel
Scomber scombrus Linnaeus, 1758

KEY FEATURES   Dorsal fin with 11–13 spines; 5 finlets posterior to dorsal and anal fins; dorsum with wavy blackish oblique to vertical bars or streaks; blotches and lines absent on lower side and belly; dorsal fins widely separated, the distance between them greater than length of base of first dorsal fin.

OTHER CHARACTERISTICS   Body elongate and rounded; head long and slender; snout pointed; teeth small and in single row in jaws; front and hind portions of eye covered by adipose eyelid; entire body covered by small scales;

caudal peduncle slender, with small keel above and below midline; caudal fin broadly forked; anal fin similar and perpendicular to second dorsal fin; pelvic fin small; pectoral fin short; swim bladder absent. Bluish black dorsally; bright silvery ventrally. Maximum adult size 50 cm FL (1.6 ft), with females typically larger than males.

GEOGRAPHIC DISTRIBUTION   Inhabiting both coasts of the northern Atlantic and the Mediterranean. In the western Atlantic, Atlantic mackerel are found from Labrador to North Carolina.

ECOLOGY   Atlantic mackerel are occasional visitors to the lower Chesapeake Bay in early spring and late fall. The species is pelagic, schools by

FISHING INTEREST   Of commercial importance throughout the North Atlantic and the Mediterranean and generally fished there with

FIGURE 165. Atlantic mackerel, *Scomber scombrus.*

size, and is most abundant in cold and temperate shelf areas. Atlantic mackerel overwinter in deeper waters south of Cape Hatteras but move north and closer to shore in spring when water temperatures are 11°–14°C (52°–57°F). Most have left the bay area by mid-June to spend their summer and early fall north of Cape Cod. In the Chesapeake Bay region, spawning begins offshore in the spring and progresses to more northerly waters during the summer. The Atlantic mackerel is primarily a plankton feeder, subsisting on pelagic crustaceans as well as fish eggs and fry.

purse seines. In the Chesapeake Bay area this species is of minor importance. In the bay region most Atlantic mackerel are taken offshore by anglers from mid-February through mid-April. The general low abundance and low variety of fishes available during the early spring makes this species popular with anglers who are willing to venture offshore.

LITERATURE   Hildebrand and Schroeder 1928:201; Musick 1972; Fritzsche 1978; Collette and Nauen 1983; Whitehead et al. 1986a.

King mackerel
Scomberomorus cavalla (Cuvier, 1829)

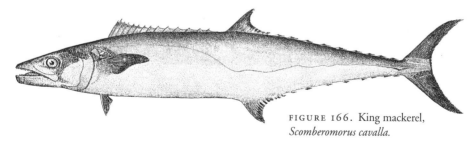

FIGURE 166. King mackerel, *Scomberomorus cavalla.*

KEY FEATURES   Lateral line abruptly curving downward below second dorsal fin; dorsal fins contiguous; first dorsal fin with 14–16 slender spines (usually 15); black area absent on anterior third of first dorsal fin; bars and spots absent on body of adults.

OTHER CHARACTERISTICS   Body elongate and strongly compressed; head compressed; snout pointed; mouth large and oblique; teeth in jaws

compressed; body entirely covered by small scales; second dorsal fin tall anteriorly, short-based, and followed by 7–10 finlets (usually 9); caudal peduncle slender; 2 small keels and 1 large median keel between them present on either side of caudal peduncle; caudal fin broadly forked; anal fin similar to second dorsal fin and originating ventroposterior to it; second dorsal fin followed by 7–10 finlets (usually 8); pelvic fin small; pectoral fin short. Iridescent blue green dorsally; side plain silver, without bars or spots in adults and with small bronze spots in 5 or 6 irregular rows in juveniles. Maximum adult size 1.7 m FL (5.7 ft), with females larger than males.

GEOGRAPHIC DISTRIBUTION   Occurring from Massachusetts to Brazil, including the Gulf of Mexico and the Caribbean Sea.

ECOLOGY   King mackerel are occasional visitors to the lower Chesapeake Bay and rare to occasional visitors in the upper bay. They occur during the warm months of the year (June to October), with peak abundance in September. The king mackerel is a surface-dwelling, nearshore species that is often found around wrecks, towers, reefs, and other structures. Large schools of similar-sized king mackerel migrate over considerable distances along the Atlantic coast. Some apparently overwinter in the Gulf of Mexico, whereas others may move farther south. Spawning occurs over the middle and outer portions of the continental shelf from July through September along the Atlantic coast. Fishes are the primary component of the king mackerel's diet, but shrimps and squids are also eaten. Females may live as long as 14 years.

FISHING INTEREST   Of importance to recreational and commercial fisheries throughout range. In Chesapeake Bay the king mackerel is of minimal commercial importance but is occasionally taken in pound nets near the bay mouth. In Florida waters it is landed commercially with gill nets and hook and line and is an important fishery. Anglers pursue king mackerel by slow trolling, drifting, or anchoring and using a variety of live, cut, or artificial baits. The Chesapeake Bay record for king mackerel is a fish weighing 23 kg (50.5 lb) that was taken near Parker's Island in 1963.

LITERATURE   Musick 1972; Berrien and Finan 1977a; DeVane 1978; Fischer 1978; Benson 1982; Collette and Nauen 1983; Collette and Russo 1984; Manooch 1984; Collins et al. 1989.

Spanish mackerel
Scomberomorus maculatus (Mitchill, 1815)
PLATE 27

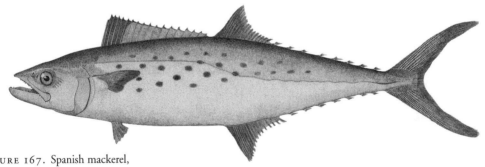

FIGURE 167. Spanish mackerel, *Scomberomorus maculatus.*

KEY FEATURES   Lateral line gradually curving downward to caudal peduncle; dorsal fins contiguous; first dorsal fin with 17–19 slender spines (usually 19); anterior third of first dorsal fin black; side silvery, marked with about 3 rows of round to elliptical dusky spots (orange in life), and without longitudinal stripes.

OTHER CHARACTERISTICS   Body elongate and strongly compressed; head compressed; snout pointed; mouth large and oblique; teeth in jaws compressed; body entirely covered by small scales; second dorsal fin tall anteriorly and short-based, followed by 7–9 finlets; caudal peduncle slender; 2 small keels and 1 large median keel between them present on either side of caudal peduncle; caudal fin broadly forked; anal fin similar in size and shape to second dorsal fin and originating posterior to it; anal fin followed by 7–10 finlets; pelvic fin small; pectoral fin short. Dusky blue dorsally; silvery ventrally. Maximum adult size 77 cm FL (2.5 ft).

GEOGRAPHIC DISTRIBUTION   Occurring from Cape Cod to Florida and coastally from Florida to Yucatán.

ECOLOGY   The Spanish mackerel is a common visitor to the middle-lower Chesapeake Bay from spring to autumn, extending at least as far north as the mouth of the Patuxent River. It is a surface-dwelling, nearshore species that undertakes long-distance migrations in large schools traveling along the shore. With increasing water temperatures in late February, Spanish mackerel migrate northward and westward from Florida waters, entering Chesapeake Bay by May when water temperatures exceed about 17°C (63°F). They spread out in the lower bay, with the major concentration along the lower Western Shore. Spawning occurs off Virginia from late spring through late summer. Spanish mackerel return in autumn to Florida waters, where they overwinter. Their food consists mainly of small fishes, shrimps, and squids. Spanish mackerel can attain 8 years of age.

FISHING INTEREST   Of recreational and commercial importance throughout range. In the late 1800s, the Spanish mackerel fishery in Chesapeake Bay was the largest in the United States. The abundance of Spanish mackerel in the bay has fluctuated over the years, but in recent times they have again become abundant and now constitute an important fishery in the lower bay. Commercial landings in Virginia in 1990 were 220,000 kg (485,000 lb), of which nearly 90% came from the lower western bay south of the Potomac River. The commercial catch is primarily taken by pound nets (88%), with gill nets and haul seines also producing minor contributions. Anglers also pursue Spanish mackerel by trolling feathers or pork rind or by casting fly and spinning lures into surface schools. Spanish mackerel often bite gold-colored spoons trolled at 6–10 km/hour (4–6 mi/hour). The peak fishing months are June, July, and August.

LITERATURE   Hildebrand and Schroeder 1928:203; Musick 1972; Berrien and Finan 1977b; Fischer 1978; Fritzsche 1978; Collette and Nauen 1983; Collette and Russo 1984; Manooch 1984; Chittenden et al. 1993.

Atlantic bonito
Sarda sarda (Bloch, 1793)
PLATE 28

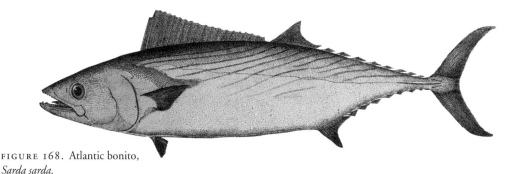

FIGURE 168. Atlantic bonito, *Sarda sarda.*

KEY FEATURES   Dorsum and upper side with 7–12 oblique stripes extending below lateral line; spots absent on chest; dorsal surface of tongue without cartilaginous longitudinal ridges; entire body covered with small scales; first dorsal fin with 20–23 spines; dorsal finlets numbering 7–9 (typically 8); anal finlets numbering 6–8 (typi-

cally 7); first dorsal fin low and with straight margin.

OTHER CHARACTERISTICS   Body elongate, fusiform, and slightly compressed; caudal peduncle slender and broader than deep; central keel separating 2 smaller keels on caudal peduncle; head long; snout pointed; mouth large, oblique, and with maxilla terminating ventro-posterior to eye; teeth in jaws strong and in single series; spinous dorsal fin long and with straight margin and slender spines; second dorsal fin short, originating dorsoanterior to anal fin; caudal fin broadly forked; anal fin with 14–17 rays and similar in shape to second dorsal fin; pectoral and pelvic fins short; pelvic fin inserting ventroposterior to pectoral fin origin; pelvic fins separated by 2 small flaps (interpelvic processes); lateral line distinctly wavy. Steel blue dorsally; lower side and venter silvery. Maximum adult size 91 cm FL (3 ft), commonly to 50 cm FL (1.6 ft).

GEOGRAPHIC DISTRIBUTION   Found in tropical and temperate waters of the Atlantic Ocean. In the western Atlantic, the Atlantic bonito is known from Massachusetts to Florida and the northern Gulf of Mexico but apparently is absent in most of the Caribbean. It is also known from Colombia and Venezuela as well as northern Argentina.

ECOLOGY   The Atlantic bonito is an occasional visitor to the lower and upper Chesapeake Bay from spring to fall. It is a pelagic migratory species that often schools near the surface in nearshore waters. The Atlantic bonito tolerates temperatures of 12°–27°C (54°–81°F) and salinities of 14–39‰ and occasionally enters estuaries. Spawning is in June and July in the northwestern Atlantic; however, spawning occurs during the winter months in waters south of Cape Hatteras. This species feeds on small schooling fishes (including other bonitos), squids, and shrimps.

FISHING INTEREST   Sought by commercial fisheries over entire range where abundant. In the western Atlantic, most commercial landings of Atlantic bonito come from coastal waters from Mexico to Venezuela. A small fishery also exists in the Gulf of Maine during June–October. Anglers pursue this species by trolling or casting lures to schooling fish at the surface. The eating quality of the Atlantic bonito is reported as excellent.

LITERATURE   Hildebrand and Schroeder 1928:206; Mansueti 1962; Musick 1972; Collette and Chao 1975; Fischer 1978; Collette and Nauen 1983; Fahay 1983; Whitehead et al. 1986a.

Little tunny
Euthynnus alletteratus (Rafinesque, 1810)

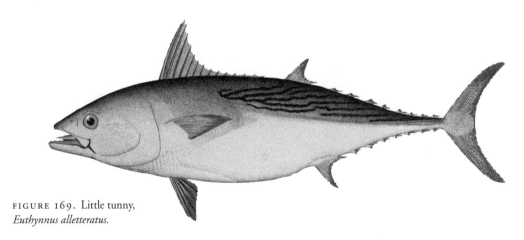

FIGURE 169. Little tunny, *Euthynnus alletteratus.*

KEY FEATURES   Dorsum above lateral line with wavy, dark, reticulated lines; chest below pectoral fin with 4 or 5 dusky spots; spinous dorsal fin high anteriorly, with concave margin, and with 15 or 16 spines; 8 dorsal and 7 anal finlets present; upper surface of tongue with 2 cartilaginous longitudinal ridges; scales absent from posterior part of body.

OTHER CHARACTERISTICS   Body elongate and robust; caudal peduncle slender, broader than deep, and with prominent central keel between 2 smaller keels; head long; snout pointed;

mouth large and oblique; lower jaw slightly pro-jecting; maxilla terminating ventroposterior to middle of eye; teeth in jaws small, conical, and in single series; second dorsal fin short, originat-ing dorsoanterior to anal fin; caudal fin broadly forked and falcate; anal fin with 11–15 rays and similar in shape to second dorsal fin; pectoral and pelvic fins short; pelvic fin inserting perpen-dicular to pectoral fin origin; pelvic fins separated by 2 flaps (interpelvic processes); lateral line dis-tinctly wavy. Lower side and venter silvery white. Maximum adult size 1 m FL (3.3 ft), commonly to 75 cm FL (2.5 ft).

GEOGRAPHIC DISTRIBUTION   Found in tropical and subtropical waters of the Atlantic Ocean. In the western Atlantic, the little tunny is known from New England to Brazil, including the Gulf of Mexico and the Caribbean Sea.

ECOLOGY   Little tunny are occasional visitors to both the lower and the upper Chesapeake Bay from late spring to fall. This inshore, schooling species occurs in near-surface waters. During the seasonal north–south migrations the schools can be very large, consisting of thousands of fish and often marked by the presence of diving birds that

are feeding on the same food source. Spawning occurs along the edge of the continental shelf from spring through fall. Little tunny are oppor-tunistic feeders on crustaceans, fishes, and squids. This species lives about 5 years.

FISHING INTEREST   Taken by mixed-species fisheries but not a targeted species in U.S. waters. In areas of greater abundance, along the coasts of northern South America and Africa, large numbers of little tunny are landed. In open waters, the species is landed with purse seines and trolling lines; juveniles can be collected with beach seines. Anglers pursue little tunny by troll-ing or casting lures to schooling fish at the sur-face. The bloody flesh limits the popularity of little tunny as a food fish, and they are often used as bait for billfishes. We are told that an-glers who take the trouble to bleed and ice the fish immediately upon landing find little tunny highly acceptable, especially if the dark lateral muscle mass is discarded.

LITERATURE   Mansueti and Mansueti 1962; Musick 1972; Fischer 1978; Fritzsche 1978; Col-lette and Nauen 1983; Fahay 1983; Collette and Russo 1984; Whitehead et al. 1986a.

Mullets
FAMILY MUGILIDAE

Mullets are medium-sized fishes that inhabit coastal marine waters, estuaries, and fresh waters. They are characterized by thick bodies, large heads, blunt snouts, and small mouths. Many species have an adipose eyelid that partially covers the eye anteriorly and posteriorly. Most mullet species are highly migratory and display seasonal inshore–offshore migration patterns. Spawning apparently occurs offshore. Inshore, mul-lets are usually found schooling in shallow waters. Mullets are renowned for their propensity to jump, sometimes clearing the water by as much as 10 m (3 ft). The purpose of their jumping is unclear, but it occasionally results in a surprise landing in the boat of an angler. They feed on plant detritus, filamentous algae, diatoms, and small animals that are sucked up along with mud. Mullets may be seen expelling the inorganic sediment from their gill openings. They possess a muscular crop (stomach) and a very long intestine commensurate with their largely herbivorous diet. They have been important food fishes since ancient times and are fished commercially wherever they occur in abundance. The taxonomy of the Mugi-lidae is very confused. At present there are about 17 recognized genera in the family and least 70 valid spe-cies found in all tropical and temperate seas. Two species of mullets are recorded from Chesapeake Bay.

KEY TO THE SPECIES OF MULLETS IN CHESAPEAKE BAY

Young mullets of 3.5–6.5 cm SL (1.4–2.5 in) are in transition to the juvenile stage, and many have not de-veloped the scalation or pigment patterns of juveniles and adults. At these sizes both mullet species found in Chesapeake Bay are simply silvery little fishes that may be reliably distinguished only by the number of anal fin elements.

KEY TO MULLETS SMALLER THAN 6.5 CM SL (2.5 IN)

1a. Anal fin with total of 11 elements, either 2 spines and 9 rays or 3 spines and 8 rays . . . .
. . . . **striped mullet,** *Mugil cephalus* (p. 186)
1b. Anal fin with total of 12 elements, either 2 spines and 10 rays or 3 spines and 9 rays . . . .
. . . .**white mullet,** *Mugil curema* (p. 187)

KEY TO MULLETS LARGER THAN 6.5 CM SL (2.5 IN)

1a. Anal fin with 3 spines and 8 rays; second dorsal fin and anal fin with few or no scales; lateral scales
with central dusky blotch forming longitudinal dusky stripe on each scale row . . . .
. . . . **striped mullet,** *Mugil cephalus* (p. 186)
1b. Anal fin with 3 spines and 9 rays; second dorsal fin and anal fin densely scaled nearly to margin; lateral
scale rows without definite dusky stripes . . . .**white mullet,** *Mugil curema* (p. 187)

Striped mullet
Mugil cephalus Linnaeus, 1758
PLATE 29

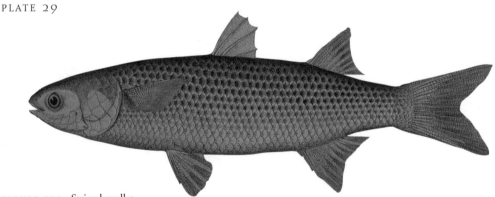

FIGURE 170. Striped mullet,
Mugil cephalus.

KEY FEATURES   Anal fin with 3 spines and 8 rays; second dorsal fin and anal fin with few or no scales; lateral scales with central dusky blotch forming longitudinal dusky stripe on each scale row.

OTHER CHARACTERISTICS   Body rather robust, somewhat compressed; head broad, with flat interorbital area; lips thin; mouth terminal, forming inverted V when viewed from below; adipose tissue covering most of eye; dorsal fins well separated; first dorsal fin near midpoint of body; origin of second dorsal fin slightly dorsoposterior to anal fin origin; caudal peduncle rather strongly compressed; caudal fin with shallow fork; pelvic fin abdominal; lateral scales numbering 37–43; elongate pointed scale present in axil of pectoral and pelvic fins. Blue gray or greenish dorsally; sil-ver laterally, shading to white ventrally; dusky purplish blotch present on upper base of pectoral fin. Maximum adult size 1.2 m TL (4 ft), most commonly 35 cm TL or less (≤1.1 ft) in Chesapeake Bay region.

GEOGRAPHIC DISTRIBUTION   Found worldwide in tropical and temperate waters. The striped mullet occurs along the western Atlantic coast from Cape Cod to Brazil, including the Gulf of Mexico and the Caribbean Sea.

ECOLOGY   The striped mullet is a common visitor to Chesapeake Bay during the summer and autumn. Most striped mullet enter the bay as prejuveniles or juveniles (3.5–6.5 cm, or 1.4–2.5 in, SL) and migrate out of the bay and southward during the winter. This species occurs in coastal waters, estuaries, and brackish-water lagoons, frequently penetrating freshwater. Like other mullets, the striped mullet is a schooling fish that often jumps from the water. Spawning takes place in surface waters offshore in large aggregations during winter. Spawning is thought not to occur north of Cape Hatteras. The food of this mullet consists largely of microscopic organisms, mainly diatoms and foraminifera, mixed with considerable quantities of mud and plant detritus.

FISHING INTEREST   Of minor commercial value in the Chesapeake Bay region but an important resource farther south. Along the Atlantic seaboard, striped mullet are mainly valued as a baitfish, but along the Gulf coast, where they reach their maximum size and abundance, they are prized for the eating quality of both the flesh and the roe. In the past decade striped mullet have been overfished in response to a growing Japanese demand for mullet roe, and sharp declines in American stocks have resulted. Commercial catches are taken with gill nets and cast nets. Recreational pursuit of striped mullet is mainly by cast netting, a particularly effective technique because of their near-surface schooling habits. As bottom-feeding herbivores, they rarely take a hook. The largest record for striped mullet in Chesapeake Bay is 51 cm TL (1.7 ft).

LITERATURE   Hildebrand and Schroeder 1928:193; Anderson 1958; Musick 1972; Fahay 1975; Fischer 1978; Martin and Drewry 1978; Benson 1982; Fritzsche 1982; Manooch 1984.

White mullet
Mugil curema Valenciennes, 1836

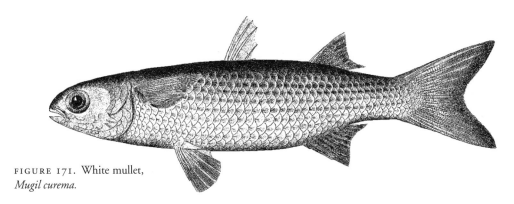

FIGURE 171. White mullet, *Mugil curema.*

KEY FEATURES   Anal fin with 3 spines and 9 rays; second dorsal fin and anal fin densely scaled nearly to margin; lateral scale rows without definite dusky stripes.

OTHER CHARACTERISTICS   Body moderately compressed; interorbital area almost flat; lips thin; mouth terminal, forming inverted V when viewed from below; adipose tissue covering most of eye; dorsal fins well separated; first dorsal fin near midpoint of body; origin of second dorsal fin slightly dorsoposterior to anal fin origin; caudal peduncle rather strongly compressed; caudal fin moderately forked; pelvic fin abdominal; lateral scales numbering 37–40; elongate pointed scale in axil of pectoral and pelvic fins. Dusky greenish with bluish tints dorsally; silver laterally and ventrally; small black blotch present on upper base of pectoral fin; ventral fins yellowish.

Maximum adult size 45 cm TL (1.5 ft), most commonly 30 cm TL or less (≤1 ft) in Chesapeake Bay region.

GEOGRAPHIC DISTRIBUTION   Known from both the eastern and western Atlantic coasts as well as the eastern Pacific. The white mullet is distributed along the western Atlantic coast from Cape Cod to Brazil, including the Gulf of Mexico and the Caribbean Sea.

ECOLOGY   The white mullet is a visitor to Chesapeake Bay during summer and autumn; it is occasional in the upper bay and occasional to common in the lower bay. Like striped mullet, white mullet enter the bay as prejuveniles or juveniles (3.5–6.5 cm, or 1.4–2.5 in, SL) and migrate out of the bay and southward during the winter. They inhabit shallow coastal waters, typically occurring in murky water over muddy bottoms of estuaries and brackish-water lagoons, but they are also often found in clean seawater close to the surface. Like other mullets, the white mullet is a schooling species. Spawning occurs in offshore surface waters south of Cape Hatteras, with a strong peak in spring and limited activity through the year. The feeding habits of the white mullet are similar to those of the striped mullet. FISHING INTEREST   Highly valued as a baitfish for cut bait and supporting a modest fishery in the south Atlantic Bight for that purpose. White mullet are little pursued for other commercial or recreational uses and are not held in esteem as a food fish. Most are taken with gill nets, cast nets, and beach seines. LITERATURE   Hildebrand and Schroeder 1928:196; Anderson 1957; Musick 1972; Fahay 1975; Fischer 1978; Martin and Drewry 1978; Fritzsche 1982.

Barracudas

FAMILY SPHYRAENIDAE

Barracudas are elongate fishes with a large mouth that contains a formidable array of long, sharp-edged teeth. These fishes are nearly cylindrical anteriorly and have two widely separated dorsal fins, abdominally located pelvic fins, and a forked caudal fin. Voracious lurking predators, they remain motionless until they make a rapid short strike on their prey, typically a fish. A barracuda is capable of cutting another fish in two with a single bite. Schooling or aggregating behavior is primarily observed in small species or in young fish, whereas large adults are mostly solitary. The young of most species and the adults of some are common in estuarine areas. Although attacks on humans have been documented, this danger is considered minimal. The barracuda family is found in all tropical to warm-temperate seas, typically in surface waters, and comprises a single genus and 20 species. Two species are recorded from Chesapeake Bay.

KEY TO THE SPECIES OF BARRACUDAS IN CHESAPEAKE BAY

1a. Scales in lateral line series typically numbering fewer than 115; origin of pelvic fin more anterior than origin of dorsal fin or tip of pectoral fin; fleshy tip absent on lower jaw. . . . . **guaguanche, *Sphyraena guachancho*** (p. 188)

1b. Scales in lateral line series typically numbering more than 120; origin of pelvic fin more posterior than origin of dorsal fin or tip of pectoral fin; fleshy tip present on lower jaw. . . . . **northern sennet, *Sphyraena borealis*** (p. 189)

Guaguanche

Sphyraena guachancho Cuvier, 1829

FIGURE 172. Guaguanche, *Sphyraena guachancho*.

KEY FEATURES   Scales in lateral line series numbering 102–119 (typically fewer than 115); origin of pelvic fin slightly more anterior than origin of dorsal fin; tip of appressed pectoral fin perpendicular to or dorsoposterior to pelvic fin origin; last rays of second dorsal fin and anal fin longer than preceding rays and extending beyond anterior rays when fins are folded; distinct fleshy tip absent on lower jaw.

OTHER CHARACTERISTICS   Body elongate, nearly cylindrical; head large and slightly compressed; snout long and pointed; mouth large; lower jaw projecting beyond upper jaw; teeth in jaws and on palatines strong and posteriorly directed; scales small; dorsal fins small and well separated; first dorsal fin with 5 slender spines; second dorsal fin with 1 slender spine and 9 soft rays and with origin almost perpendicular to anal fin origin; caudal fin forked; pelvic and pectoral fins small. Gray to olive dorsally; side and venter silvery; faint yellow or golden lateral stripe present in life; top of head dark; margins of pelvic and anal fins and rays of central caudal fin black. Maximum adult size 1.0 m TL (3.3 ft).

GEOGRAPHIC DISTRIBUTION   Known

from both sides of the Atlantic. In the western Atlantic, the guaguanche is known from Massachusetts to Brazil, including the Gulf of Mexico and the Caribbean Sea.

ECOLOGY   The guaguanche is a rare summer visitor to the lower Chesapeake Bay. A schooling species, it occurs in shallow and generally turbid coastal waters over muddy bottoms, often around estuaries. Its prey consists mainly of small fishes and shrimps.

FISHING INTEREST   Of no commercial or recreational value in the Chesapeake Bay region, because of rarity. In areas where the guaguanche is more common, it is valued as a food fish and is landed by trawls and handlines.

LITERATURE   Hildebrand and Schroeder 1928:198; Musick 1972; Fischer 1978; Martin and Drewry 1978; Fischer et al. 1981; DeSylva 1984.

Northern sennet
Sphyraena borealis DeKay, 1842

FIGURE 173. Northern sennet, *Sphyraena borealis.*

KEY FEATURES   Scales in lateral line series numbering 115–130 (typically more than 120); origin of pelvic fin more posterior than origin of dorsal fin; tip of appressed pectoral fin dorsoanterior to pelvic fin origin; last rays of second dorsal fin and anal fin shorter than preceding rays; anterior rays of second dorsal fin and anal fin extending beyond posterior rays when fins are folded; distinct fleshy tip present on lower jaw.

OTHER CHARACTERISTICS   Body elongate, nearly cylindrical; head large and slightly compressed; snout long and pointed; mouth large; lower jaw projecting beyond upper jaw; teeth in jaws and on palatines strong and pointed; scales very small; dorsal fins small and well separated; first dorsal fin with 5 slender spines; second dorsal fin with 1 slender spine and 8 or 9 soft rays

and slightly more anterior than anal fin origin; caudal fin forked; pelvic and pectoral fins small. Dusky olive dorsally; side and venter silvery; top of head and snout black; side with dark longitudinal stripe sometimes broken into blotches; dorsal and caudal fins dusky; other fins pale. Maximum adult size 45 cm TL (1.5 ft).

GEOGRAPHIC DISTRIBUTION   Known from Cape Cod to Florida, throughout the Gulf of Mexico and along the Central American coast to Panama.

ECOLOGY   The northern sennet is an occasional summer visitor to the lower Chesapeake Bay. Juveniles may be found most summers near the bay mouth. The northern sennet inhabits coastal waters to depths of 65 m (215 ft) and forms large schools over all kinds of substrates, but especially over muddy bottoms. Spawning occurs off Florida during winter. This species feeds mainly on small fishes, squids, and shrimps.

FISHING INTEREST   Of no commercial or recreational value in the Chesapeake Bay region, because of infrequent occurrence. In areas where the northern sennet is more common, it is valued as a food fish.

LITERATURE   Hildebrand and Schroeder 1928:198; Musick 1972; Fischer 1978; Martin and Drewry 1978; Fahay 1983; DeSylva 1984.

Stargazers
FAMILY URANOSCOPIDAE

Stargazers are thick-bodied fishes with their eyes located on the top of their dorsally flattened head. A grooved spine with a venom gland at its base is present just dorsal to the pectoral fin base. Some stargazers have a wormlike tentacle attached to the floor of the mouth that is used as a lure to attract small fishes near the mouth, where they are immediately engulfed. Some stargazer species have electric organs on the head that are capable of producing strong electric discharges. The anatomical features of most stargazers and especially those of the genus *Astroscopus,* which enters Chesapeake Bay, appear to be strongly adapted to their burrowing, lie-in-wait predatory habits. Stargazers are found from inshore waters to depths of 550 m (1,805 ft). The family, found in all oceans, comprises 8 genera and about 50 species, 1 of which is found in Chesapeake Bay.

Northern stargazer
Astroscopus guttatus Abbott, 1861

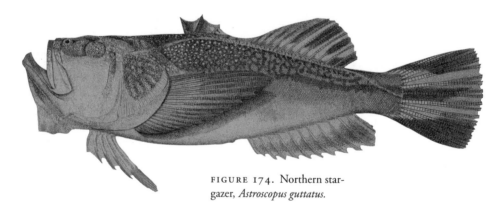

FIGURE 174. Northern stargazer, *Astroscopus guttatus.*

KEY FEATURES   Head flattened and about as wide as deep; mouth nearly vertical, with fringed lips; eye located dorsally; nasal opening fringed, with posterior opening located posteromedial to eye and formed into elongate groove.

OTHER CHARACTERISTICS   Body robust, becoming slender posteriorly; eye small; mouth broad; teeth small and in bands on jaws; scales very small; short, skin-covered poisonous spine (cleithral spine) located just dorsal to pectoral fin base; dorsal fins separate; spinous dorsal fin with 4 or 5 short spines; second dorsal fin higher than first and with 13–15 soft rays; caudal fin with slightly convex margin; anal fin with 1 spine and 12 soft rays; pelvic fin jugular; pectoral fin large. Dorsal part of body with many small irregular white spots on dusky background; ventral part of body grayish, with obscure blotches; caudal peduncle with dusky midlateral stripe; first dorsal fin blackish; second dorsal fin with several oblique bars; caudal fin with alternating black and white longitudinal stripes; pectoral fin dusky, with white margin. Maximum adult size 31 cm SL (1 ft).

GEOGRAPHIC DISTRIBUTION   Found in coastal waters from New York to Virginia.

ECOLOGY   The northern stargazer is a year-round resident of the lower Chesapeake Bay and is encountered in the upper bay only during autumn. Northern stargazers lie buried just below the surface of the sediment with only the lips, the top of the head, and the eyes exposed. The large vertically oriented mouth bears fringes on the lips, presumably to prevent sand from entering the mouth. The nasal openings are also externally fringed, and unlike all but a few fishes, northern stargazers have nasal passages that open into the mouth cavity, thus allowing them to respire without taking water in through the mouth when they are buried. A most unusual feature of *Astroscopus* species is the modification of the posterior rectus muscles of the eyes to form electric organs. In adults these organs have been reported to produce as much as 50 volts of electricity, and it is speculated that the discharge is used both to stun prey and to drive off predators. The northern stargazer spawns in the lower bay in May and June, but little is known of the early life history of this species. Its diet consists of small fishes and crustaceans.

FISHING INTEREST   Of no commercial or recreational value but occasionally collected in pound nets and trawls.

LITERATURE   Hildebrand and Schroeder 1928:330; Berry and Anderson 1961; Musick 1972; Fritzsche 1978; Smith 1985; Nelson 1994.

Drums
FAMILY SCIAENIDAE

Drums are primarily coastal marine and estuarine fishes, but some are restricted to freshwater. The common name derives from the large and elaborate swim bladder found in many species that is resonated by special muscles to produce croaking or drumming sounds. The large majority of drums live over sandy or muddy bottoms, whereas others are adapted to life in coral reefs or the surf zone. Most utilize estuarine areas as nursery grounds during the larval and juvenile period and as feeding grounds as adults, but some species are year-round residents of estuaries. Drums are typically demersal fishes and live singly or in small groups, although large aggregates are known during the spawning and feeding seasons. They feed on other fishes and invertebrates. Many species of the family are valuable food fishes. The family, found in all temperate and tropical waters, comprises 70 genera and approximately 270 species, 14 of which are found in Chesapeake Bay.

KEY TO THE SPECIES OF DRUMS IN CHESAPEAKE BAY

1a. Lower jaw with 1 or more barbels (sometimes minute and easily overlooked) 2
1b. Lower jaw without barbels 7

2a. Preopercular margin entire and without spines or bony "teeth" . . . .
. . . . **black drum, *Pogonias cromis*** (p. 192)
2b. Preopercular margin strongly to finely serrate and with spines or bony "teeth" 3

3a. Lower jaw with row of minute barbels on each side; preopercular margin strongly serrate (Figure 175)
. . . . **Atlantic croaker, *Micropogonias undulatus*** (p. 194)
3b. Lower jaw with single thick barbel at tip; preopercular margin finely serrate 4

FIGURE 175. Preopercular margin of a croaker.

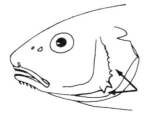

4a. Anal fin with 2 spines .... **sand drum,** *Umbrina coroides* (p. 195)

4b. Anal fin with 1 spine **5**

5a. Scales on chest much smaller than scales on side above lateral line; scales on breast much reduced in size; posterior margin of pectoral fin pale .... **gulf kingfish,** *Menticirrhus littoralis* (p. 196)

5b. Scales on chest not much smaller than scales on side above lateral line; scales on breast not distinctly reduced in size; posterior margin of pectoral fin dusky or edged in black **6**

6a. Anal fin typically with 8 soft rays (sometimes 7 or 9); longest spine of first dorsal fin extending beyond origin of second dorsal fin; side typically with blackish bars; nape with black bars forming V; pectoral fin with 18–21 rays .... **northern kingfish,** *Menticirrhus saxatilis* (p. 197)

6b. Anal fin typically with 7 soft rays (rarely 6 or 8); spines of first dorsal fin not extending beyond origin of second dorsal fin; side with faint dusky bars; pectoral fin with 21 or 22 rays .... **southern kingfish,** *Menticirrhus americanus* (p. 198)

7a. Upper jaw with 1 or 2 canine teeth **8**

7b. Upper jaw without canine teeth **10**

8a. Side silvery and without conspicuous spots .... **silver seatrout,** *Cynoscion nothus* (p. 199)

8b. Back and upper side with conspicuous black spots or blotches in rows **9**

9a. Spots irregularly spaced; soft portion of dorsal fin unscaled .... **spotted seatrout,** *Cynoscion nebulosus* (p. 200)

9b. Spots forming oblique streaks along scale rows; soft portion of dorsal fin with scales basally .... **weakfish,** *Cynoscion regalis* (p. 201)

10a. One or more black spots present dorsally on caudal peduncle; gill rakers on first arch numbering 12–14 .... **red drum,** *Sciaenops ocellatus* (p. 202)

10b. Spots absent at caudal fin base; gill rakers on first arch numbering 20–36 .... **11**

11a. Dorsal fin typically with 30 or 31 rays; dusky spot present on shoulder .... **spot,** *Leiostomus xanthurus* (p. 203)

11b. Dorsal fin with 19–27 rays; dusky spot absent on shoulder **12**

12a. Preopercle entire or weakly serrate; mouth large and often very oblique; side marked with 7–9 dusky vertical bars .... **banded drum,** *Larimus fasciatus* (p. 205)

12b. Preopercle strongly serrate; mouth not large; side without dusky vertical bars **13**

13a. Anal fin typically with 7 or 8 rays; skull cavernous and spongy-feeling to the touch .... **star drum,** *Stellifer lanceolatus* (p. 205)

13b. Anal fin typically with 10 rays; skull not cavernous or noticeably spongy-feeling .... **silver perch,** *Bairdiella chrysoura* (p. 206)

Black drum
Pogonias cromis (Linnaeus, 1766)

KEY FEATURES   Lower jaw with 5 pores and 12 or 13 pairs of barbels; margin of preopercle without spines or serration; snout with 5 upper pores and 5 marginal pores; lower pharyngeal tooth plates united and paved with large molariform teeth.

OTHER CHARACTERISTICS   Body long, deep, and robust; dorsal profile elevated; ventral profile nearly straight; snout blunt; mouth subterminal; jaw teeth small and in broad bands; gill rakers short, numbering 14–16 on lower limb of first arch; scales ctenoid, large, thick, and numbering 41–45 in lateral series; dorsal fin continuous but deeply notched, with 10 spines in anterior portion and with 1 spine and 19–22 soft rays in posterior portion; caudal fin margin slightly indented; anal fin with 5–7 soft rays and 2 spines, the second spine greatly enlarged; pelvic fin long and inserting dorsoposterior to origin of pectoral fin; pectoral fin long and pointed. Body blackish, with brassy luster dorsally; grayish white ventrally; fins dusky to black; young with 4–6 vertical bars on side. Maximum adult size 1.7 m TL (5.5 ft), with weight of 66 kg (146 lb). The black drum is the largest member of the family Sciaenidae on the Atlantic coast.

corded from among the bay's spawning population. The black drum uses its sensory chin barbels to detect bottom-dwelling prey and is able to crush clams, oysters, mussels, and crabs by mean of its pharyngeal tooth plates.

FISHING INTEREST   Supplying a small commercial gill net fishery on the seaside of the lower Delmarva Peninsula in the early spring and

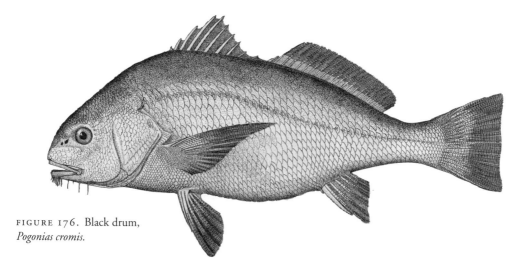

FIGURE 176. Black drum, *Pogonias cromis.*

GEOGRAPHIC DISTRIBUTION   Occurring in coastal waters and estuaries from Massachusetts to Argentina. The black drum is uncommon north of Delaware Bay.

ECOLOGY   Adult black drum enter Chesapeake Bay in April and concentrate just north of the bay mouth west of Cape Charles, where spawning begins in mid- to late April and continues through early June. Black drum eggs are common during the spawning season, but larvae and young are not. There is evidence that larvae may be heavily preyed upon by jellyfishes and comb jellies, and the contributions of Chesapeake Bay spawners may be highly variable from year to year. After the end of spawning, adult black drum spread out in the bay; they are recorded as far north in the bay as the Elk River. Black drum migrate southward in late fall. The species is long-lived, with fish from 7 to 57 years old re-

on the bay side late in the season. The black drum catch shows great annual variation, with catches varying from 2,250 kg (5,000 lb) in 1980 to 91,000 kg (200,000 lb) in 1986. An intense 4- to 6-week recreational fishery in late April to early June is centered on and around the spawning ground west of Cape Charles. The best time to catch black drum is during a full moon. Anglers frequently use a 5/0 hook baited with soft crab and drift-fish on the bottom in 5.5–6.1 m (18–20 ft) of water. The Chesapeake Bay record is a fish weighing 50.5 kg (111.0 lb) that was caught off Cape Charles in 1973.

LITERATURE   Welsh and Breder 1923; Hildebrand and Schroeder 1928:287; Musick 1972; Chao and Musick 1977; Chao 1978; Fischer 1978; Powles and Stender 1978; Manooch 1984; Bobko 1991; Cowan et al. 1992; Daniel and Graves 1994.

Atlantic croaker
Micropogonias undulatus (Linnaeus, 1766)

FIGURE 177. Atlantic croaker,
Micropogonias undulatus.

KEY FEATURES   Chin with 3–5 pairs of small barbels and 5 pores; caudal fin double concave, with middle rays longest; preopercular margin strongly serrate; mouth horizontal and inferior.

OTHER CHARACTERISTICS   Body elongate, somewhat compressed; back slightly elevated; snout conical, projecting beyond mouth; teeth small and in bands; gill rakers short, numbering 14–18 on lower limb of first arch; scales ctenoid, moderately large, and numbering 64–72 in lateral line; scales absent from all fins except caudal fin; dorsal fin deeply notched, with 10 spines in anterior portion and with 1 spine and 26–30 soft rays in posterior portion; anal fin with 2 spines and 7–9 soft rays; pelvic fin inserting ventroposterior to origin of pectoral fin; pectoral fin long. Silvery greenish or grayish dorsally; silvery to brassy white ventrally; upper side with numerous brassy spots that form oblique wavy bars (bars less distinct in large individuals); dorsal fin with numerous dusky spots that form indistinct dusky streaks in posterior portion; pectoral fin greenish, with dusky base; caudal fin greenish; anal and pelvic fins pale to yellowish; large individuals with bronze or yellowish cast to body and fins. Maximum adult size 50 cm TL (1.6 ft) in Chesapeake Bay area, with fish north of Cape Hatteras of larger average size than those south.

GEOGRAPHIC DISTRIBUTION   Found in the western Atlantic from Massachusetts to Florida and throughout the Gulf of Mexico. This species is uncommon north of New Jersey.

ECOLOGY   The Atlantic croaker is one of the most abundant inshore demersal fishes along the southeastern coast of the United States. Adults move into Chesapeake Bay in April and are found throughout the bay most often in salinities above about 5‰. (This species has been collected as far north in the bay as the Susquehanna Flats.) Young of the year of about 20 mm TL (0.8 in) enter the estuary beginning in August and move into the nursery habitat of low-salinity to freshwater creeks. In autumn the young move into the deeper portions of tidal rivers, where they overwinter and leave the bay with adults the following fall. The first spawning occurs at age 2–3 in continental shelf waters from July through February, with peak spawning from August through October for Atlantic croakers in Chesapeake Bay. This species displays greater interannual variability in abundance than any other bay fish. There is evidence suggesting that these fluctuations may be weather-related, with colder winters causing increased mortality in overwintering young of the year. Also, during colder winters, the spawning population may be pushed farther south along the coast, thus reducing the number of postlarval fish that are able to reach the bay nursery areas. Atlantic croakers are opportunistic bottom feeders that consume polychaete worms, mollusks, a variety of small crustaceans, and occasionally small fishes. This species can live as long as 7 years.

FISHING INTEREST   Forming the basis of an important but highly variable commercial fishery in Chesapeake Bay. Atlantic croakers are taken with pound nets, gill nets, and haul seines, with the Virginia portion of the bay providing the bulk of the landings. Bay catches peaked in the mid-1930s through the mid-1940s, with Virginia landings of 26 million kilograms (57 million pounds) reported in 1937. From the late 1940s through the early 1970s, the fishery was in decline except for a brief resurgence in the late 1950s. Bay catches in the late 1960s through 1970 were insignificant, but by 1977 the catch had rebounded to nearly 4 million kilograms (9 million pounds). Another downward trend began in the late 1970s, and in the 1980s and early 1990s the catch averaged between 0.9 and 1.4 million kilograms (2 and 3 million pounds) per year. Prior to 1960, the Atlantic croaker was a mainstay of the recreational fishery, but its highly variable availability in the mid-1960s to mid-1980s reduced its popularity. However, the recreational catch still exceeds the commercial catch. Croakers are taken by recreational anglers from mid-April through September while bottom-fishing with a variety of baits. The bay angling record is a fish weighing 2.8 kg (6.2 lb), taken in 1980. The record for this species is 66 cm SL (2.2 ft), for a fish from the northern Gulf of Mexico.

LITERATURE   Welsh and Breder 1923; Hildebrand and Schroeder 1928:283; Haven 1957; Massmann and Pacheco 1960; Joseph 1972; Musick 1972; Chao and Musick 1977; White and Chittenden 1977; Chao 1978; Fischer 1978; Powles and Stender 1978; Morse 1980; Weinstein et al. 1980; Norcross and Austin 1981; Manooch 1984; Atlantic States Marine Fisheries Commission 1987a; Ross 1988.

Sand drum
Umbrina coroides Cuvier, 1830

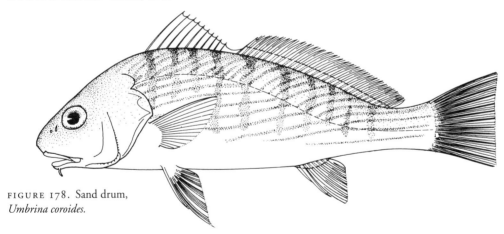

FIGURE 178. Sand drum, *Umbrina coroides.*

KEY FEATURES   Chin with short, blunt, and rigid barbel; preopercular margin serrate; anal fin with 2 spines and 6 soft rays.

OTHER CHARACTERISTICS   Body elongate, compressed; back moderately elevated; head short; snout conical, projecting beyond mouth; mouth inferior; teeth small and in bands; gill rakers numbering approximately 11 on lower limb of first arch; scales small, ctenoid, and numbering about 58 in lateral series; dorsal fin continuous but notched, with 9 or 10 spines in anterior portion and with 1 spine and 26–30 soft rays in posterior portion; caudal fin truncate; anal fin small and with second spine long and strong; pelvic fin originating ventroposterior to origin of pectoral fin; pectoral fin short. Body silvery; back and upper side with undulating longitudinal streaks and 9 vertical black bars; venter and lower side pale. Maximum adult size 35 cm TL (1.1 ft).

GEOGRAPHIC DISTRIBUTION   Found coastally from Chesapeake Bay to Brazil, including much of the Gulf of Mexico and the Caribbean Sea. The sand drum is absent from the northern Gulf of Mexico and much of the Central American coast, and it is uncommon north of Florida.

ECOLOGY   The sand drum is a rare visitor to the lower Chesapeake Bay in late summer. It is typically found in shallow water along sandy beaches. The sand drum can also be encountered over muddy bottoms in estuaries and sometimes near coral reefs. It feeds on bottom-dwelling organisms.

FISHING INTEREST   None in the Chesapeake Bay area. A commercial fishery exists in more tropical waters where the species is more abundant.

LITERATURE   Welsh and Breder 1923; Hildebrand and Schroeder 1928:289; Musick 1972; Chao and Musick 1977; Chao 1978; Fischer 1978; Powles and Stender 1978.

Gulf kingfish
Menticirrhus littoralis (Holbrook, 1855)

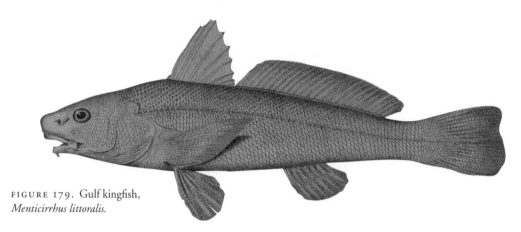

FIGURE 179. Gulf kingfish, *Menticirrhus littoralis.*

KEY FEATURES   Chin with single, short, median barbel; nape and side without bars or stripes; anal fin with 1 spine and 6–8 rays (typically 7); prepelvic scales distinctly smaller than scales on rest of body.

OTHER CHARACTERISTICS   Body elongate and rounded, with back slightly elevated and belly nearly straight; snout conical, projecting beyond mouth; mouth inferior; chin with 5 pores, the median pore at tip of barbel; teeth small and in bands; gill rakers small nubs to absent, numbering 0–8 on lower limb of first arch; preopercular margin serrate; scales small, ctenoid, and numbering 72–74 in row just above lateral line; dorsal fin continuous but deeply notched, with 10 or 11 flexible spines (typically 10) in anterior portion and with 1 spine and 19–26 soft rays in posterior portion; caudal fin with concave upper portion and elongate lower portion; pelvic fin inserting ventroposterior to origin of pectoral fin; pectoral fin broad and moderately long. Body silvery gray dorsally, with bronze cast to side and on cheek; belly white; spinous dorsal fin light brown, with dusky tip; caudal fin pale, with dusky margin; other fins pale to dusky. Maximum adult size 46 cm TL (1.5 ft).

GEOGRAPHIC DISTRIBUTION   Occurring from Delaware south and throughout the Gulf of Mexico to Brazil. This species is most common south of Cape Hatteras and in the Gulf of Mexico.

ECOLOGY   The gulf kingfish is the least common of the three species of *Menticirrhus* that occur in Chesapeake Bay. Like other members of this genus, it is more frequently found along coastal beaches, especially in the surf zone. Its distribution within the bay is primarily in the polyhaline waters near the bay mouth, and its diet and habits appear similar to those of the northern kingfish.

FISHING INTEREST   See under discussion for the northern kingfish, below.

LITERATURE   Welsh and Breder 1923; Hildebrand and Schroeder 1928:294; Musick 1972; Chao 1978; Fischer 1978; Powles and Stender 1978.

Northern kingfish
Menticirrhus saxatilis (Bloch and Schneider, 1801)
PLATE 30

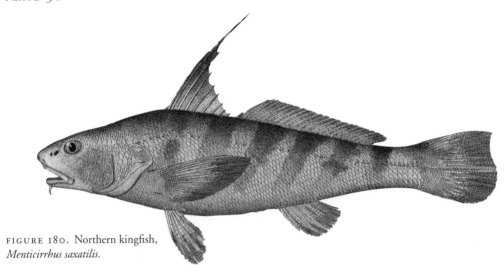

FIGURE 180. Northern kingfish, *Menticirrhus saxatilis.*

KEY FEATURES   Chin with single, short, median barbel; dorsal fin spines flexible, the second or third spine elongate; side and nape with 5 or 6 oblique blackish bars; bar that precedes spinous dorsal fin and bar that follows it converging behind pectoral fin base to form prominent V; anal fin with 1 spine and 7–9 rays (typically 8); prepelvic scales similar in size to those on body.

OTHER CHARACTERISTICS   Body elongate and rounded, with back slightly elevated and belly nearly straight; snout conical, projecting beyond mouth; mouth inferior; chin with 5 pores, the median pore at tip of barbel; teeth small and in bands; gill rakers small nubs to absent, numbering 0–7 on lower limb of first arch; preopercular margin serrate; scales small, ctenoid, and numbering 91–96 in row just above lateral line; dorsal fin continuous but deeply notched; anterior portion of dorsal fin with 10 or 11 spines; posterior portion of dorsal fin with 1 spine and 22–27 soft rays; caudal fin with concave upper portion and elongate lower portion; pelvic fin

short, inserting perpendicular to pectoral fin; pectoral fin broad and moderately long. Body silvery gray or tan dorsally; dusky longitudinal streak present on posterior flank and extending onto caudal fin in larger specimens; distal margin of pectoral fin black; other fins pale to dusky. Maximum adult size 50 cm TL (1.7 ft), with weight of 1.3 kg (3 lb).

GEOGRAPHIC DISTRIBUTION   Found from Maine to the northern coast of Yucatán. The northern kingfish is most common from New York through North Carolina.

ECOLOGY   Northern kingfish enter Chesapeake Bay in April and May and leave in the fall for wintering grounds on the continental shelf. They are most abundant in the lower bay in salinities above 10‰ over firm bottoms. This species has been collected as far north in the bay as the Chester River. Spawning occurs at age 2–3 from May through August in coastal waters. The northern kingfish is known to live at least 4 years. This species is a bottom feeder, primarily on small crustaceans and polychaete worms.

FISHING INTEREST   Of limited commercial importance and taken along with other species by gill nets, haul seines, and pound nets. The northern kingfish is also called sea mullet, round-head, or whiting. Catch data, as well as anglers, rarely distinguish this species from the southern kingfish *(Menticirrhus americanus)* and the gulf kingfish *(M. littoralis),* with which it is often co-incidental. Commercial catches of kingfishes peaked in Chesapeake Bay in the 1940s but have been insignificant for the past 30 years. Recreational anglers take kingfishes while bottom-fishing over firm bottoms with a variety of baits. The fishing season runs from April through mid-November but is best from August through October. The typical catch weighs 0.23–0.68 kg (0.5–1.5 lb).

LITERATURE   Welsh and Breder 1923; Hildebrand and Schroeder 1928:290; Musick 1972; Chao and Musick 1977; Chao 1978; Fischer 1978; Powles and Stender 1978; Ralph 1982.

Southern kingfish
Menticirrhus americanus (Linnaeus, 1758)

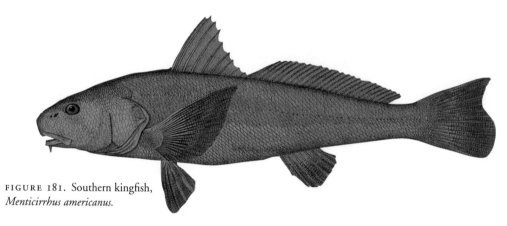

FIGURE 181. Southern kingfish, *Menticirrhus americanus.*

KEY FEATURES   Chin with single, short, median barbel; nape and side with 7 or 8 faint oblique dusky bars, none forming prominent V; anal fin with 1 spine and 6–8 rays (typically 7); prepelvic scales similar in size to those on body.

OTHER CHARACTERISTICS   Body elongate and rounded, with back slightly elevated and belly nearly straight; snout conical, projecting beyond mouth; mouth inferior; chin with 5 pores, the median pore at tip of barbel; teeth small and in bands; gill rakers small nubs to absent, numbering 0–7 on lower limb of first arch; preopercular margin serrate; scales small, ctenoid, and numbering 86–96 in row just above lateral line; dorsal fin continuous but deeply notched, with 9 or 10 flexible spines (typically 10) in anterior portion and with 1 spine and 20–26 soft rays in posterior portion; caudal fin with concave upper portion and elongate lower portion; pelvic fin short and inserting slightly ventroposterior to origin of pectoral fin; pectoral fin broad and moderately long. Body silvery gray or tan dorsally; belly silvery white; spinous dorsal fin dusky along margin; soft dorsal fin pale; caudal fin dusky, the upper portion often with tan pigment; pectoral fin dusky, sometimes with blackish edge; pelvic and anal fins white to yellowish. Maximum adult size 42 cm SL (1.4 ft), with weight of 1 kg (2.2 lb).

GEOGRAPHIC DISTRIBUTION   Occurring from New York south through the Gulf of Mexico to Buenos Aires, Argentina. The southern kingfish is most common from Chesapeake Bay to the Bay of Campeche, Mexico, but is rare to absent in South Florida and the Antilles.

ECOLOGY   Southern kingfish are similar to northern kingfish in their ecology. They enter Chesapeake Bay in the spring and leave in the fall for wintering grounds on the continental shelf. They are most abundant in the polyhaline waters of the lower bay. Southern kingfish are demersal and occur over a wide variety of substrates from mud to sand-mud mixtures; adults frequent the sand bottoms of ocean beaches and the mouths of large coastal sounds. The southern kingfish is found in a wider range of water temperatures (8°–30°C, or 46°–86°F) and salinities (6–35‰) than either the gulf kingfish or the northern kingfish. Spawning occurs outside bay waters from April through September. This species is a bottom feeder, primarily on small crustaceans and polychaete worms. It may attain 5–6 years of age.

FISHING INTEREST   See under discussion

for the northern kingfish, page 198. In some years the southern kingfish is apparently more abundant in Chesapeake Bay than the northern kingfish.

LITERATURE   Welsh and Breder 1923; Hildebrand and Schroeder 1928:291; Musick 1972; Chao and Musick 1977; Chao 1978; Powles and Stender 1978; Manooch 1984; Smith and Wenner 1985.

Silver seatrout
Cynoscion nothus (Holbrook, 1855)

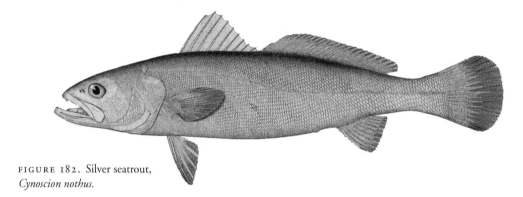

FIGURE 182. Silver seatrout, *Cynoscion nothus.*

KEY FEATURES   Pair of enlarged canine teeth present at tip of upper jaw; posterior margin of caudal fin rounded or with lower rays elongate; body without conspicuous spots.

OTHER CHARACTERISTICS   Body elongate fusiform; mouth large; snout pointed; lower jaw projecting; chin without barbels; preopercle with smooth posterior margin; scales moderately large, weakly ctenoid, and numbering about 67–72 in lateral series; soft dorsal and anal fins scaled about halfway to margin; gill rakers long and slender, numbering about 8–10 on lower limb of first arch; dorsal fins narrowly separated in adults, with 10 spines in anterior portion and with 1 spine and 26–31 soft rays in posterior portion; anal fin with 2 spines and 8–10 soft rays; pelvic fin short, inserting slightly ventroposterior to origin of pectoral fin; pectoral fin pointed and slightly shorter than pelvic fin. Grayish brown dorsally; silvery ventrally; back and upper side sometimes marked with faint irregular rows of spots; dorsal fin dusky; other fins pale. Maximum adult size 38 cm TL (1.3 ft).

GEOGRAPHIC DISTRIBUTION   Occurring from Chesapeake Bay to the Bay of Campeche,

Mexico. The silver seatrout is most abundant in the Gulf of Mexico.

ECOLOGY   Adult silver seatrout are occasionally found in the lower Chesapeake Bay in summer and fall in salinities above 18‰, but they are more common in outside coastal waters. This species is the least abundant of the seatrouts that enter the bay, and little is known of its ecology in Virginia and Maryland waters. Spawning occurs from May through August in nearshore coastal waters in North Carolina. There appears to be no significant spawning in Virginia waters. The silver seatrout feeds on crustaceans and small fishes.

FISHING INTEREST   Occasionally taken in pound nets near the Chesapeake Bay mouth but not the subject of a commercial fishery. Anglers take silver seatrout as a rarity when angling for other species.

LITERATURE   Welsh and Breder 1923; Hildebrand and Schroeder 1928:299; Musick 1972; Chao and Musick 1977; Chao 1978; Fischer 1978; Powles and Stender 1978.

Spotted seatrout
Cynoscion nebulosus (Cuvier, 1830)

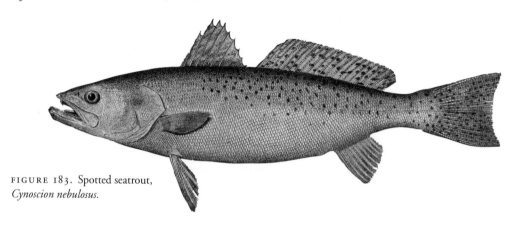

FIGURE 183. Spotted seatrout,
Cynoscion nebulosus.

KEY FEATURES   Numerous black spots scattered on upper side and on dorsal and caudal fins; pair of enlarged canine teeth present at tip of upper jaw; posterior margin of caudal fin concave; fins scaleless except for several basal rows of scales on first dorsal fin and anal fin.

OTHER CHARACTERISTICS   Body elongate fusiform; mouth large; snout pointed; lower jaw projecting; chin without barbels; preopercle with smooth posterior margin; scales small, weakly ctenoid, and numbering about 90–102 in lateral series; gill rakers short, numbering 6–9 on lower limb of first arch; dorsal fins narrowly separated or continuous but deeply notched, with 10 spines (rarely 9 or 11) in anterior portion and with 1 spine and 24–28 soft rays in posterior portion; anal fin with 2 spines and 9–12 soft rays; pelvic fin short, inserting slightly ventroposterior to origin of pectoral fin; pectoral fin shorter than pelvic fin. Body dusky gray dorsally, with bluish reflections and silvery ventrally; first dorsal fin dusky; other fins pale yellowish green. Maximum adult size about 90 cm TL (3 ft), with weight of 7.25 kg (16 lb).

GEOGRAPHIC DISTRIBUTION   Found from Cape Cod to Mexico but rare north of Delaware Bay.

ECOLOGY   Spotted seatrout, also known as speckled trout, prefer shallow water over sandy bottoms near submerged aquatic vegetation or structures. Adults display a wide salinity tolerance and may be found in salinities as low as 5‰ in Chesapeake Bay tributaries. Adult spotted sea-

trout are migratory in the bay, usually arriving in late April and moving offshore and south in late November. They are most abundant in the lower bay but are found throughout bay waters. Spawning occurs at night from late May through July near the bay mouth and in nearby coastal waters. In summer and fall, young of the year are common in intertidal creeks and may also be found in nearshore beds of submerged aquatic vegetation. Spotted seatrout are opportunistic carnivores whose food habits change with size; when they are small, their diet consists primarily of crustaceans, and as they mature, it shifts to fish. The major food items of adults are peneid shrimps and numerous fishes such as striped mullet, pinfish, and anchovies. Spotted seatrout feed sporadically but primarily during morning hours. A maximum age of 15 years has been reported for Chesapeake Bay spotted seatrout.

FISHING INTEREST   Spotted seatrout rank second by weight in catches by U.S. saltwater anglers, primarily in the Southeast. No reliable catch records exist for the recreational fishery for spotted seatrout in Chesapeake Bay, but the catch likely exceeds that of the commercial fishery. The largest catches occur from May through November in the lower bay and the York and Rappahannock rivers. During spring and autumn, spotted seatrout are taken at high tide over shallow eelgrass beds at dawn and dusk, by using peeler crabs or artificial lures and bait. In November, spotted seatrout are caught by anglers in the deep channel areas of the Chesapeake Bay Bridge Tunnel, where they are associated with weakfish. In addition to their importance as a recreational species, spotted seatrout are taken by haul seines, pound nets, and gill nets; however, the catch is of minor commercial importance in Chesapeake Bay. Maryland landings have been less than 455 kg (1,000 lb) annually since the 1940s. Virginia's annual catch reached 345,000 kg (760,000 lb) in 1944 but has steadily declined since, and in recent times it has not exceeded 8,600 kg (19,000

lb). The typical spotted seatrout in Chesapeake Bay weighs 1–2 kg (2–4 lb); however, the world all-tackle record of 7.5 kg (16.5 lb) was taken in 1977 near Roaring Point, Maryland.

LITERATURE   Welsh and Breder 1923; Hildebrand and Schroeder 1928:296; Musick 1972; Chao and Musick 1977; Chao 1978; Fischer 1978; Powles and Stender 1978; Brown 1981; Atlantic States Marine Fisheries Commission 1984; Kostecki 1984; Manooch 1984; Mercer 1984b.

Weakfish
Cynoscion regalis (Bloch and Schneider, 1801)
PLATE 31

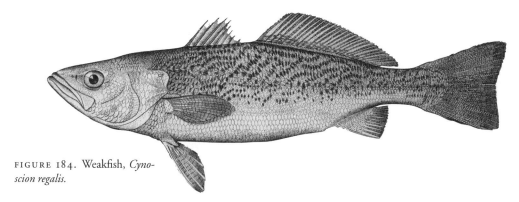

FIGURE 184. Weakfish, *Cynoscion regalis.*

KEY FEATURES   Back and upper side with dusky blotches and spots formed into oblique wavy lines; soft dorsal and anal fins partially scaled; pair of enlarged canine teeth present at tip of upper jaw; posterior margin of caudal fin concave in adults.

OTHER CHARACTERISTICS   Body elongate fusiform; mouth large; snout pointed; lower jaw projecting; chin without barbels; preopercle with smooth posterior margin; scales small, weakly ctenoid, and numbering about 76–86 in lateral series; soft dorsal and anal fins scaled about halfway to margin; gill rakers long and slender, numbering 10–12 on lower limb of first arch; dorsal fins narrowly separated in adults, with 10 spines in anterior portion and with 1 spine and 24–29 soft rays (typically 26–28) in posterior portion; anal fin with 2 spines and 10–13 soft rays; pelvic fin short, inserting slightly ventroposterior to origin of pectoral fin; pectoral fin somewhat rounded and shorter than pelvic fin. Dark olive green dorsally; back and side variously burnished

with blue or copper; underside white or silvery; fins dark yellow. Maximum adult size 91 cm TL (3 ft), with weight of 8.5 kg (19 lb).

GEOGRAPHIC DISTRIBUTION   Occurring from Nova Scotia to about Cape Canaveral, Florida. The weakfish is most abundant from North Carolina through Long Island.

ECOLOGY   North of Cape Hatteras, weakfish (also known as gray trout) display a spring and summer migration northward and inshore, and a fall and winter movement southward and offshore. Larger fish (year 2 and older) appear in the lower Chesapeake Bay in April–May, with age-1 fish becoming abundant in summer. In the estuary, adult weakfish occur in schools and frequent shallow, sandy bottom areas in salinities above 10‰. However, weakfish are found throughout bay waters. Weakfish feed on a variety of small fishes, larger zooplankton, shrimps, and crabs and become increasingly piscivorous with age. North of Cape Hatteras, weakfish tend to be larger after age 1 and attain a greater longevity than those farther south. Maturity is reached at age 1–2, and spawning takes place near the bay mouth and in adjacent nearshore waters. The spawning period is protracted (April–August), with peak spawning from May through June. Larvae are taken throughout the lower bay in late summer, and young of the year of about 4 cm TL (1.6 in) appear in low-salinity river habitats in August. The young fish grow rapidly in the rivers through October. At about 12 cm TL (4.7 in) they begin to move into more saline waters, and they apparently leave the estuary by early winter. Weakfish live as long as 9 years.

FISHING INTEREST   Weakfish landings by pound nets, gill nets, and haul seines constitute an important fishery in the lower Chesapeake Bay, but the fishery has been in decline since the 1940s. Maryland reported bayside landings of 318,000 kg (700,000 lb) in 1948, but the catch has averaged less than 91,000 kg (200,000 lb) in the 1980s and 1990s. In Virginia the bay catch peaked at 7.2 million kilograms (16 million pounds) in 1946 but has not exceeded 2.7 million kilograms (6 million pounds) since 1948. Recent Virginia landings have rarely exceeded 1.1 million kilograms (2.5 million pounds). Much of the decline in the weakfish fishery appears attributable to overfishing and degradation in the estuarine environment. Weakfish are a major recreational species in the bay, with the 1985 estimated catch exceeding 460,000 kg (1 million pounds). Anglers slowly troll bucktails in the spring and bottom-fish using hooks baited with soft crab or jig-baited bucktails in the summer and autumn. Typical weakfish catches weigh 0.5–3.5 kg (1–8 lb). The bay size record, also the world record, is a fish weighing 8.5 kg (19 lb) that was taken at the Chesapeake Bay Bridge Tunnel in 1983.

LITERATURE   Welsh and Breder 1923; Hildebrand and Schroeder 1928:300; Massmann 1963; Joseph 1972; Musick 1972; Merriner 1976; Chao and Musick 1977; Chao 1978; Fischer 1978; Powles and Stender 1978; Mercer 1983; Olney 1983; Sheperd and Grimes 1983, 1984; Manooch 1984; Atlantic States Marine Fisheries Commission 1985; Graves et al. 1992; Daniel and Graves 1994.

Red drum
Sciaenops ocellatus (Linnaeus, 1766)

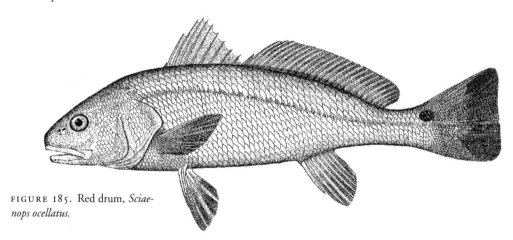

FIGURE 185. Red drum, *Sciaenops ocellatus.*

KEY FEATURES   One to several black ocellar spots present on upper portion of caudal peduncle; mouth inferior and horizontal; chin without barbels.

OTHER CHARACTERISTICS   Body elongate and robust; back moderately elevated; ventral profile nearly straight; head and snout long; teeth in several bands; gill rakers short, numbering 12–14 on first arch; margin of preopercle serrate in young, becoming smooth in adults; scales large, ctenoid, and numbering about 40–45 in lateral series; dorsal fin continuous but deeply notched, with 10 spines in anterior portion and with 1 spine and 23–25 soft rays in posterior portion;

anal fin with 2 spines and 7–9 soft rays; posterior margin of caudal fin straight to slightly S-shaped; pelvic fin short, inserting ventroposterior to origin of pectoral fin; pectoral fin shorter than pelvic fin. Coloration somewhat variable; most frequently silvery, tinged with copper dorsally; white ventrally; dorsal and caudal fins dusky; anal and pelvic fins white; pectoral fin rusty distally. Maximum adult size 1.5 m TL (5 ft), with weight of 42 kg (92 lb).

GEOGRAPHIC DISTRIBUTION   Known from the Gulf of Maine to the northern coast of Mexico but uncommon north of New Jersey. The red drum is more abundant in the Gulf of Mexico than along the Atlantic coast.

ECOLOGY   Adults red drum occur in Chesapeake Bay from May through November and are most abundant in the spring and fall near the bay mouth in salinities above 15‰. However, in the bay area they are most frequently taken along seaside beaches. This species extends as far north in the bay as the Patuxent River. Adult red drum are most common in nearshore marine waters, where they may travel in large schools. Red drum occasionally move offshore, but there is no specific information available on timing, duration, or extent of these movements. Red drum display a northerly migration in the spring and southerly movement in the fall, but they may occasionally overwinter in the bay in mild winters. Spawning occurs in nearshore coastal waters from late summer through fall, with young of the year appearing in the estuary from August through September. The food of the red drum consists of small to moderate-sized crustaceans and fishes. The red drum can live as long as 35 years.

FISHING INTEREST   Supporting an important sport and commercial fishery in the Gulf of Mexico and, to a lesser extent, along the south Atlantic coast but not constituting an important fishery in the Chesapeake Bay area. Virginia's commercial catch, once as high as 82,000 kg (180,000 lb) per year, has been insignificant since 1965, and Maryland's annual catch has not exceeded 910 kg (2,000 lb) since 1954. A modest recreational fishery exists, with most fish taken by surf casting from seaside beaches and some by bait fishing along the bay side of the lower Eastern Shore. The Chesapeake Bay size record is unknown, but the Virginia record is a fish weighing 38.8 kg (85.3 lb) that was taken from the seaside of Wreck Island in 1981.

LITERATURE   Welsh and Breder 1923; Hildebrand and Schroeder 1928:276; Mansueti 1960; Musick 1972; Chao and Musick 1977; Chao 1978; Fischer 1978; Powles and Stender 1978; Buckley 1984; Manooch 1984; Mercer 1984a; Murphy and Taylor 1990.

Spot
Leiostomus xanthurus Lacepède, 1802

KEY FEATURES   Caudal fin distinctly forked; 12–15 oblique dusky bars present on upper side; distinct dusky to black spot present on body just behind dorsal end of gill opening; head short; snout blunt; mouth small and inferior.

OTHER CHARACTERISTICS   Body rather deep, compressed; back elevated; teeth small and in bands; chin without barbels; gill rakers short and slender, numbering 20–23 on lower limb of first arch; scales small, ctenoid, and numbering 72–77 in lateral line; small scales extending onto bases of fins; dorsal fin deeply notched, with 9–11 spines in anterior portion and with 1 spine and 29–35 soft rays (typically 30 or 31) in posterior portion; anal fin with 2 spines and 12–13 soft rays; pelvic fin short, inserting ventroposterior to origin of pectoral fin; pectoral fin pointed and longer than pelvic fin. Body bluish gray dorsally; brassy white ventrally; fins pale to yellowish. Maximum adult size 29 cm TL (11 in).

GEOGRAPHIC DISTRIBUTION   Known from the Gulf of Maine to the Bay of Campeche off northern Mexico. Spot are most abundant from Chesapeake Bay through the Carolinas.

ECOLOGY   Spot migrate seasonally between coastal and estuarine waters. Adults and juveniles enter Chesapeake Bay during the spring and remain until fall, when they migrate to south of Cape Hatteras. Adult spot are primarily found in salinities above 5‰, but the young of the year often penetrate tributaries to the lower reaches of freshwater. Spot are found throughout the bay. Spawning occurs at age 2–3 in offshore coastal waters in late fall to early spring, with a peak in

February. After spawning, adult spot may remain offshore. Larval spot enter the bay in winter and spring and appear in nursery habitats (low-salinity tidal creeks) in April and May when they are about 25 mm TL (1.0 in). The young spot grow rapidly through the summer and by fall have reached an average total length of about 125 mm (4.9 in). Most young of the year leave the estuary by December, but some apparently

million kilograms (6.4 million pounds) were landed. Chesapeake Bay catches in recent years have rarely exceeded 900,000 kg (2 million pounds). Catch declines may be associated with the degradation of the estuarine nursery habitat. Recreational anglers take spot from shore or boat while bottom fishing with a wide variety of baits. Oftentimes, anglers drift-fish over the bottom, using small hooks baited with bloodworms. The

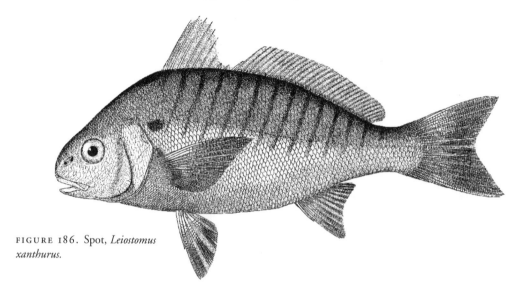

FIGURE 186. Spot, *Leiostomus xanthurus*.

overwinter. Newly arrived young spot feed predominantly on crustacean zooplankton, but they make the transition to bottom feeding as they grow. Both juveniles and adults are nocturnal predators on polychaete worms, small crustaceans, and mollusks. Spot often congregate over oyster beds.

FISHING INTEREST   One of Chesapeake Bay's most important commercial and recreational species. Commercial catches come from pound nets, gill nets, and haul seines, with landings in Virginia typically an order of magnitude larger than those in Maryland. Spot catches have shown considerable interannual fluctuation but peaked in 1949 at 3.9 million kilograms (8.7 million pounds) and have generally declined since. The last large catch was made in 1970, when 2.9

spot season in the bay extends from about May through October and peaks in late summer to early fall. The Chesapeake Bay angling record is a fish that weighed 1.1 kg (2.3 lb) and was caught off Poquoson, Virginia, in 1980.

LITERATURE   Welsh and Breder 1923; Hildebrand and Schroeder 1928:271; Dawson 1958; Pacheco 1962; Joseph 1972; Musick 1972; Chao and Musick 1977; Chao 1978; Fischer 1978; Powles and Stender 1978; Powell and Gordy 1980; Weinstein et al. 1980; Weinstein 1981, 1983; Weinstein and Walters 1981; Manooch 1984; Warlen and Chester 1985; Atlantic States Marine Fisheries Commission 1987b; O'Neil and Weinstein 1987; Hales and Van Den Avyle 1989; Virginia Marine Resources Commission 1990.

Banded drum
Larimus fasciatus Holbrook, 1855

FIGURE 187. Banded drum,
Larimus fasciatus.

KEY FEATURES   Seven to 9 dusky vertical
bars present on back, extending to midline of
body; body short, deep, and compressed; mouth
large and obliquely oriented.

OTHER CHARACTERISTICS   Dorsal profile
elevated; snout short; lower jaw projecting; teeth
small and in single row in each jaw; chin without barbels; gill rakers long and slender, numbering 23–25 on lower limb of first arch; scales
ctenoid, moderate in size, and numbering 50–56
in lateral series; dorsal fin continuous but deeply
notched, with 10 spines in anterior portion and
with 1 spine and 24–27 soft rays in posterior portion; caudal fin with median rays the longest;
anal fin with 2 spines and 6 or 7 soft rays; pelvic
fin moderately long, inserting slightly ventroposterior to origin of pectoral fin; pectoral fin
pointed and approximately as long as pelvic fin.
Grayish green dorsally; silvery white ventrally; inner surface of opercle darkly pigmented; lower
portion of caudal fin yellowish; pelvic fin yellowish, dusky toward tip; anal fin yellowish; dorsal
fin dusky. Maximum adult size 23 cm TL (9 in).

GEOGRAPHIC DISTRIBUTION   Found
from Massachusetts to Florida and the northern
Gulf of Mexico but not abundant north of Cape
Hatteras.

ECOLOGY   The banded drum is occasionally
taken in salinities above 15‰ in the lower Chesapeake Bay. This species is more typically found
over mud and sandy mud bottoms in coastal waters to depths of about 60 m (200 ft) and is only
rarely encountered in estuaries. Banded drum
feed in the water column at dawn and dusk.
Their diet comprises primarily shrimps and copepods.

FISHING INTEREST   Not the subject of a
commercial fishery, because of small size and low
abundance. Banded drum are occasionally caught
in pound nets, and anglers rarely take them on
hook and line in the lower Chesapeake Bay.

LITERATURE   Welsh and Breder 1923; Hildebrand and Schroeder 1928:278; Musick 1972;
Chao and Musick 1977; Chao 1978; Fischer
1978; Powles and Stender 1978; Powles 1980;
Ross 1984, 1989.

Star drum
Stellifer lanceolatus (Holbrook, 1855)

KEY FEATURES   Head broad; interorbital region and occiput with greatly enlarged sensory canals, giving spongy appearance to top of head;
preopercle with 4–6 spines; anal fin with 2 spines
and 7–9 soft rays (typically 7 or 8); caudal fin
pointed.

OTHER CHARACTERISTICS   Body compressed, oblong; head broad, with nape slightly concave; snout blunt; mouth oblique and moderate-sized; teeth small and in narrow bands;

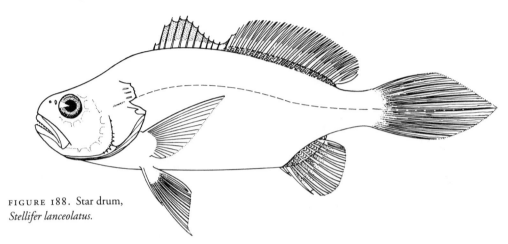

FIGURE 188. Star drum, *Stellifer lanceolatus.*

chin without barbels; gill rakers long and slender, numbering 21–23 on lower limb of first arch; scales ctenoid, extending onto fins, and numbering about 47–50 in lateral series; dorsal fin continuous but deeply notched, with 11 or 12 spines in anterior portion and with 1 spine and 20–25 soft rays in posterior portion; pelvic fin short to moderately long, inserting perpendicular to origin of pectoral fin; pectoral fin pointed and longer than pelvic fin. Olive gray dorsally; silvery ventrally; spinous dorsal fin with dusky margin. Maximum adult size 20 cm TL (8 in).

GEOGRAPHIC DISTRIBUTION   Occurring in inshore waters from Virginia to Texas but not common north of South Carolina.

ECOLOGY   The star drum strays infrequently north to the Chesapeake Bay mouth during the summer. It is typically found over sand-mud bottoms in coastal waters to depths of about 20 m (66 ft). The star drum is also encountered in river estuaries. It apparently feeds both in the water column and from the bottom, predominantly on small crustaceans.

FISHING INTEREST   None in the Chesapeake Bay area.

LITERATURE   Welsh and Breder 1923; Hildebrand and Schroeder 1928:282; Musick 1972; Chao and Musick 1977; Chao 1978; Fischer 1978; Powles and Stender 1978; Powles 1980.

Silver perch
Bairdiella chrysoura (Lacepède, 1802)

KEY FEATURES   Preopercle with serrate margin; top of head not spongy to the touch; anal fin with 2 spines and 8–10 soft rays (typically 10); caudal fin with median rays slightly longer than other rays.

OTHER CHARACTERISTICS   Body moderately elongate, compressed; back somewhat elevated; mouth moderate-sized, terminal, and slightly oblique; snout not projecting; teeth small and conical; teeth in upper jaw in several rows, with those in outer row moderately enlarged;

teeth of lower jaw on narrow ridge, with those in median row slightly larger; chin without barbels; gill rakers moderately long, numbering 22–24 on first arch; scales ctenoid, numbering 55–59 in lateral series; scales present on bases of pectoral and pelvic fins and extending onto and covering most of soft dorsal, anal, and caudal fins; dorsal fin continuous but notched nearly to base, with 10 or 11 spines in anterior portion and 1 spine and 19–23 soft rays in posterior portion; pelvic fin broad, inserting ventroposterior to origin of pectoral fin; pectoral fin shorter than pelvic fin. Greenish or bluish gray dorsally, with faint dusky stripes along scale rows; side and belly silvery; fins yellowish. Maximum adult size 30 cm TL (1 ft).

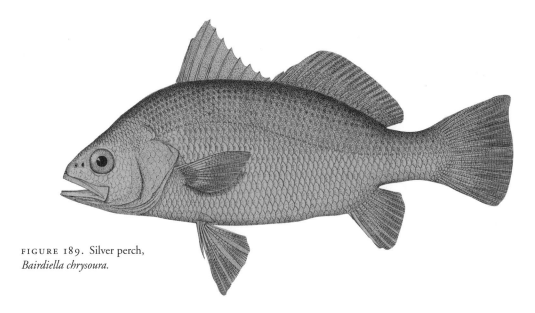

FIGURE 189. Silver perch, *Bairdiella chrysoura*.

GEOGRAPHIC DISTRIBUTION   Found from New York to the Gulf coast of northern Mexico.

ECOLOGY   Silver perch occur in Chesapeake Bay throughout the year but are most frequently taken from April through November, with peak abundance in September and October. They retreat to deeper bay waters in the colder months and may migrate to coastal waters during especially cold winters. The abundance of silver perch declines in the northern portion of the bay, and the species is rare north of Baltimore. The diet consists mostly of small crustaceans, with some polychaete worms and fishes. Spawning occurs along the bayside and seaside Eastern Shore beginning in early to mid-April and lasting through June. Juveniles settle in shallow sea grass beds, where they are abundant.

FISHING INTEREST   Taken in pound nets but of limited commercial value because of small size. Silver perch are often caught by anglers with hook and line but are rarely a targeted species.

LITERATURE   Welsh and Breder 1923; Hildebrand and Schroeder 1928:279; Musick 1972; Chao and Musick 1977; Chao 1978; Fischer 1978; Powles and Stender 1978; Powles 1980; Manooch 1984; Daniel and Graves 1994.

Spadefishes
FAMILY EPHIPPIDAE

Spadefishes are compressed, deep-bodied coastal fishes that inhabit depths to about 30 m (100 ft). Most spadefishes frequent rocky bottoms and reefs as well as wrecks and pilings, sometimes forming dense schools. They feed on a variety of benthic and planktonic invertebrates. The young of several species in this family resemble floating leaves, a characteristic that is thought to reduce their risk of predation. The color pattern typically includes four to six dusky vertical bars on the head and side, but these bars are often obscure or absent in large adults. The family, inhabiting all tropical and subtropical waters, comprises 7 genera and 20 species, 1 of which frequents Chesapeake Bay waters.

Atlantic spadefish
Chaetodipterus faber (Broussonet, 1782)

FIGURE 190. Atlantic spadefish,
Chaetodipterus faber.

KEY FEATURES   Body very deep and compressed; spinous and soft fins separate; anterior portion of soft dorsal and anal fins prolonged into filaments; adults usually with 4–6 broad dusky vertical bars on body (fading with age).

OTHER CHARACTERISTICS   Head blunt; mouth small and terminal; teeth in bands; spinous portion of dorsal fin low in adults; third spine of dorsal fin produced in juveniles; dorsal fin with 9 spines and 21–23 soft rays; caudal fin emarginate; anal fin with 3 spines and 17–20 soft rays; pelvic fin longer than and originating slightly ventroposterior to pectoral fin. Body silvery gray; first vertical bar passing through eye; last bar located on caudal peduncle; most fins blackish; juveniles typically all black. Maximum adult size 90 cm TL (3 ft), with weights exceeding 9 kg (20 lb).

GEOGRAPHIC DISTRIBUTION   Known from New England to southern Brazil, including the Gulf of Mexico and the Caribbean Sea, but rare north of Chesapeake Bay. This species is the only family member that is native to the western Atlantic Ocean.

ECOLOGY   The Atlantic spadefish is an occasional to common visitor during summer and autumn to the mid-lower Chesapeake Bay, extending as far north as Solomons Island. It occurs in schools of a few to more than 500 individuals, most frequently around towers, buoys, or other structures. Spawning occurs offshore from May to August, and large spawning aggregations can be found near the surface on warm, sunny days when the water temperature is 24°–29°C (75°–85°F). The young of the year are common in nearshore habitats of the lower bay in late summer and early fall. Atlantic spadefish feed on the bottom or near the surface on a wide variety of invertebrates, including jellyfishes, hydroids, polychaetes, amphipods, sponges, and sea anemones. Atlantic spadefish attain at least 8 years of age.

FISHING INTEREST   Of only minor commercial importance but pursued by anglers fishing near the Chesapeake Bay mouth and offshore. Because of the Atlantic spadefish's small mouth, small hooks baited with pieces of jelly-fishes, clams, or mussels are used. Most catches run 1.4–3.6 kg (3–8 lb); however, the weight record for Chesapeake Bay is 5.9 kg (13 lb). The flesh is of excellent quality.

LITERATURE   Hildebrand and Schroeder 1928:306; Musick 1972; Fischer 1978; Johnson 1978; Fritzsche 1982; Fahay 1983; Manooch 1984; Hayse 1990.

Bluefishes
FAMILY POMATOMIDAE

The family Pomatomidae comprises two genera and three species. Two species in the family are smallish, deep-dwelling predators of the outer continental shelf. However, the bluefish, the single species in the genus *Pomatomus,* is a moderate-sized to large fish with a sturdy compressed body and a large head. It occurs on continental shelves and in estuaries of temperate and tropical waters around much of the world except the eastern Pacific. The bluefish is a pelagic schooling species that is considered a bloodthirsty pred-ator of other fishes. It has the rare reputation among predators of wantonly killing prey that it does not eat. Bluefish have occasionally bitten human bathers who were unfortunate enough to encounter a feed-ing school in the surf zone. The bluefish is among the most abundant and most frequently caught food and sport fishes along the Atlantic coast and supports important recreational and commercial fisheries.

Bluefish
Pomatomus saltatrix (Linnaeus, 1766)
PLATE 32

FIGURE 191. Bluefish, *Pomatomus saltatrix.*

KEY FEATURES   Body elongate, moderately compressed; head rather long; snout pointed; mouth large, with lower jaw projecting; both jaws with series of sharp, somewhat compressed and triangular teeth; upper jaw with additional inner series of small depressible teeth; dorsal fins separate; spines of first dorsal fin connected by membrane; second dorsal fin and anal fin covered with scales; black blotch present at base of pecto-ral fin.

OTHER CHARACTERISTICS   Scales small; lateral line nearly straight, extending onto base of caudal fin; preopercle serrate; first dorsal fin com-posed of 7 or 8 short slender spines; second dor-

sal fin with 23–26 soft rays; anal fin similar to second dorsal fin, slightly elevated anteriorly, and with 2 spines and 25–27 soft rays; caudal fin forked; pelvic and pectoral fins short. Greenish blue dorsally; silvery ventrally. Maximum adult size 1.1 m TL (3.6 ft).

GEOGRAPHIC DISTRIBUTION   In the western Atlantic, occurring from Nova Scotia to Brazil, including the Gulf of Mexico, but rare or absent in most of the Caribbean Sea.

ECOLOGY   The bluefish, a visitor to Chesa-peake Bay waters from spring to autumn, is abun-dant in the lower bay and common most years in the upper bay, although it is rare north of Baltimore. It is a migratory pelagic species that primarily travels in schools. These schools are generally groups of like-sized fish that can form aggregations that cover tens of square miles. Bluefish undergo extensive inshore–offshore and north–south migrations. Adults overwinter off the southeastern coast of Florida and begin a northerly migration in the spring. During the migration north, a spring spawning period occurs from southern North Carolina to Florida. A second spawning occurs during the summer off the mid-Atlantic coast. In the Chesapeake Bay area, peak spawning is in July over the outer continental shelf. After the spring spawn, bluefish move shoreward; the smaller fish generally enter Chesapeake and Delaware bays, whereas the larger fish head farther north. (Some researchers argue that bluefish exhibit a pattern of continuous spawning that begins in the spring off the southeastern United States and ends in August in the northern part of the Mid-Atlantic Bight.) Early juveniles (25–50 mm, or 1.0–2.0 in, TL) enter the lower bay and its tributaries in late summer and fall. In early autumn, bluefish begin to migrate out of the bay and move south along the coast. Peak abundance near the bay mouth occurs in April–July and again in October–November. Bluefish are voracious predators and will strike at almost any object. They are sight feeders throughout the water column, with smaller individuals feeding on a wide variety of fishes and invertebrates and with large bluefish feeding almost exclusively on fishes. Bluefish reach sexual maturity at age 2 when about 36 cm TL (1.2 ft), and they can live more than 12 years.

FISHING INTEREST   Among the most important sport fishes in Chesapeake Bay and usually ranking first in both weight and number caught every year. Although the recreational catch of bluefish greatly outweighs the commercial harvest in the bay, the commercial fishery is an important one and accounts for about 20% of the total U.S. landings of bluefish. Bluefish are harvested almost entirely for the fresh market and sold as whole fish or fillets—they have relatively poor freezing qualities because their flesh is oily and soft. Bluefish abundance displays considerable year-to-year variation and also long-term cycles. Commercial landings from the bay were generally high during the 1930s, modest to poor from the 1940s through the 1960s, and again high from the early 1970s through the mid-1980s. Historically, Virginia's landings have exceeded Maryland's about 10-fold. The peak commercial catch in recent years occurred in 1976, when landings were just under 1.8 million kilograms (4 million pounds), of which nearly 90% (1.6 million kilograms, or 3.5 million pounds) was from Virginia waters. In comparison, Virginia landings in 1990 were just over 182,000 kg (400,000 lb). These fluctuations in abundance probably have multiple causes, some of which are likely to be natural factors. However, in recent years overfishing has also become a concern. Within the bay, the bulk of the commercial landings of bluefish comes from gill nets and pound nets. Although the statistical data are scant, recreational landings are estimated to be five to six times greater than commercial landings. For this reason, the recent bluefish conservation effort by anglers is encouraging. Bluefish are well known to anglers for having an incredible biting power and voracious feeding habits. Relatively easy to catch, bluefish can be taken by using a wide variety of techniques, including trolling, casting, live-bait fishing, jigging, still fishing, and drift fishing. This species is caught from boats, piers, bridges, jetties, and the surf.

LITERATURE   Hildebrand and Schroeder 1928:231; Musick 1972; Norcross et al. 1974; Wilk 1977; Kendall and Walford 1979; Benson 1982; Manooch 1984; Smith 1985; Whitehead et al. 1986a; Jones et al. 1988; Nyman and Conover 1988; Pottern et al. 1989; McBride and Conover 1991; Nelson et al. 1991; Hare and Cowen 1993; Smith et al. 1994; Stone et al. 1994.

Gobies
FAMILY GOBIIDAE

The Gobiidae is the largest family of marine fishes and comprises more than 200 genera and 1,500 species. These fishes are usually secretive in their habits and typically very small. The smallest known vertebrate *(Trimmatom nanus),* which matures at 8 mm TL (0.3 in), is a goby. In most gobies the pelvic fins are united to form a ventral sucking disk. This highly successful family primarily inhabits shallow tropical and subtropical waters but has invaded nearly all benthic habitats from the shoreline to depths exceeding 500 m (1,640 ft). Gobiid fishes dwell on a variety of substrata from mud to rubble, and coral reefs are particularly rich in goby species. Some gobies associate with other organisms such as shrimps, sponges, soft corals, and other fishes. For a few species, symbiotic relationships with other organisms are a necessary part of the goby's lifestyle. For instance, the cleaner gobies of the Caribbean (i.e., the genus *Elacatinus*) feed on ectoparasites of other fishes, whereas the Indo-Pacific gobies of the genera *Amblyeleotris* and *Cryptocentrus* share a burrow with a snapping shrimp *(Alphaeus).* Typically, female gobies lay a small mass of eggs, each attached by an adhesive stalk to the underside of a dead shell or some other firm overhanging substrate. The eggs are guarded and tended by the male. The family has five representatives in Chesapeake Bay.

KEY TO THE SPECIES OF GOBIES IN CHESAPEAKE BAY

1a. First dorsal fin with 6 flexible spines **2**
1b. First dorsal fin with 7 flexible spines **3**

2a. Teeth bicuspid in males smaller than 60 mm SL (2.4 in) and in females (Figure 192a); dark blotches separated by median pale area present at base of caudal fin in adults . . . .
. . . . **lyre goby,** *Evorthodus lyricus* (p. 212)
2b. Teeth conical (Figure 192b); large dark spot present above pectoral fin base . . . .
. . . . **darter goby,** *Gobionellus boleosoma* (p. 213)

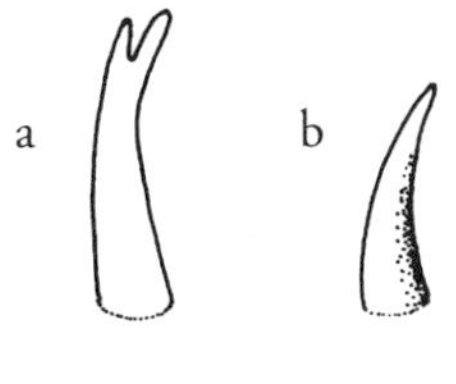

a

b

FIGURE 192. Examples of goby teeth: *(a)* bicuspid, *(b)* conical.

3a. Body largely scaled; single median interorbital pore present; second dorsal fin typically with 1 spine and 15 or 16 rays; caudal fin pointed **4**
3b. Body scaleless or only 2 scales present on each side of caudal fin base; 2 median interorbital pores present; second dorsal fin typically with 1 spine and 11 or 12 rays; caudal fin rounded **5**

4a. Body iridescent greenish blue, with 4 or 5 tan to golden bars behind pectoral fin; yellow green bands present on cheek; first dorsal fin with some red pigment; postorbital lateralis canal with 2 pores . . . . .
. . . . **green goby,** *Microgobius thalassinus* (p. 214)
4b. Body with numerous large dark blotches and no bright colors; postorbital lateralis canal with 3 pores
. . . . **clown goby,** *Microgobius gulosus* (p. 288)

5a. Body scaleless, except for pair of large ctenoid scales on each side of caudal fin base; second dorsal fin typically with 1 spine and 11 rays . . . . **seaboard goby,** *Gobiosoma ginsburgi* (p. 215)
5b. Body entirely scaleless; second dorsal fin typically with 1 spine and 12 rays **6**

6a. Posttemporal lateralis canal segment with 2 pores; midline without series of dark dots and dashes . . . . **naked goby, *Gobiosoma bosc*** (p. 215)

6b. Posttemporal lateralis canal segment absent; midline with series of dark dots and dashes . . . . **code goby, *Gobiosoma robustum*** (p. 288)

Lyre goby
Evorthodus lyricus (Girard, 1858)

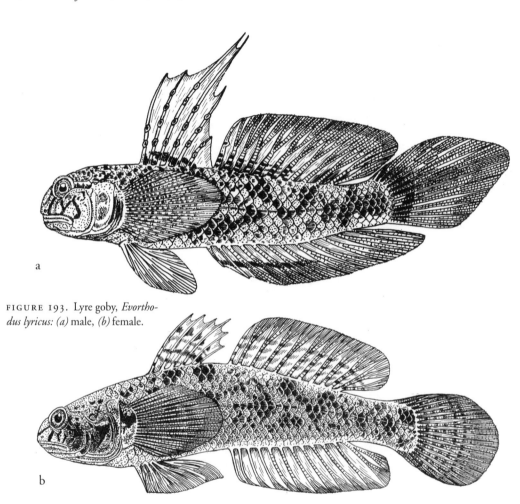

FIGURE 193. Lyre goby, *Evorthodus lyricus: (a)* male, *(b)* female.

KEY FEATURES   First dorsal fin with 6 flexible spines; teeth bicuspid in males smaller than 60 mm SL (2.4 in) and in females; second dorsal fin with 1 spine and 10 rays; anal fin with 1 spine and 11 rays; caudal fin rounded; 2 large spots present on base of caudal fin in adults greater than 50 mm SL (2.0 in); males with 1 or 2 ocelli on dorsal part of caudal fin.

OTHER CHARACTERISTICS   Body elongate, compressed; head deeper than broad; snout short and blunt; mouth large and slightly inferior; scales large, ctenoid, and absent anteriorly; dorsal fins well separated; spines of first dorsal fin long and filamentous in males; second dorsal fin and anal fin equal in size; caudal fin long, with margin somewhat rounded in females and pointed in large males; pelvic fins united to form sucking disk; pectoral fin moderately large. Head and body with varying shades of brown and gray; lateral body markings irregular but usually with some indication of 5 or 6 vertical bars and faint median blotches; caudal fin base with distinctive upper and lower dusky blotches; dorsal and caudal fins marked with narrow brown lines in females and young males; first dorsal fin of males with several ocelli; pectoral fin with narrow vertical brown bars. Maximum adult size 77 mm TL (3 in).

GEOGRAPHIC DISTRIBUTION   Occurring from Chesapeake Bay to Suriname, including the Gulf of Mexico.

ECOLOGY   The lyre goby is rare in Chesapeake Bay, which is the species' northern limit,

and has most frequently been recorded from the Lynnhaven River subestuary near the bay mouth. This species in not common anywhere along the Atlantic coast, and little is known of its biology. It inhabits fresh and brackish waters in shallow muddy estuarine environments as well as tidal marshes and ponds.

FISHING INTEREST   Of no commercial or recreational value.

LITERATURE   Hildebrand and Schroeder 1928:327; Ginsburg 1931; Musick 1972; Fischer 1978; Fritzsche 1978.

Darter goby
Gobionellus boleosoma (Jordan and Gilbert, 1882)

FIGURE 194. Darter goby, *Gobionellus boleosoma.*

KEY FEATURES   First dorsal fin with 6 flexible spines; teeth conical and with tips pointed; large dusky spot present above pectoral fin base; side with markings between lateral midline and second dorsal fin forming diffuse bars that diverge upward to form distinct V; caudal fin pointed, arrow-shaped, and longer in males than in females.

OTHER CHARACTERISTICS   Body moderately elongate, slender, and compressed; mouth small, nearly horizontal, and low on head; second dorsal fin with 1 spine and 9–11 rays (typically 10); anal fin with 1 spine and 10–12 rays (typically 11); anal fin similar in shape to second dorsal fin; pelvic fins long and united to form sucking disk. Body predominantly pale tan, but occasionally dusky in largest males; side with 4 or 5 narrow longitudinal brown spots or bars along midline; dorsal and caudal fins streaked

with small brown spots; caudal fin of older males sometimes with 2 pink stripes. Maximum adult size 62 mm TL (2.5 in).

GEOGRAPHIC DISTRIBUTION   Found from Delaware Bay to Brazil, including the Gulf of Mexico.

ECOLOGY   The darter goby is rare in Chesapeake Bay. It inhabits mud and sand bottoms in freshwater to salt water in lower estuaries and sounds. Spawning occurs in coastal waters in March–August. The darter goby feeds by taking mouthfuls of sediment and sifting out the small interstitial organisms with its gill rakers. Copepods and ostracods are the primary food items.

FISHING INTEREST   Of no direct commercial or recreational value.

LITERATURE   Ginsburg 1932; Musick 1972; Fischer 1978; Fritzsche 1978; Carle and Hastings 1982; Fahay 1983.

Green goby
Microgobius thalassinus (Jordan and Gilbert, 1883)

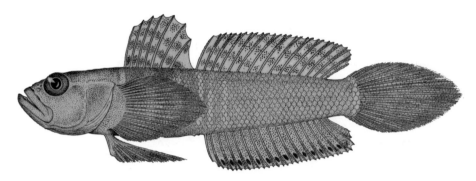

FIGURE 195. Green goby, *Micro-gobius thalassinus.*

KEY FEATURES   First dorsal fin with 7 flexible spines; body largely scaled, with scales numbering about 45–50 in lateral series; single median interorbital pore present; second dorsal fin typically with 1 spine and 15 rays; caudal fin pointed.

OTHER CHARACTERISTICS   Body elongate and compressed; eye large; mouth large and strongly inclined toward vertical; tongue with 2 lobes; second dorsal fin and anal fin long; anal fin elements numbering 16; caudal fin nearly lanceolate; pelvic fins long and joined together to form sucking disk; pectoral fin long and somewhat pointed; postorbital lateralis canal with 2 pores. Life color pattern complex, color intensity variable, and sexes dichromatic. Both sexes with iridescent greenish blue as dominant body ground color and with 2 yellow green bands on cheek. Males with 5 golden tan bars on side, mostly covered by pectoral fin; first tan bar extending to shoulder from pectoral base; first dorsal fin reddish; anal fin with submarginal row of dark spots. Females with reddish spot on anterior of first dorsal fin and with several submarginal black spots on posterior of same fin; anal fin without submarginal row of dark spots. Maximum adult size 40 mm SL (1.6 in).

GEOGRAPHIC DISTRIBUTION   Known from Chesapeake Bay to Galveston, Texas, but apparently absent from southeast Florida and the Florida Keys.

ECOLOGY   The green goby is a year-round resident of Chesapeake Bay and is occasional to common in the lower reaches of tributaries throughout the bay. This species apparently prefers mud or muddy sand bottoms, and in the bay it is frequently found in mud and oyster habitats, often in association with the sponge *Microciona prolifera.* Several other goby species of this genus are known to dig burrows in soft substrate. Most collections of green goby have been made in depths of less than 6 m (20 ft). In the winter months, the green goby retreats to channels or channel edges. In the aquarium, it frequently hovers just above the bottom at an oblique angle, a common feeding posture among the species of this genus. Its food is likely to consist of small planktonic crustaceans.

FISHING INTEREST   Of no direct commercial or recreational value but serving as a forage resource for other fishes.

LITERATURE   Hildebrand and Schroeder 1928:326; Hildebrand and Cable 1938; Schwartz 1971; Musick 1972; Richardson and Joseph 1975; Birdsong 1981.

Seaboard goby
Gobiosoma ginsburgi Hildebrand and Schroeder, 1928

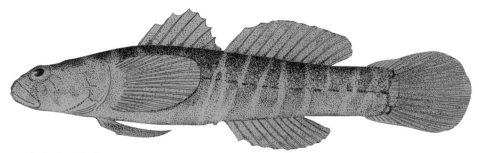

FIGURE 196. Seaboard goby,
Gobiosoma ginsburgi.

KEY FEATURES   Body entirely scaleless except for pair of large ctenoid scales on each side of caudal fin base; second dorsal fin typically with 1 spine and 11 rays; first dorsal fin with 7 flexible spines; tongue tip usually rounded; 2 median interorbital pores present.

OTHER CHARACTERISTICS   Body rather slender; head depressed and broader than deep; snout short; mouth terminal and slightly oblique; teeth in jaws pointed and in bands; second dorsal fin and anal fin similar in size and opposite each other; caudal fin rounded; pelvic fins united to form sucking disk; pectoral fin moderately broad. Body brownish, with 6–8 whitish crossbars; lateral line with longitudinally elongate dusky spots; males darker than females, especially when guarding territory. Maximum adult size 52 mm TL (2 in).

GEOGRAPHIC DISTRIBUTION   Known from Massachusetts to Georgia. The original description of this species was based on specimens collected from several localities in Chesapeake Bay.

ECOLOGY   The seaboard goby is a year-round resident of Chesapeake Bay that is common to abundant in the lower bay and occasional to common in the upper bay. This species typically inhabits deeper flats (to 45 m, or 150 ft) and oyster reefs from spring to autumn, retreating to channels in winter. This is the most abundant goby in open waters of the bay. Spawning occurs from May through October. Dead shells are the primary spawning sites. The seaboard goby feeds on small crustaceans.

FISHING INTEREST   Of no direct commercial or recreational value but constituting an important forage resource for other fishes.

LITERATURE   Hildebrand and Schroeder 1928:324; Hildebrand and Cable 1938; Schwartz 1961; Böhlke and Robins 1968; Musick 1972; Dahlberg and Conyers 1973; Hoff 1976; Fritzsche 1978.

Naked goby
Gobiosoma bosc (Lacepède, 1800)

KEY FEATURES   Body without scales; second dorsal fin typically with 1 spine and 12 rays; first dorsal fin with 7 flexible spines; tongue tip usually rounded; 2 median interorbital pores present.

OTHER CHARACTERISTICS   Body robust; head depressed and broader than deep; snout short; mouth terminal; teeth in jaws pointed and in bands; second dorsal fin and anal fin similar in size and perpendicular to each other; caudal fin short and rounded; pelvic fins united to form sucking disk; pectoral fin broad. Greenish gray dorsally; pale ventrally; nape and side with narrow pale crossbars; males darker than females, especially when guarding territory. Maximum adult size 60 mm TL (2.4 in).

GEOGRAPHIC DISTRIBUTION   Known from Massachusetts to Cape Canaveral, Florida, and along the northern Gulf of Mexico from Pearl Bay, Florida, to Campeche, Mexico.

ECOLOGY   The naked goby is a year-round resident of Chesapeake Bay that is common to
abundant throughout most of the bay, extending
as far north as Havre de Grace, Maryland. The
naked goby inhabits fresh to marine shallow waters (as shallow as 10 cm, or 4 in) and is common on vegetated flats, oyster reefs, and among

the water column during flood tide and down
near the bottom during the ebb flow. Maximum
densities of larvae are reached at salinities of 2–
4‰. At about 20 days after hatching, planktonic
larvae have been observed to school just above
oyster reefs prior to settling. The naked goby
feeds on small crustaceans and worms.

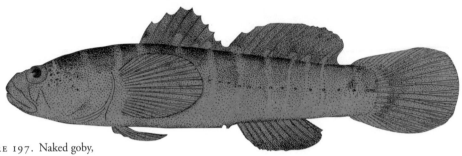

FIGURE 197. Naked goby,
Gobiosoma bosc.

the growth on pilings, seawalls, and other firm
substrates. In the winter, individuals may retreat
to channels or bury themselves in muddy bottoms. Spawning occurs from May to November
when water temperatures exceed 20°C (68°F).
The most common nesting sites are dead shells.
After hatching, the larvae are planktonic until
they reach about 12–15 mm TL (0.5–0.6 in).
The planktonic larvae of the naked goby are
known to migrate upstream at rates of up to
1 km (0.6 mi) per day. This migration is apparently accomplished by alternately moving up into

FISHING INTEREST   Of no direct commercial or recreational value. Based on the density of
larvae, the population of this species in Chesapeake Bay must be exceedingly large and must
therefore constitute a major forage resource for
other fishes.
LITERATURE   Hildebrand and Schroeder
1928:323; Hildebrand and Cable 1938; Schwartz
1961; Böhlke and Robins 1968; Musick 1972;
Dahlberg and Conyers 1973; Fritzsche 1978;
Crabtree and Middaugh 1982; Fahay 1983;
Shenker et al. 1983; Breitburg 1989.

Striped Basses
FAMILY MORONIDAE

Members of the striped bass family are moderate-sized to large fishes that occur in marine, brackish, and
freshwater habitats, mostly in temperate waters. They are typically oblong, moderately elongate, perchlike
fishes. The dorsal fins are separate (or nearly so), and the anal fin possesses three strong spines. The family, found in North America, North Africa, and Europe, comprises fewer than 10 species, some of which
are commercially important. Two species are found in Chesapeake Bay.

KEY TO THE SPECIES OF STRIPED BASSES IN CHESAPEAKE BAY

1a. Body short, deep, and compressed; second spine of anal fin as long as third spine; anal fin with 10 or
     fewer soft rays .... **white perch, *Morone americana*** (p. 217)
1b. Body elongate and stout; second spine of anal fin shorter than third spine; anal fin with 10 or more
     soft rays .... **striped bass, *Morone saxatilis*** (p. 218)

White perch
Morone americana (Gmelin, 1789)
PLATE 33

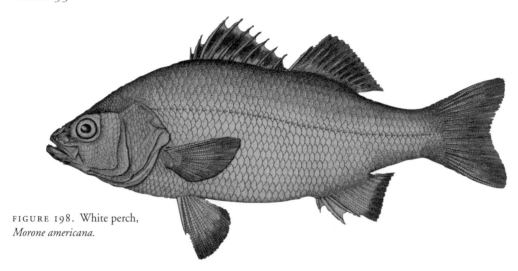

FIGURE 198. White perch,
Morone americana.

KEY FEATURES   Body rather short, deep, and compressed; dorsal fins connected by low membrane; anal fin with 8–10 soft rays; second and third spines of anal fin of approximately same length.

OTHER CHARACTERISTICS   Head low; snout pointed; mouth large and terminal; teeth small, pointed, and in bands on jaws; teeth absent on base of tongue; scales strongly ctenoid; spines of dorsal fins large and strong; first dorsal fin with 7–11 spines; second dorsal fin with 1 spine and 10–13 soft rays; caudal fin slightly forked; anal fin with 3 strong spines; pelvic fin large, inserting slightly ventroposterior to pectoral fin origin; pectoral and pelvic fins of similar size and shape. Coloration variable; body mostly silvery; often greenish to bluish and blackish dorsally; sometimes brassy laterally; frequently with irregular dusky longitudinal lines; pelvic fin sometimes white. Maximum adult size 48 cm TL (1.7 ft).

GEOGRAPHIC DISTRIBUTION   Known from Nova Scotia to South Carolina but most abundant from Hudson River to Chesapeake Bay.

ECOLOGY   The white perch is an abundant year-round resident found in all tributaries of Chesapeake Bay from Havre de Grace, Maryland, to Cape Henry, Virginia. From spring through autumn the white perch is present on flats and in channels, and it retreats to deep channels in winter. White perch are ubiquitous in estuaries and freshwater ecosystems, living in waters ranging in salinity from zero to full-strength seawater, but they usually inhabit waters of less than 18‰ salinity. Because white perch tolerate a wide range of salinities, they become easily acclimated in freshwater ponds and other impoundments. White perch frequent areas with level bottoms composed of compact silt, mud, sand, or clay and show little preference for vegetation, structures, or other shelter. They exhibit semianadromous spawning migrations and move into the fresh to low-salinity waters of large rivers, where they spawn from April through June when water temperatures are about 11°–16°C (52°–61°F). The young utilize the quiet-water shore margins of the spawning area as nursery grounds. White perch are predaceous carnivores whose diet changes with age and habitat. Juveniles feed on aquatic insects and small crustaceans, whereas larger white perch prey on crabs, shrimps, and small fishes. White perch may live as long as 17 years.

FISHING INTEREST   Among the most important recreational and commercial fishes in Chesapeake Bay, especially in Maryland waters, where more than 80% of the bay landings occur. Commercial landings of white perch in the bay peaked in 1969 at about 1.3 million kilograms (2.8 million pounds) and have generally declined since. Maryland landings during 1959–1972 averaged about 600,000 kg (1.4 million pounds) per year, whereas catches during 1973–1986 averaged only about 230,000 kg (500,000 lb). A similar decline has occurred in Virginia, where commercial landings of white perch fell from an average of 182,000 kg (400,000 lb) per year for the period 1959–1972 to about 45,000 kg (100,000 lb) for the period 1972–1986. Commercial landings are made with a variety of gear types, especially haul seines, fyke nets, pound nets, and gill nets. Catches are greatest during the spring spawning season and also from September through November, when white perch school to feed on migrating clupeids. The recreational fishery for white perch is significant, especially in Maryland. In recent years recreational catches in the bay have exceeded commercial catches; recreational landings in 1991 were estimated to have exceeded 5 million fish. The recreational fishery is also concentrated in the spring and autumn, when white perch are taken by drifting live bait or by trolling artificial lures near the surface. The Chesapeake Bay sport catch record is a fish taken in Maryland waters that weighed 1.2 kg (2.6 lb).

LITERATURE   Hildebrand and Schroeder 1928:244; Mansueti 1961b, 1964; Wallace 1971; Musick 1972; St. Pierre and Davis 1972; Hardy 1978b; Manooch 1984; Smith 1985; Jones et al. 1988; Jenkins and Burkhead 1994.

Striped bass
Morone saxatilis (Walbaum, 1792)
PLATE 34

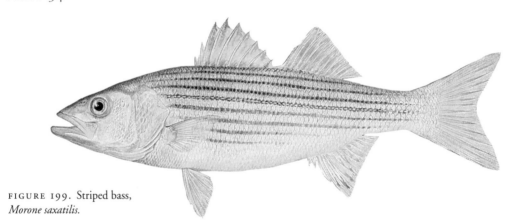

FIGURE 199. Striped bass, *Morone saxatilis.*

KEY FEATURES   Body compressed, moderately elongate in young fishes and becoming stouter in adults; side with 7 or 8 narrow dusky lateral stripes; dorsal fins well separated; anal fin with 10–12 soft rays (usually 11); second spine of anal fin shorter than third spine.

OTHER CHARACTERISTICS   Head low and long; snout pointed; mouth large and oblique; teeth small, in bands on jaws and in 2 lateral patches on tongue; scales small and ctenoid; first dorsal fin with 8–11 (typically 9) strong spines; second dorsal fin with 1 spine and 10–14 soft rays (typically 11 or 12); caudal fin forked; anal fin with 3 strong, graduated spines; pelvic fin of moderate size, inserting ventroposterior to pectoral fin origin; pectoral and pelvic fins similar in size and shape. Olive green, blue, or black dorsally; ground color of side silvery, becoming white ventrally; lateral stripes aligning with scale rows; stripes frequently interrupted and obscure on young fish. Maximum adult size 1.8 m TL (6 ft).

ADDITIONAL REMARKS   Hatchery-reared hybrids of the striped bass and the white bass *(Morone chrysops)* have been introduced in several Chesapeake Bay tributaries and are proving very popular with anglers. Generally, the hybrid has the shape of the white bass and the coloration and dentition of the striped bass.

GEOGRAPHIC DISTRIBUTION   Naturally ranging along the Atlantic coast from the St. Lawrence River in Canada to the St. Johns River in Florida, and in the Gulf of Mexico from western Florida to Louisiana. Striped bass were introduced on the Pacific coast in the 1870s with transplants from the east coast, and their range now extends from British Columbia to the California–Mexico border. They have also been widely introduced into lakes and reservoirs with varying success.

ECOLOGY   The striped bass is an abundant year-round resident found in all tributaries of Chesapeake Bay from Havre de Grace, Maryland, to Cape Henry, Virginia. It tolerates a variety of environmental conditions and may be found in marine, estuarine, riverine, and lacustrine habitats. During summer and winter, striped bass are found in deep channels of the bay. In autumn, they are more concentrated in the lower reaches of rivers. In summer, a portion of the bay population of second-year and older striped bass migrates north along the coast as far as southern Canada and returns to the bay vicinity in fall and winter. Females typically mature in their fourth or fifth year, and males in their second or third. In the Chesapeake Bay region, the striped bass is anadromous, and spawning migrations begin as early as March, with peak spawning activity at the end of April or early May when water temperatures are 13°–20°C (55°–68°F). The tributaries of Chesapeake Bay constitute the principal spawning areas for striped bass along the mid-Atlantic coast, and spawning activity is most intense in the first 40 km (25 mi) of freshwater in the tributary over sand or mud bottom. Spawning behavior often involves a single large female's being courted simultaneously by a number of smaller males. Larval nurseries are the nearshore areas of the spawning sites and the brackish waters immediately downstream. The larvae are often found in association with larvae of the white perch. Postlarval striped bass move downstream as they grow, and some year-1 fish may move into the bay. Adult and subadult striped bass form schools in estuarine and inshore ocean waters where at least some current is running. Females grow larger than males, and most fish older than 11 years are females, with ages exceeding 30 years reported. The largest striped

bass ever recorded, a female, weighed 56.8 kg (125 lb) and was taken in a net off North Carolina in 1891. Males rarely exceed 13.5 kg (30 lb). Adult and juvenile striped bass are predators on a variety of fishes, crustaceans, squids, mussels, and worms; larval striped bass feed on small planktonic crustaceans.

FISHING INTEREST   Traditionally among the most important recreational and commercial species in Chesapeake Bay, especially in Maryland. The Chesapeake Bay population of striped bass shows great year-to-year variability in recruitment success, and it is not unusual for one or two strong year-classes to dominate the population. However, in the early 1980s the bay population dropped to a historical low, as indicated by landings and by the juvenile indexes (relative estimates of the annual recruitment success of juveniles based on standardized seining programs in Maryland and Virginia). In Maryland, commercial landings of striped bass averaged 1.7 million kilograms (3.7 million pounds) per year in 1958–1975 but fell to an average of less than 600,000 kg (1.3 million pounds) during 1976–1984. A similar trend was noted in Virginia, where landings averaged more than 800,000 kg (1.8 million pounds) per year in 1958–1974 and only 273,000 kg (600,000 lb) per year during 1976–1984. Overfishing was generally considered to be the primary cause of the drastic decline in the striped bass stock, and this realization prompted greatly increased regulation. A moratorium was instituted in Maryland waters during 1985–1989, and size, catch, and length-of-season restrictions were put into effect in both Maryland and Virginia (and elsewhere in the mid-Atlantic region). Because of these measures, along with estuarine habitat protection and restocking efforts, a significant improvement in the fishery was evident by the early 1990s. The juvenile striped bass index in Maryland in 1993 was the highest in the 40-year history of the indexing program. Commercial landings are made primarily with haul seines, gill nets, and pound nets, whereas recreational anglers troll artificial lures or bottom-fish with natural baits such as eel. Casting for breaking fish is also an effective method. The all-tackle record for striped bass is a fish weighing 34.5 kg (76 lb) that was taken from Montauk Point, Long Island, in 1981. The Chesapeake

Bay sport catch record is a fish weighing 30.6 kg (67.5 lb) that was taken near Bloody Point, Maryland, in 1995.

LITERATURE   Hildebrand and Schroeder 1928:247; Raney 1952; Mansueti 1961a; Mass-

mann and Pacheco 1961; Musick 1972; Smith and Wells 1977; Fischer 1978; Hardy 1978b; Manooch 1984; Smith 1985; Jones et al. 1988; Hill et al. 1989; Grant and Olney 1991; Jenkins and Burkhead 1994.

Perches
FAMILY PERCIDAE

Perches are an important group of freshwater fishes characterized by a dorsal fin that is completely divided into a spiny portion and a separate soft-rayed portion. The anal fin contains only one or two spines. Several of the larger species in the family, such as the yellow perch and the walleye, are favorites of anglers and may be fished commercially. Members of this family spawn during the spring in a variety of ways: some lay their eggs in gelatinous strings over vegetation; others deposit eggs at random in shallow water; and some place their eggs on the underside of objects, where they are cared for by the males. All members of this family are predaceous. The larger species are highly piscivorous, and the smaller species prey on minute insects and crustaceans. The family, found in freshwaters of the Northern Hemisphere, comprises 10 genera and about 160 species, 3 of which are known from Chesapeake Bay waters.

KEY TO THE SPECIES OF PERCHES IN CHESAPEAKE BAY

1a. Dorsal fin with more than 10 spines; branchiostegal rays numbering 7 or 8; posterior margin of preopercle serrate **2**

1b. Dorsal fin with 10 or fewer spines; branchiostegal rays numbering 5 or 6; posterior margin of preopercle smooth . . . . **tessellated darter, *Etheostoma olmstedi*** (p. 220)

2a. Body with 6–8 dark olive crossbars; anal fin with 2 spines and 6–9 soft rays; jaws without enlarged caninelike teeth; lower lobe of caudal fin without whitish tip . . . **yellow perch, *Perca flavescens*** (p. 221)

2b. Body without dark crossbars; anal fin with 2 spines and 12 or 13 soft rays; jaws with numerous enlarged caninelike teeth; lower lobe of caudal fin with whitish tip . . . . . **walleye, *Stizostedion vitreum*** (p. 288)

Tessellated darter
Etheostoma olmstedi Storer, 1842

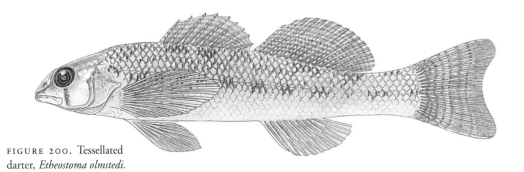

FIGURE 200. Tessellated darter, *Etheostoma olmstedi*.

KEY FEATURES   Dorsal fins contiguous; anal fin with only 1 spine; 8 or more dusky irregular X-shaped or W-shaped markings present on back and upper side; posterior margin of preopercle smooth.

OTHER CHARACTERISTICS   Body slender, little compressed; head low; snout short; mouth horizontal and terminal; opercle ending in strong spine; scales strongly ctenoid and covering entire body; lateral line complete; first dorsal fin arched and with 8–10 spines; second dorsal fin higher than first dorsal fin; caudal fin truncate; anal fin shorter and lower than second dorsal fin; pelvic fin originating slightly ventroposterior to pectoral fin base; pectoral fin pointed. Pale olive dorsally, shading to whitish ventrally; dorsal, caudal, and pectoral fins spotted and barred with black; males with black blotch between first 2 spines of first dorsal fin; pelvic and anal fins black during breeding. Maximum adult size 10 cm TL (4 in).

GEOGRAPHIC DISTRIBUTION   Found from St. Lawrence Seaway west to Lake Ontario and south to Florida.

ECOLOGY   The tessellated darter is common to abundant in all tributaries to Chesapeake Bay and has been collected in brackish waters with salinities as great as 13‰. This species is most abundant in clear, running streams but also occurs in quiet, standing waters. Sexual maturity is reached in the first or second year. Spawning occurs from late April to June, with the eggs deposited on the underside and sides of rocks. The eggs are guarded and cleaned by the male. The tessellated darter feeds primarily on small crustaceans, insects, insect larvae, snails, and algae. It may exceed 3 years of age.

FISHING INTEREST   Because of small size, of no recreational or commercial value except as food for larger species.

LITERATURE   Hildebrand and Schroeder 1928:237; Cole 1967; Musick 1972; Eddy and Underhill 1978; Hardy 1978b; Page 1983; Smith 1985; Page and Burr 1991; Jenkins and Burkhead 1994.

Yellow perch
Perca flavescens (Mitchill, 1814)
PLATE 35

FIGURE 201. Yellow perch, *Perca flavescens.*

KEY FEATURES   Dorsal fins well separated; anal fin with 2 long, slender spines and 6–9 soft rays; body with 6–8 dark olive crossbars; posterior margin of preopercle serrate.

OTHER CHARACTERISTICS   Body elongate, moderately compressed; head long; snout pointed; mouth large and terminal; scales small; first dorsal fin with 11–15 spines; second dorsal fin with 1–3 spines and 12–16 soft rays; caudal fin emarginate; pelvic fins close together and originating ventroposterior to pectoral fin base; pectoral fin short and rounded. Green to gold dorsally; yellow laterally; anal, pelvic, and pectoral fins red or orange, brightest in males during spawning season. Maximum adult size 45 cm TL (1.5 ft).

GEOGRAPHIC DISTRIBUTION   Widely distributed in the upper Mississippi Valley, many eastern states, the Great Lakes, and Canada. Along the east coast, yellow perch are known from Canada to South Carolina. The species has been introduced elsewhere.

ECOLOGY   The yellow perch is common to abundant in most of the tributaries of Chesapeake Bay and is sometimes found in brackish water (<13‰ salinity) at river mouths. Yellow perch often travel in schools and inhabit cool-water lakes and reservoirs as well as coastal rivers, streams, and low-salinity estuaries. They require freshwater for spawning and begin their spawning migrations from the river mouths into tributaries in late February and early March. Spawning occurs in shallow water when water temperatures are 7°–13°C (45°–55°F). Eggs are laid in gelatinous strands in and around aquatic vegetation and submerged tree branches. Some exposed strands can be observed at low tide. Yellow perch are frequently associated with shoreline areas where moderate amounts of vegetation (such as pondweed, *Potamogeton*) provide food, cover, and spawning habitat. Adults can be found in moderate currents but prefer sluggish currents or slack-water habitat, particularly during spawning. Habitat requirements of juvenile yellow perch are similar to those of adults. The diet of yellow perch is diverse and includes insect larvae, crustaceans, and small fishes. Yellow perch are known to live as long as 13 years. FISHING INTEREST   Of commercial and recreational interest in the Chesapeake Bay region, albeit minor, because of the flavor of the flesh and the fish's proclivity to take a baited hook. Most yellow perch are caught during their spring spawning runs. Commercial yellow perch landings primarily come from fyke nets, with pound

nets, gill nets, and haul seines contributing lesser amounts. As with other anadromous fishes in the region, declines in abundance were noted in the 1970s and 1980s. In Maryland waters, commercial landings of yellow perch averaged 55,000 kg (122,000 lb) per year in 1959–1972 but only 14,500 kg (32,000 lb) per year during 1973–1986. Similarly, commercial landings in Virginia averaged about 5,900 kg (13,000 lb) per year in 1959–1972 but decreased to less that 454 kg (1,000 lb) per year in 1973–1986. These decreases in average annual landings indicate that the yellow perch fishery is in serious decline. Studies have shown that spawning runs are virtually nonexistent in many tributaries. Restocking and habitat improvement efforts have been initiated in an attempt to reverse this decline. The yellow perch is of excellent eating quality and is popular with shore anglers, who use a variety of natural baits. The world-record yellow perch is a 1.9-kg (4.3-lb) fish from New Jersey. LITERATURE   Hildebrand and Schroeder 1928:236; McClane 1965; Musick 1972; Eddy and Underhill 1978; Smith 1979; Manooch 1984; Smith 1985; Jones et al. 1988; Page and Burr 1991; Jenkins and Burkhead 1994.

Combtooth Blennies
FAMILY BLENNIIDAE

Combtooth blennies are small, scaleless, bottom-dwelling fishes that typically have fleshy flaps or cirri on the head. They are further characterized by having many close-set, fine, comblike teeth. Most species are marine, but some occur in freshwater or brackish water. The majority of combtooth blennies are found inshore in shallow water, although some are pelagic as young. Members of this family are typically very secretive and live on the bottom close to cover or among the growth on rocks, pilings, and shell reefs. Most species spawn in crevices or under rocks and shells. The eggs are deposited in clumps and are guarded by one or both parents. Combtooth blennies feed on a wide variety of food that includes algae, crustaceans, fishes, worms, and other invertebrates. This large family, comprising about 53 genera and at least 345 species, is found in all tropical and temperate seas. Three species of combtooth blennies are recorded from Chesapeake Bay.

KEY TO THE SPECIES OF COMBTOOTH BLENNIES IN CHESAPEAKE BAY

1a. Branchiostegal membranes fused with body on breast, not forming pronounced fold under which a probe can be inserted (Figure 202a); enlarged posterior canine teeth absent in jaws **2**

1b. Branchiostegal membranes forming free fold across breast, not fused with body (Figure 202b); large canine teeth present posteriorly in jaws .... **seaweed blenny,** ***Parablennius marmoreus*** (p. 289)

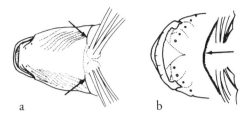

FIGURE 202. Ventral view of
(a) head of feather blenny and
(b) head of seaweed blenny.

a   b

2a. Interorbital area strongly concave; anterior pores of lateral line vertically paired; pectoral fin typically
    with 14 rays; dorsal fin typically with 25–27 elements; supraorbital cirri long and branched . . . .
    . . . . **feather blenny,** ***Hypsoblennius hentz*** (p. 223)
2b. Interorbital area flat; anterior pores of lateral line in longitudinal series, not vertically paired; pectoral
    fin typically with 12 rays; dorsal fin typically with 29 or 30 elements; supraorbital cirri small to absent
    in adults . . . . **striped blenny,** ***Chasmodes bosquianus*** (p. 224)

Feather blenny
Hypsoblennius hentz (Lesueur, 1825)

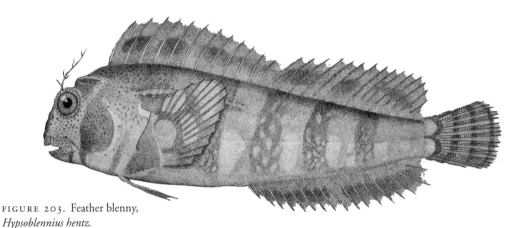

FIGURE 203. Feather blenny,
Hypsoblennius hentz.

KEY FEATURES   Interorbital area strongly concave; anterior pores of lateral line vertically
paired; pectoral fin typically with 14 rays; dorsal
fin typically with 25–27 elements; supraorbital
cirri long and branched; branchiostegal membranes fused with body on breast, not forming
pronounced fold under which a probe can be inserted; enlarged posterior canine teeth absent in
jaws.
OTHER CHARACTERISTICS   Body compressed; head short and deep; mouth broad and
terminal; dorsal fin long, continuous, and
attached to caudal fin; dorsal fin with 11–13
spines (typically 12); caudal fin rounded and typically with 13 segmented rays; anal fin lower than
dorsal fin and not attached to caudal fin; pelvic
fin well developed and jugular in position; pecto-

ral fin large, much longer than head. Head and
body with multitude of small, deep brown spots,
varying in intensity and sometimes forming irregular bands; spots more numerous on head and
larger posteriorly on body; large dark ovoid area
posterior to eye; underside of head with 2 or 3
chevron-shaped bands; dorsal fin typically with
dusky spot over second spine; pelvic fin nearly
black; anal fin dark and with pale margin in males,
barred in females; other fins variously barred or
spotted. Maximum adult size 10 cm SL (4 in).
GEOGRAPHIC DISTRIBUTION   Found in
nearshore waters from Nova Scotia southward to
Florida, around the Florida tip, and westward to
Campeche, Mexico.
ECOLOGY   The feather blenny, a year-round
resident of Chesapeake Bay, is common through-

out the bay, frequenting grass flats and oyster reefs and firm, live-bottom habitats during the summer and deeper channels during the winter. It is typically found in waters with salinities of 12–30‰. Spawning extends from May to August; empty oyster shells in live oyster reefs near the low tide line are the preferred nest sites. This

blenny feeds on small crustaceans, mollusks, and ascidians.

FISHING INTEREST   Of no direct commercial or recreational value.

LITERATURE   Hildebrand and Schroeder 1928:334; Hildebrand and Cable 1938; Musick 1972; Fritzsche 1978; Smith-Vaniz 1980.

Striped blenny
Chasmodes bosquianus (Lacepède, 1800)

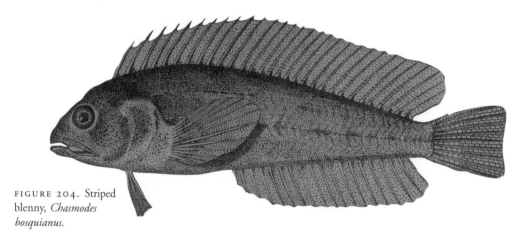

FIGURE 204. Striped blenny, *Chasmodes bosquianus.*

KEY FEATURES   Interorbital area flat; anterior pores of lateral line in longitudinal series, not vertically paired; pectoral fin typically with 12 rays; dorsal fin typically with 29 or 30 elements; supraorbital cirri small to absent in adults, decreasing in size with increasing standard length of fish.

OTHER CHARACTERISTICS   Body compressed; mouth moderately large and oblique; dorsal fin continuous, very long, and with 10–12 spines (typically 11); caudal fin truncate; anal fin long, low, and not connected to caudal fin; pelvic fin narrow and jugular in position; pectoral fin broad. Coloration varying from pattern of pale longitudinal lines to pale blotches or diffuse bands on olivaceous background; head with small dark spots dorsally and laterally; blue spot present anteriorly in dorsal fin of adult males. Maximum adult size 8 cm SL (3 in).

GEOGRAPHIC DISTRIBUTION   Found in nearshore waters from New York southward to northern Florida. A different subspecies ranges from Pensacola, Florida, to Veracruz, Mexico.

The striped blenny is rarely encountered north of Chesapeake Bay.

ECOLOGY   The striped blenny is a common to abundant resident of the entire Chesapeake Bay and is usually found in grass beds or over hard substrates such as oysters reefs or sand bottoms. The striped blenny inhabits shallow areas during spring and summer and moves to deeper flats and reefs in autumn and to channels during winter. It usually inhabits waters that range in salinity from 15‰ to 25‰. The spawning season begins in mid-March and extends through August. Dead shells are the preferred spawning sites, and males vigorously defend their established spawning territory. The food of this blenny is primarily small crustaceans and mollusks.

FISHING INTEREST   Of no direct commercial or recreational value.

LITERATURE   Hildebrand and Schroeder 1928:332; Springer 1959; Musick 1972; Fritzsche 1978; Williams 1983.

Butterflyfishes
FAMILY CHAETODONTIDAE

The family of butterflyfishes, primarily found in shallow tropical waters, comprises some of the most colorful and conspicuous of coral reef fishes. Butterflyfishes are typically diurnal, feeding from the bottom or on plankton. Their prey consists of small invertebrates, such as coral polyps and copepods, although some species browse on algae. All species are deep-bodied, highly compressed fishes, and in some species the snout is elongate, enabling them to retrieve food from places that are inaccessible to other fishes. A few species form aggregations, but most are solitary or occur in pairs. The young are often quite differently colored from the adults. Little is known of the reproductive habits of this family. Found in all tropical and subtropical waters, the family comprises 10 genera and more than 110 species, of which 1 is recorded from Chesapeake Bay.

Spotfin butterflyfish
Chaetodon ocellatus Bloch, 1787

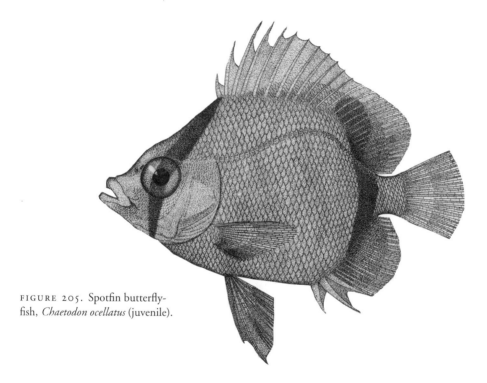

FIGURE 205. Spotfin butterfly-fish, *Chaetodon ocellatus* (juvenile).

KEY FEATURES   Body deep and strongly compressed, oval to orbicular in profile; jet black band present, extending from dorsal fin origin through eye and across cheek; large blackish blotch present near center of soft dorsal fin base (often obscured by second body bar in small juveniles); teeth arranged in brushlike bands in jaws; scales extending onto soft portions of vertical fins; dorsal fin continuous.

OTHER CHARACTERISTICS   Head short and deep; snout pointed; mouth terminal, small, and protractile; lateral line coursing high on side, terminating beneath posterior part of dorsal fin; scales ctenoid, large on side and smaller on head and caudal peduncle; dorsal fin long, with 12 or 13 strong spines and 18–21 soft rays; caudal fin nearly rounded; anal fin similar to soft portion of dorsal fin, with 3 strong spines and 15–17 soft rays; pelvic fin inserting ventroposterior to pectoral fin; pectoral fin broad. Head and body grayish to yellowish; caudal peduncle yellowish orange; second, indefinite bar coursing from middle of anal fin to middle of soft dorsal fin in juveniles; narrow yellow bar running along upper margin of gill opening to pectoral fin base; all fins slightly yellowish orange. Maximum adult size 15 cm TL (6 in).

GEOGRAPHIC DISTRIBUTION   Inhabiting coral reefs from Florida to Brazil. Juveniles are carried northward by the Gulf Stream, accounting for their occurrence as far north as Nova Scotia.

ECOLOGY   The spotfin butterflyfish is a rare to occasional visitor to the lower Chesapeake Bay during summer and autumn. All spotfin butterflyfish that enter the bay are juveniles and may grow to a length of 4–5 cm (1.6–2.0 in) before succumbing to the low water temperatures of winter. In the bay, they are most common around eel grass beds.

FISHING INTEREST   Of no commercial or recreational importance. The spotfin butterflyfish makes an attractive aquarium fish and will subsist on frozen tubifex worms and brine shrimps. It may be taken with seines around shallow grass beds in late summer.

LITERATURE   Musick 1972; Allen 1978; Burgess 1978; Fischer 1978; Fritzsche 1978; Randall 1983.

Mojarras

FAMILY GERREIDAE

Mojarras are small to medium-sized coastal fishes that inhabit marine and brackish waters and sometimes freshwater. They are generally associated with sand or mud bottoms in habitats ranging from the continental shelf and the surf zone to sea grass beds and mangroves. Mojarras are silvery fishes that are compressed and occasionally deep-bodied. Their mouth is extremely protrusible and is pointed downward when protracted. They are reported to feed on bottom-dwelling organisms. The dorsal fin is long and single, but moderately to deeply notched. The pectoral fins are long and pointed. Inhabiting coastal waters of all warm seas, the family comprises 8 genera and approximately 40 species, 6 of which are recorded from Chesapeake Bay.

KEY TO THE SPECIES OF MOJARRAS IN CHESAPEAKE BAY

Morphometric characters apply only to specimens greater than 40 mm SL (1.6 in).

1a. Margin of preopercle serrated; 10 or more gill rakers present on lower limb of first arch (including 1 at angle); anal fin with 8 soft rays (11 fin elements in total) . . . . **Irish pompano, *Diapterus auratus*** (p. 227)

1b. Margin of preopercle entire; 9 or fewer gill rakers present on lower limb of first arch; anal fin with 7 soft rays (10 fin elements in total) **2**

2a. Nine gill rakers present on lower limb of first arch; spinous dorsal fin distinctly tricolored, with jet black blotch at tip, longitudinal white band (clear in preserved specimens) at middle of fin, and dusky pigment near base . . . . **flagfin mojarra, *Eucinostomus melanopterus*** (p. 289)

2b. Eight gill rakers present on lower limb of first arch; spinous dorsal fin often dusky to black at tip but not tricolored **3**

3a. Anal fin base typically more than 16% of standard length; groove formed on snout by ascending processes of premaxilla (i.e., premaxillary groove, readily seen by pulling upper jaw out and down) often constricted or crossed by scales, especially in larger specimens **4**

3b. Anal fin base typically less than 16% of standard length; premaxillary groove present but not constricted or crossed by scales **5**

4a. Last spine of dorsal fin typically less than 7.5% of standard length; pelvic fin typically less than 21.5% of standard length; V-shaped or U-shaped area on snout between nares, and longitudinal band posterior to this area, often unpigmented (especially in juveniles) .... **spotfin mojarra, *Eucinostomus argenteus*** (p. 228)

4b. Last spine of dorsal fin typically more than 7.5% of standard length; pelvic fin typically more than 21.5% of standard length; V and band on snout generally clearly discernible but pigmented .... **silver jenny, *Eucinostomus gula*** (p. 229)

5a. Lateral line typically with 46 or more scales (most frequently 47); least depth of caudal peduncle typically less than 10.5% of standard length; pelvic fin typically less than 19% of standard length; V and band on snout generally quite distinct and often nearly unpigmented in smaller specimens .... **slender mojarra, *Eucinostomus jonesi*** (p. 289)

5b. Lateral line typically with 45 or fewer scales (modally 45); least depth of caudal peduncle typically greater than 10.5% of standard length; pelvic fin typically more than 19% of standard length; V and band on snout generally darkly pigmented and often nearly obscured by pigment .... **tidewater mojarra, *Eucinostomus harengulus*** (p. 289)

Irish pompano
Diapterus auratus Ranzani, 1840

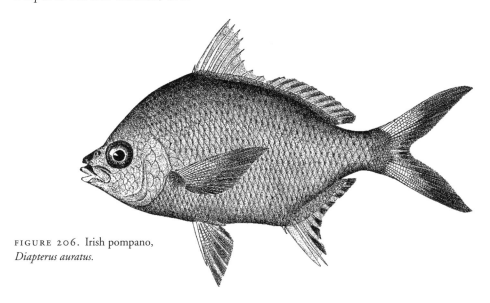

FIGURE 206. Irish pompano, *Diapterus auratus.*

KEY FEATURES   Mouth strongly protrusible; body very deep in large individuals; margin of preopercle serrated; second spine of anal fin very strong (generally greater than 20% of standard length in larger juveniles and adults); anal fin with 3 spines and 8 soft rays (third spine often jointed in smaller individuals); 10 or more gill rakers present on lower limb of first gill arch.

OTHER CHARACTERISTICS   Body rhomboidal and compressed; small villiform teeth present in both jaws and absent on roof of mouth; dorsal fin deeply notched, with notably high spinous portion, and with 9 spines and 10 soft rays; caudal fin deeply forked; pelvic fin inserting ventroposterior to pectoral fin base; pectoral fin pointed, with dorsalmost rays longest. Body silvery; somewhat dusky dorsally; anal and pelvic fins yellowish; side of body generally with 4–6 pale vertical bars in juveniles. Maximum adult size 34 cm TL (1.1 ft).

GEOGRAPHIC DISTRIBUTION   Inhabiting coastal waters of the western Atlantic from New Jersey to Brazil, including the Gulf of Mexico and the Caribbean Sea.

ECOLOGY   A rare summer visitor to both the upper and the lower Chesapeake Bay, Irish pompano inhabit shallow coastal waters; they are common in sea grass beds, mangrove-lined creeks, and lagoons and are often found in low-salinity areas of coastal rivers. With its tubelike protractile mouth, the Irish pompano feeds on bottom-living invertebrates and plant material.

FISHING INTEREST   Of no commercial or recreational value in the Chesapeake Bay region but of commercial value in Florida and in various Neotropical countries. Where abundant, the Irish pompano is collected in seines and trawls.

LITERATURE   Austin and Austin 1971; Musick 1972; Fischer 1978; Johnson 1978; Deckert and Greenfield 1987.

Spotfin mojarra
Eucinostomus argenteus Baird and Girard, 1855

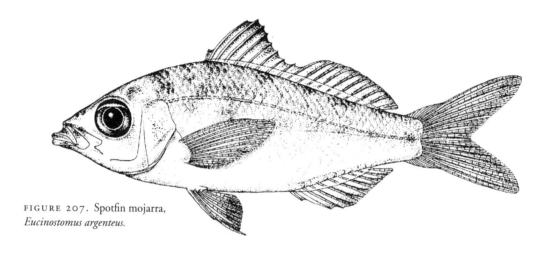

FIGURE 207. Spotfin mojarra, *Eucinostomus argenteus.*

KEY FEATURES   Mouth strongly protrusible; body slender to moderately deep (in adults); edge of preopercle entire; anal fin with 3 spines and 7 soft rays (third spine often jointed in smaller individuals); second spine of anal fin relatively weak (generally less than 15% of standard length in larger juveniles and adults); 8 gill rakers present on lower limb of first gill arch; spinous dorsal fin often dusky and with distinct concentration of pigment near tip (spot at tip not as dark as in flagfin mojarra, and fin definitely not tricolored); anal fin base typically more than 16% of standard length; groove formed on snout by ascending processes of premaxilla (i.e., premaxillary groove, readily seen by pulling upper jaw out and down) often constricted or crossed by scales, especially in larger specimens; last spine of dorsal fin typically less than 7.5% of standard length; pelvic fin typically less than 21.5% of standard length; V-shaped or U-shaped area on snout between nares, and longitudinal band posterior to this area, often unpigmented (especially in juveniles).

OTHER CHARACTERISTICS   Body fusiform to ovoid and compressed; small villiform teeth present in both jaws and absent on roof of mouth; dorsal fin deeply notched, with moderately high spinous portion, and with 9 spines and 10 soft rays; caudal fin deeply forked; pelvic fin inserting slightly ventroposterior to pectoral fin base; pectoral fin pointed, with dorsalmost rays longest. Body silvery, with bluish reflections and often noticeably mottled. Maximum adult size 19 cm TL (7.5 in).

GEOGRAPHIC DISTRIBUTION   Inhabiting coastal waters of the western Atlantic from New Jersey to Brazil, including the Gulf of Mexico and the Caribbean Sea.

ECOLOGY   The spotfin mojarra is a rare summer and fall visitor to Chesapeake Bay. Juveniles occur sporadically in estuarine habitats, and adults are often collected over the continental shelf. This species probably feeds on benthic invertebrates. Much of the ecological information ascribed to this species in the literature probably applies to the tidewater mojarra *(E. harengulus),* with which the spotfin mojarra has been frequently confused.

FISHING INTEREST   Of no commercial or recreational value in the Chesapeake Bay area.

The spotfin mojarra may be used as bait where it is more abundant. It is collected with seines and trawls.

LITERATURE   Matheson and McEachran 1984.

Silver jenny
Eucinostomus gula (Quoy and Gaimard, 1824)

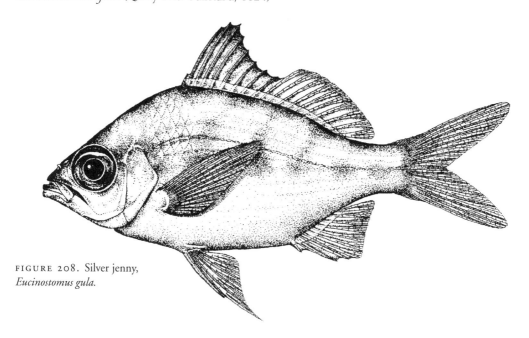

FIGURE 208. Silver jenny, *Eucinostomus gula.*

KEY FEATURES   Mouth strongly protrusible; body moderately deep (especially in adults); edge of preopercle entire; second spine of anal fin relatively weak (generally less than 15% of standard length in larger juveniles and adults); anal fin with 3 spines and 7 soft rays (third spine often jointed in smaller individuals); 8 gill rakers present on lower limb of first gill arch; spinous dorsal fin often dusky and with distinct but moderate concentration of pigment near tip (spot at tip not as dark as in flagfin mojarra, and fin definitely not tricolored); anal fin base typically more than 16% of standard length; groove formed on snout by ascending processes of premaxilla (i.e., premaxillary groove, readily seen by pulling upper jaw out and down) often constricted or crossed by scales, especially in larger specimens; last spine of dorsal fin typically more than 7.5% of standard length; pelvic fin typically more than 21.5% of standard length; V and lon-

gitudinal band on snout generally clearly discernible but pigmented.

OTHER CHARACTERISTICS   Body ovoid and compressed; small villiform teeth present in both jaws and absent on roof of mouth; dorsal fin deeply notched, with moderately high spinous portion, and with 9 spines and 10 soft rays; caudal fin deeply forked; pelvic fin inserting ventroposterior to pectoral fin base; pectoral fin pointed, with dorsalmost rays longest. Body silvery, with bluish reflections. Maximum adult size 15 cm TL (6 in).

GEOGRAPHIC DISTRIBUTION   Found in coastal waters of the western Atlantic from New Jersey to Brazil, including the Gulf of Mexico and the Caribbean Sea.

ECOLOGY   A rare summer and fall visitor to Chesapeake Bay, the silver jenny inhabits shallow coastal waters and is occasionally taken on the continental shelf. It is abundant in various estuarine

habitats, including sea grass beds and mangrove forests, but generally does not penetrate far up coastal rivers. This species feeds on benthic invertebrates, especially polychaetes and crustaceans.
FISHING INTEREST   Of no commercial or recreational value in the Chesapeake Bay region.

The silver jenny is commonly used as bait where it is more abundant. It is collected with seines and trawls.
LITERATURE   Livingston 1984; Matheson and McEachran 1984; Kerschner et al. 1985.

Porgies
FAMILY SPARIDAE

The porgies are primarily marine fishes, although some species are occasionally found in estuaries. Most species have a moderately deep, compressed body and a small, horizontal, and only slightly protractile mouth. The teeth at the front of the jaws are prominent and either conical or incisor-like; those at the sides of the jaws are molarlike. The rear nasal opening is slitlike. Most porgies are carnivorous, feeding principally on mollusks and crustaceans that they crush with their molarlike teeth. Some plant material is often included in the diet. Young fishes often form aggregations, but larger fishes are less gregarious. Porgies are considered to be excellent food fishes, and many species are commercially important. The family, found in all tropical and temperate waters, comprises 29 genera and more than 100 species, of which 4 are known from Chesapeake Bay.

KEY TO THE SPECIES OF PORGIES IN CHESAPEAKE BAY

1a. Anterior teeth narrow, in close-set bands, and almost conical ... **scup, _Stenotomus chrysops_** (p. 231)
1b. Anterior teeth very broad and incisor-like **2**

2a. Large dusky "saddle" present on caudal peduncle; first dorsal spine not procumbent (not directed forward) . . . . **spottail pinfish, _Diplodus holbrooki_** (p. 232)
2b. Dusky saddle absent on caudal peduncle; first dorsal spine procumbent (directed forward) **3**

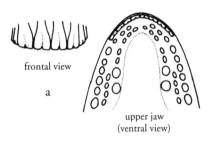

frontal view

a

upper jaw
(ventral view)

frontal view

b

upper jaw
(ventral view)

FIGURE 209. Teeth of _(a)_ pinfish and _(b)_ sheepshead.

3a. Anterior teeth deeply notched; 2½ rows of molarlike teeth present laterally in each jaw (Figure 209a); dusky blotch present near origin of lateral line, followed by 4–6 dusky vertical bars on body . . . . **pinfish, _Lagodon rhomboides_** (p. 233)
3b. Anterior teeth with shallow notches or not notched (Figure 209b); 3 rows of molarlike teeth present laterally in upper jaw and 2 rows in lower jaw; incomplete dark bar present across top of head, followed by 6 distinct dark vertical bars on body . . . . **sheepshead, _Archosargus probatocephalus_** (p. 234)

Scup
Stenotomus chrysops (Linnaeus, 1766)
PLATE 36

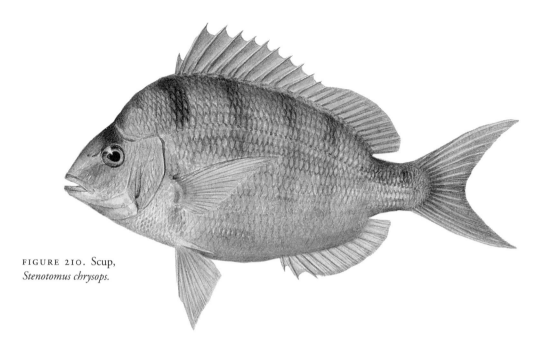

FIGURE 210. Scup,
Stenotomus chrysops.

KEY FEATURES   Anterior teeth narrow, in close-set bands, not notched, and almost conical; 2 rows of molars present laterally in jaws; side with 6 or 7 faint dusky bars; small black spot present in dorsal part of axil of pectoral fin; procumbent spine absent anterior to dorsal fin.

OTHER CHARACTERISTICS   Body deep and compressed; head short and deep; snout pointed; mouth small and terminal; 49–54 scales present in lateral series; scales extending onto caudal fin base and forming low sheath on dorsal and anal fins; snout and preopercular margin without scales; chin without pores; dorsal fin long and continuous, with 12 spines and 12 soft rays; spinous portion of dorsal fin high; soft portion of dorsal fin rounded; caudal fin forked; anal fin low and rounded, with 3 spines and 11 soft rays; pelvic fin long and narrow, inserting ventroposterior to pectoral fin base; pectoral fin long and pointed, reaching to or beyond origin of anal fin. Bluish silver dorsally; silvery ventrally; side with 12–15 indistinct longitudinal stripes in addition to dusky bars; dorsal, anal, and caudal

fins with blue flecks. Maximum adult size 45 cm TL (1.5 ft).

GEOGRAPHIC DISTRIBUTION   Found from Nova Scotia to eastern Florida, but rare south of North Carolina.

ECOLOGY   The scup is a common to abundant visitor to the lower Chesapeake Bay from spring to autumn, extending as far north as the York River, and migrates offshore to deeper waters during the winter. Young of the year also inhabit polyhaline waters of the bay from June to October. Scup prefer hard-bottom areas and submerged structures, where they browse on bottom-dwelling invertebrates. With their strong molars, scup are able to crush crabs, sea urchins, snails, and clams. Spawning apparently occurs from May through August in nearshore waters north of Chesapeake Bay, but eggs and larvae are rarely collected. Scup may attain 15 years of age.

FISHING INTEREST   Of minor commercial and recreational importance in Chesapeake Bay. Commercial landings in the bay are typically less than 2,270 kg (5,000 lb) per year, with most landed by pound nets and haul seines in the fall as the fish begin to move out to deeper water. Anglers catch scup by bottom-fishing with natural baits and by jigging small artificial lures. The scup is a tasty panfish.

LITERATURE   Hildebrand and Schroeder 1928:261; Musick 1972; Morse 1977; Fischer 1978; Johnson 1978, 1980; Fahay 1983; Manooch 1984; Bourne and Govoni 1988.

Spottail pinfish
Diplodus holbrooki (Bean, 1878)

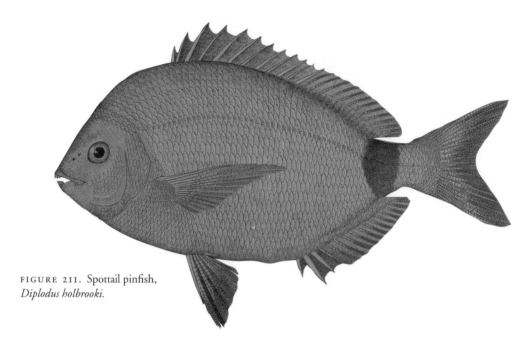

FIGURE 211. Spottail pinfish, *Diplodus holbrooki.*

KEY FEATURES   Front of both jaws with 6 well-developed, incisor-like teeth; large dusky "saddle" present across caudal peduncle, reaching well below lateral line; 3 rows of molars present laterally in jaws; procumbent spine absent anterior to dorsal fin.

OTHER CHARACTERISTICS   Body very deep, oval-shaped, and compressed; head short and deep; snout pointed; snout and preopercular margin without scales; chin without pores; dorsal fin long, low, continuous, and with 12 spines and 13–16 soft rays; caudal fin forked; anal fin low, with 3 spines and 13–15 soft rays; pelvic fin inserting ventroposterior to pectoral fin base; pectoral fin long and pointed, reaching to or beyond anal fin origin. Steel blue dorsally; silvery ventrolaterally; juveniles with about 5 narrow dusky crossbars on upper side. Maximum adult size 32 cm TL (1 ft).

GEOGRAPHIC DISTRIBUTION   Known from New Jersey to northern Florida on the Atlantic coast and from the Florida Keys to southern Texas in the Gulf of Mexico. The spottail pinfish is not common anywhere north of Cape Hatteras.

ECOLOGY   The spottail pinfish is a rare visitor to the lower Chesapeake Bay during the summer and can be found around pilings and jetties and over vegetated bottoms. Although typically a shallow-water species, spottail pinfish do range offshore. Spottail pinfish feed during daylight, primarily on plants and invertebrates such as worms, sponges, and hydroids that are picked from the substrate. Spawning occurs offshore from winter to early spring in areas south of Cape Hatteras.

FISHING INTEREST   Of no commercial or recreational importance in the Chesapeake Bay region. This species is caught only incidentally by commercial fisheries and anglers throughout its range.

LITERATURE   Hildebrand and Schroeder 1928:268; Musick 1972; Fischer 1978; Johnson 1978, 1980; Manooch 1984; Stoner and Livingston 1984; Darcy 1985a.

Pinfish
Lagodon rhomboides (Linnaeus, 1766)

FIGURE 212. Pinfish, *Lagodon rhomboides.*

KEY FEATURES   Front of both jaws with 8 broad, anteriorly directed, incisor-like teeth that have deeply notched edges; 2½ rows of molars present laterally in jaws; procumbent spine present anterior to dorsal fin; blackish blotch present near origin of lateral line; 4–6 diffuse dusky yellow bars present on side.

OTHER CHARACTERISTICS   Body oval-shaped and compressed; snout pointed; mouth small; snout and preopercular margin without scales; chin without pores; dorsal fin continuous, with 11–13 spines (typically 12) and 10–12 soft rays (typically 11); caudal fin forked; anal fin with 3 spines and 10–12 soft rays (typically 11); pelvic fin inserting ventroposterior to pectoral fin origin; pectoral fin long, reaching almost to anal fin origin. Body silvery, with yellow and blue stripes; pectoral and caudal fins yellow; anal fin yellow with broad, light blue margin; dorsal fin

striped with blue and yellow. Maximum adult size 40 cm TL (1.3 ft).

GEOGRAPHIC DISTRIBUTION   Known from Cape Cod through the Gulf of Mexico to Yucatán, as well as Bermuda.

ECOLOGY   The pinfish is an occasional visitor to the lower Chesapeake Bay from spring to autumn, extending as far north as Kent Island. It is most commonly found over shallow vegetated bottoms and occasionally over rocky bottoms and near pilings. Pinfish are tolerant of a wide range of salinities and are sometimes found in brackish waters and freshwater. Spawning occurs from mid-October to March in offshore waters from North Carolina to Florida. Daytime feeders, small pinfish are omnivorous, feeding on epiphytes and small invertebrates that are picked from the substrate. Fish larger than about 12 cm SL (4.7 in) appear to be mainly herbivorous, feeding on epiphytes and sea grasses. Pinfish can live at least as long as 7 years.

FISHING INTEREST   Of no commercial or recreational importance in the Chesapeake Bay region and caught only incidentally by commercial fisheries and anglers. In the nineteenth century, pinfish were a popular panfish, but their rather strong flavor apparently does not suit today's taste. In areas where small pinfish are more abundant, they are popular with anglers as live bait.

LITERATURE   Hildebrand and Schroeder 1928:265; Musick 1972; Fischer 1978; Johnson 1978, 1980; Fahay 1983; Manooch 1984; Stoner and Livingston 1984; Darcy 1985b.

Sheepshead
Archosargus probatocephalus (Walbaum, 1792)
PLATE 37

FIGURE 213. Sheepshead, *Archosargus probatocephalus.*

KEY FEATURES   Front of both jaws with 8 broad incisor-like teeth that have straight or only slightly notched edges; 3 rows of molars present laterally in upper jaw and 2 rows in lower jaw; procumbent spine anterior to dorsal fin; incomplete dark bar present across top of head, followed by 6 distinct dark vertical bars on body.

OTHER CHARACTERISTICS   Body oval-shaped, deep, and compressed; snout blunt; mouth small; snout and preopercular margin without scales; chin without pores; dorsal fin continuous, with 10–12 spines (typically 12) and 10–13 soft rays (typically 11); caudal fin forked; anal fin with 3 spines (the second spine quite stout) and 10 or 11 soft rays (typically 10); pelvic fin inserting ventroposterior to origin of pectoral fin; pectoral fin long, reaching beyond anal fin origin. Body silvery to greenish yellow; fins dusky. Maximum adult size 75 cm TL (2.5 ft), with weight exceeding 8 kg (>18 lb).

GEOGRAPHIC DISTRIBUTION   Distributed in three populations from Nova Scotia to Rio de Janeiro, Brazil, including the Gulf of Mexico and the Caribbean Sea. The population that ranges from Nova Scotia to Cedar Key, Florida, is regarded as a subspecies, *A. p. probatocephalus.*

ECOLOGY   The sheepshead is a rare to occasional summer visitor to the mid-lower Chesapeake Bay, extending as far north as the Potomac River. It frequents jetties, wharves, pilings, shipwrecks, and other structures that become encrusted with barnacles, mussels, and oysters. Sheepshead will enter brackish waters and are not usually found in waters of less than 15.5°C (60°F). Spawning occurs offshore of Florida during the spring, and the young inhabit grassy flats, feeding on small animals and plants. As the fish mature, they disperse to more high-relief, hard-bottom areas, where they prey on barnacles, shellfish, and crabs that are crushed by their strong molars and incisors. Sheepshead can live longer than 8 years.

FISHING INTEREST   Of no commercial interest in Chesapeake Bay, although occasionally taken in pound nets. The sheepshead is not com-

mon enough in the bay to be targeted by anglers, but where it is abundant, it is highly prized. Anglers often use a live fiddler crab bait when bottom-fishing around structures for the sheepshead. It is regarded as an excellent food fish.

LITERATURE   Hildebrand and Schroeder 1928:267; Musick 1972; Fischer 1978; Johnson 1978, 1980; Fahay 1983; Manooch 1984; Schwartz 1990.

Snappers

FAMILY LUTJANIDAE

Snappers are found from brackish estuarine waters to the continental slope, but most frequently they are nearshore, reef-dwelling fishes. Most species live near the bottom and are usually associated with underwater structures, where they often form schools or aggregations. Snappers are active predators that feed mainly at night on a variety of crustaceans and fishes. Many members of this family are excellent food fishes and are fished commercially, although some large reef-dwelling individuals have been implicated in cases of ciguatera (poisoning caused by eating the flesh of a fish in which a toxic substance has accumulated). Snappers are characterized by a continuous dorsal fin, large ctenoid scales, and large canine teeth in both jaws. The family, mainly confined to tropical and subtropical marine waters, comprises 21 genera and 125 species, 2 of which are known from Chesapeake Bay.

KEY TO THE SPECIES OF SNAPPERS IN CHESAPEAKE BAY

FIGURE 214. Tooth patch on roof of mouth in *(a)* gray snapper and *(b)* cubera snapper.

1a. Tooth patch on roof of mouth V-shaped or crescentic, with posterior extension (Figure 214a); prominent canine teeth in upper jaw much larger than canines in lower jaw; dusky stripe present from snout through eye to upper margin of opercle in juveniles . . . . **gray snapper,** *Lutjanus griseus* (p. 235)

1b. Tooth patch on roof of mouth triangular, without posterior extension (Figure 214b); canine teeth in both jaws very strong and equally well developed; stripe on snout through eye absent in fish at any size . . . . **cubera snapper,** *Lutjanus cyanopterus* (p. 236)

Gray snapper
Lutjanus griseus (Linnaeus, 1758)
PLATE 38

KEY FEATURES   Vomerine tooth patch V-shaped or crescentic, with medial posterior extension; outer pair of canine teeth in upper jaw much larger than those of lower jaw; dusky stripe present from snout through eye to upper margin of opercle in juveniles; caudal fin emarginate.

OTHER CHARACTERISTICS   Body relatively slender; snout long and pointed; dorsal fin with 10 spines and 14 soft rays (occasionally 13); scales strongly ctenoid; 44–47 pored scales present in lateral line; snout and preopercular margin without scales; chin pores absent; anal fin margin rounded, with 3 spines and 7 or 8 soft rays; pectoral fin short, not reaching as far as anus; pelvic fin origin ventroposterior to pectoral fin base. Coloration variable, depending on surroundings; typically gray, greenish gray, or dusky olive dorsally and laterally, sometimes with reddish tinge;

offshore waters to depths of 180 m (590 ft), with larger fish generally found offshore. Inshore, gray snapper are found over smooth bottoms around pilings, rock piles, sea grass meadows, and mangrove thickets. Offshore, this species frequents irregular-bottom areas such as coral reefs, ship-

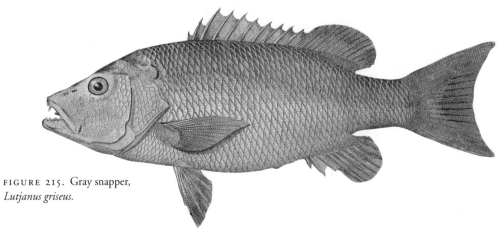

FIGURE 215. Gray snapper,
Lutjanus griseus.

venter grayish or with vertical blotches; young specimens with dusky stripe from snout through eye to upper opercle and with blue stripe on cheek below eye; margin of spinous dorsal fin dusky in young. Maximum adult size 60 cm TL (2 ft).

GEOGRAPHIC DISTRIBUTION   Known from Massachusetts to Brazil, including the Gulf of Mexico and the Caribbean Sea. Adults are rare north of the Carolinas.

ECOLOGY   Small juvenile gray snapper, typically about 2.5 cm TL (1.0 in) upon arrival, are regular visitors to the lower Chesapeake Bay during summer and fall, extending as far north as the Rappahannock River. The breeding population does not extend north of Cape Hatteras, but to the south, spawning occurs offshore during summer. Gray snapper inhabit coastal as well as

wrecks, and rocky areas. Gray snapper often form large aggregations in the daytime and disperse at night as they move into grass flats to feed. The diet changes with age and consists mainly of a variety of small fishes and crustaceans. Gray snapper become more piscivorous with increasing size. This species may live as long as 21 years. The U.S. weight record is 7.5 kg (16.5 lb).

FISHING INTEREST   Important as a recreational and commercial species around Florida, where the species is abundant. On light tackle, gray snapper provide good sport, and they are an excellent food fish.

LITERATURE   Hildebrand and Schroeder 1928:257; Anderson 1967; Starck 1971; Musick 1972; Fischer 1978; Hardy 1978b; Johnson 1980; Manooch 1984; Allen 1985.

Cubera snapper
Lutjanus cyanopterus (Cuvier, 1828)

KEY FEATURES   Vomerine tooth patch triangular, without medial posterior extension; canine teeth in both jaws very strong; 1 pair of canine teeth notably enlarged and visible when mouth is closed; caudal fin nearly truncate.

OTHER CHARACTERISTICS   Body relatively elongate and slender; mouth large, with

thick lips; dorsal fin with 10 spines and 14 soft rays; scales strongly ctenoid; 45–50 pored scales present in lateral line; snout and preopercular margin without scales; chin pores absent; anal fin rounded, with 3 spines and 7 or 8 soft rays; pectoral fin short, not reaching as far as anus; pelvic fin origin ventral to pectoral fin base. Pale to dusky gray dorsally and laterally, often with reddish tinge; whitish gray ventrally; anal and pelvic fins reddish. Maximum adult size 1.6 m TL (5.3 ft).

FIGURE 216. Cubera snapper, *Lutjanus cyanopterus.*

GEOGRAPHIC DISTRIBUTION   Known from Chesapeake Bay to Brazil, including the Gulf of Mexico and the Caribbean Sea. The cubera snapper is not common anywhere and is rare north of Florida.

ECOLOGY   Adult cubera snapper are rare visitors to the lower Chesapeake Bay during autumn. In more southerly waters the adults are found mainly around ledges over rocky bottoms or around reefs at depths to about 40 m

(130 ft). The young sometimes inhabit mangrove areas. The cubera snapper feeds mainly on fishes.

FISHING INTEREST   Of little commercial or recreational interest in Chesapeake Bay, because of rarity. Cubera snapper are rarely taken in pound nets near the bay mouth. The species is highly prized as a food fish where it is abundant and is caught on hook and line and with bottom longlines. It is also landed with gill nets and bottom trawls.

LITERATURE   Anderson 1967; Randall 1967; Musick 1972; Fischer 1978; Hardy 1978b; Johnson 1980; Allen 1985.

Grunts
FAMILY HAEMULIDAE

Grunts are small to medium-sized perchlike fishes that primarily inhabit shallow tropical to subtropical waters. Most are found in association with coral reefs, wrecks, or other structures, but the pigfish, the most common grunt entering Chesapeake Bay, is found over sand and mud bottoms. Many species form schools during the day and then disperse for feeding at night on bottom-living invertebrates and fishes. Grunts obtained their common name from their habit of grinding their pharyngeal teeth, which causes resonation of the swim bladder. The family, distributed in nearly all tropical and subtropical seas, comprises 17 genera and approximately 150 species, 3 of which are recorded from Chesapeake Bay.

KEY TO THE SPECIES OF GRUNTS IN CHESAPEAKE BAY

1a. Inside of mouth red; soft portions of dorsal and anal fins scaled nearly to outer margins **2**

1b. Inside of mouth not red; soft portions of dorsal and anal fins without scales . . . . **pigfish, *Orthopristis chrysoptera*** (p. 238)

2a. Dorsal fin with 12 spines . . . . **white grunt, *Haemulon plumieri*** (p. 290)

2b. Dorsal fin with 13 spines . . . . **tomtate, *Haemulon aurolineatum*** (p. 290)

Pigfish
Orthopristis chrysoptera (Linnaeus, 1766)

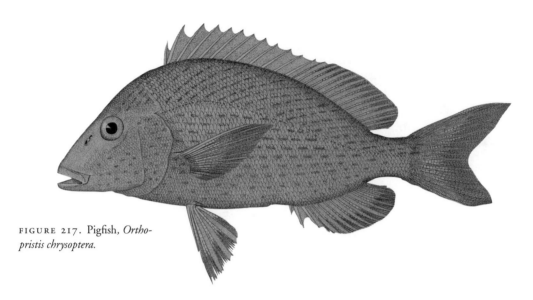

FIGURE 217. Pigfish, *Ortho-pristis chrysoptera*.

KEY FEATURES   Enlarged canine teeth absent in jaws; chin with 2 anterior pores and with central groove just posterior to symphysis of lower jaw; teeth absent on roof of mouth; anal fin with 3 spines and 12 or 13 rays; 71–77 scales present in lateral series; snout and opercular margin scaled.

OTHER CHARACTERISTICS   Body considerably compressed; snout sloping; mouth terminal; jaws with narrow band of slender teeth; preopercular margin slightly serrate; posterior margin of suborbital bone not exposed; scales strongly ctenoid; dorsal fin continuous, rather low, and with origin slightly dorsoanterior to pectoral fin base; dorsal fin spines rather slender and sharp; caudal fin deeply concave, with upper lobe longer than lower lobe; pelvic fin inserting slightly ventroposterior to pectoral fin base; pectoral fin long. Bluish gray dorsally, shading to silver ventrally; each body scale with blue center and with bronze spot on edge; spots on scales forming very distinct orange brown oblique stripes; head with bronze spots; fins yellow bronze, with dusky margins; body dull brownish gray in death. Maximum adult size 46 cm TL (1.5 ft).

GEOGRAPHIC DISTRIBUTION   Found in coastal waters from New Jersey to Florida and throughout the Gulf of Mexico.

ECOLOGY   The pigfish is occasional to common in Chesapeake Bay from spring to autumn and is more common in the lower bay than in the upper bay, extending as far north as the Potomac River on the Western Shore and Love Point on the Eastern Shore. Pigfish enter the bay after spawning occurs in the Mid-Atlantic Bight in the spring and early summer. They leave the bay in late fall and apparently overwinter in deeper offshore waters. Pigfish are bottom dwellers, most frequently occurring over mud bottoms and occasionally over sandy, vegetated areas. They feed on a variety of benthic invertebrates, including worms, mollusks, amphipods, shrimps, and crabs.

FISHING INTEREST   Of minor commercial and recreational importance in Chesapeake Bay but the basis of a significant fishery south of Cape Hatteras. In the bay area, pigfish are landed with seines, gill nets, and pound nets. Anglers catch pigfish by using bottom rigs baited with bloodworms, shrimps, or squids. The species is highly esteemed as a food fish.

LITERATURE   Hildebrand and Schroeder 1928:258; Musick 1972; Fischer 1978; Johnson 1978, 1980; Fritzsche 1982; Fahay 1983; Manooch 1984.

Bigeyes
FAMILY PRIACANTHIDAE

The priacanthids are predominantly red, big-eyed fishes that possess extremely rough, spiny scales and have the innermost ray of the pelvic fin connected to the body by a membrane. They are primarily tropical and subtropical in distribution, but the young stray into temperate waters in summer. Typically solitary as adults, priacanthids generally remain concealed under ledges or other cover during the day. As suggested by their color and eye size, bigeyes are most active nocturnally, emerging from cover at night to feed on small fishes and large zooplankton. Although the coloration is predominantly red in the daytime, some species become silvery pink, mottled, or barred at times. Most species occur in relatively deep water, some to depths greater than 400 m (1,310 ft). The family, found in all tropical and subtropical seas, comprises 4 genera and 18 species, 2 of which are recorded from Chesapeake Bay.

KEY TO THE SPECIES OF BIGEYES IN CHESAPEAKE BAY

1a. Anal fin with 10 soft rays; dorsal fin with 10–12 soft rays; lateral line with 36–40 scales; body depth 50–60% of standard length . . . . **short bigeye, *Pristigenys alta*** (p. 239)

1b. Anal fin typically with 15 soft rays; dorsal fin with 13–15 soft rays; lateral line with 71–84 scales; body depth 33–40% of standard length . . . . **bigeye, *Priacanthus arenatus*** (p. 240)

Short bigeye
Pristigenys alta (Gill, 1862)

FIGURE 218. Short bigeye, *Pristigenys alta* (juvenile).

KEY FEATURES   Anal fin with 10 soft rays; dorsal fin typically with 11 soft rays (rarely 10 or 12); body scales relatively large, numbering 36–40 in lateral line; body depth 50–60% of standard length.

OTHER CHARACTERISTICS   Body short, very deep, and compressed; eye very large; mouth large and oblique, with lower jaw strongly projecting; teeth pointed and in narrow bands in jaws; dorsal fin continuous and rounded posteriorly; caudal fin rounded; anal fin high and rounded; pelvic fin larger than pectoral fin; innermost pelvic ray broadly connected to body by membrane. Body uniformly dark red in life, pink to orange when freshly dead; tip of pelvic fin black. Maximum adult size 26 cm SL (10 in).

GEOGRAPHIC DISTRIBUTION   Known from Maine to Florida and throughout the Gulf of Mexico and the Caribbean Sea.

ECOLOGY   The short bigeye is a rare to occasional visitor to the lower Chesapeake Bay during summer. Juvenile and larval fish occur in drifting weed lines near the surface offshore and are commonly recorded as far north as Maine. However, no large adults are known from north of Cape Hatteras, and the juveniles probably do not survive the winter in those latitudes. Adults typically occur in rocky bottom habitats at depths greater than 100 m (330 ft).

FISHING INTEREST   Of no commercial or recreational importance in the Chesapeake Bay region. Adult short bigeyes are occasionally caught with hook and line in more southern latitudes, where they are more common.

LITERATURE   Hildebrand and Schroeder 1928:254; Caldwell 1962a,b; Musick 1972; Hardy 1978b; Starnes 1988.

Bigeye
Priacanthus arenatus Cuvier, 1829
PLATE 39

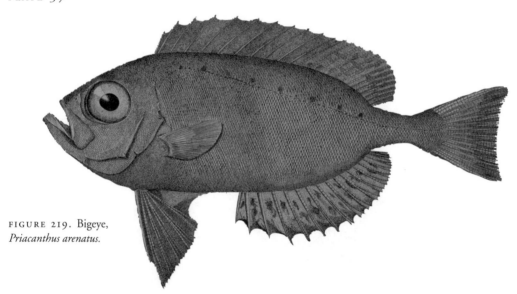

FIGURE 219. Bigeye, *Priacanthus arenatus.*

KEY FEATURES   Anal fin with 14–16 soft rays (typically 15); dorsal fin with 13–15 soft rays (typically 14); body scales relatively small, numbering 71–84 in lateral line; body depth 33–40% of standard length.

OTHER CHARACTERISTICS   Body elongate, relatively deep, and compressed; eye large; mouth large and oblique, with lower jaw strongly projecting; teeth small, pointed, and in narrow bands in jaws; dorsal fin continuous and rounded posteriorly; caudal fin slightly emarginate; anal fin high and rounded; pelvic fin larger than pectoral fin; innermost pelvic ray broadly connected to body by membrane. Body uniformly bright scarlet; pelvic fin blackish. Maximum adult size 36 cm SL (1.2 ft).

GEOGRAPHIC DISTRIBUTION   Known from both coasts of the Atlantic. In the western Atlantic, the bigeye is recorded from Nova Scotia to Argentina and throughout the Gulf of Mexico and the Caribbean Sea.

ECOLOGY   Like the short bigeye, the bigeye is a rare to occasional visitor to the lower Chesapeake Bay during summer. Although juvenile and larval bigeyes are commonly recorded as far north as Nova Scotia, no adults are known from north of North Carolina, and thus juveniles probably do not survive the winter in more northerly latitudes. The bigeye occurs at depths from about 20 m (66 ft) to more than 200 m (660 ft), where it is usually associated with reefs or patch reefs and occasionally with open sandy bottoms. Loose aggregations of adults occur over patch reef areas, and the spacing of these individuals may indicate territorial behavior. The bigeye is a nocturnal predator that feeds mainly on small fishes and fish larvae, small crustaceans, and polychaetes.

FISHING INTEREST   Of no commercial or recreational importance. Adult bigeye are caught at night with hook and line where common. They are also occasionally collected in bottom trawls.

LITERATURE   Hildebrand and Schroeder 1928:253; Caldwell 1962b; Musick 1972; Hardy 1978b; Starnes 1988.

Sunfishes
FAMILY CENTRARCHIDAE

The sunfish family, which includes the crappies and the black basses as well as the sunfishes, are native to freshwaters of North America. However, many species of this family have been introduced all over the world. The members of this family somewhat resemble those of the perch family and the striped bass family; centrarchids differ in having the spinous and soft portions of the dorsal fin confluent. All members of the family are nest builders. The male hollows out a depression on the bottom during the spring. He then guards the adhesive eggs that are deposited in this nest. Most sunfishes feed on insects and other small invertebrates, but the larger basses are voracious piscivores. Most of the larger sunfishes are popular with anglers. The largemouth bass is one of the world's most popular game fishes and has been widely introduced throughout the United States and also in Europe and southern Africa. The family, indigenous to North American lakes and streams, comprises 8 genera and fewer than 30 species, all but 1 of which were originally confined to east of the Rocky Mountains. In the Chesapeake Bay region, 6 genera and 10 species are occasionally encountered in brackish waters of 5‰ or greater salinities.

KEY TO THE SPECIES OF SUNFISHES IN CHESAPEAKE BAY

1a. Anal fin with 5–8 spines **2**
1b. Anal fin typically with 3 spines **3**

2a. First dorsal fin with 11–13 spines . . . . **flier, *Centrarchus macropterus*** (p. 242)
2b. First dorsal fin with 6–8 spines **8**

3a. Caudal fin forked **4**
3b. Caudal fin rounded **9**

4a. Body elongate, its depth contained about 3 times in standard length **5**
4b. Body short and deep, its depth contained less than 3 times in standard length **6**

5a. Upper jaw terminating ventral or ventroposterior to posterior margin of orbit; typically 68 or fewer scales present in lateral series . . . . **largemouth bass, *Micropterus salmoides*** (p. 243)
5b. Upper jaw terminating ventral to middle of orbit; typically 68 or more scales present in lateral series . . . . **smallmouth bass, *Micropterus dolomieu*** (p. 244)

6a. Pectoral fin short and rounded; when bent forward, tip of pectoral fin usually not reaching front of eye . . . . **redbreast sunfish, *Lepomis auritus*** (p. 245)
6b. Pectoral fin long and sharply pointed; when bent forward, tip of pectoral fin reaching at least to front of eye **7**

7a. Opercular flap flexible, blackish on posterior margin, and without red spot; posterior portion of second dorsal fin with dusky smudge or distinct black spot . . . . **bluegill, *Lepomis macrochirus*** (p. 246)

7b. Opercular flap stiff or moderately flexible, with orange or red spot on posterior tip; posterior portion of second dorsal fin without dusky smudge or distinct black spot . . . . **pumpkinseed, *Lepomis gibbosus*** (p. 247)

8a. Dorsal spines typically numbering 7 or 8; scattered spots present on side . . . . **black crappie, *Pomoxis nigromaculatus*** (p. 248)

8b. Dorsal spines typically numbering 6; dusky markings present on side, forming rough vertical bars . . . . **white crappie, *Pomoxis annularis*** (p. 290)

9a. Anterior part of dorsal fin darkly pigmented; vertical bars present on side . . . . **blackbanded sunfish, *Enneacanthus chaetodon*** (p. 249)

9b. Anterior part of dorsal fin not darkly pigmented; blue or silver spots present on side . . . . **bluespotted sunfish, *Enneacanthus gloriosus*** (p. 250)

Flier
Centrarchus macropterus (Lacepède, 1801)

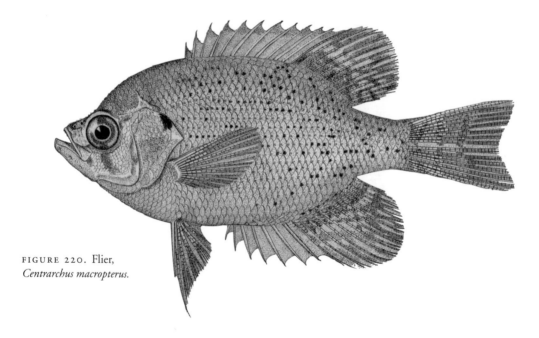

FIGURE 220. Flier,
Centrarchus macropterus.

KEY FEATURES   First dorsal fin with 11 or 12 spines (rarely 13); anal fin with 6–8 spines (typically 7 or 8); dorsal fin origin much dorsoanterior to anal fin origin; mouth small, with posterior end of upper jaw terminating ventral to front of eye; dusky bar below eye vertically aligned.

OTHER CHARACTERISTICS   Body short, deep, and compressed; head short; snout blunt; mouth terminal; 38–45 scales present in lateral series; lateral line arched anteriorly; dorsal fin long-based, with 12–14 soft rays, and with margin broadly rounded posteriorly; caudal fin emarginate; anal fin with 13–15 soft rays and with margin broadly rounded posteriorly; pelvic fin origin almost perpendicular to origin of dorsal fin; pelvic fin pointed; pectoral fin long, originating ventral to tip of gill cover. Entire body olive green, slightly darker dorsally than ventrally; each scale with brown spot, and scale spots forming longitudinal rows of dots; median fins with pale bands; smaller individuals with prominent orange-and-black ocellus in posterior portion of dorsal fin. Maximum adult size 20 cm TL (8 in).

GEOGRAPHIC DISTRIBUTION   Occurring in the south-central and southeastern United States and known along the Atlantic coast from southern Maryland to Florida.

ECOLOGY   The flier is locally common in some small coastal-plain streams in Virginia from the York River drainage southward but is uncommon northward. In Maryland it is known from only a single site in St. Marys County. A typical flier habitat is an acidic, well-vegetated, slow-moving water body such as a pond, a swamp, or a sluggish stream. This species occasionally penetrates into Chesapeake Bay waters of 5‰ or greater salinity and can tolerate salinities as great as 7‰. The flier eats insects, crustaceans, and other fishes such as young bluegill. Spawning occurs from March to May.

FISHING INTEREST   Of no commercial or recreational importance.

LITERATURE   Musick 1972; Pflieger 1975; Hardy 1978b; Smith 1979; Lee et al. 1981; Jenkins and Burkhead 1994.

Largemouth bass
Micropterus salmoides (Lacepède, 1802)
PLATE 40

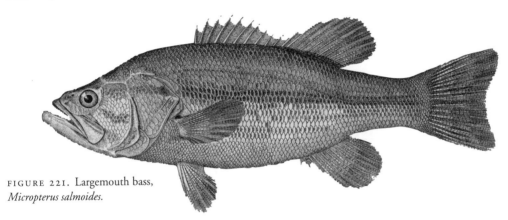

FIGURE 221. Largemouth bass, *Micropterus salmoides.*

KEY FEATURES   Mouth very large; upper jaw terminating ventral or ventroposterior to posterior margin of eye; 51–77 scales (typically 60–68) present in lateral series; irregular black midlateral stripe usually present.

OTHER CHARACTERISTICS   Body elongate and compressed; head long and low; snout pointed; mouth very large and slightly oblique; scales moderate-sized; lateral line complete and slightly arched anteriorly; dorsal fin long and low, deeply notched, and with spinous portion lower than soft portion; dorsal fin with 9–11 spines (typically 10) and 11–14 soft rays (typically 12 or 13); caudal fin moderately forked; anal fin shaped liked soft dorsal fin, with 3 short graduated spines and 10–12 soft rays; pelvic fin short, originating perpendicular to pectoral fin base; pectoral fin rounded. Dull green dorsally; silver laterally; venter white; 3 dusky bars on head ventroposterior to eye; midlateral black stripe sometimes indistinct or blotchy, less distinct in large adults. Maximum adult size is 88 cm TL (2.9 ft).

GEOGRAPHIC DISTRIBUTION   Native to the central and eastern United States, excluding the northeastern and central Atlantic states. The largemouth bass has been widely introduced elsewhere in North America and the world. The species was introduced to the Chesapeake Bay region in the mid-1800s.

ECOLOGY   The largemouth bass is common to abundant in all tributaries of Chesapeake Bay and can tolerate mesohaline conditions to almost 13‰. Optimal habitat conditions for largemouth bass are lakes with extensive shallow areas (<6 m, or <20 ft, deep) that support submerged vegetation. Largemouth bass are also found in large slow-moving rivers or pools of streams with soft bottoms, some aquatic vegetation, and relatively clear water. Spawning occurs in the spring when water temperatures are 12°–18°C (54°–64°F). A gravel substrate is preferred for spawning, but largemouth bass will nest on a wide variety of other substrates, including vegetation, roots, sand, mud, and rocks. Nests are constructed by the male at depths less than 1 m (<3.3 ft). Largemouth bass juveniles consume mostly insects and small fishes, whereas adults feed primarily on fishes and crayfishes. Adults often feed near vegetation within shallow areas; peak feeding is in early morning and late evening. The maximum known age for largemouth bass is 25 years.

FISHING INTEREST   One of the most sought-after game fishes in the United States, particularly throughout the Atlantic seaboard, the Mississippi Valley, and the tributaries to the Gulf of Mexico. The world record is a fish from Georgia that weighed 10 kg (22 lb). In tributaries of Chesapeake Bay, the largemouth bass is an important food and game fish, but it is not abundant enough in brackish waters to be of value to the commercial fisheries of the bay.

LITERATURE   Hildebrand and Schroeder 1928:243; Musick 1972; Eddy and Underhill 1978; Hardy 1978b; Stuber et al. 1982; Smith 1985; Jenkins and Burkhead 1994.

Smallmouth bass
Micropterus dolomieu Lacepède, 1802
PLATE 41

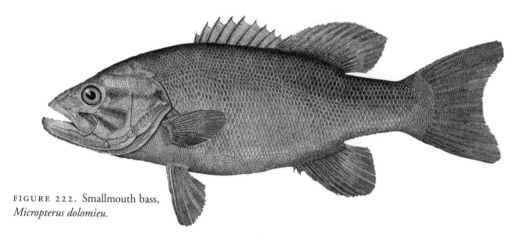

FIGURE 222. Smallmouth bass, *Micropterus dolomieu.*

KEY FEATURES   Mouth moderate-sized; upper jaw terminating ventral to middle of eye; 67–85 scales (typically 68–78) present in lateral series; body almost uniformly pale brown or olive green.

OTHER CHARACTERISTICS   Body elongate, compressed; head long and low; snout pointed; mouth slightly oblique; lower jaw projecting; scales small; lateral line complete and slightly arched anteriorly; dorsal fin long and low, with spinous portion lower than soft portion; dorsal fin with 9–11 spines (typically 10) and 12–15 soft rays; caudal fin moderately forked; anal fin shaped liked soft dorsal fin and with 3 short graduated spines and 9–12 soft rays (typically 11); pelvic fin short, originating almost perpendicular

to pectoral fin base; pectoral fin rounded. Body often with numerous small dusky brown blotches and sometimes with 5–15 indistinct dusky bars laterally; 3–5 brownish stripes present on head ventroposterior to eye; caudal fin tricolored in juveniles, with orange base, black middle, and white margin. Typical adult size 20–56 cm TL (8–22 in).

GEOGRAPHIC DISTRIBUTION   Originally extending from the Great Lakes south to northern Georgia and Alabama, east to the Appalachian range, and west to eastern Oklahoma. The smallmouth bass has been widely introduced in the northeastern United States, including the Chesapeake Bay region, and in areas west of the Mississippi drainage.

ECOLOGY   The smallmouth bass tolerates salinities to about 7‰ and is occasional to common in Chesapeake Bay tributaries from the Rappahannock River northward, rare to occasional south of the Rappahannock, and absent from Eastern Shore streams and rivers. The optimal smallmouth bass habitat is a cool, clear stream with abundant shade and cover and with deep pools, moderate currents, and a gravel or rubble substrate. These fish are also found in large clear lakes and reservoirs containing rocky shoals. Smallmouth bass exhibit strong cover-seeking behavior and prefer protection from light in all life stages. Nest building and spawning occur from spring to early summer, usually mid-April to July, on rocky lake shoals or in river shallows when the water temperatures reach 13°–21°C (55°–70°F). Juvenile smallmouth bass eat large insects, crayfishes, and fishes, whereas adults primarily feed on fishes and crayfishes. The maximum known age for smallmouth bass is 18 years, but individuals older than 7 years are uncommon.

FISHING INTEREST   Known as an important game fish that will take live bait, lures, or artificial flies. The largest recorded smallmouth bass is a fish from Kentucky that measured 68.6 cm TL (2.3 ft) and weighed 5.4 kg (11.9 lb). Because the smallmouth bass only occasionally enters brackish waters, it is not considered a valuable species by Chesapeake Bay's commercial fisheries.

LITERATURE   Hildebrand and Schroeder 1928:242; Musick 1972; Eddy and Underhill 1978; Hardy 1978b; Edwards et al. 1983; Jenkins and Burkhead 1994.

Redbreast sunfish
Lepomis auritus (Linnaeus, 1758)

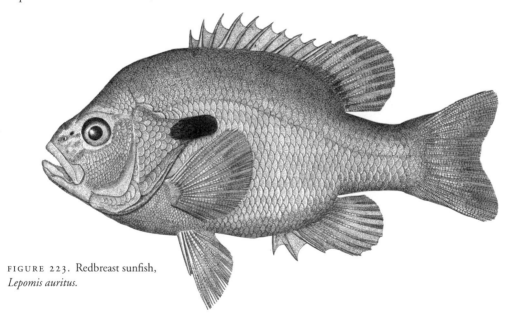

FIGURE 223. Redbreast sunfish, *Lepomis auritus.*

KEY FEATURES   Pectoral fin short and rounded; opercular flap black, very long in adults.

OTHER CHARACTERISTICS   Body deep and highly compressed; head short; mouth small and terminal; lower jaw projecting; scales small; lateral line complete, arched anteriorly, and with 39–54 scales; dorsal fin continuous, moderately emarginate at junction of spinous and soft portions, and with soft portion rounded; dorsal fin with 9–11 spines and 10–12 soft rays; caudal fin slightly forked and with rounded lobes; anal fin shaped liked soft dorsal fin and with 3 short graduated spines (rarely 2 or 4) and 8–11 soft rays (typically 9 or 10); pelvic fin short, originating perpendicular or slightly ventroposterior to pectoral fin base. Uniformly brownish olive dorsally; yellowish green ventrally; scales with dusky centers and pale margins; breast yellowish in females and reddish in males. Maximum adult size 30 cm TL (1 ft), typically 13–20 cm TL (5–8 in).

GEOGRAPHIC DISTRIBUTION   Originally distributed from New Brunswick to Florida. The redbreast sunfish has been introduced in many central and midwestern states.

ECOLOGY   The redbreast sunfish is common to abundant in all tributaries of Chesapeake Bay. It is only occasionally encountered in brackish waters with salinities of 5‰ or greater; 7‰ is its maximum recorded salinity tolerance. Typically a solitary species, it sometimes forms small groups. It is found in standing waters and the slower parts of streams. This species will seek cover under rocks and is commonly associated with the

rock bass *(Ambloplites rupestris)* and the smallmouth bass. The redbreast sunfish feeds on a variety of invertebrate organisms, including insects and plankton, but also eats fishes and crayfishes. Spawning in Maryland and Virginia waters occurs in June and July among plants near the shoreline; nests are scooped out of gravel bottoms. Redbreast sunfish can live 6 years or slightly longer.

FISHING INTEREST   Known as an important recreational species. The most abundant sunfish in tidewater streams of Chesapeake Bay, the redbreast sunfish can be taken with a fly rod as well as with spinning lures and baited hooks. It is an excellent panfish.

LITERATURE   Musick 1972; Eddy and Underhill 1978; Hardy 1978b; Smith 1985; Jenkins and Burkhead 1994.

Bluegill
Lepomis macrochirus Rafinesque, 1819
PLATE 42

FIGURE 224. Bluegill, *Lepomis macrochirus.*

KEY FEATURES   Pectoral fin long and sharply pointed; opercular flap blackish; dusky smudge or black spot present on basal half of last 4 rays of soft dorsal fin; 6–8 ill-defined vertical bars present on side.

OTHER CHARACTERISTICS   Body deep and highly compressed; head short; mouth small; lower jaw projecting; scales small; lateral line complete, arched anteriorly, and with approximately 38–50 scales; dorsal fin continuous, with spinous

portion arched and with soft portion rounded; dorsal fin with 9–12 spines (typically 10) and 9–13 soft rays; caudal fin slightly forked and with rounded lobes; anal fin shaped liked soft dorsal fin and with 3 short graduated spines and 8–12 soft rays (typically 10–12); pelvic fin short, originating ventroposterior to pectoral fin base. Body olive green, with blue and purple iridescence on cheek and opercle; yellowish green ventrally; vertical bars on side olive-colored and chainlike. Maximum adult size 31 cm TL (1 ft), typically 10–15 cm TL (4–6 in).

GEOGRAPHIC DISTRIBUTION Originally distributed from the Great Lakes and the Mississippi Valley to Texas and Florida. The bluegill has been widely introduced elsewhere, including Hawaii.

ECOLOGY This species is common to abundant in all tributaries of Chesapeake Bay and can tolerate salinities at least as great as 18‰. Bluegills are apt to be found in quiet waters of lakes, ponds, and slow-flowing rivers and streams with sand, mud, or gravel bottoms, bordered with aquatic vegetation. Spawning in the Chesapeake Bay region is from April to September when water temperatures reach about 12°C (54°F). Multiple spawning is common. Males build nests in colonies where many nests are close together. The circular nest, 20–30 cm (8–12 in) in diameter, is constructed in shallow waters (usually less than 1 m, or 3.3 ft, deep) and consists of a shallow depression in a sandy or fine gravel bottom from which the detrital covering has been fanned away. The male vigorously guards the nest both before and after spawning. Bluegills feed throughout the water column on a wide variety of organisms, including insects, crayfishes, and some plant material. Bluegills can live as long as 11 years.

FISHING INTEREST Popular with anglers of all ages because of its readiness to take a baited hook. Artificial lures and flies are also used to catch bluegills. The largest recorded bluegill is an individual from Alabama that weighed 2.2 kg (4.8 lb). The bluegill is considered an excellent food fish.

LITERATURE Musick 1972; Pflieger 1975; Eddy and Underhill 1978; Hardy 1978b; Smith 1979; Smith 1985; Jenkins and Burkhead 1994.

Pumpkinseed
Lepomis gibbosus (Linnaeus, 1758)

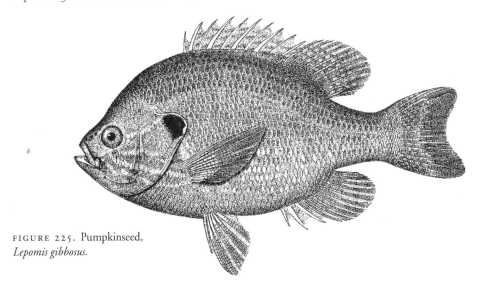

FIGURE 225. Pumpkinseed, *Lepomis gibbosus.*

KEY FEATURES Pectoral fin long and sharply pointed; opercular lobe ("ear flap") with spot of orange or red; cheek of adults with wavy blue lines.

OTHER CHARACTERISTICS Body deep and highly compressed; head short; mouth small; lower jaw projecting; scales small; lateral line complete, arched anteriorly, and with 34–47 scales; dorsal fin continuous, with spinous portion arched and with soft portion rounded; dorsal fin with 9–12 spines (typically 10) and 11–13 soft rays; caudal fin slightly forked and with rounded lobes; anal fin shaped liked soft dorsal fin and with 3 short graduated spines and 7–12 soft rays (typically 10 or 11); pelvic fin short, originating ventroposterior to pectoral fin base. Dorsum and side olive green to bluish, with many irregular spots of bright copper or gold; orange ventrally; blue and orange streaks radiating from mouth onto cheek. Maximum adult size 31 cm TL (1 ft), typically 10–15 cm TL (4–6 in).

GEOGRAPHIC DISTRIBUTION   Known from Quebec to North Dakota and south to Georgia, Ohio, and Iowa. The pumpkinseed has been widely introduced elsewhere in the United States.

ECOLOGY   This sunfish is common to abundant in all tributaries of Chesapeake Bay and is frequently found in brackish waters with salinities greater than 5‰. It is tolerant of salinities as great as 18‰ for short periods. The pumpkinseed typically occupies well-vegetated natural lakes, coastal ponds, and pools of rivers. Spawn-

ing behavior is similar to that of the bluegill and takes place in the spring and early summer when waters warm to about 20°C (68°F). Males construct nests over a sandy or gravel bottom in shallow waters, often near weed beds. Pumpkinseeds feed on a wide variety of small animals, including worms, mollusks, insects, and small fishes. They can live as long as 10 years.

FISHING INTEREST   Well known for beauty and tastiness and sought by anglers of all ages. The world record is a fish from Virginia that weighed 0.5 kg (1 lb). Pumpkinseeds will take natural and artificial baits.

LITERATURE   Hildebrand and Schroeder 1928:241; Musick 1972; Eddy and Underhill 1978; Hardy 1978b; Smith 1979; Manooch 1984; Smith 1985; Jenkins and Burkhead 1994.

Black crappie
Pomoxis nigromaculatus (Lesueur, 1829)

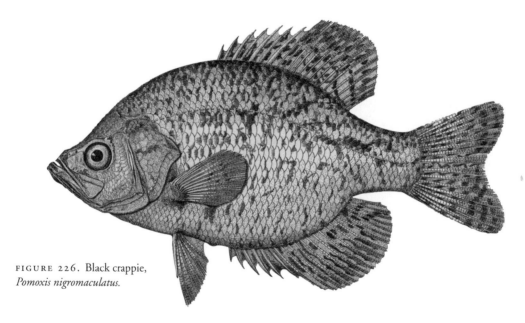

FIGURE 226. Black crappie,
Pomoxis nigromaculatus.

KEY FEATURES   Anal fin with 5–8 spines (typically 6); dorsal fin with 6–8 spines (typically 7 or 8); pattern of scattered dusky blotches present laterally.

OTHER CHARACTERISTICS   Body deep and strongly compressed; mouth large and oblique; head long; 36–46 scales present in lat-

eral series; dorsal fin continuous, with soft portion high and rounded; caudal fin slightly forked and with blunt lobes; anal fin similar to dorsal fin and typically with 16–18 soft rays; pelvic fin moderate-sized, originating slightly ventroposterior to pectoral fin base; pectoral fin moderate-sized and rounded. Dark green dorsally, with patches of dusky scales coalescing to form irregular blotches; black bar often present ventral to eye. Maximum adult size 49 cm TL (1.6 ft).

GEOGRAPHIC DISTRIBUTION   Known in freshwater lakes and streams from the St. Lawrence Valley west to Manitoba, south to Texas and Florida. The black crappie was introduced to the Chesapeake Bay region in the 1860s and has been widely introduced elsewhere in North America.

ECOLOGY   Black crappies are occasional to abundant inhabitants in all major tributaries of Chesapeake Bay and can tolerate salinities at least as great as 5‰. They are most abundant in well-vegetated lakes and clear backwaters of rivers. Young black crappies are plankton feeders, but adults feed primarily on small fishes and also eat benthic insects. Spawning occurs from March to July when water temperatures are 15°–20°C (59°–68°F). Male black crappies construct and guard nests in sandy bottoms of weedy areas at depths of 1.0–2.5 m (3.3–8.2 ft). The maximum age for black crappie is about 10 years.

FISHING INTEREST   Considered an excellent game and food fish and pursued by many freshwater anglers. The rod-and-reel world record is a fish from Virginia that weighed 2 kg (4.5 lb). The black crappie is only rarely encountered in brackish waters and is of no commercial importance.

LITERATURE   Musick 1972; Pflieger 1975; Hardy 1978b; Smith 1979; Smith 1985; Jenkins and Burkhead 1994.

Blackbanded sunfish
Enneacanthus chaetodon (Baird, 1855)

FIGURE 227. Blackbanded sunfish, *Enneacanthus chaetodon.*

KEY FEATURES   Anterior part of dorsal fin darkly pigmented; 6–8 vertical black bars present on side; dorsal fin with 8–11 spines; anal fin with 3 spines; caudal fin rounded.

OTHER CHARACTERISTICS   Body short, deep, and compressed; head short; snout blunt; mouth small and terminal; scales large, numbering 23–32 in lateral series; lateral line arched anteriorly; dorsal fin long-based, with margin broadly rounded posteriorly, and with 10–13 soft rays; anal fin with margin broadly rounded posteriorly and with 10–14 soft rays; pelvic fin origin almost perpendicular to dorsal fin origin; pelvic fin pointed; pectoral fin rounded, originating ventral to opercular flap. Grayish brown to black dorsally; venter whitish or pale; pelvic fin, basal portion of anal fin, and anterior membranes of dorsal fin blackish; pelvic spine orange; opercle with black spot. Maximum adult size 10 cm TL (4 in).

GEOGRAPHIC DISTRIBUTION   Known from New Jersey to Florida, including the Gulf coast of Florida.

ECOLOGY   The blackbanded sunfish inhabits nutrient-poor, acidic waters that are heavily vegetated. It is less common in Chesapeake Bay than the bluespotted sunfish. In Maryland the blackbanded sunfish is found only on the Eastern Shore in the Pocomoke drainage, where it is not uncommon in brackish waters near stream mouths. It is rare in Virginia (known only from three sites in the upper Chowan drainage) and is classified there as endangered. Nests are made in

shallows about 30 cm (1.0 ft) deep. Spawning is reported to occur in March in North Carolina and from May to late June in Delaware. The species is apparently nocturnal, feeding on insects and some plant materials. Blackbanded sunfish live about 4 years in the wild.

FISHING INTEREST   Of no commercial or recreational importance, because of small size. The blackbanded sunfish is a handsome aquarium fish and is popular with aquarists. However, because the species is classified as endangered in Virginia, it is unlawful to take or possess the blackbanded sunfish in that state.

LITERATURE   McClane 1965; Musick 1972; Hardy 1978b; Lee et al. 1981; Jenkins and Burkhead 1994.

Bluespotted sunfish
Enneacanthus gloriosus (Holbrook, 1855)

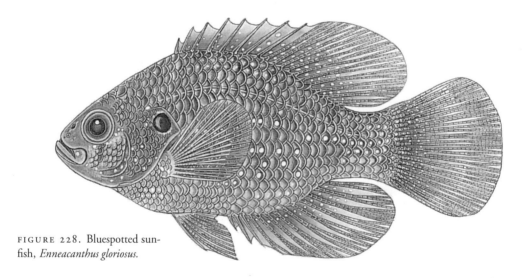

FIGURE 228. Bluespotted sunfish, *Enneacanthus gloriosus.*

KEY FEATURES   Caudal fin rounded; anterior part of dorsal fin not darkly pigmented; blue or silver spots usually present, forming irregular patterns on side; dorsal fin with 7–11 spines (typically 9); anal fin with 3 or 4 spines (typically 3); vertical bars absent on body.

OTHER CHARACTERISTICS   Body short, deep, and compressed; head short; snout blunt; mouth small and terminal; scales large, numbering 25–35 in lateral series; lateral line arched anteriorly; dorsal fin long-based, with margin

broadly rounded posteriorly, and with 9–13 soft rays; anal fin with margin broadly rounded posteriorly and with 8–13 soft rays; pelvic fin pointed, originating ventroposterior to origin of dorsal fin; pectoral fin rounded, originating ventral to opercular flap. Greenish or olive brown dorsally; venter yellow or pale; adult males with bright turquoise spots on fins and body and with prominent black spot on opercle; females drabber than males and sometimes without bluish spots. Maximum adult size 8.5 cm TL (3.4 in).

GEOGRAPHIC DISTRIBUTION   Known from New York to Florida, including the Gulf coast of Florida.

ECOLOGY   The bluespotted sunfish inhabits slow-moving, darkly stained waters that are typically densely packed with aquatic vegetation. The species is not uncommon in brackish waters near stream mouths. Bluespotted sunfish have been collected in Chesapeake Bay waters with salinities as great as 13‰. The species feeds primarily on crustaceans but also eats insects and worms.

Spawning is reported to occur in May and June in the bay region. Spawning and nest building take place both on the bottom and in vegetation.

FISHING INTEREST   Of no commercial or recreational importance, because of small size. This species is a beautiful fish that is valued by aquarists.

LITERATURE   Hildebrand and Schroeder 1928:240; McClane 1965; Musick 1972; Hardy 1978b; Smith 1985; Jenkins and Burkhead 1994.

Wrasses
FAMILY LABRIDAE

The family of wrasses is among the most diverse families of marine fishes. Most members of the family are found in tropical waters, usually associated with coral reef habitats. Many species have complex and often brilliant color patterns that change with growth. Another characteristic displayed by many species is a type of hermaphroditism called protogyny (meaning "first female"), in which the majority of individuals commence adult life as reproductive females and later may change, both morphologically and functionally, into males. Most wrasses prey on benthic invertebrates or fishes, but some species are planktivores, corallivores, or cleaners that feed on the ectoparasites of other fishes. All wrasses are active in daytime, and many species bury themselves with sand at night. Wrasses normally swim by using only their pectoral fins, which creates the impression that they are dragging their tail; the tail is used for locomotion only when a burst of speed is needed. The family, comprising approximately 60 genera and 500 species, is represented by 2 species in Chesapeake Bay.

KEY TO THE SPECIES OF WRASSES IN CHESAPEAKE BAY

1a. Snout pointed; scales large, numbering about 40 in lateral series; cheek and opercle with scales . . . . **cunner,** *Tautogolabrus adspersus* (p. 251)

1b. Snout blunt; scales small, numbering about 70 in lateral series; cheek and opercle with few or no scales . . . . **tautog,** *Tautoga onitis* (p. 252)

Cunner
Tautogolabrus adspersus (Walbaum, 1792)
PLATE 43

KEY FEATURES   Snout pointed; scales large, numbering about 40 in lateral series; cheek and opercle nearly fully scaled; margin of preopercle serrated.

OTHER CHARACTERISTICS   Body moderately deep and compressed; mouth terminal; lips thin; outer row of teeth enlarged and caninelike, protruding anteriorly; dorsal fin long, continuous, with 16–18 spines and 9–11 soft rays, and with soft rays longer than spines; caudal fin rounded; anal fin with 3 pungent spines and 8 or 9 soft rays; pelvic fin moderate-sized, inserting slightly ventroposterior to pectoral fin base; pectoral fin moderately broad. Coloration highly variable; body sometimes uniformly brownish to olive green or blue, sometimes mottled; body color frequently matching that of the bottom the fish inhabits; fins reddish; dusky spot present on base of anterior soft rays. Maximum adult size 38 cm TL (15 in).

GEOGRAPHIC DISTRIBUTION   Known from Labrador to Virginia but more common north of New Jersey.

ECOLOGY   The cunner is a rare to occasional visitor to the lower Chesapeake Bay during summer, autumn, and winter. The cunner lives close

a diet comprising a wide variety of bottom-dwelling animals, especially mussels.

FISHING INTEREST   Of no commercial or recreational importance in the Chesapeake Bay area. The cunner has excellent eating qualities, however, and where it is abundant, it is caught

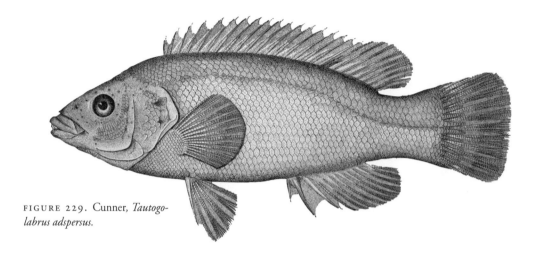

FIGURE 229. Cunner, *Tautogo-labrus adspersus.*

to shore, particularly in bays and sounds and seldom moves far from a rocky outcrop or similar structures. Spawning in the Mid-Atlantic Bight takes place from nearshore to the edge of the shelf from May to October. This species feeds both on the bottom and in the water column on

frequently by anglers. The cunner is well known for its bait-stealing ability.

LITERATURE   Hildebrand and Schroeder 1928:320; Musick 1972; Olla et al. 1975, 1979; Fritzsche 1978; Fahay 1983; Smith 1985; Morse et al. 1987.

Tautog
Tautoga onitis (Linnaeus, 1758)
PLATE 44

KEY FEATURES   Snout blunt; scales small, numbering about 70 in lateral series; cheek and opercle with few or no scales; margin of preopercle smooth.

OTHER CHARACTERISTICS   Body deep and compressed; mouth slightly inferior; lips broad and thick; teeth in jaws strong; anterior teeth compressed and incisor-like; dorsal fin long, continuous, with 16–18 spines and 10–11 soft rays, and with soft rays longer than spines; caudal fin truncate; anal fin with 3 sharp spines and 7 or 8 soft rays; pelvic fin moderate-sized, inserting ventroposterior to pectoral fin base; pectoral fin broad. Dull black to greenish black or

brown dorsally, with irregular blackish lateral bars or blotches; small males often uniformly blackish; most large males with enlarged white chin and with white dorsal and ventral margins on pectoral and caudal fins; juveniles of less than about 5 cm TL (2 in) often bright green. Maximum adult size 95 cm SL (3.1 ft).

GEOGRAPHIC DISTRIBUTION   Known from the Bay of Fundy to South Carolina and most abundant from Cape Cod to Delaware.

ECOLOGY   The tautog is a year-round resident near the Chesapeake Bay mouth and seasonally extends as far north as the Chester River. It is locally abundant in the lower bay from autumn to spring. There is a population shift to more off-shore locations in summer and perhaps again in January and February. Spawning occurs from late April to early August both in the lower bay and

crustaceans such as mussels, barnacles, and crabs, which are crushed by its strong molars.

FISHING INTEREST   Of minor commercial value but very popular with anglers. Anglers take

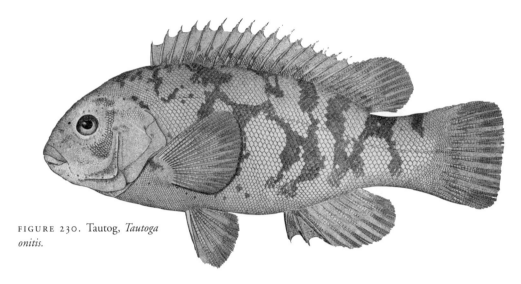

FIGURE 230. Tautog, *Tautoga onitis.*

offshore. The young are planktonic for about 3 weeks and then take up residence in shallow sea grass beds, with which the green coloration of the young blends well. Tautog mature at 3 years of age in the bay area. The tautog is a slow-growing fish that is known to live as long as 34 years. Hermaphroditism has not been established for the tautog; however, males are dimorphic, with some having an enlarged white chin, as described above, and others, usually smaller males, being blackish and similar to females. The sex ratio is also known to be strongly skewed toward males in older fishes. This species frequents rock piles, bridge pilings, artificial reefs, and old wrecks, much as the sheepshead does. Also like the sheepshead, the tautog feeds on a variety of mollusks and

tautog by bottom-fishing with hook and line baited with crabs or clams. Tautog are also a popular spearfishing target. In the lower Chesapeake Bay, tautog are most available around wrecks and structures in the spring and fall. Recreational catches of tautog in Virginia waters were estimated to exceed 318,000 kg (700,000 lb) per year in the early 1990s. The Chesapeake Bay record is unknown, but the world-record tautog, which weighed 10.9 kg (24 lb), was taken in Virginia waters off Wachapreague in 1987.

LITERATURE   Hildebrand and Schroeder 1928:318; Musick 1972; Olla et al. 1974; Olla and Samet 1977; Fritzsche 1978; Olla et al. 1981; Fahay 1983; Manooch 1984; Smith 1985; Sogard et al. 1992; Hostetter and Munroe 1993.

Medusafishes
FAMILY CENTROLOPHIDAE

Medusafishes are pelagic and are usually found on the high seas and over the edge of the continental shelves, although a few are found in shallow water. Young medusafishes live in association with jellyfishes, floating wood, or other debris. The young feed on medusae, fishes, and crustaceans. Medusafishes are slender to deep-bodied fishes with a single dorsal fin. The maximum size exceeds 1 m TL (3.3 ft). The mouth is large, with the maxilla extending to below the eye. The pharyngeal sacs have papillae with irregularly shaped bases arranged in 10–20 longitudinal bands. The family, found in most tropical and temperate seas, comprises 7 genera and 27 species, 1 of which is found in Chesapeake Bay.

Barrelfish
Hyperoglyphe perciformis (Mitchill, 1818)

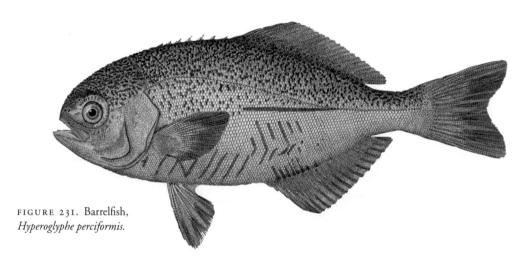

FIGURE 231. Barrelfish,
Hyperoglyphe perciformis.

KEY FEATURES   Spinous portion of dorsal fin much lower than rayed portion; pelvic fin present; toothed saccular outgrowths (pharyngeal sacs) present in gullet immediately posterior to last gill arch.

OTHER CHARACTERISTICS   Body stout, oblong, and moderately compressed; head short; snout rounded; eye moderate-sized; dorsal fin continuous, with 6–8 very short, stout spines and 19–23 soft rays; caudal fin slightly forked; anal fin with 3 spines and 15–17 soft rays; bases of anal and dorsal fins covered with scales; pelvic fin origin slightly ventroposterior to base of pectoral fin. Adults brownish black dorsally, grading to brownish white ventrally; some individuals, collected near surface, with greenish flecks laterally and ventrally. Maximum adult size 90 cm TL (3 ft).

GEOGRAPHIC DISTRIBUTION   Known from Nova Scotia to Key West, Florida.

ECOLOGY   This species is a rare visitor to the upper and lower Chesapeake Bay during summer and autumn. The barrelfish owes its common name to its habit of congregating around floating wood, planks, or wreckage and on occasion drifting inside boxes in flotsam. Near-surface drifting is primarily a habit of the young fish (5–10 cm, or 2–4 in, TL), which are also found in sargassum clumps. Only juvenile barrelfish are likely to be observed in the bay, because juveniles typically drift close inshore. The adult barrelfish is thought to be a deep-dwelling species over the continental slope and in submarine canyons. The young feed on hydroids, ctenophores, barnacles, and salps and other tunicates, as well as on young fishes of various kinds.

FISHING INTEREST   None.

LITERATURE   Musick 1972; Martin and Drewry 1978; Fritzsche 1982.

Tripletails
FAMILY LOBOTIDAE

The deep-bodied and compressed fishes known as tripletails are so named because their dorsal and anal fins are rounded and symmetrical and, in combination with the caudal fin, give the appearance of a three-lobed caudal fin. The general configuration of tripletails is often likened to that of the crappie, a common freshwater sunfish. Both adult and young tripletails are found in coastal waters, including the mouths of coastal streams and estuaries, as well as in the open-ocean epipelagic zone. However, tripletails do not appear to be abundant anywhere. The young have often been observed drifting on their sides at the surface, giving the appearance, in both posture and coloration, of floating dead mangrove leaves. The family comprises only two genera and four species and is found in all warm seas. A single species, *Lobotes surinamensis,* is known from the Atlantic and exhibits an unusually broad geographic range that includes the Mediterranean and the Indo-Pacific from Korea to southern Australia.

Tripletail
Lobotes surinamensis (Bloch, 1790)

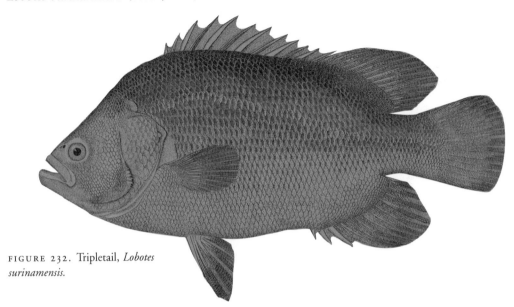

FIGURE 232. Tripletail, *Lobotes surinamensis.*

KEY FEATURES   Body deep and compressed; soft dorsal and anal fins large and broadly rounded, reaching past caudal fin base; rounded symmetrical lobes of dorsal and anal fins resembling caudal fin in size and shape and suggesting presence of 3 caudal fins; preopercle coarsely serrate; vomer, roof of mouth, and tongue toothless.

OTHER CHARACTERISTICS   Eye small; mouth large; upper jaw slightly protrusible; jaws with outer row of short, close-set canines and inner band of much smaller teeth; dorsal fin single, without pronounced notch, and with 11–13 strong spines and 13–16 soft rays; anal fin with 3 spines and 9–12 soft rays; scales moderately large, numbering about 45 in lateral series; pelvic fin rounded and longer than pectoral fin; pectoral fin rounded. Color pattern variable; body usually olive to dusky brown, mottled with dusky spots; fins blackish; juveniles often yellowish. Maximum adult size 1 m TL (3.3 ft).

GEOGRAPHIC DISTRIBUTION   A cosmopolitan species found in all warm seas. In the western Atlantic, the tripletail is known from Massachusetts to Argentina. This species apparently is not abundant anywhere in its range, but in the Atlantic it is more common south of Virginia along the seaboard.

ECOLOGY   The tripletail is an occasional visitor to the lower Chesapeake Bay during summer and autumn. Tripletails are sluggish fish found offshore and inshore near floating objects such as buoys and debris. Juveniles have been collected from patches of sargassum far offshore. Spawning occurs in spring and summer, probably inshore. Prey items consist primarily of bottom-dwelling fishes and crustaceans. Tripletails may live as long as 7–10 years and attain a weight of 20 kg (45 lb).

FISHING INTEREST   Caught incidentally by commercial fisheries, mostly in pound nets. Although not a common catch in the Chesapeake Bay area, the tripletail is regarded as a good fighting sport fish. Most tripletails are landed from May to October near wrecks, buoys, and drifting debris. The flesh is said to be of excellent quality.

LITERATURE   Hildebrand and Schroeder 1928:255; Caldwell 1955; Musick 1972; Fischer 1978; Hardy 1978b; Fritzsche 1982; Manooch 1984; Whitehead et al. 1986a; Böhlke and Chaplin 1993.

Sea Basses and Groupers
FAMILY SERRANIDAE

Members of the family of sea basses and groupers are typically large-mouthed, robust bottom dwellers that range in length from several centimeters to several meters. The family is relatively unspecialized and therefore is difficult to characterize briefly. The species in this family inhabit a wide range of habitats from the shoreline to depths of 200 m (660 ft) or more. They are carnivores of crustaceans and fishes and readily take a baited hook. Many species are commercially important. Some of the genera in the family are sequential hermaphrodites, maturing first as females and then changing to males. Small species may reach maturity in as little as a year, and large ones may take several years. Some groupers can attain weights greater than 295 kg (650 lb); such individuals are probably decades old. The family, primarily inhabitants of tropical and temperate seas, comprises 62 genera and approximately 450 species, of which 3 are known from Chesapeake Bay.

KEY TO THE SPECIES OF SEA BASSES AND GROUPERS IN CHESAPEAKE BAY

1a. Dorsal fin with 10 spines; scales relatively large, numbering 48–50 in lateral line; caudal fin rounded to trilobate; adults often with 1 upper ray of caudal fin elongate; predominant color pattern consisting of dark brown to bluish black ground color with light spots that form longitudinal stripes; young with broad dark lateral stripe and dark blotch at base of spinous dorsal fin .... **black sea bass, *Centropristis striata*** (p. 256)

1b. Dorsal fin with 11 spines; scales in lateral series too small to count accurately but numbering many more than 50; caudal fin emarginate or rounded, without elongate upper ray; predominant color pattern not as described above **2**

2a. Anal fin with 3 spines and 8 soft rays; caudal fin rounded; dorsal spines short, with membranes between them deeply notched; predominant color pattern consisting of gray or greenish ground color with small dark spots scattered on upper part of head and body .... **jewfish, *Epinephelus itajara*** (p. 257)

2b. Anal fin with 3 spines and 11 soft rays; caudal fin emarginate; dorsal spines not noticeably short and membranes between them not deeply notched; predominant color pattern consisting of brownish gray ground color with dusky wormlike markings on side ...... **gag, *Mycteroperca microlepis*** (p. 258)

Black sea bass
Centropristis striata (Linnaeus, 1758)
PLATE 45

KEY FEATURES   Dorsal fin with 10 spines, each with fleshy filament at tip in adults; lateral line scales numbering 48–50; caudal fin rounded to trilobate; large individuals often with 1 upper ray of caudal fin produced.

OTHER CHARACTERISTICS   Body elongate, moderately compressed; head pointed; mouth large and oblique; teeth pointed; distinct canine teeth absent anteriorly; preopercular margin finely serrate; opercle with 3 flat spines; dorsal fin continuous but notched, with 10 slender spines and 11 soft rays; anal fin with 3 spines and 7 soft rays; pelvic fin long and inserting slightly ventroanterior to pectoral fin; pectoral fin longer than pelvic fin. Body bluish black in adults, brownish in juveniles; centers of scales pale blue or white, forming longitudinal lines along back and side; dorsal fin with longitudinal rows of pale streaks; females paler than males; fleshy hump, often bright blue, developing on nape of males during spawning season; juveniles with prominent, dark, broad lateral stripe and with dark blotch at base of posterior dorsal spines. Maximum adult size 61 cm TL (2 ft).

GEOGRAPHIC DISTRIBUTION   Recorded in the western Atlantic from Massachusetts to Florida.

ECOLOGY   The black sea bass is common in

the mid-lower Chesapeake Bay from spring to late autumn, extending as far north as Solomons Island. In the winter, it migrates offshore and south. Adult black sea bass are most often found on rocky bottoms near pilings, wrecks, and jetties. Juveniles are found in deep, vegetated flats. Black sea bass are visual feeders during daylight hours. The adults feed chiefly on crabs, mussels, razor clams, and fishes, whereas the young prey

Large fish are more common offshore than in the bay.

FISHING INTEREST   Of modest commercial importance in Chesapeake Bay, but forming the basis of an important sport fishery. Commercial landings of black sea bass from the bay average less than 2,275 kg (5,000 lb) per year. However, an estimated 1.5 million black sea bass were taken by anglers in the lower bay in 1991.

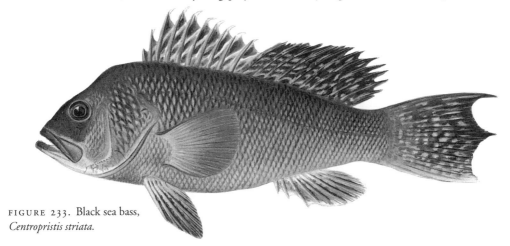

FIGURE 233. Black sea bass, *Centropristis striata*.

on shrimps, isopods, and amphipods. Black sea bass are protogynous hermaphrodites—that is, initially they are females, but larger fish reverse sex to become males. Spawning begins in June, peaks in August, and continues through October in the Mid-Atlantic Bight. Black sea bass are reported to live as long as 20 years. However, individuals longer than 38 cm TL (15 in), the size of an approximately 8-year-old fish, are uncommon.

Bottom-fishing from boats, anglers use squids and other natural baits fished over firm bottoms near rocks, wrecks, and reefs to catch this highly esteemed and flavorful fish.

LITERATURE   Hildebrand and Schroeder 1928:251; Musick 1972; Kendall 1977; Musick and Mercer 1977; Fischer 1978; Hardy 1978b; Fahay 1983; Manooch 1984; Wenner et al. 1986.

Jewfish
Epinephelus itajara (Lichtenstein, 1822)

KEY FEATURES   Anal fin with 3 spines and 8 soft rays; caudal fin rounded; dorsal spines short, with membranes between them deeply notched; predominant color pattern consisting of gray or greenish ground color with small dark spots scattered on upper part of head and body.

OTHER CHARACTERISTICS   Body robust and thick, almost terete; head broad and flat between orbits, with large interorbital width; mouth very large; canine teeth only slightly enlarged; eye proportionally very small; preopercular margin with distinct notch; opercle with 3 flat spines; scales very small and rugose; scales in lat-

eral line with radiating ridges; dorsal fin with 11 short spines and 15 or 16 soft rays; dorsal spines tuberculate in large fish; pelvic fin inserting perpendicular or slightly ventroposterior to pectoral fin base. Large specimens gray or greenish, with small distinct dark spots scattered over upper parts of head, body, and pectoral fin; specimens under about 1 m TL (3.3 ft) also marked with small scattered spots, but ground color tan to greenish and 5 or 6 irregular dusky bars present on side. Maximum adult size 2.4 m TL (8 ft), with weight more than 320 kg (700 lb).

GEOGRAPHIC DISTRIBUTION   In the Atlantic, known from Virginia to Brazil, including the Gulf of Mexico, the Caribbean Sea, and Bermuda. In the eastern Pacific, the jewfish occurs from Costa Rica to Peru.

when the jewfish's enormous mouth cavity is rapidly opened and expanded. Jewfish are very slow-growing and long-lived; a 37-year-old individual is known to the literature.

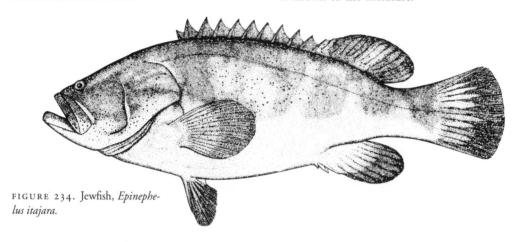

FIGURE 234. Jewfish, *Epinephelus itajara*.

ECOLOGY   The jewfish is a tropical and subtropical species that only rarely strays into warm-temperate waters. It is a shallow-water species that usually inhabits depths of less than 30 m (100 ft) and is sometimes seen in depths as shallow as 1 m (3.3 ft). Jewfish inhabit areas of reefs, ledges, and wrecks offshore and bridge pilings, jetties, and submerged mangrove roots inshore. In Florida, spawning in aggregations occurs in July and August. There is evidence that jewfish are protogynous hermaphrodites, transforming from females to males when very large. A large female taken in Chesapeake Bay in the month of August showed signs of having recently spawned. Jewfish are primarily predators on large crustaceans such as crabs and lobsters but also eat fishes, turtles, and octopi. The prey item is engulfed by suction

FISHING INTEREST   Not pursued by commercial or recreational fisheries, because of rarity. In Florida, where the jewfish is common, it is protected from commercial harvest as a game fish but is a popular sport species that is taken on bottom rigs by using whole or cut mullet or crabs as bait. The all-tackle record for jewfish is 306 kg (675 lb). The jewfish is also vulnerable to divers with spears because it is easily approached. A female jewfish weighing 218 kg (480 lb) was taken near New Point Comfort Light in Chesapeake Bay and is arguably the largest bony fish ever landed in bay waters.
LITERATURE   Richards 1963; Smith 1971; Musick 1972; Fischer 1978; Hardy 1978b; Heemstra and Randall 1993.

Gag
Mycteroperca microlepis (Goode and Bean, 1879)
PLATE 46

KEY FEATURES   Anal fin with 3 spines and 11 soft rays; dorsal fin with 11 slender spines (rarely 10 or 12); dorsal spines without fleshy tips, not noticeably short, and with membranes between them not deeply notched; caudal fin emarginate, with no rays produced; predominant color pattern consisting of brownish gray ground color with dusky wormlike markings on side.

OTHER CHARACTERISTICS   Body elongate, compressed; head pointed; mouth large; 2 canine teeth present anteriorly in each jaw; preopercular margin angulate, with distinct notch at angle; scales very small, numbering 120–140 in lateral line series; dorsal fin continuous and with 16–19 soft rays; pelvic fin inserting perpendicular to pectoral fin. Adults with narrow pale or white margin on dusky median fins; juveniles much paler and with numerous dusky brown marks laterally. Maximum adult size 1.2 m TL (4 ft).

GEOGRAPHIC DISTRIBUTION   Found as adults from North Carolina to Brazil, including the Gulf of Mexico but excluding the West Indies. Juveniles inhabit estuaries as far north as Massachusetts.

curs off the southeast Atlantic coast in February at depths greater than 70 m (230 ft). Gags feed on fishes, crabs, shrimps, and squids. Individuals may live for 15 years.

FISHING INTEREST   Of no commercial or recreational importance in the Chesapeake Bay area, because of scarcity. Where more common, gags are highly prized as food fish and are caught

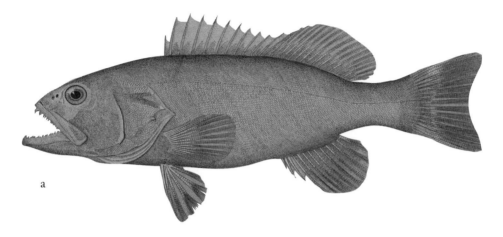

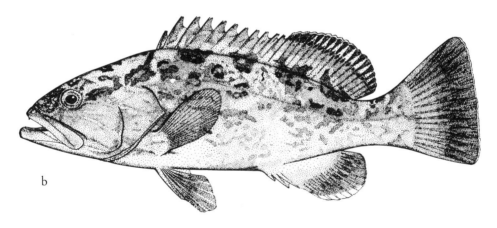

FIGURE 235. Gag, *Mycteroperca microlepis:* (a) subadult, (b) adult.

ECOLOGY   Juvenile gags are occasional visitors to the lower Chesapeake Bay during summer and early autumn. Adults frequent waters from 20 to 80 m (65 to 265 ft) in depth in rocky areas and on coral reefs. Juveniles occur in estuaries and sea grass beds. Like many other sea basses and groupers, gags are protogynous hermaphrodites, with sexual transition from female to male occurring between 10 and 11 years of age. Spawning oc-

by bottom-fishing with hook and line. The all-tackle record for gag is 32 kg (70 lb) for a fish caught off Florida. Gags are occasionally taken in pound nets or by anglers bottom-fishing near the bay mouth.

LITERATURE   Hildebrand and Schroeder 1928:250; Smith 1971; Musick 1972; Fischer 1978; Hardy 1978b; Manooch 1984; Heemstra and Randall 1993.

Puffers and Triggerfishes
ORDER TETRAODONTIFORMES

The order of puffers and triggerfishes has nine families, six of which are known from Chesapeake Bay.

KEY TO THE FAMILIES OF PUFFERS AND TRIGGERFISHES IN CHESAPEAKE BAY

1a. Body abruptly truncate, without caudal peduncle and normal caudal fin; dorsal and anal fins high . . . . **molas—Molidae**
. . . . (1 species recorded from Chesapeake Bay: ocean sunfish, *Mola mola,* p. 290)
1b. Not fitting above description **2**

2a. Jaws with distinct teeth **3**
2b. Jaws with teeth modified into short beak with enamel-like covering **5**

3a. Spinous dorsal fin absent; body "box-shaped" and covered by immovable bony plates, with only jaws, fins, and tail free . . . . **boxfishes—Ostraciidae** (p. 260)
3b. Spinous dorsal fin present; body covered with scales or flexible bony plates **4**

4a. First dorsal fin with 3 spines; scales relatively large, bony, and rough, forming very flexible but tough external covering . . . . **triggerfishes—Balistidae** (p. 261)
4b. First dorsal fin with 1 or 2 spines; scales minute, not bony, and not readily distinguishable from one another to the unaided eye . . . . **filefishes—Monacanthidae** (p. 263)

5a. Body covered with prominent spines; beak not divided in either jaw . . . . **porcupinefishes—Diodontidae** (p. 265)
5b. Body naked or with small spines or prickles; beak divided in 2 anteriorly in each jaw . . . . **puffers—Tetraodontidae** (p. 267)

Boxfishes
FAMILY OSTRACIIDAE

Boxfishes are marine oddities, so named because their external carapace of bony plates covers most of the head and body, with the jaws, eyes, and fins protruding from it. Some species possess sharp spines that project anteriorly and/or posteriorly from the carapace. As would be expected from their appearance, boxfishes are slow swimmers and propel themselves primarily by a sculling action of the dorsal and anal fins. Boxfishes are bottom dwellers found primarily in shallow sea grass beds, but some species have been taken at depths of more than 270 m (890 ft). They are diurnal predators that feed on a wide variety of benthic invertebrates and algae. Though one would think that their carapace would provide adequate protection from most predators, at least some species have another defense in the form of a poison, ostracitoxin, which is secreted from the skin and is powerful enough to kill other fish in a confined area. The family, distributed worldwide in tropical seas, comprises 14 genera and approximately 33 species, 2 of which are recorded from Chesapeake Bay.

KEY TO THE SPECIES OF BOXFISHES IN CHESAPEAKE BAY

1a. Prominent carapace spines projecting anteriorly from near eye . . . . **scrawled cowfish, *Lactophrys quadricornis*** (p. 291)
1b. Carapace spines absent near eye . . . . **trunkfish, *Lactophrys trigonus*** (p. 261)

Trunkfish
Lactophrys trigonus (Linnaeus, 1758)

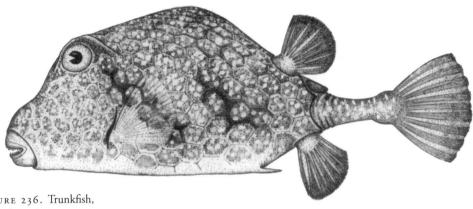

FIGURE 236. Trunkfish,
Lactophrys trigonus.

KEY FEATURES   Spinous dorsal fin absent; body "box-shaped" and covered by carapace with only jaws, fins, and tail free; carapace incomplete posteriorly, partially open posterior to dorsal fin; carapace spines absent near eye.

OTHER CHARACTERISTICS   Body deep, wide ventrally, and almost completely encased in bony carapace; mouth small and terminal; dorsal fin without spines and with 9 or 10 soft rays; caudal fin rounded; posteriorly directed spine present on each side of carapace posterior to anal fin; anal fin with 9 rays; pelvic fin absent; pectoral fin broad. Body greenish to tannish, with small white spots and 2 dusky blotches on side. Maximum adult size 45 cm TL (1.5 ft).

GEOGRAPHIC DISTRIBUTION   Known from Massachusetts to Brazil, including the Gulf of Mexico and the Caribbean Sea.

ECOLOGY   The trunkfish is a rare summer visitor to the lower Chesapeake Bay. Typically only juveniles enter the bay as tropical strays. Primarily a resident of sea grass beds in shallow water to depths of 50 m (165 ft), the trunkfish feeds on a variety of small bottom-dwelling organisms such as mollusks, crustaceans, and worms.

FISHING INTEREST   Of no commercial or recreational importance. The trunkfish is caught incidentally with traps or by seining.

LITERATURE   Hildebrand and Schroeder 1928: 346; Musick 1972; Fischer 1978; Fritzsche 1982.

Triggerfishes
FAMILY BALISTIDAE

Triggerfishes typically are brightly colored, highly compressed, and deep-bodied tropical marine fishes. They have a thick, tough skin consisting of armorlike, nonoverlapping scales. The pelvic fins are replaced by a single spinous knob at the end of a long, depressible pelvic bone. The first dorsal fin spine can be locked in place by the second spine (the "trigger"). When alarmed or at night, these fishes take refuge in a rock or coral crevice and lock their dorsal spine up, erect their pelvic bone, and thus become effectively wedged in and protected from attack. They swim by undulating the second dorsal fin and the anal fin, using their tail only to move quickly. Triggerfishes have powerful jaws and chisellike teeth, with which they feed on a variety of invertebrate organisms, including crabs, mollusks, sea urchins, and corals. Triggerfishes are usually solitary, typically found in and around rocky or coral reefs in depths of 90 m (295 ft) or less. Eggs are laid in a nest that is aggressively guarded by the male. The family, found worldwide in tropical seas, comprises 11 genera and approximately 40 species, 1 of which is recorded from Chesapeake Bay.

Gray triggerfish
Balistes capriscus Gmelin, 1789

FIGURE 237. Gray triggerfish,
Balistes capriscus.

KEY FEATURES   First dorsal fin with 3 spines; scales relatively large, bony, and rough, forming very flexible but tough external covering; teeth notched, uneven, and of distinctly increasing length toward middle; dorsal and ventral rays of caudal fin slightly prolonged.

OTHER CHARACTERISTICS   Head and body deep, strongly compressed; snout long; eye small; mouth small and terminal; teeth large and strong; gill opening in form of relatively short, vertical to oblique slit anterior to pectoral fin base; scales implanted in thick leathery skin and with edges not free; dorsal fins separate; first dorsal fin with 3 short strong spines and with first spine longest; second dorsal fin and anal fin similar and highest anteriorly; pelvic fins represented by single, multibarbed, blunt spiny process at terminus of pelvic bone; pectoral fin short. Body grayish green, with 3 dusky blotches and with small purplish or bluish spots dorsally, and with pale spots ventrally; second dorsal fin and anal fin with dusky spots that tend to form rows. Maximum adult size 40 cm TL (16 in).

GEOGRAPHIC DISTRIBUTION   Known from both the eastern and the western Atlantic coasts. In the western Atlantic, the gray trig-gerfish ranges from Nova Scotia to Argentina, including the Gulf of Mexico and the Caribbean Sea.

ECOLOGY   The gray triggerfish is an occasional summer visitor to the lower Chesapeake Bay, reaching as far north as the mouth of the Potomac River. This species frequents coral reef environments, including sand or grass flats as well as rocky bottoms to depths of about 50 m (165 ft). It feeds on bottom-dwelling invertebrates such as mollusks and crustaceans, relying on its powerful teeth to dislodge and crush its prey. Spawning occurs from July to September and only after water temperatures exceed 21°C (70°F). Eggs are laid in a shallow depression made by the female in sand bottoms, and the nest is guarded by the male.

FISHING INTEREST   Of no commercial or recreational importance. The gray triggerfish is caught incidentally in bottom trawls, in traps, and on handlines.

LITERATURE   Hildebrand and Schroeder 1928:341; Musick 1972; Fischer 1978; Martin and Drewry 1978; Fritzsche 1982; Manooch 1984; Whitehead et al. 1986b.

Filefishes

FAMILY MONACANTHIDAE

Filefishes are closely related and similar in appearance to triggerfishes. The former differ by having more compressed bodies, a longer and thinner first dorsal spine (sometimes adorned with spikes), a very small second spine (sometimes absent), no third dorsal spine, somewhat smaller and fewer teeth, and much smaller nonoverlapping scales. Unlike triggerfishes, most filefishes are able to change their color to match their surroundings closely. Filefishes are relatively secretive, hiding in sea grass or algae. They feed on a wide variety of benthic animal and plant life. The family, found worldwide in tropical seas, comprises 31 genera and approximately 95 species. Two genera and 3 species are recorded from Chesapeake Bay.

KEY TO THE SPECIES OF FILEFISHES IN CHESAPEAKE BAY

1a. Pelvic spine prominent, in form of barbed process in midline at end of pelvis .... **planehead filefish, *Monacanthus hispidus*** (p. 263)

1b. Pelvic spine absent or rudimentary **2**

2a. Head and body olive-colored, with blue or green reticulation and numerous black or maroon spots; dorsal fin with 43 or more rays; anal fin with 46 or more rays .... **scrawled filefish, *Aluterus scriptus*** (p. 264)

2b. Head and body grayish to brownish, with large irregular whitish blotches and numerous small orange yellow spots; dorsal fin with 40 or fewer rays; anal fin with 41 or fewer rays .... **orange filefish, *Aluterus schoepfi*** (p. 265)

Planehead filefish
Monacanthus hispidus (Linnaeus, 1766)

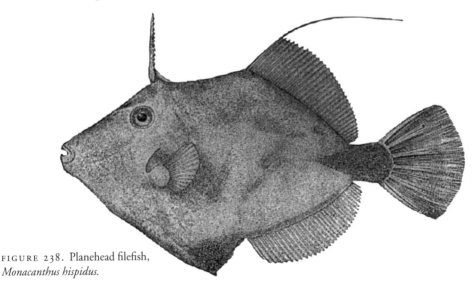

FIGURE 238. Planehead filefish,
Monacanthus hispidus.

KEY FEATURES   Pelvic spine prominent, represented as barbed process in midline at end of pelvis; caudal peduncle without enlarged spines in fish at any size; second ray of dorsal fin elongate in males.

OTHER CHARACTERISTICS   Body short and deep, strongly compressed; profile from snout to dorsal fin slightly concave; snout long; mouth very small and terminal; teeth in jaws broad and sharp-edged; gill opening in form of oblique slit, located between eye and pectoral fin base; scales minute, with short rough bristles; first dorsal fin consisting of single barbed spine originating perpendicular to posterior part of eye; second dorsal fin and anal fin similar in form and located opposite each other; caudal fin convex; ventral flap, or dewlap, present between end of pelvis and anus; pectoral fin small. Coloration varying with background; body typically grayish or greenish; side with irregular black blotches; caudal fin dusky. Maximum adult size 20 cm TL (8 in).

GEOGRAPHIC DISTRIBUTION　Found in both the eastern and the western Atlantic. Along the western Atlantic coast, the planehead filefish is known from Nova Scotia to Brazil and throughout the Gulf of Mexico.

ECOLOGY　The planehead filefish is an occasional visitor to the lower Chesapeake Bay during summer and autumn. Adults are often associated with sea grass beds; juveniles occasionally associate with floating seaweed. The planehead filefish feeds on bryozoans, small crustaceans, mollusks, annelids, sea urchins, and algae.

FISHING INTEREST　Of no commercial or recreational value.

LITERATURE　Hildebrand and Schroeder 1928:342; Musick 1972; Martin and Drewry 1978; Whitehead et al. 1986b.

Scrawled filefish
Aluterus scriptus (Osbeck, 1765)

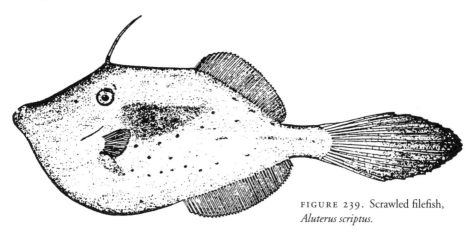

FIGURE 239. Scrawled filefish, *Aluterus scriptus.*

KEY FEATURES　Head and body olive-colored, with blue or green reticulation extending from snout to tail; numerous round black or maroon spots present on body; spinous pelvic projection absent; dorsal fin with 43–50 rays; anal fin with 46–52 rays; pectoral fin with 13–15 rays (typically 14).

OTHER CHARACTERISTICS　Body elongate, very strongly compressed; mouth very small and nearly vertical; teeth in jaws broad; teeth of lower jaw usually deeply notched and with sharp edge; gill opening in form of oblique slit dorsoanterior to pectoral fin base; scales minute; first dorsal spine originating perpendicular to eye, barbed in juveniles and barbless in adults; second dorsal fin and anal fin similar in form and located opposite each other; caudal fin long and rounded; pectoral fin small. Dorsal and anal fins yellowish; caudal fin reddish. Maximum adult size 90 cm TL (3 ft).

GEOGRAPHIC DISTRIBUTION　Known from all tropical seas. In the western Atlantic, the scrawled filefish ranges from Georges Bank, Massachusetts, to Brazil, including the Gulf of Mexico. This species is rare north of South Carolina.

ECOLOGY　The scrawled filefish is a rare summer visitor to the lower Chesapeake Bay. It typically inhabits patch reefs and grass beds. The young mimic blades of sea grass and are observed drifting head-down, looking at the bottom for food.

FISHING INTEREST　Of no commercial or recreational value.

LITERATURE　Berry and Vogele 1961; Böhlke and Chaplin 1993.

Orange filefish
Aluterus schoepfi (Walbaum, 1792)

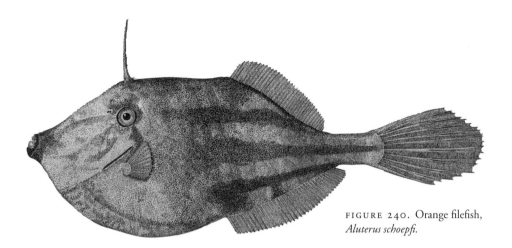

FIGURE 240. Orange filefish,
Aluterus schoepfi.

KEY FEATURES   Head and body grayish to brownish, with large irregular whitish blotches and numerous small orange yellow spots; spinous pelvic projection absent; dorsal fin with 32–40 rays; anal fin with 35–41 rays; pectoral fin with 11–14 rays (typically 12 or 13); obviously enlarged, encasing scales absent at end of pelvis; first spine of dorsal fin relatively weak and slender, without barbs along posterior edge.

OTHER CHARACTERISTICS   Body elongate, very strongly compressed; mouth very small and nearly vertical; teeth in jaws broad; teeth of lower jaw usually deeply notched and with sharp edge; gill opening in form of oblique slit dorsoanterior to pectoral fin base; scales minute; first dorsal spine originating perpendicular to eye; second dorsal fin and anal fin similar in form and located opposite each other; caudal fin long and rounded; pectoral fin small. Maximum adult size 60 cm TL (2 ft).

GEOGRAPHIC DISTRIBUTION   Ranging from Nova Scotia to Brazil, including the Gulf of Mexico and the Caribbean Sea.

ECOLOGY   The orange filefish is a summer visitor to Chesapeake Bay that is common in the lower bay but only occasionally encountered in the upper bay, extending as far as the Choptank River. This species typically associates with sea grass beds, where it grazes on algae and other plants.

FISHING INTEREST   Of no commercial or recreational value. The orange filefish is taken as bycatch in trawls.

LITERATURE   Hildebrand and Schroeder 1928:344; Berry and Vogele 1961; Musick 1972; Fischer 1978; Martin and Drewry 1978; Fritzsche 1982.

Porcupinefishes
FAMILY DIODONTIDAE

Porcupinefishes are characterized by large eyes, round bodies, and small caudal fins. These small to medium-sized fishes have a blunt head and a wide body that bears enormously enlarged scales in the form of fixed short spines or long, erectile quills. When disturbed, these fishes inflate to an almost spherical shape, with their long spines directed outward. They swim slowly, propelled by undulations of the dorsal and anal fins, and use their tail as a rudder. They are distinguished from the puffers (Tetraodontidae) by having larger sharp, stout spines covering their head and body and by having teeth that form a continuous unsutured plate in each jaw. These oral plates have a sharp cutting edge anteriorly and a strong crushing surface posteriorly. Many species of porcupinefishes are found in shallow water, in sandy bays, or over reefs. Most porcupinefishes are nocturnal carnivores that use their parrotlike beak to crush the hard-shelled benthic invertebrates on which they feed. Porcupinefishes are often dried in the inflated state and used for curio lampshades and souvenirs. The family, which inhabits all tropical seas, comprises 6 genera and 19 species, 2 of which are known from Chesapeake Bay.

KEY TO THE SPECIES OF PORCUPINEFISHES IN CHESAPEAKE BAY

1a. Spines on head and body long and quill-like . . . . **porcupinefish, *Diodon hystrix*** (p. 291)
1b. Spines on head and body short and massive . . . . . **striped burrfish, *Chilomycterus schoepfi*** (p. 266)

Striped burrfish
Chilomycterus schoepfi (Walbaum, 1792)

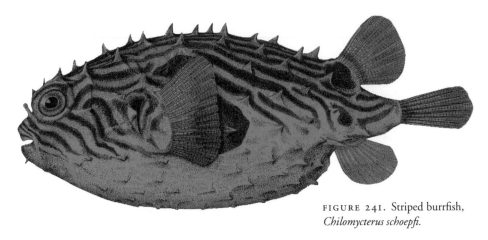

FIGURE 241. Striped burrfish, *Chilomycterus schoepfi.*

KEY FEATURES   Jaws with teeth modified into short beak with enamel-like covering; spines relatively short and massive, covering head and body; beak not divided in either jaw.

OTHER CHARACTERISTICS   Body robust, broader than deep; head short and broad; snout very short and broad; mouth small and terminal; gill opening restricted to small round opening; dorsal and anal fins located posteriorly and opposite each other; caudal fin rounded; pectoral fin short and broad; pelvic fin or pelvic process absent. Yellowish green dorsally; whitish orange ventrally; numerous dusky brown or blackish irregular wavy stripes present on dorsum; several large black ocelli (eyelike spots) present laterally on body and varying in number; 1 ocellus commonly present dorsal to pectoral fin, 1 immediately posterior to pectoral fin, 1 ventral to dorsal fin, and 1 just anterior to caudal peduncle; fins greenish yellow or orange. Maximum adult size 25 cm TL (10 in).

GEOGRAPHIC DISTRIBUTION   Found from New England to Brazil, including the Gulf of Mexico.

ECOLOGY   The striped burrfish is a common visitor to the lower to middle Chesapeake Bay from late spring to autumn, reaching as far north as the Patuxent River. It moves out of the bay and southward in wintertime. Striped burrfish are typically found in deep flats, in grass flats, and along channel margins. Their locomotion is reported to be assisted by jetting water from the restricted gill openings. The striped burrfish feeds primarily on benthic invertebrates, especially hermit crabs, which are consumed shell and all.

FISHING INTEREST   Of no commercial or recreational value. The striped burrfish is occasionally collected in seines and pound nets.

LITERATURE   Hildebrand and Schroeder 1928:350; Musick 1972; Martin and Drewry 1978; Fritzsche 1982; Böhlke and Chaplin 1993.

Puffers
FAMILY TETRAODONTIDAE

The puffers are so named for their ability, when provoked, to inflate themselves greatly by drawing water (or air if they are out of the water) into a specialized chamber near the stomach. The resulting prickly ball deters many predators. They have a tough skin, which may be scaleless or may have scales that are modified into small spines or prickles. They lack true teeth but have beaklike dental plates with a median suture. Fin spines are absent, as are pelvic fins. Puffers are well known for possessing tetraodontoxin, one of nature's most powerful toxins, particularly in their liver and ovaries. Serious illness and death may result from eating those tissues of puffers. The muscle tissue of puffers is usually safe to eat and is considered a delicacy by some people. Puffers feed on invertebrates such as sponges, crustaceans, polychaetes, sea urchins, and hydroids. All species lay adhesive demersal eggs that are guarded by the male. Puffers are inhabitants of tropical and temperate seas; they are most frequently found in shallow inshore waters, but they sometimes enter brackish waters and freshwaters. The family comprises 19 genera and more than 120 species. Two genera and 3 species are known from Chesapeake Bay.

KEY TO THE SPECIES OF PUFFERS IN CHESAPEAKE BAY

1a. Dorsal fin with 13 or more rays; anal fin usually with 12 or more rays; caudal fin margin distinctly concave or slightly crescent-shaped; scales (prickles) restricted to belly . . . . **smooth puffer, *Lagocephalus laevigatus*** (p. 267)

1b. Dorsal fin with 9 or fewer rays; anal fin with 8 or fewer rays; caudal fin slightly rounded or truncate; prickles present over most of body and more pronounced on dorsum **2**

2a. Back grayish green, with ill-defined black spots and blotches; side yellowish, with several irregular bars; intense black spot present in pectoral fin axil . . . . . **northern puffer, *Sphoeroides maculatus*** (p. 268)

2b. Back greenish brown, with pale lines forming reticulated pattern that approximates concentric circles from dorsal view; numerous dusky spots present on side and back; intense black spot absent in pectoral fin axil . . . . **checkered puffer, *Sphoeroides testudineus*** (p. 291)

Smooth puffer
Lagocephalus laevigatus (Linnaeus, 1766)
PLATE 47

KEY FEATURES   Upper and lower tooth plates divided into left and right halves; prickles (scales) short and restricted to belly; caudal fin margin deeply concave, with upper lobe slightly longer than lower lobe; dorsal fin usually with 13 or 14 soft rays and no spines; anal fin usually with 12 or 13 soft rays and no spines.

OTHER CHARACTERISTICS   Body elongate, deeper than broad; head long; snout conical; eye large; mouth small and nearly terminal; ventral edge of body with longitudinal fold or keel; anal and dorsal fins opposite one another, similar in size and shape, and originating posterior to midpoint of body; pectoral fin short and broad. Dorsum and upper side uniformly dusky gray or greenish gray; lower side silver; venter white; young fish with several broad dark bars on upper side. Maximum adult size 1 m TL (3.3 ft). This species is the largest of the American puffers.

GEOGRAPHIC DISTRIBUTION   Known from both the eastern and the western Atlantic coasts. In the western Atlantic, the smooth puffer's range is from Massachusetts to Argentina, including the Gulf of Mexico and the Caribbean Sea.

ECOLOGY   The smooth puffer is an occasional summer and autumn visitor to the lower Chesapeake Bay and is rarely encountered in the upper bay, extending as far as Annapolis. Smooth puffers inhabit inshore and nearshore areas to about 60 m (200 ft) deep, over sand, rocky, or mud bottoms, and they are known to form small aggregations.

with hook and line. The tail flesh is of excellent quality, but puffers must be cleaned with care because the viscera are toxic and can contaminate the meat. Only the tail flesh should be eaten.

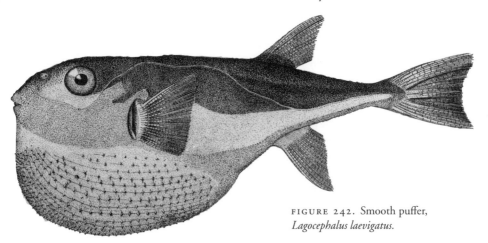

FIGURE 242. Smooth puffer, *Lagocephalus laevigatus.*

FISHING INTEREST   Of no commercial or recreational importance. Smooth puffers are caught primarily by anglers while bottom-fishing

LITERATURE   Hildebrand and Schroeder 1928:347; Musick 1972; Fischer 1978; Nelson 1994.

Northern puffer
Sphoeroides maculatus (Bloch and Schneider, 1801)

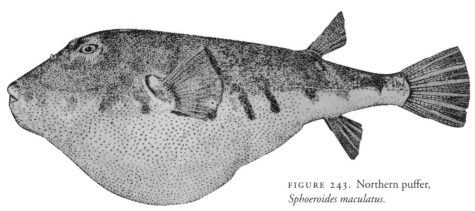

FIGURE 243. Northern puffer, *Sphoeroides maculatus.*

KEY FEATURES   Upper and lower tooth plates divided into left and right halves; small spines or prickles present on body except on caudal peduncle; dorsal fin usually with 8 soft rays and no spines; anal fin usually with 7 soft rays and no spines; caudal fin rounded.

OTHER CHARACTERISTICS   Body elongate, deeper than broad; head long; snout coni-

cal; eye small; mouth small and nearly terminal; anal and dorsal fins similar in size and shape and originating posterior to midpoint of body, with origin of dorsal fin dorsoanterior to anal fin origin; pectoral fin short and broad. Back grayish green, with ill-defined black blotches and small black spots; side yellowish, with several irregular bars; intense black spot present in pectoral fin axil; venter white to yellow. Maximum adult size 36 cm TL (14 in).

GEOGRAPHIC DISTRIBUTION Occurring coastally from Newfoundland to southern Florida.

ECOLOGY The northern puffer is a common visitor to Chesapeake Bay from spring to autumn, exiting the bay during winter. It is more common in the lower bay than in the upper bay, extending as far as Love Point, at the mouth of the Chester River. It inhabits channel margins and flats of bays and estuaries, as well as offshore waters to depths of 60 m (200 ft) or more. Spawning occurs from May to August in nearshore waters, where the eggs are attached to the substrate. The northern puffer feeds on small crustaceans, including crabs, shrimp, isopods, and amphipods.

FISHING INTEREST Important as a food fish along the mid-Atlantic coast through the 1960s, usually marketed as "sea squab." Subsequently, the numbers of northern puffers have decreased dramatically, and the species is now only an incidental catch for commercial fisheries. In the bay, northern puffers are caught during the spring in pound nets and in the summer and autumn in crab pots. The species is of minor recreational value to hook-and-line anglers fishing from boats or the shore.

LITERATURE Hildebrand and Schroeder 1928:348; Robinson and Schwartz 1968; Musick 1972; Fischer 1978; Martin and Drewry 1978; Fahay 1983; Manooch 1984.

Flatfishes
ORDER PLEURONECTIFORMES

The order of flatfishes comprises 10 families, 5 of which are known from Chesapeake Bay.

KEY TO THE FAMILIES OF FLATFISHES IN CHESAPEAKE BAY

1a. One or both pectoral fins absent; margin of preopercle not free **2**
1b. Both pectoral fins present; margin of preopercle free **3**

2a. Eyes sinistral (located on left side of head); median fins continuous with caudal fin; lateral line absent . . . . **tonguefishes—Cynoglossidae** (p. 269)
2b. Eyes dextral (located on right side of head); median fins separate from caudal fin; lateral line present or absent . . . . **American soles—Achiridae** (p. 270)

3a. Eyes dextral . . . . **righteye flounders—Pleuronectidae** (p. 272)
3b. Eyes sinistral **4**

4a. Anterior rays of dorsal fin branched . . . . **windowpanes—Scophthalmidae** (p. 273)
4b. Anterior rays of dorsal fin unbranched . . . . **paralichthyid flounders—Paralichthyidae** (p. 274)

Tonguefishes
FAMILY CYNOGLOSSIDAE

Members of the family of tonguefishes are small bottom-dwelling flatfishes. Tonguefishes have both eyes on the left side, and the posterior two-thirds of the body tapers to a point without a caudal peduncle region. The dorsal and anal fins are attached to the pointed caudal fin, and the pectoral fins are both typically absent. Only the left pelvic fin is developed. Most species are small and found on muddy bottoms of shelf areas. The family is found worldwide in tropical and subtropical waters and comprises more than 100 species in only 3 genera. One species of tonguefish is resident in Chesapeake Bay.

Blackcheek tonguefish
Symphurus plagiusa (Linnaeus, 1766)

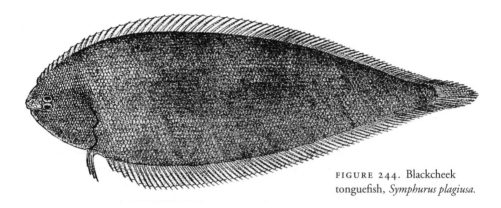

FIGURE 244. Blackcheek tonguefish, *Symphurus plagiusa.*

KEY FEATURES   Eyes small and located on left side of head; preopercular margin covered with skin and scales and not free; pectoral fins absent; dorsal and anal fin rays confluent with caudal fin; posterior two-thirds of body tapering to a point.
OTHER CHARACTERISTICS   Body extremely compressed; head length shorter than head width; snout blunt; mouth small and nearly horizontal; scales small, ctenoid, and numbering about 76–86 in lateral series; dermal papillae well developed on snout, chin, and dorsal portion of blind side of head; dorsal fin long-based, originating dorsoanterior to eyes, and with 81–91 rays; anal fin long-based, originating ventroposterior to gill opening, and with 66–75 rays; single pelvic fin present, originating perpendicular to gill opening. Ocular side brownish and sometimes with 6 or 7 indistinct broad crossbars formed by small dusky spots; large dusky spot usually present on upper portion of opercle; blind side white. Maximum adult size 20 cm TL (8 in).
GEOGRAPHIC DISTRIBUTION   Ranging from New York to Florida and throughout the Gulf of Mexico, including the Greater Antilles and the Bahamas.
ECOLOGY   The blackcheek tonguefish is a year-round resident of Chesapeake Bay that is common in the lower bay but only occasionally encountered in the upper bay, extending as far as Kent Island. Juveniles are abundant in tidal creeks and salt-marsh fringes and move into deeper bay waters as they grow. This species primarily inhabits mud bottoms, feeding on mollusks, worms, and small crustaceans. Spawning occurs from late spring through summer in the bay.
FISHING INTEREST   Of no commercial or recreational value and taken only incidentally with seines and bottom trawls.
LITERATURE   Hildebrand and Schroeder 1928:177; Musick 1972; Olney and Grant 1976; Stickney 1976; Fischer 1978; Martin and Drewry 1978; Fritzsche 1982; Fahay 1983; Munroe 1987; Chapleau 1988; Norcross and Hata 1990; Bonzek et al. 1993.

American Soles
FAMILY ACHIRIDAE

The American soles share many characteristics with the tonguefishes. However, the eyes of American soles are located on the right side (rather than on the left side, as in tonguefishes). Additionally, American soles have a rounded caudal fin and a distinct caudal peduncle region, and in most American sole species the dorsal and anal fins are not continuous with the caudal fin. Although most species in this family are marine, some are freshwater. The family is restricted to the New World and comprises 9 genera and approximately 28 species. One species in the family is resident in Chesapeake Bay.

Hogchoker
Trinectes maculatus (Bloch and Schneider, 1801)
PLATE 48

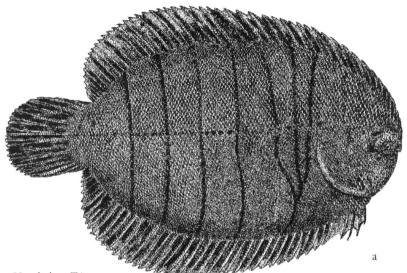

a

FIGURE 245. Hogchoker, *Tri-nectes maculatus: (a)* dorsal surface, *(b)* ventral surface.

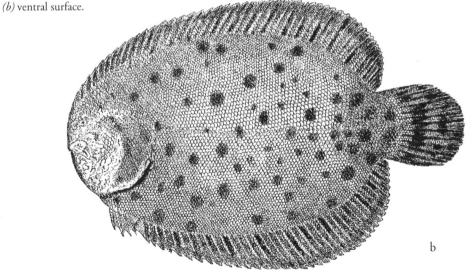

b

KEY FEATURES Eyes small and located on right side of head; body rounded or oval in outline; preopercular margin covered with skin and scales and not free; dorsal and anal fin rays not connected to caudal fin; distinct caudal peduncle present; pectoral fins usually absent (with single ray when present).

OTHER CHARACTERISTICS Body broad, with dorsal and ventral outlines convex; head short; snout blunt; scales small, ctenoid, and numbering 66–75 in lateral series; dorsal fin long-based, originating on tip of snout, and with 50–56 rays; anal fin long-based, originating perpendicular to opercle, and with 36–46 rays; caudal fin rounded; right pelvic fin continuous with anal fin. Color pattern highly variable and rapidly changeable (in seconds to minutes); most common pattern of ocular side (right side) brownish gray with 7 or 8 thin black vertical lines but often with variable number of small to large spots; blind side sometimes plain white or pale brown with variable number of dark spots, sometimes with same pattern as ocular side, and occasionally partially pigmented and partially white; fins mottled or with spots. Maximum adult size 20 cm TL (8 in).

GEOGRAPHIC DISTRIBUTION   Known from Massachusetts to Florida and throughout the Gulf of Mexico.

ECOLOGY   The hogchoker, typically found on mud bottoms, is an abundant year-round resident of the entire Chesapeake Bay. It also ascends coastal rivers and enters freshwater. Spawning occurs from May to September in inshore waters and estuaries, with the majority of the spawning activity taking place in July. Young of the year migrate upstream and congregate on shallow mud flats. Hogchokers feed on a variety of worms and crustaceans and may attain 7 years of age.

FISHING INTEREST   Of no commercial or recreational importance and considered a trash fish. Hogs that are fed trash fish reportedly have great difficulty in swallowing this sole—hence the common name "hogchoker." This species is collected incidentally in seines and bottom trawls.

LITERATURE   Hildebrand and Schroeder 1928:175; Massmann 1954; Dovel et al. 1969; Musick 1972; Fahay 1983; Manooch 1984; Chapleau and Keast 1988; Chapleau 1993.

Righteye Flounders
FAMILY PLEURONECTIDAE

Members of the family of righteye flounders typically have eyes on the right side of the head and have a free preopercular margin. The pelvic fins lack spines. This family includes several commercially important species, such as the Atlantic halibut, a giant flatfish reaching a weight of more than 250 kg (550 lb). The family is found in all oceans and comprises more than 40 genera and about 100 species. Three species are recorded from Chesapeake Bay, but 2 of them are very rare; only the winter flounder is commonly encountered.

KEY TO THE SPECIES OF RIGHTEYE FLOUNDERS IN CHESAPEAKE BAY

1a. Dorsal fin with 95 or more rays; caudal fin margin concave ....
.... **Atlantic halibut, *Hippoglossus hippoglossus*** (p. 291)
1b. Dorsal fin with 91 or fewer rays; caudal fin margin convex **2**

2a. Dorsal fin with 73–91 rays; lateral line distinctly arched over pectoral fin ....
.... **yellowtail flounder, *Pleuronectes ferrugineus*** (p. 291)
2b. Dorsal fin with 60–76 rays; lateral line nearly straight anteriorly ....
.... **winter flounder, *Pleuronectes americanus*** (p. 272)

Winter flounder
Pleuronectes americanus Walbaum, 1792
PLATE 49

KEY FEATURES   Both pectoral fins present; margin of preopercle free; eyes located on right side of head; lateral line nearly straight; caudal fin margin convex.

OTHER CHARACTERISTICS   Body elliptical; dorsal and ventral outlines about evenly curved; head small; mouth small; teeth small and present only on left side of each jaw; scales rather small; dorsal fin long-based, with 60–76 rays, and originating near anterior portion of dorsalmost eye; anal fin base shorter than dorsal fin base and originating posterior to pelvic fin; pectoral fin small; pelvic fin small and originating ventroanterior to pectoral fin. Coloration varying considerably, depending on substrate and on size of fish; body olive green, with reddish brown spots on ocular side; blind side white; background color pale or dusky; spots prominent, obscure, or almost absent. Maximum adult size 64 cm TL (2 ft), with inshore specimens (espe-

flounder is more abundant in the upper bay than in the lower bay. This species is found most frequently on muddy or vegetated bottoms. Spawning occurs in nearshore and estuarine waters from late winter to early spring. The winter flounder primarily feeds on small crustaceans and worms.

FISHING INTEREST   Collected by pound and fyke nets in the early part of the twentieth

FIGURE 246. Winter flounder,
Pleuronectes americanus.

cially from Chesapeake Bay) 20–40 cm TL (8–16 in).

GEOGRAPHIC DISTRIBUTION   Occurring coastally from Labrador to Georgia.

ECOLOGY   The winter flounder is found throughout Chesapeake Bay from the Susquehanna River to the bay mouth. It is less common during the summer months, when it retreats to deeper water or migrates offshore. In contrast to most other marine fishes of the bay, the winter

century as a valuable food fish. Commercial fishing of winter flounders is still conducted from November to June in Chesapeake Bay, but the yield is much smaller than historically. Along the middle Atlantic and New England coasts, the winter flounder is pursued by both recreational and commercial fisheries.

LITERATURE   Hildebrand and Schroeder 1928:168; Musick 1972; Martin and Drewry 1978; Fritzsche 1982; Fahay 1983.

Windowpanes
FAMILY SCOPHTHALMIDAE

Windowpanes are typically large flatfishes with their eyes located on the left side. The mouth of windowpanes is large, with a prominent lower jaw. No spines are present in the fins. The origin of the dorsal fin is well anterior to the upper eye. The bases of the pelvic fins are elongate and of equal size. The lateral line is visible on both sides of windowpanes. Distributed in the North Atlantic and the Mediterranean Sea, the family comprises about 5 genera and 18 species. One species is recorded from Chesapeake Bay.

Windowpane
Scophthalmus aquosus (Mitchill, 1814)

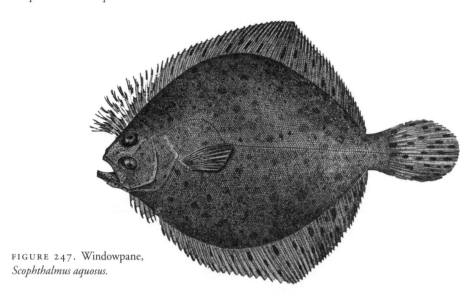

FIGURE 247. Windowpane,
Scophthalmus aquosus.

KEY FEATURES   Anterior rays of dorsal fin long, branched, and distally free (unconnected by membrane); eyes located on left side of head; lateral line arched anteriorly; both pectoral fins present; margin of preopercle free.

OTHER CHARACTERISTICS   Body rhomboid, very strongly compressed, and with depth 60–70% of standard length; head short, its length 25–30% of standard length; mouth large and nearly vertical, with upper jaw length about 45% of head length; scales small and numbering 85–95 in lateral line; dorsal fin originating near snout tip and with 64–71 rays; anal fin with 48–55 rays; pelvic fin bases long. Ocular side pale brown, mottled with numerous brown and black spots of various small sizes that continue onto fins; blind side white. Maximum adult size 46 cm TL (18 in). The common name "windowpane" refers to the thinness of the body, which is almost transparent in some places.

GEOGRAPHIC DISTRIBUTION   Known from the Gulf of St. Lawrence to Florida.

ECOLOGY   The windowpane is a year-round Chesapeake Bay resident that is occasional to common in the upper bay, extending as far north as the Choptank River, and common to abundant in the lower bay. Spawning occurs from spring to autumn, with a possible hiatus during the warmest summer months. The windowpane is reported to feed on fishes, crustaceans, and worms.

FISHING INTEREST   Of no commercial or recreational value.

LITERATURE   Hildebrand and Schroeder 1928:171; Gutherz 1967; Musick 1972; Martin and Drewry 1978; Fahay 1983.

Paralichthyid Flounders
FAMILY PARALICHTHYIDAE

The paralichthyid flounders have both eyes on the left side and a shortened pelvic fin on the blind side. The lateral line is usually highly arched anteriorly. Like most flatfishes, the paralichthyids can change their color to match the substratum on which they are lying. They typically burrow partially in the sediment and are lie-in-wait predators on small fishes and crustaceans. Most paralichthyids are valued as food fishes. The family, which is distributed worldwide in tropical and temperate seas, comprises 16 genera and about 90 species, 7 of which are known from Chesapeake Bay.

KEY TO THE SPECIES OF PARALICHTHYID FLOUNDERS IN CHESAPEAKE BAY

1a. Lateral line strongly arched above pectoral fin **2**

1b. Lateral line nearly straight throughout length **4**

2a. Ocular side with prominent ocellated spots **3**

2b. Ocular side without prominent ocellated spots . . **southern flounder,** *Paralichthys lethostigma* (p. 275)

3a. Interorbital distance much less than diameter of pupil; ocular side with 4 prominent ocellated black
    spots . . . . **fourspot flounder,** *Paralichthys oblongus* (p. 276)

3b. Interorbital distance about equal to diameter of pupil; ocular side with triangular pattern of ocelli,
    consisting of 1 ocellus on midline and 2 ocelli on body edges at caudal peduncle . . . .
    . . . . **summer flounder,** *Paralichthys dentatus* (p. 277)

4a. Mouth small; maxilla about 25% of head length, terminating posteriorly near anterior edge of lower
    eye; jaws on blind side arched; front teeth in both jaws same size as posterior teeth **5**

4b. Mouth moderately large; maxilla about 35% of head length, extending to middle of lower eye; jaws
    on blind side not arched; front teeth in jaws larger than posterior teeth . . . .
    . . . . **bay whiff,** *Citharichthys spilopterus* (p. 278)

5a. Body elongate, with depth about 43–51% of standard length; primary body scales with overlapping
    secondary scales; gill rakers numbering about 13 on lower limb of first arch . . . .
    . . . . **smallmouth flounder,** *Etropus microstomus* (p. 279)

5b. Body ovate, with depth about 50–58% of standard length; primary body scales without overlapping
    secondary scales; gill rakers numbering 6–9 on lower limb of first arch . . . .
    . . . . **fringed flounder,** *Etropus crossotus* (p. 280)

Southern flounder
Paralichthys lethostigma Jordan and Gilbert 1884

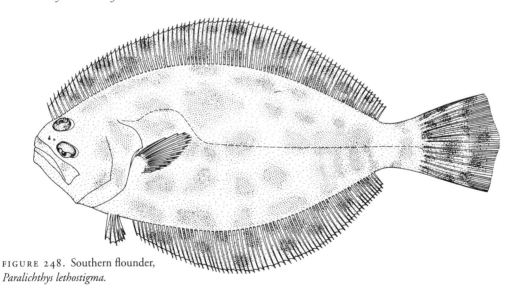

FIGURE 248. Southern flounder,
Paralichthys lethostigma.

KEY FEATURES   Body without prominent ocellated spots; ocular side with numerous inconspicuous dusky spots and blotches (frequently absent in large individuals); lateral line strongly curved anteriorly; eyes located on left side and widely set, with interorbital distance greater than width of pupil; dorsal fin elements numbering 80–95; gill rakers on first arch usually numbering 10–13.

OTHER CHARACTERISTICS   Body oval, moderately elongate, and with depth about 39–47% of standard length; dorsal profile of head slightly concave; mouth large, with upper jaw extending past posterior margin of pupil; teeth in jaws strong; dorsal fin originating slightly dorsoanterior to upper eye; caudal fin margin with double concavity and with median rays longest; anal fin elements numbering 63–74; pelvic fins smaller than pectoral fins. Ocular side olive brown; blind side white or dusky. Maximum adult size 75 cm TL (2.5 ft), commonly to 50 cm TL (1.7 ft).

GEOGRAPHIC DISTRIBUTION   Known from Chesapeake Bay to Texas, but absent from southern Florida.

ECOLOGY   The southern flounder is an infrequent visitor to the lower Chesapeake Bay during late summer. Tolerating a wide salinity range, southern flounder are frequently found in brackish and freshwater habitats. Juveniles and adults are typically most abundant in shallow areas with aquatic vegetation on a muddy bottom. From October to November there is a large migration of adults and older juveniles from estuaries to offshore waters, where they overwinter. Spawning occurs offshore from autumn to winter. Like other flounders, the southern flounder partially buries itself in the sand in order to ambush prey such as shrimps, crabs, and small fishes.

FISHING INTEREST   Highly prized recreationally and commercially where common (in waters more southern than Chesapeake Bay). Much of the commercial catch of southern flounder is bycatch from the shrimp fishery in the Gulf of Mexico. Southern flounder are collected as a sport fish by nighttime gigging in tidal creeks and salt marshes.

LITERATURE   Ginsburg 1952; Gutherz 1967; Fischer 1978; Benson 1982; Manooch 1984.

Fourspot flounder
Paralichthys oblongus (Mitchill, 1815)

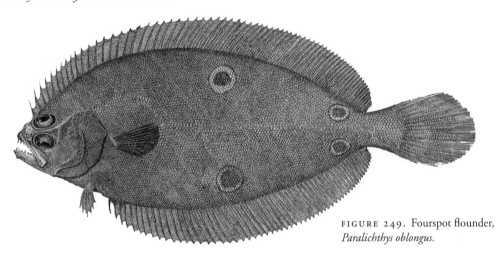

FIGURE 249. Fourspot flounder, *Paralichthys oblongus.*

KEY FEATURES   Four large conspicuous ocellated spots present on posterior half of ocular side, forming trapezoidal pattern; eyes located on left side, large, and close-set, with interorbital distance much less than diameter of pupil; lateral line strongly curved anteriorly; dorsal fin elements numbering 72–86; gill rakers numbering 9–13 on outer arch.

OTHER CHARACTERISTICS   Body oblong, very compressed, and with depth 38–44% of standard length; mouth large, with upper jaw extending dorsoventrally to posterior edge of pupil; large canine teeth present anteriorly in jaws; dorsal fin originating near anterior margin of eye; caudal fin margin rounded; anal fin elements numbering 58–72; pelvic fins smaller than pectoral fins. Ocular side mottled brownish gray; typically 1 pair of ocelli present near midbody and another pair near caudal peduncle; blind side of caudal, dorsal, and anal fins with small dark spots distally. Maximum adult size 40 cm TL (1.3 ft).

GEOGRAPHIC DISTRIBUTION   Known from Georges Bank to Dry Tortugas.

ECOLOGY   The fourspot flounder is a rare visitor to the lower Chesapeake Bay. Although this species has an extensive north–south distribution, it is common inshore only in the northern portion of its range. South of New York it typically occurs at depths exceeding 30 m (100 ft) on sand and mud bottoms. Spawning apparently occurs offshore near the midshelf from late spring through early fall. The fourspot flounder feeds on small crabs, shrimps, and other crustaceans as well as on worms, mollusks, and small fishes.

FISHING INTEREST   Of little commercial or recreational importance in the Chesapeake Bay area, because of small size and infrequency of occurrence. However, the fourspot flounder is taken in shelf waters by the winter trawl fishery, at least in small numbers.

LITERATURE   Ginsburg 1952; Liem and Scott 1966; Gutherz 1967.

Summer flounder
Paralichthys dentatus (Linnaeus, 1766)

FIGURE 250. Summer flounder, *Paralichthys dentatus.*

KEY FEATURES   Ocular side with triangular pattern of ocelli, consisting of 1 ocellus on midline and 2 ocelli on body edges at caudal peduncle; eyes moderately large; interorbital distance about equal to diameter of pupil; lateral line strongly curved anteriorly; dorsal fin elements numbering 80–96; gill rakers numbering 16–24 on outer arch.

OTHER CHARACTERISTICS   Body moderately elongate, with depth 41–47% of standard length; mouth large, terminating ventroposterior to margin of pupil in specimens of about 1.0 m SL (3.3 ft) and posterior to eye in specimens of 3.0 m SL (9.8 ft); teeth prominent and pointed; scales small, numbering 91–106 in lateral line; anal fin rays numbering 61–73; dorsal fin originating dorsoanterior to eye; caudal fin with double concavity and with median rays longest; pelvic fins smaller than pectoral fins. Coloration varying, depending on background; ocular side typically brownish; spots on anterior half of body smaller and variable in number and placement; spots sometimes obscure in larger specimens. Maximum adult size 95 cm TL (3 ft).

GEOGRAPHIC DISTRIBUTION   Occurring from Nova Scotia to South Florida, with greatest abundance between Massachusetts and North Carolina.

ECOLOGY   Most summer flounder are visitors to Chesapeake Bay from spring to autumn and then migrate offshore during the winter months. However, some overwinter in the bay. The summer flounder is more common in the lower bay than in the upper bay, extending as far north as the Gunpowder River. Larvae enter the bay during October through May. Juvenile summer flounder utilize eelgrass beds in Chesapeake Bay. Adults typically occur in deep channels, ridges, or sandbars. After age 3, summer flounder primarily inhabit coastal waters. Spawning occurs during the offshore migration from late summer to midwinter. Like other flounders, this species partially conceals itself with sand and feeds on unsuspecting prey that venture too close. The diet of summer flounder consists primarily of shrimps, fishes, and squids. Summer flounder can live to 20 years of age, with females living longer and growing larger than males.

FISHING INTEREST   Of major recreational and commercial importance north of Cape Hatteras. Commercial landings in Virginia have historically been an order of magnitude higher than those in Maryland. During 1981–1986, Virginia averaged 2.6 million kilograms (5.7 million pounds) per year and Maryland averaged 265,000 kg (583,000 lb). However, more than 90% of the landings recorded for both states has come from outside state waters. The great bulk of the catch is produced by the winter trawl fishery that operates in midshelf waters. Within Chesapeake Bay, summer flounder are commercially caught by haul seines, pound nets, and gill nets, but the species does not form a significant commercial fishery. In 1990 only 22,000 kg (48,000 lb) were taken in Virginia waters, bay

side and seaside combined. Anglers catch summer flounder from shore, piers, and boats with hook and line; live minnows are especially good bait. The recreational catch far exceeds the commercial catch in the bay and nearshore coastal waters, with the lower bay and seaside inlets producing the bulk of the recreational landings. For the period 1979–1985, the combined recreational harvest in Maryland and Virginia averaged 2.5 million kilograms (5.5 million pounds) per year, with 90% coming from Virginia waters. Since the mid-1980s, both commercial and recreational catches have declined precipitously because of overfishing and year-class failure. The Chesapeake Bay record for summer flounder is a fish weighing 6.8 kg (15 lb) that was taken in Maryland waters.

LITERATURE   Hildebrand and Schroeder 1928:165; Ginsburg 1952; Gutherz 1967; Musick 1972; Smith 1972; Martin and Drewry 1978; Fritzsche 1982; Fahay 1983; Rogers and Van Den Avyle 1983; Manooch 1984; Jones et al. 1988; Able et al. 1990; Szedlmayer et al. 1992; Keefe 1993.

Bay whiff
Citharichthys spilopterus Günther, 1862

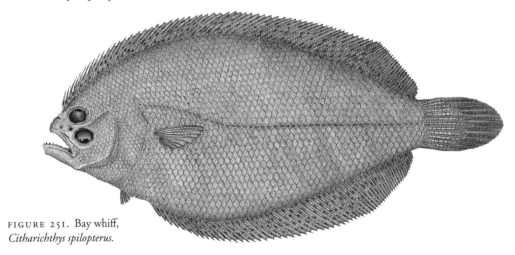

FIGURE 251. Bay whiff,
Citharichthys spilopterus.

KEY FEATURES   Mouth moderately large; upper jaw about 31–38% of head length, terminating ventroposterior to anterior margin of pupil; jaws on blind side not arched; front teeth in jaws larger than posterior teeth; lateral line nearly straight.

OTHER CHARACTERISTICS   Body moderately elongate, much compressed, and with depth 41–51% of standard length; gill rakers numbering 9–15 on lower limb of first arch; dorsal fin with 75–84 unbranched rays and originating near anterior nostril of blind side; anal fin with 56–63 unbranched rays and originating perpendicular to pectoral fin base. Ocular side greenish brown, with or without dusky spots. Maximum adult size 20 cm TL (8 in).

GEOGRAPHIC DISTRIBUTION   Known from New Jersey to Brazil, including the Gulf of Mexico and the Caribbean Sea. The bay whiff is rare north of Virginia.

ECOLOGY   The bay whiff is a rare late-summer visitor to the lower Chesapeake Bay. Al-though reported from depths as great as 73 m (240 ft), this species is typically found in shallow waters with mud bottoms. The bay whiff moves offshore in winter. Little information on the ecology and natural history of this species is known.

FISHING INTEREST   Of no commercial or recreational interest, because of small size.

LITERATURE   Gutherz 1967; Martin and Drewry 1978; Tucker 1982.

Smallmouth flounder
Etropus microstomus (Gill, 1864)

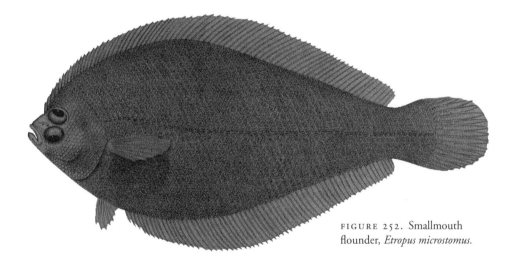

FIGURE 252. Smallmouth flounder, *Etropus microstomus.*

KEY FEATURES   Mouth small; upper jaw 24–28% of head length, terminating posteriorly near anterior margin of eye; depth of body 43–51% of standard length; primary body scales with small overlapping secondary scales; gill rakers numbering about 13 on lower limb of first gill arch; scales present on snout; lateral line nearly straight.

OTHER CHARACTERISTICS   Body strongly compressed; head short, measuring about 21–27% of standard length; snout blunt; mouth oblique; eyes small and separated by ridge; teeth small; primary scales large, numbering 37–45 in lateral line; dorsal fin with 67–82 unbranched fin rays and originating at anterior margin of orbit; anal fin with 50–63 rays; caudal fin rounded; pectoral fin on ocular side much larger than its mate on blind side. Ocular side typically pale brown, with or without dusky blotches along lateral line; dark pigment between orbits and around mouth; diffuse dusky spots often present in row near bases of dorsal and anal fins. Maximum adult size 15 cm TL (6 in).

GEOGRAPHIC DISTRIBUTION   Found coastally from New York to Florida, but rare south of North Carolina.

ECOLOGY   The smallmouth flounder is a common year-round resident of the lower Chesapeake Bay that frequents channels and mud bottoms. Smallmouth flounder are distributed from near-shore to about 37 m (120 ft) in depth. Spawning apparently occurs from June into autumn north of Cape Hatteras and throughout the year south of Cape Hatteras. Little is known about the habits of this species.

FISHING INTEREST   Of no commercial or recreational value, because of small size.
LITERATURE   Hildebrand and Schroeder 1928:172; Gutherz 1967; Musick 1972; Richardson and Joseph 1973; Martin and Drewry 1978; Tucker 1982; Fahay 1983; Leslie and Stewart 1986.

Fringed flounder
Etropus crossotus Jordan and Gilbert, 1882

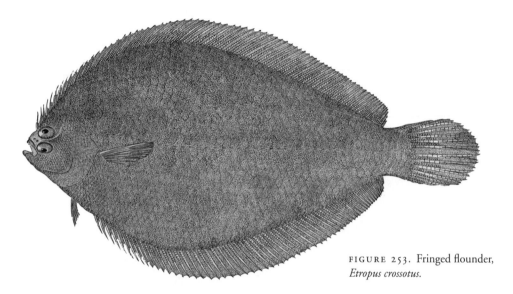

FIGURE 253. Fringed flounder, *Etropus crossotus*.

KEY FEATURES   Body strongly compressed; mouth small; upper jaw 21–27% of head length, terminating posteriorly at anterior margin of eye; depth of body 50–58% of standard length; primary body scales without overlapping secondary scales; gill rakers numbering 6–9 on lower limb of first gill arch; scales absent on snout; lateral line nearly straight.
OTHER CHARACTERISTICS   Head short, measuring 20–25% of standard length; snout blunt; teeth small; scales large, numbering 41–47 in lateral line; dorsal fin with 75–87 unbranched fin rays and originating at anterior margin of orbit; anal fin with 58–68 unbranched fin rays and originating perpendicular to pectoral fin; caudal fin rounded; pectoral fin on ocular side longer than its mate on blind side. Ocular side uniformly dusky olive brown, with 2 or 3 dusky blotches sometimes present along lateral line; dorsal and anal fins with dusky spots and blotches; caudal fin with dark margin in large specimens; gill cover on blind side with distinct white fringe. Maximum adult size 12 cm SL (5 in).

GEOGRAPHIC DISTRIBUTION   Found from Chesapeake Bay to Brazil, including the Gulf of Mexico and parts of the Caribbean Sea. The southern limits of the range are uncertain.
ECOLOGY   The fringed flounder is a rare to occasional visitor to the lower Chesapeake Bay from spring to autumn and probably migrates southward during the winter months. It inhabits mud, sand, and crushed-shell bottoms in depths to 60 m (200 ft) and is known to enter freshwater occasionally. Spawning apparently occurs in late spring in the mid-Atlantic region. Little is known about the habits of this species.
FISHING INTEREST   Of no commercial or recreational value, because of small size and infrequent occurrence.
LITERATURE   Hildebrand and Schroeder 1928:173; Gutherz 1967; Musick 1972; Richardson and Joseph 1973; Eddy and Underhill 1978; Martin and Drewry 1978; Tucker 1982; Leslie and Stewart 1986.

APPENDIX I

Sportfishing Records

of Largest Fishes Caught in Chesapeake Bay, by Species and State

Maryland state records: Chesapeake Bay Division

COMMON NAME	SCIENTIFIC NAME	WEIGHT KG	WEIGHT LB	DATE	LOCATION
bass, largemouth	*Micropterus salmoides*	4.1	9.1	13 Sep 1975	Pocomoke River
bass, smallmouth	*Micropterus dolomieu*	2.7	6.0	23 Jul 1971	Susquehanna River
bass, striped	*Morone saxatilis*	30.6	67.5	13 May 1995	Bloody Point
bluefish	*Pomatomus saltatrix*	10.0	22.0	18 Oct 1979	Queen Anne Marina
		10.0	22.0	31 May 1986	Hackett's Point
		10.0	22.0	8 May 1991	Chesapeake Beach
carp, common	*Cyprinus carpio*	20.2	44.4	28 Apr 1978	Morgantown Beach
catfish, channel	*Ictalurus punctatus*	12.9	28.3	8 Aug 1993	Piscataway Creek
cobia	*Rachycentron canadum*	44.4	97.8	12 Sep 1969	Middle Grounds
crappie, black	*Pomoxis nigromaculatus*	1.2	2.6	28 Apr 1979	Tuckahoe River
croaker, Atlantic	*Micropogonias undulatus*	2.8	6.2	9 Jul 1980	Puppy Hole
drum, black	*Pogonias cromis*	47.0	103.5	23 Sep 1973	Buoy #16
drum, red	*Sciaenops ocellatus*	33.8	74.4	15 May 1977	Tangier Sound
flounder, summer	*Paralichthys dentatus*	6.8	15.0	14 Oct 1978	Buoy #50
perch, white	*Morone americana*	1.2	2.6	18 May 1979	Dundee Creek
perch, yellow	*Perca flavescens*	1.0	2.2	21 Nov 1979	Marsh Creek
pickerel, chain	*Esox niger*	3.0	6.5	19 May 1965	Susquehanna River
seatrout, spotted	*Cynoscion nebulosus*	7.5	16.5	15 May 1977	Roaring Point
shad, American	*Alosa sapidissima*	3.7	8.1	3 May 1975	Wicomico River
shad, hickory	*Alosa mediocris*	1.8	4.0	5 May 1972	Susquehanna River
spot	*Leiostomus xanthurus*	0.9	2.0	5 Sep 1978	Tangier Sound

Virginia state records

Virginia sportfishing records are not divided into Chesapeake Bay and Atlantic Ocean divisions. Therefore, the following records include both bay and nearshore catches for fish species that occur in the bay. Although Virginia records are known for many other species treated in this book, the following list reflects only those fishes that were likely collected near or in Chesapeake Bay waters.

		WEIGHT			
COMMON NAME	SCIENTIFIC NAME	KG	LB	DATE	LOCATION
amberjack, greater	*Seriola dumerili*	53.6	118.0	1986	Chesapeake Light Tower
bass, black sea	*Centropristis striata*	4.3	9.5	1987	Off Virginia Beach
bass, striped	*Morone saxatilis*	27.7	61.0	1981	Mattaponi River
bluefish	*Pomatomus saltatrix*	11.5	25.3	1986	Bluefish Rock
catfish, channel	*Ictalurus punctatus*	14.3	31.5	1992	Rappahannock River
catfish, flathead	*Pylodictis olivaris*	30.1	66.3	1994	Occoquan Reservoir
cobia	*Rachycentron canadum*	47.0	103.5	1980	Mobjack Bay
croaker, Atlantic	*Micropogonias undulatus*	2.6	5.8	1982	The Cell (Chesapeake Bay)
drum, black	*Pogonias cromis*	50.4	111.0	1973	Cape Charles
drum, red	*Sciaenops ocellatus*	38.7	85.3	1981	Wreck Island
flounder, summer	*Paralichthys dentatus*	8.0	17.5	1971	Baltimore Channel
seatrout, spotted	*Cynoscion nebulosus*	7.3	16.0	1977	Masons Beach
sheepshead	*Archosargus probatocephalus*	8.6	19.0	1979	Bay Bridge Tunnel
spadefish, Atlantic	*Chaetodipterus faber*	5.9	13.0	1988	The Cell (Chesapeake Bay)
spot	*Leiostomus xanthurus*	1.1	2.4	1980	Off Poquoson
tarpon	*Megalops atlanticus*	59.0	130.0	1975	Off Oyster Reef
tautog	*Tautoga onitis*	10.9	24.0	1987	Off Wachapreague
tiger, sand	*Odontaspis taurus*	153.8	339.0	1983	Cape Charles
tunny, little	*Euthynnus alletteratus*	11.5	25.3	1964	Off Virginia Capes
weakfish	*Cynoscion regalis*	8.6	19.0	1983	Bay Bridge Tunnel

Fish Species
Rarely Recorded from Chesapeake Bay

The fish species listed here have been recorded from Chesapeake Bay, but in many instances their occurrence has been reported only once. A specimen that validates such an occurrence may or may not exist; the Virginia Institute of Marine Science (VIMS) holds many of the voucher (validating) specimens. Species listed in this appendix are not expected to be found in the bay in any abundance or with any regularity. Families not described here are described in the main text.

Nurse Sharks
FAMILY GINGLYMOSTOMATIDAE

Members of the family of nurse sharks (order Orectolobiformes) are sluggish bottom dwellers that possess a well-developed nasal barbel. The family is circumtropical, and its members are often found in shallow water. The larger species can be dangerous when provoked. The family comprises only three or four species, one of which has been reported from Chesapeake Bay.

Nurse shark
Ginglymostoma cirratum (Bonnaterre, 1788)

REASON FOR INCLUSION   The nurse shark was reported from the "southern part of Chesapeake Bay" in 1877. It has not been recorded from the bay since that time. The nurse shark is common in the tropical and subtropical waters of the western Atlantic, where it frequents mangrove areas, rocky reefs, and sand flats. It is also found in the eastern Pacific and along the coast of West Africa.
PERTINENT LITERATURE   Lugger 1877; Hildebrand and Schroeder 1928:45; Musick 1972; Fischer 1978.

Requiem Sharks
FAMILY CARCHARHINIDAE

Lemon shark
Negaprion brevirostris (Poey, 1868)

REASON FOR INCLUSION   Lemon sharks are common in coastal lagoons along the Eastern Shore as

well as along Atlantic beaches. There is a single VIMS record (uncataloged, specimen released) of a lemon shark collected near Fisherman Island on 22 June 1981. The lemon shark is a slow-moving, bottom-dwelling species typically found in tropical and subtropical coastal waters, including river mouths.
PERTINENT LITERATURE   Compagno 1984b.

Tiger shark
Galeocerdo cuvier (Peron and Lesueur, 1822)

REASON FOR INCLUSION   The tiger shark is a rare visitor to the lower Chesapeake Bay, although it is common in coastal waters in summer. A single record (VIMS 7382) is known from the Smith Island shoal at the bay mouth. The tiger shark is a common, wide-ranging species that is found in a variety of habitats from intertidal waters to depths of 140 m (460 ft). It occurs in estuaries, near wharves and jetties, and in coral atolls and lagoons; it is also found far offshore. The tiger shark occurs circumglobally in temperate and tropical seas.
PERTINENT LITERATURE   Musick 1972; Compagno 1984b; Branstetter et al. 1987; Randall 1992.

Blacktip shark
Carcharhinus limbatus (Valenciennes, 1841)

REASON FOR INCLUSION   Blacktip sharks are common in coastal lagoons along the Eastern Shore as well as along Atlantic beaches. They have been occasionally taken at Fisherman Island, and there is a single VIMS record (uncataloged, specimen released) of a blacktip shark collected there 20 June 1980. The blacktip shark occurs in coastal as well as offshore surface waters and sometimes enters brackish waters. It is more common in tropical and subtropical waters.

PERTINENT LITERATURE   Compagno 1984b.

Electric Rays
FAMILY TORPEDINIDAE

Electric rays have a rounded disk and a short, thick tail. Members of this family possess powerful electric organs posterior to the head that generate sufficient electricity to stun unsuspecting prey. The family comprises 9 genera and approximately 35 species, of which 1 is known from Chesapeake Bay.

Atlantic torpedo
Torpedo nobiliana (Bonaparte, 1835)

REASON FOR INCLUSION   Known from both tropical and temperate waters, the Atlantic torpedo is a rare visitor to the lower Chesapeake Bay. The last recorded collection was from 1922. The Atlantic torpedo can reach almost 2 m (6.6 ft) in length and attain a weight of 90 kg (200 lb). A large Atlantic torpedo is capable of emitting electric shocks that are sufficient to immobilize a careless human temporarily.

PERTINENT LITERATURE   Hildebrand and Schroeder 1928:62; Musick 1972.

Eagle Rays
FAMILY MYLIOBATIDAE

Spotted eagle ray
Aetobatis narinari (Euphrasen, 1790)

REASON FOR INCLUSION   The spotted eagle ray is a circumtropical species that has been reported in Chesapeake Bay only rarely, most recently in 1956. This coastal species is often observed at or near the water's surface. During the summer, it undergoes spawning migrations, and a spotted eagle ray might enter the bay only during this season.

PERTINENT LITERATURE   Hildebrand and Schroeder 1928:70; Massmann 1957; Musick 1972; Fischer 1978.

Snake Eels
FAMILY OPHICHTHIDAE

The family Ophichthidae contains the snake eels and the worm eels. Snake and worm eels possess an elongate, nearly cylindrical body and a hard, pointed tail, giving these species a snakelike appearance. They are found from the intertidal zone to depths of 750 m (2,500 ft) or more, and from coral reefs to sand and mud substrates. They also enter rivers and estuaries. Many species burrow or live in crevices and are seldom seen, although they occasionally emerge to traverse sand, rubble, or sea grass habitats. Snake eels and worm eels are reported to be more active at night; some species are attracted to light. This large, diverse family, found in all tropical oceans, comprises 52 genera and more than 250 species, 1 of which is known from Chesapeake Bay.

Speckled worm eel
Myrophis punctatus Lütken, 1851

REASON FOR INCLUSION   Although the speckled worm eel is common in the lower Chesapeake Bay in the larval stage, adults are rare visitors to the lower bay during the late summer and fall. The species is usually found in brackish waters of tidal creeks and protected bays in depths to 7 m (23 ft). Adults migrate offshore to spawn and are sometimes collected at the surface by night-light. The typical range of adults is from the Carolinas and Bermuda to Brazil, including the Gulf of Mexico.

PERTINENT LITERATURE   Lippson and Moran 1974; Robins et al. 1986; McCosker et al. 1989.

Sea Catfishes
FAMILY ARIIDAE

Hardhead catfish
Arius felis (Linnaeus, 1766)

REASON FOR INCLUSION   The hardhead catfish is a rare summer visitor to the lower Chesapeake Bay and reaches as far as the York River. This species is found in shallow turbid waters over muddy bottoms. Although primarily a marine species, it occasionally enters estuaries and sometimes freshwater. The hardhead catfish more commonly occurs in subtropical waters.

PERTINENT LITERATURE   Musick 1972; Fischer 1978; Jones et al. 1978; Muncy and Wingo 1983; Robins et al. 1986.

Trouts
FAMILY SALMONIDAE

Coho salmon
Oncorhynchus kisutch (Walbaum, 1792)

REASON FOR INCLUSION   The coho salmon is a Pacific salmon, found from northern Asia to Alaska and Monterey Bay, California. It has been successfully introduced into the Great Lakes and in the northeastern United States. A single record of the coho salmon from

Chesapeake Bay is known. The specimen (VIMS 2473) was collected near the mouth of Back River (York County, Virginia); its fins had been clipped and it had apparently been released as a smolt in North River, Massachusetts, the previous year.

PERTINENT LITERATURE   Scott and Crossman 1973; Smith 1985; Hassler 1987.

Frogfishes
FAMILY ANTENNARIIDAE

Frogfishes are bulbous, with a large, almost vertical mouth and leglike pectoral fins. Typically, they are lie-in-wait predators that spend considerable time sitting camouflaged on the bottom or clinging to floating seaweed while waiting for small fishes to be attracted to the "lure" that dangles near their cavernous mouth. The lure, or esca, is the tip of the modified first dorsal spine, or illicium. The family comprises 43 species, 1 of which has been reported from Chesapeake Bay.

Sargassumfish
Histrio histrio (Linnaeus, 1758)

REASON FOR INCLUSION   Although known from as far north as Woods Hole, Massachusetts, no specimens of sargassumfish collected in Chesapeake Bay are known to the present authors. From an 1876 publication, the sargassumfish reportedly "occurs in the oyster regions of Chesapeake Bay, but is perhaps quite uncommon." Although the sargassumfish is primarily a tropical species, it is conceivable that it could be carried northward with sargassum seaweed and drift or be blown into the bay.

PERTINENT LITERATURE   Uhler and Lugger 1876; Hildebrand and Schroeder 1928:353; Musick 1972; Johnson 1978.

Batfishes
FAMILY OGCOCEPHALIDAE

Members of the batfish family are bottom dwellers that typically occur well offshore. Batfishes are closely related to frogfishes. Rather than being derived from a dorsal fin spine (as in frogfishes), the illicium of batfishes is glandular and is located beneath the rostrum. The family, found in all oceans, comprises 9 genera and 62 species, 1 of which has been reported in Chesapeake Bay.

Longnose batfish
Ogcocephalus corniger Bradbury, 1980

REASON FOR INCLUSION   The longnose batfish was reported as rare in the lower Chesapeake Bay during the late 1800s. No recent records of the species are known from the bay. Longnose batfish typically inhabit sandy bottoms at depths of 20–180 m (66–590 ft) in tropical and subtropical waters.

PERTINENT LITERATURE   Uhler and Lugger 1876; Musick 1972; Johnson 1978.

Cods
FAMILY GADIDAE

White hake
Urophycis tenuis (Mitchill, 1814)

REASON FOR INCLUSION   Ranging from Labrador and the Grand Banks of Newfoundland as far south as North Carolina, the white hake is a rare springtime visitor to the lower Chesapeake Bay. It is typically associated with soft muddy bottoms of the continental shelf and upper slope. As bay waters warm in late spring, this species migrates to deeper waters offshore.

PERTINENT LITERATURE   Musick 1972, 1973, 1974; Robins et al. 1986; Whitehead et al. 1986a; Fahay and Able 1989; Cohen et al. 1990; Comyns and Grant 1993.

Flyingfishes
FAMILY EXOCOETIDAE

Members of the family of flyingfishes typically inhabit the surface waters of the open ocean and are only infrequently found inshore. They possess exceptionally large pectoral fins and use these appendages for gliding flights over the water. The family comprises approximately 52 species in 8 genera. One species is recorded from Chesapeake Bay.

Atlantic flyingfish
Cypselurus melanurus (Valenciennes, 1847)

REASON FOR INCLUSION   In 1876 the Atlantic flyingfish was reported (dubiously) to occur as far north in Chesapeake Bay as the mouth of the Potomac River. Recent records of Atlantic flyingfish from bay waters are not known. This surface-dwelling coastal species occasionally enters bays and may be a rare summer visitor to the lower Chesapeake Bay. It is found primarily in tropical and subtropical waters.

PERTINENT LITERATURE   Uhler and Lugger 1876; Hildebrand and Schroeder 1928:154; Musick 1972; Hardy 1978a; Whitehead et al. 1986a.

Needlefishes
FAMILY BELONIDAE

Agujon
Tylosurus acus (Lacepède, 1803)

REASON FOR INCLUSION   The agujon is primarily an offshore species but is an occasional late spring and summer visitor to Chesapeake Bay, extending as far up the bay as the lower Susquehanna River. It is distributed worldwide in tropical and warm-temperate waters.
PERTINENT LITERATURE   Hildebrand and Schroeder 1928:149; Berry and Rivas 1962; Musick 1972; Fischer 1978; Hardy 1978a; Fahay 1983.

Searobins
FAMILY TRIGLIDAE

Leopard searobin
Prionotus scitulus Jordan and Gilbert, 1882

REASON FOR INCLUSION   The leopard searobin is a warmwater species that has been recorded from the Virginia portion of Chesapeake Bay, extending as far north in the bay as the Potomac River. The leopard searobin tolerates a wide range of salinities, from 7‰ to 38‰.
PERTINENT LITERATURE   Musick 1972; Fritzsche 1978.

Bighead searobin
Prionotus tribulus Cuvier, 1829

REASON FOR INCLUSION   The bighead searobin is a rare late-summer visitor to the lower Chesapeake Bay, recorded from the York River and near the bay mouth. This species can tolerate a wide range of salinities, from 1.0‰ to 40.8‰. It is most commonly found south of Cape Hatteras in waters 10–30 m (33–100 ft) deep.
PERTINENT LITERATURE   Musick 1972; Fischer 1978; Fritzsche 1978; Russell et al. 1992.

Sculpins
FAMILY COTTIDAE

Sea raven
Hemitripterus americanus (Gmelin, 1789)

REASON FOR INCLUSION   The sea raven inhabits cold-temperate waters and is a rare visitor to the lower Chesapeake Bay. It is not abundant south of New Jersey and may be expected to occur in the Chesapeake Bay region during the winter and early spring. The sea raven cannot tolerate water temperatures greater than 16°C (61°F).
PERTINENT LITERATURE   Uhler and Lugger 1876; Hildebrand and Schroeder 1928:310; Musick 1972; Fritzsche 1978.

Jacks
FAMILY CARANGIDAE

Lesser amberjack
Seriola fasciata (Bloch, 1797)

REASON FOR INCLUSION   The lesser amberjack is a rare visitor to the lower Chesapeake Bay in late summer. Adults of this species apparently frequent bottom waters at depths of 55–125 m (181–410 ft); juveniles inhabit nearshore waters. The species is known from the Gulf of Mexico to Massachusetts.
PERTINENT LITERATURE   Musick 1972; Fischer 1978; Johnson 1978.

Remoras
FAMILY ECHENEIDAE

Marlinsucker
Remora osteochir (Cuvier, 1829)

REASON FOR INCLUSION   The marlinsucker is a rare summer visitor to the lower Chesapeake Bay, reaching as far north as the York River. Although occasionally free-living, this species is usually found attached to billfishes, especially the white marlin *(Tetrapturus albidus)* and the sailfish *(Istiophorus platypterus)*. Large marlinsuckers are usually attached to the host's body, but small individuals are frequently found inside the gill cavity or the mouth of the host.
PERTINENT LITERATURE   Strasburg 1959; Cressey and Lachner 1970; Musick 1972; Fischer 1978; Martin and Drewry 1978.

Whalesucker
Remora australis (Bennett, 1840)

REASON FOR INCLUSION   The whalesucker is a rare summer visitor to the lower Chesapeake Bay. Whalesuckers have been found attached to marine mammals.
PERTINENT LITERATURE   Massmann 1957; Musick 1972; Fischer 1978; Martin and Drewry 1978.

Whitefin sharksucker
Echeneis neucratoides Zuieuw, 1789

REASON FOR INCLUSION   The whitefin sharksucker is a rare summer visitor to the lower Chesapeake Bay, reaching as far north as Gloucester Point. This species is far less common than the sharksucker (*E. naucrates*), and there is little published information on this fish. It has been found attached to sharks and sturgeons.

PERTINENT LITERATURE   Fischer 1978; Martin and Drewry 1978; Böhlke and Chaplin 1993.

Dolphins
FAMILY CORYPHAENIDAE

The family of dolphins comprises only two species, one of which is known from Chesapeake Bay. These pelagic fishes are found in all oceans and typically associate with ships and other floating objects.

Dolphin
Coryphaena hippurus Linnaeus, 1758

REASON FOR INCLUSION   Although adult dolphins are not known (and not expected) from Chesapeake Bay, two small juveniles (44 and 66 mm, or 1.7 and 2.6 in, SL) have been collected in the lower bay. The smaller specimen was caught near the mouth of the York River; the larger was seined from Hampton Creek. Both of these dolphins were collected in the late summer of 1955.

PERTINENT LITERATURE   Massmann 1957; Musick 1972.

Threadfins
FAMILY POLYNEMIDAE

Threadfins are so named because the pectoral fins of the species in this family are divided into two sections, and the ventral, more anterior section comprises long, unattached threadlike rays. The detached rays of the pectoral fins probably serve both tactile and chemosensory functions. This shallow-water group lives on sand or mud bottoms, often in turbid water. Threadfins are usually found inshore but are occasionally taken at depths to 70 m (230 ft). They are carnivorous, feeding as adults on planktonic crustaceans and fishes. Threadfins are most common in brackish-water environments; some species enter rivers. The family, found in all tropical and subtropical seas, is composed of 7 genera and approximately 33 species, 2 of which are recorded from Chesapeake Bay. The Atlantic threadfin has eight filamentous pectoral fin rays, whereas the barbu has only seven.

Atlantic threadfin
Polydactylus octonemus (Girard, 1858)

REASON FOR INCLUSION   Rare visitors to the lower Chesapeake Bay in late summer, Atlantic threadfins occur on sand bottoms near beaches, often in water only a few centimeters deep. They also inhabit brackish waters near river mouths. The species is recorded in the western Atlantic from New York to Brazil.

PERTINENT LITERATURE   Hildebrand and Schroeder 1928:199; Musick 1972; Fischer 1978; Martin and Drewry 1978; Fritzsche 1982; Dentzau and Chittenden 1990.

Barbu
Polydactylus virginicus (Linnaeus, 1758)

REASON FOR INCLUSION   The barbu is a rare tropical stray recorded from the lower Chesapeake Bay. Its ecology is similar to that of the Atlantic threadfin.

PERTINENT LITERATURE   Richards 1963; Musick 1972; Fischer 1978; Martin and Drewry 1978.

Mackerels
FAMILY SCOMBRIDAE

Cero
Scomberomorus regalis (Bloch, 1795)

REASON FOR INCLUSION   The cero was once recorded from "Chesapeake Bay near the ocean" in the 1870s. Cero are uncommon north of Florida. In tropical waters, they may be found over reefs and turtle grass beds.

PERTINENT LITERATURE   Uhler and Lugger 1876; Hildebrand and Schroeder 1928:205; Fritzsche 1978; Collette and Nauen 1983.

Bluefin tuna
Thunnus thynnus (Linnaeus, 1758)

REASON FOR INCLUSION   The bluefin tuna, an oceanic species, is reported to have been collected once in the twentieth century (in 1909) by pound net near the Chesapeake Bay mouth. This epipelagic species is commonly taken in June in Virginia coastal waters. It summers to the north, from New England to Newfoundland, and spends the winter in the tropics.

PERTINENT LITERATURE   Hildebrand and Schroeder 1928:207; Fritzsche 1978; Collette and Nauen 1983.

Goatfishes
FAMILY MULLIDAE

The family of goatfishes, distributed worldwide in tropical inshore waters, comprises 6 genera and approximately 55 species, 2 of which are recorded from Chesapeake Bay. The red goatfish has eight spines in the first dorsal fin, which differentiate it from the dwarf goatfish, which has only seven spines in the first dorsal fin. The first spine of the dorsal fin in the red goatfish is minute, whereas the first spine is the longest dorsal fin spine in the dwarf goatfish.

Red goatfish
Mullus auratus Jordan and Gilbert, 1882

REASON FOR INCLUSION   Although recorded from as far north as Cape Cod, the red goatfish is primarily a tropical-subtropical species. It is a rare summer visitor to the lower Chesapeake Bay, reaching as far north as the York River. This species inhabits shallow coastal waters, typically 10–60 m (33–200 ft) deep, especially over soft sand and mud bottoms. Young red goatfish are frequently associated with sea grass beds.
PERTINENT LITERATURE   Caldwell 1962c; Fischer 1978; Johnson 1978.

Dwarf goatfish
Upeneus parvus Poey, 1853

REASON FOR INCLUSION   The dwarf goatfish is a rare summer visitor to Chesapeake Bay that has been collected as far north as New Point Comfort. This species typically inhabits more southerly waters, at depths of 40–100 m (131–330 ft).
PERTINENT LITERATURE   Lachner 1954; Caldwell 1962c; Fischer 1978.

Gobies
FAMILY GOBIIDAE

Clown goby
Microgobius gulosus (Girard, 1858)

REASON FOR INCLUSION   The clown goby has been recorded only once from within Chesapeake Bay. That record is of 32 specimens collected in a single trawl tow at the mouth of the Patuxent River in February 1962. This record is considered doubtful and perhaps the result of a collection label error, given that the typical range of this species is from St. Johns River, Florida, to Corpus Christi, Texas.
PERTINENT LITERATURE   Schwartz 1971; Musick 1972; Birdsong 1981.

Code goby
Gobiosoma robustum Ginsburg, 1933

REASON FOR INCLUSION   Ten specimens of the code goby were reported as having been collected in the same tow with the clown goby at the mouth of the Patuxent River in February 1962 (see preceding species account). Like the clown goby record, this record is considered doubtful, given the considerable northerly extension from the code goby's typical range of Cape Canaveral to Yucatán.
PERTINENT LITERATURE   Schwartz 1971; Musick 1972; Birdsong 1981.

Sleepers
FAMILY ELEOTRIDAE

Sleepers are similar to gobies, but the absence of united pelvic fins distinguishes sleepers from most gobies. Members of the family Eleotridae are typically small to medium-sized bottom-dwelling fishes. Many are relatively inactive—hence the common name "sleeper." Sleepers are typically found in fresh or brackish waters, although some species are truly marine. The family, found in all subtropical and tropical waters (except the Mediterranean Sea and its tributaries), comprises approximately 40 genera and 150 species, of which 1 is recorded from Chesapeake Bay.

Fat sleeper
Dormitator maculatus (Bloch, 1785)

REASON FOR INCLUSION   The fat sleeper occurs in brackish marshes, estuarine ponds, and mangrove areas. A single record of the fat sleeper is known from Chesapeake Bay: an individual of 21 mm SL (0.8 in) was collected in White Creek (part of the Wicomico River drainage) in October 1990 by electrofishing in less than 1 m (3.3 ft) of water. There is presently no evidence of the existence of a breeding population of the fat sleeper in the bay; however, these small sedentary fishes have eggs attached by an adhesive stalk to a firm substrate and would seem to be poor candidates for waif dispersal (dispersal of larval fish by currents).
PERTINENT LITERATURE   Dawson 1969; Fritzsche 1982; Smith 1985.

Perches
FAMILY PERCIDAE

Walleye
Stizostedion vitreum (Mitchill, 1818)

REASON FOR INCLUSION   The walleye is an introduced freshwater species that occurs in clear, cool lakes as well as rapidly flowing streams and rivers. It is re-corded from various Western Shore tributaries to Chesapeake Bay. Reported to enter brackish waters, the walleye rarely penetrates waters of 5‰ or greater salinities.

PERTINENT LITERATURE   Musick 1972; Hardy 1978b; Lee et al. 1981; Jenkins and Burkhead 1994.

Combtooth Blennies
FAMILY BLENNIIDAE

Seaweed blenny
Parablennius marmoreus (Poey, 1876)

REASON FOR INCLUSION   Only a single specimen (VIMS 9086) of seaweed blenny is known from Chesapeake Bay. That individual, of 58 mm SL (2.3 in), was collected in a bottom trawl near the bay mouth on 10 June 1993. The seaweed blenny typically inhabits warm shallow waters with algae-covered rocks. The algae provide food for this fish, and the rocks provide shelter. This species is known to excavate small holes in sandy bottoms.

PERTINENT LITERATURE   Randall 1983; Böhlke and Chaplin 1993.

Mojarras
FAMILY GERREIDAE

Flagfin mojarra
Eucinostomus melanopterus (Bleeker, 1863)

REASON FOR INCLUSION   Primarily a tropical and subtropical species, the flagfin mojarra is a rare visitor to Chesapeake Bay in summer and fall. It has been collected in various habitats, ranging from the continental shelf to the surf zone and low-salinity coastal streams.

PERTINENT LITERATURE   Fagade and Olaniyan 1973; Matheson 1981; Albaret and Desfossez 1988.

Slender mojarra
Eucinostomus jonesi (Günther, 1879)

REASON FOR INCLUSION   The slender mojarra is a rare visitor to Chesapeake Bay in summer and fall. This species is most common near inlets and over the continental shelf in Florida waters and typically does not penetrate far up coastal rivers.

PERTINENT LITERATURE   Matheson and McEachran 1984; Kerschner et al. 1985.

Tidewater mojarra
Eucinostomus harengulus Goode and Bean, 1879

REASON FOR INCLUSION   A single specimen (VIMS 0759) is known from Chesapeake Bay waters. This individual, of 63 mm SL (2.5 in), was collected at Gloucester Point in 1948. The tidewater mojarra occurs in various habitats, ranging from the continental shelf to coastal rivers. It is primarily a tropical and subtropical species. It is frequently taken in low-salinity waters of coastal rivers.

PERTINENT LITERATURE   Matheson and McEachran 1984.

Sea Chubs
FAMILY KYPHOSIDAE

Sea chubs are a family of primarily plant-eating marine fishes found throughout the world's tropical and warm-temperate seas. They are typically associated with shallow reefs and other rocky habitats, but the young are found near the surface, often among floating plants and debris. The family comprises 15 genera and more than 40 species, 2 of which are known from Chesapeake Bay. Those 2 species (Bermuda chub and yellow chub) can be distinguished based on the following combination of features: the Bermuda chub possesses 11–13 (typically 12) soft dorsal fin rays, 10–12 (typically 11) soft anal fin rays, and 16–18 gill rakers on the lower limb of the anterior gill arch, whereas the yellow chub possesses 13–15 (typically 14) soft dorsal fin rays, 12–13 (typically 13) soft anal fin rays, and 19–22 gill rakers on the lower limb of the anterior gill arch.

Bermuda chub
Kyphosus sectatrix (Linnaeus, 1758)

REASON FOR INCLUSION   A juvenile Bermuda chub has been collected at Fisherman Island near the Chesapeake Bay Bridge Tunnel. Other Bermuda chubs are expected to enter the lower bay as rare summer stragglers. Juvenile strays are known from as far north as Cape Cod; however, adults are not known north of the Bahamas.

PERTINENT LITERATURE   Hildebrand and Schroeder 1928:269; Musick 1972; Johnson 1978.

Yellow chub
Kyphosus incisor (Cuvier, 1831)

REASON FOR INCLUSION   A yellow chub was collected off Kiptopeke, Virginia (VIMS 0017). This individual, the only adult yellow chub recorded north of the Bahamas, was a female that measured 36 cm SL (1.4 in).

Juvenile yellow chubs are expected to enter the lower Chesapeake Bay as rare summer stragglers.
PERTINENT LITERATURE   Richards 1970; Musick 1972; Johnson 1978.

Grunts
FAMILY HAEMULIDAE

White grunt
Haemulon plumieri (Lacepède, 1801)

REASON FOR INCLUSION   Known from Chesapeake Bay (the mouth of the Potomac River) from a record in 1876, the white grunt has not been recorded in Chesapeake Bay since that time. The white grunt is not frequently encountered north of South Carolina. It is commonly found on shallow turtle grass beds and around mangroves.
PERTINENT LITERATURE   Uhler and Lugger 1876; Hildebrand and Schroeder 1928:260; Musick 1972; Johnson 1978.

Tomtate
Haemulon aurolineatum Cuvier, 1830

REASON FOR INCLUSION   Known from Chesapeake Bay from a record in 1876, the tomtate has not been recorded in Chesapeake Bay since that time. The tomtate is a warm-temperate to tropical species that frequents grass beds and reefs.
PERTINENT LITERATURE   Uhler and Lugger 1876; Musick 1972; Johnson 1978.

Sunfishes
FAMILY CENTRARCHIDAE

White crappie
Pomoxis annularis Rafinesque, 1818

REASON FOR INCLUSION   This introduced freshwater species occurs in lakes, ponds, and slow-moving streams of the Chesapeake Bay region. Although tolerant of very low-salinity waters, the white crappie rarely penetrates into waters of 5‰ or greater salinity.
PERTINENT LITERATURE   Hildebrand and Schroeder 1928:239; Musick 1972; Hardy 1978b; Jenkins and Burkhead 1994.

Parrotfishes
FAMILY SCARIDAE

Parrotfishes are marine fishes typically associated with coral reefs. Most feed by grazing on algae that grow on coral reefs. Parrotfishes are often brilliantly colored, and in many species the jaw teeth are fused to form a parrot-like beak—hence the common name. The family comprises about 9 genera and more than 80 species, 1 of which has been reported from Chesapeake Bay.

Blue parrotfish
Scarus coeruleus (Bloch, 1786)

REASON FOR INCLUSION   A single record of the blue parrotfish from Chesapeake Bay waters is known and is based on an 1894 collection by pound net from the Potomac River off St. George Island. Adult blue parrotfish are found on coral reefs, whereas juveniles inhabit sea grass beds as well as reefs.
PERTINENT LITERATURE   Hildebrand and Schroeder 1928:322; Musick 1972; Fischer 1978; Fritzsche 1978.

Molas
FAMILY MOLIDAE

Molas, or ocean sunfishes, are subtropical fishes of the open ocean and coastal waters that are found in depths from the surface to more than 300 m (100 ft). These large bizarre-looking fishes are often sighted near the surface. Molas appear to be all head and no tail; the body terminates posterior to the dorsal and anal fins. The posterior fin, which serves as a rudder, is derived from the posterior parts of the dorsal and anal fins and is therefore not a true caudal fin. As in puffers, the teeth of molas are fused into a single beak on each jaw. Molas feed primarily on jellyfishes and ctenophores. The family, comprising three genera and three species, is found in all tropical and temperate waters. A single species is recorded from Chesapeake Bay waters.

Ocean sunfish
Mola mola (Linnaeus, 1758)

REASON FOR INCLUSION   A single record of the ocean sunfish is known from Chesapeake Bay waters. This specimen (VIMS 8120) was foundering off the beach of the Great Wicomico River in Northumberland County, Virginia. Adult ocean sunfish are typically observed at or near the surface, although they are known to inhabit waters of considerable depth. Movement of ocean sunfish is largely driven by currents, and they drift with their food source (jellyfishes and ctenophores). Adults are reported to occur in pairs and groups.
PERTINENT LITERATURE   Martin and Drewry 1978; Fischer et al. 1981; Fritzsche 1982.

Boxfishes
FAMILY OSTRACIIDAE

Scrawled cowfish
Lactophrys quadricornis (Linnaeus, 1758)

REASON FOR INCLUSION   A single record, dating from 1877, exists for the scrawled cowfish from Chesapeake Bay. This tropical and temperate species frequents sea grass beds and is reported from depths approaching 80 m (265 ft).
PERTINENT LITERATURE   Lugger 1877; Musick 1972; Fischer 1978; Martin and Drewry 1978.

Porcupinefishes
FAMILY DIODONTIDAE

Porcupinefish
Diodon hystrix Linnaeus, 1758

REASON FOR INCLUSION   A single record, dating from 1876, exists for the porcupinefish from Chesapeake Bay and is based on a specimen from St. Marys County, Maryland. This circumtropical species frequents shallow inshore waters and occasionally strays into temperate waters.
PERTINENT LITERATURE   Uhler and Lugger 1876; Hildebrand and Schroeder 1928:350; Musick 1972; Fischer 1978; Martin and Drewry 1978.

Puffers
FAMILY TETRAODONTIDAE

Checkered puffer
Sphoeroides testudineus (Linnaeus, 1758)

REASON FOR INCLUSION   A single record, dating from 1877, exists for the checkered puffer from Chesapeake Bay. This tropical and subtropical species is rare north of Florida and frequents mangrove areas. The checkered puffer is typically found in very shallow waters over mud-sand bottoms.
PERTINENT LITERATURE   Lugger 1877; Hildebrand and Schroeder 1928:349; Musick 1972; Fischer 1978; Martin and Drewry 1978.

Righteye Flounders
FAMILY PLEURONECTIDAE

Atlantic halibut
Hippoglossus hippoglossus (Linnaeus, 1758)

REASON FOR INCLUSION   A cold-temperate species, the Atlantic halibut is only occasionally encountered south of New York and has been recorded once from within Chesapeake Bay. That record is an individual of 1.8 m TL (6 ft), collected in a pound net near Reedville, Virginia. The Atlantic halibut, found on both sides of the North Atlantic, inhabits hard bottoms and is more likely to occur on offshore banks and the outer continental shelf.
PERTINENT LITERATURE   Walford 1946; Musick 1972; Martin and Drewry 1978.

Yellowtail flounder
Pleuronectes ferrugineus (Storer, 1839)

REASON FOR INCLUSION   Known from Chesapeake Bay from an 1876 record, the yellowtail flounder has not been recorded in the bay since that time. This species is only rarely encountered south of New York and is unlikely to occur in Chesapeake Bay except during winter months.
PERTINENT LITERATURE   Uhler and Lugger 1876; Hildebrand and Schroeder 1928:168; Musick 1972; Martin and Drewry 1978.

Glossary
of Selected Technical Terms

ABDOMINAL   Pertaining to the belly. The term is often used to refer to the ventral portion of the body from the thorax to the anal opening.

ADIPOSE EYELID   A fatty, transparent tissue that covers the eye in some fishes.

ADIPOSE FIN   A fleshy, finlike, rayless structure situated on the dorsal ridge between the dorsal and caudal fins and, in some species, fused to the tail and separated from it by only a slight notch.

ANAL FIN   The vertical fin on the ventral surface of fishes just anterior to the tail and posterior to the anus.

ANTERIOR   In front of; the front end of the body or structure.

AXIL   The armpit, or the back side of the pectoral fin base.

AXILLARY SCALE, OR AXILLARY PROCESS   A modified, usually elongate scale at the insertion of the pectoral or pelvic fin in certain fishes.

BARBEL   A fleshy, tactile, enlarged flap or icicle-shaped projection, usually situated about the lips, chin, or nose. Barbels vary considerably in number and size in the various species of fishes.

BRANCHIOSTEGAL MEMBRANES   The paired membranes situated on the ventral edges of the gill covers and containing the elongate branchiostegal rays.

BRANCHIOSTEGAL RAYS   Elongate bones arranged fanwise within the branchiostegal membranes.

CARAPACE   A bony case covering the back and sometimes other parts of the body.

CAUDAL FIN   The tail fin.

CAUDAL PEDUNCLE   The region of the body between the base of the posterior ray of the anal fin and the base of the tail fin.

CLASPER   A modified pelvic fin in male sharks, rays, and skates that is used for reproduction.

COMPRESSED   Flattened laterally.

CONCAVE   Arched and rounded inward. A concave fin is one in which the central soft rays or spines are shorter than the anterior and posterior soft rays or spines, thereby giving the fin an inwardly curved distal edge.

CONVEX   Arched or rounded outward. A convex fin is one in which the central soft rays or spines are longer than the anterior and posterior soft rays or spines, thereby giving the fin an outwardly curved distal edge.

CTENOID SCALES   Scales that have a comblike margin of tiny prickles (ctenii) on the exposed, or posterior, field. The ctenii cause the scales to feel rough to the touch when stroked.

CYCLOID SCALES   Smooth-edged scales having an evenly curved posterior border without minute spines, or ctenii.

DENTICLES   Small toothlike projections.

DEPRESSED   Flattened dorsoventrally.

DEXTRAL   Located on the right side of the head.

DISTAL   Away from the center or from the point of origin.

DORSAL   Toward, near, or pertaining to the back or upper surface.

DORSAL FINS   The fins of the midline of the back. Usually two dorsal fins, which may or may not be connected, are present: a spiny-rayed dorsal fin anterior to a soft-rayed dorsal fin.

DORSOANTERIOR   In a dorsal and anterior direction.

DORSOLATERAL   In a dorsal and lateral direction.

DORSOPOSTERIOR   In a dorsal and posterior direction.

EMARGINATE   Having a notched margin.

ESCA   A fleshy bulblike structure located at the distal end of the angling apparatus (illicium) that is characteristic of goosefishes, batfishes, and frogfishes.

EURYHALINE   Capable of withstanding wide variations in osmotic pressure or salinity.

FALCATE   Curved like a sickle. A fin is falcate if it is deeply concave—that is, if the middle rays are much shorter than the anterior and posterior rays.

FIMBRIATE   Fringed at the margin.

FINLETS   Separated parts of divided dorsal and anal fins.

FRENUM   A connecting membrane that binds a part or parts together, such as the binding together of the upper jaw to the snout with skin.

GANOID SCALES   Diamond- or rhombic-shaped scales consisting of bone covered with superficial enamel.

GENITAL PAPILLA   A small, blunt, fleshy projection behind the anal opening. Gobies have a genital papilla.

GILL   A respiratory organ in aquatic animals, consisting chiefly of filamentous outgrowths for breathing oxygen dissolved in water.

GILL ARCH   The branchial skeleton that contains the gill rakers and the gill lamellae.

GILL RAKERS   Projections on the inner edge of gill arches that prevent food particles from passing outward through the gill slits.

GULAR PLATE   A large bony plate between ventral portions of the arms of the lower jaw.

HETEROCERCAL   Describing a caudal fin when the posterior end of the vertebral column (backbone) flexes upward, enters the dorsal lobe of the fin, and continues nearly to its end (but does not enter the caudal filament if one is present), and the dorsal lobe of the fin is better developed and often longer than the lower lobe.

HOMOCERCAL   Describing a caudal fin when the posterior end of the vertebral column does not flex upward or enter either lobe of the fin but ends in a hypural plate, and the two lobes of the fin are equal or nearly equal.

ILLICIUM   The angling apparatus, or "fishing pole," of goosefishes and frogfishes. This structure constitutes the remains of the spinous dorsal fin.

INFERIOR MOUTH   Describing a mouth when it is located near or on the ventral side of the head, and the snout overhangs the upper lip.

INFRAORBITAL CANAL   The portion of the lateral line system that encircles most or all of the eye, except the upper section, and encroaches onto the snout.

INNER NARIAL GROOVE   An external groove along the front margin of the head of some hammerhead sharks, extending from the narial opening back toward the median part of the head.

INNOMINATE BONE   The pelvis, or the hip bone.

INTERDORSAL   Located between the first and second dorsal fins.

INTEROPERCLE   The membrane bone that lies just ventral to the preopercle.

INTERRADIAL MEMBRANES   Membranes between fin rays or spines.

ISTHMUS   The narrow portion of the breast lying between and separating the gill chambers.

JUGULAR   Pertaining to the throat. The pelvic fins are jugular when they are located anterior to the pectoral fins.

LACUSTRINE   Pertaining to or inhabiting lakes.

LANCEOLATE   Pointed; lance-shaped.

LATERAL   Toward, near, or pertaining to the side.

LATERAL LINE   A line formed by a series of sensory tubes and pores, extending backward from the head along the side of the body. The lateral line is complete when all pores are present and the line reaches to the base of the caudal fin; it is incomplete when it does not extend as far as the base of the caudal fin; and it is absent if no tubes or pores are present.

MANDIBLE   The lower jaw.

MAXILLAE, OR MAXILLARIES   The bones on each of the halves of the upper jaw behind the premaxillae. These bones and the premaxillae form the two sides of the upper jaw.

MEDIAL   Toward, near, or pertaining to the middle.

MESOHALINE   Waters with middle-range salinities (5–30‰); tolerating such salinities.

NAPE   The small area on the dorsal surface of a fish beginning immediately posterior to the occipital region of the head and extending posteriorly to the dorsal fin origin in most species of spiny-rayed fishes, and posteriorly from the occiput about the same distance as the length of the occiput in soft-rayed species.

NARIAL GROOVE   *See* inner narial groove.

OCELLUS, OR OCELLAR SPOT   An eyelike spot.

OCCIPUT   The back or posterior portion of the head, extending posteriorly to the point between the end of the head and the beginning of the nape.

OPERCLE, OR OPERCULUM   The large, thin, very flat bones on each side of the head that cover the gills. Also called the gill cover.

PAIRED FINS   The pectoral and pelvic fins.

PALATINES   A pair of bones on the roof of the mouth, with one bone on each side and posterior to the vomer.

PALATINE TEETH   Teeth borne on the paired palatine bones that lie posterior to the vomer on the roof of the mouth.

PAPILLA   A small fleshy projection.

PECTORAL FINS   Paired fins attached to the shoulder on the side of the body.

PELVIC FINS   Paired fins on the ventral side of the body that are sometimes called ventral fins. They may be posterior to the pectoral fins (abdominal), ventral to the pectoral fins (thoracic), or anterior to the pectoral fins (jugular).

POLYHALINE   Waters with salinities of 18–30‰; tolerating such salinities.

POSTERIOR   Behind; the back end of the body or structure.

POSTEROLATERAL   In a posterior and lateral direction.

POSTEROMEDIAL   In a posterior and medial direction.

POSTORBITAL LATERALIS CANAL   A portion of the sensory system located posterolateral to the eye.

PRECAUDAL PIT   A depression or indentation on the tail of a shark located at the dorsal and/or ventral midline just anterior to the caudal fin.

PREDORSAL   Anterior to the dorsal fin.

PREMAXILLA, OR PREMAXILLARY   The anteriormost bone of the upper jaw that forms part or all of the border of the jaw and may bear teeth.

PREOPERCLE, OR PREOPERCULUM   The bone lying anterior to the opercle and comprising the forepart of the gill cover.

PREOPERCULOMANDIBULAR CANAL   A portion of the lateral line system, located on the head and extending along the preopercle and the mandible.

PRINCIPAL RAY   A branched or unbranched ray that is not rudimentary.

PROCUMBENT   Directed forward.

PSEUDOBRANCHIAE   Small gill-like structures on the underside of the opercle near the junction with the preopercle.

RAY   Any of the soft and hard rays of the fins, as well as any spine. A *soft ray* is usually flexible, branched, bilaterally paired, and segmented; it may be either a principal or a rudimentary ray. A *hard ray* is a hardened soft ray that may be a simple spine or the consolidated product of branching, as in the catfishes. A *true spine* is an unpaired structure without segmentation, usually stiff, and sharpened apically.

ROBUST   Not compressed; sturdy.

RUDIMENTARY RAY   A small, typically poorly developed, unbranched ray.

SCUTE   A modified scale that is often spiny or keeled. Scutes are found along the ventral midline of some species and along the lateral line of others.

SERRATED   Notched or toothed, somewhat like edge of a saw blade.

SINISTRAL   Located on the left side of the head.

SPINE   *See* ray.

SPIRACLE   An opening dorsoposterior to the eye in rays and some sharks.

STAY   A short bony prominence.

SUBOPERCLE   The elongate membrane bone that lies just ventral to the opercle.

SUBORBITAL BONY STAY   A bony ridge, usually with spinous points, that is located immediately ventral to the eye.

SUBTERMINAL MOUTH   Describing a mouth whose anterior end is just ventral to the tip of the snout.

SUPRAMAXILLA   A edge-shaped, small, movable bone attached to the upper edge of the maxilla near its posterior tip.

SUPRAORBITAL CANALS   The portions of the lateral line system that extend along the upper edge of each eye anteriorly onto the snout.

SUPRATEMPORAL CANAL   The portion of the lateral line system that connects the two lateral canals by crossing the top of the head at the occiput.

SYMPHYSIS   A type of joint in which two bones are connected by cartilage.

TERMINAL MOUTH   Describing a mouth in which the upper and lower jaws form the extreme anterior tip of the head.

TERETE   Circular in cross section.

THORACIC   In the region of the thorax or chest. Pelvic fins are thoracic when inserted perpendicular to the pectoral fins rather than considerably posterior to the pectoral fin insertion, as is more often the case.

TUBERCLE   A small rounded prominence.

VENTER   The abdomen or belly.

VENTRAL   Toward, near, or pertaining to the underpart or lower surface.

VENTROANTERIOR   In a ventral and anterior direction.

VENTROPOSTERIOR   In a ventral and posterior direction.

VERTICAL FINS   The dorsal, anal, and caudal fins, which are unpaired and located on the median line of the body, in contrast to the pectoral and pelvic fins, which are paired.

VOMER   An unpaired bone located at the anterior part of the roof of the mouth. If the vomer bears teeth, they are called vomerine teeth.

Literature Cited

Able, K. W. 1976. Cleaning behavior in the cyprinodontid fishes: *Fundulus majalis, Cyprinodon variegatus,* and *Lucania parva. Chesapeake Science* 17 (1): 35–39.

Able, K. W., and M. Castagna. 1975. Aspects of an undescribed reproductive behavior in *Fundulus heteroclitus* (Pisces: Cyprinodontidae) from Virginia. *Chesapeake Science* 16 (4): 282–284.

Able, K. W., C. B. Grimes, R. A. Cooper, and J. R. Uzmann. 1982. Burrow construction and behavior of tilefish, *Lopholatilus chamaeleonticeps,* in Hudson submarine canyon. *Environmental Biology of Fishes* 7 (3): 199–205.

Able, K. W., R. E. Matheson, W. W. Morse, M. P. Fahay, and G. Shepard. 1990. Patterns of summer flounder *Paralichthys dentatus* early life history in the Mid-Atlantic Bight and New Jersey estuaries. *Fishery Bulletin, U.S.* 88 (1): 1–12.

Abraham, B. J. 1985. *Species profiles: Life histories and environmental requirements of coastal fishes and invertebrates (Mid-Atlantic Bight)—mummichog and striped killifish.* U.S. Fish and Wildlife Service, Office of Biological Services, FWS/OBS-82/11.40. U.S. Army Corps of Engineers TR EL-82-4.

Ahrenholz, D. W. 1991. Population biology and life history of the North American menhadens, *Brevoortia* spp. *Marine Fisheries Review* 53 (4): 3–19.

Ahrenholz, D. W., W. R. Nelson, and S. P. Epperly. 1987. Population and fishery characteristics of Atlantic menhaden, *Brevoortia tyrannus. Fishery Bulletin, U.S.* 85 (3): 569–600.

Albaret, J. J., and P. Desfossez. 1988. Biologie et écologie des Gerreidae (Pisces, Teleostei) en lagune Ebrié (Côte d'Ivoire). *Revue d'Hydrobiologie Tropicale* 21 (1): 71–88.

Allen, G. R. 1978. *Butterfly and angelfishes of the world.* Vol. 2. John Wiley and Sons, New York.

———. 1985. *FAO species catalogue.* Vol. 6, *Snappers of the world: An annotated and illustrated catalogue of lutjanid species known to date.* Food and Agriculture Organization of the United Nations, Fisheries Synopsis 125. Rome.

Anderson, W. D., Jr. 1967. *Field guide to the snappers (Lutjanidae) of the western Atlantic.* U.S. Fish and Wildlife Service, Bureau of Commercial Fisheries, Circular 252.

Anderson, W. W. 1957. Early development, spawning, growth, and occurrence of the silver mullet *(Mugil curema)* along the south Atlantic coast of the United States. *Fishery Bulletin, U.S.* 57 (3): 397–414.

———. 1958. Larval development, growth, and spawning of striped mullet *(Mugil cephalus)* along the south Atlantic coast of the U.S. *Fishery Bulletin, U.S.* 58 (4): 501–519.

Anderson, W. W., J. W. Gehringer, and F. H. Berry. 1966. Family Synodontidae. In *Fishes of the western North Atlantic,* Sears Foundation for Marine Research, Memoir 1, pt. 5, 30–102. Yale University, New Haven, Conn.

Armstrong, M. P., J. A. Musick, and J. A. Colvocoresses. 1992. Age, growth, and reproduction of the goosefish *Lophius americanus* (Pisces: Lophiiformes). *Fishery Bulletin, U.S.* 90 (2): 217–230.

Atlantic States Marine Fisheries Commission. 1984. *Fishery management plan for the spotted seatrout (Cynoscion nebulosus) fishery.* Fishery Management Report 4. Washington, D.C.

———. 1985. *Fishery management plan for the weakfish (Cynoscion regalis) fishery.* Fishery Management Report 7. Washington, D.C.

———. 1987a. *Fishery management plan for Atlantic croaker (Micropogonias undulatus).* Fishery Management Report 10. Washington, D.C.

———. 1987b. *Fishery management plan for spot (Leiostomus xanthurus).* Fisheries Management Report 11. Washington, D.C.

———. 1988. *Supplement to the fishery management plan for the anadromous alosid stocks of the eastern United States: American shad, hickory shad, alewife, and blueback herring.* Fisheries Management Report 12. Washington, D.C.

Austin, H., and S. Austin. 1971. The feeding habits of some juvenile marine fishes from the mangroves of western Puerto Rico. *Caribbean Journal of Science* 11 (3–4): 171–178.

Baer, L. J. 1974. Feeding and food preferences by three sympatric species of cyprinodontid fishes. Master's thesis, Old Dominion University, Norfolk, Va.

Bakker, T. C. M., and P. Sevenster. 1988. Plate morphs of *Gasterosteus aculeatus* Linnaeus (Pisces: Gasterosteidae): Comments on terminology. *Copeia* 1988 (3): 659–663.

Banford, H. M., and B. C. Collette. 1993. *Hyporhamphus meeki,* a new species of halfbeak (Teleostei: Hemiramphidae) from the Atlantic and Gulf coasts of the United States. *Proceedings of the Biological Society of Washington* 106 (2): 369–384.

Barans, C. A. 1969. Distribution, growth, and behavior of the spotted hake in the Chesapeake Bight. Master's thesis, Virginia Institute of Marine Science, College of William and Mary, Gloucester Point.

———. 1972. Spotted hake, *Urophycis regius,* of the York River and lower Chesapeake Bay. *Chesapeake Science* 13 (1): 59–62.

Bayliff, W. H., Jr. 1950. *The life history of the silverside Menidia menidia (Linnaeus).* Chesapeake Biological Laboratory Publication 90. Solomons Island, Md.

Beamish, F. W. H., and T. E. Medland. 1988. Age determination for lampreys. *Transactions of the American Fisheries Society* 117 (1): 63–71.

Benson, N. G., ed. 1982. *Life history requirements of selected finfish and shellfish in Mississippi Sound and adjacent areas.* U.S. Fish and Wildlife Service, Office of Biological Services, FWS/OBS-81/51.

Berrien, P., and D. Finan. 1977a. *Biological and fisheries data on king mackerel, Scomberomorus cavalla (Cuvier).* Sandy Hook Laboratory, Northeast Fisheries Center, National Marine Fisheries Service, National Oceanic and Atmospheric Administration, Department of Commerce, Technical Series Report 8.

———. 1977b. *Biological and fisheries data on Spanish mackerel, Scomberomorus maculatus (Mitchill).* Sandy Hook Laboratory, Northeast Fisheries Center, National Marine Fisheries Service, National Oceanic and Atmospheric Administration, Department of Commerce, Technical Series Report 9.

Berry, F. H. 1959. Young jack crevalles (*Caranx* species) off the southeastern Atlantic coast of the United States. *Fishery Bulletin, U.S.* 59 (3): 417–535.

Berry, F. H., and W. W. Anderson. 1961. Stargazer fishes from the western North Atlantic (family Uranoscopidae). *Proceedings of U.S. National Museum* 112 (3448): 563–586.

Berry, F. H., and E. S. Iverson. 1966. Pompano: Biology, fisheries, and farming potential. *Proceedings of Gulf and Caribbean Fisheries Institute* 19:116–128.

Berry, F. H., and L. R. Rivas. 1962. Data on six species

of needlefishes (Belonidae) from the western Atlantic. *Copeia* 1962 (1): 152–160.

Berry, F. H., and L. E. Vogele. 1961. Filefishes (Monacanthidae) of the western North Atlantic. *Fishery Bulletin, U.S.* 61 (1): 61–109.

Bigelow, H. B., and W. C. Schroeder. 1948. Sharks. In *Fishes of the western North Atlantic,* Sears Foundation for Marine Research, Memoir 1, pt. 1, 59–546. Yale University, New Haven, Conn.

———. 1953a. Fishes of the Gulf of Maine. *Fishery Bulletin, U.S.* 53:1–577.

———. 1953b. Sawfishes, guitarfishes, skates, and rays. In *Fishes of the western North Atlantic,* Sears Foundation for Marine Research, Memoir 1, pt. 2, 1–502. Yale University, New Haven, Conn.

Birdsong, R. S. 1981. A review of the gobiid fish genus *Microgobius. Bulletin of Marine Science* 31 (2): 267–306.

Blaylock, R. A. 1989. A massive school of cownose rays, *Rhinoptera bonasus* (Rhinopteridae), in lower Chesapeake Bay, Virginia. *Copeia* 1989 (3): 744–748.

Bobko, S. J. 1991. Age, growth, and reproduction of black drum, *Pogonias cromis,* in Virginia. Master's thesis, Old Dominion University, Norfolk, Va.

Böhlke, J. E., and C. C. G. Chaplin. 1993. *Fishes of the Bahamas and adjacent tropical seas.* 2d ed. University of Texas Press, Austin.

Böhlke, J. E., and C. R. Robins. 1968. Western Atlantic seven-spined gobies, with descriptions of ten new species and a new genus, and comments on Pacific relatives. *Proceedings of the Academy of Natural Sciences of Philadelphia* 120 (3): 45–174.

Bonzek, C. F., P. J. Geer, J. A. Colvocoresses, and R. P. Harris Jr. 1993. *Juvenile finfish and blue crab stock assessment program.* Bottom Trawl Survey, Annual Data Summary Report Series, vol. 1992, Special Scientific Report 124. Virginia Institute Marine Science, Gloucester Point.

Bourne, D. W., and J. J. Govoni. 1988. Distribution of fish eggs and larvae and patterns of water circulation in Narragansett Bay, 1972–1973. In *Larval fish and shellfish transport through inlets,* American Fisheries Society Symposium 3, ed. M. P. Weinstein, 132–148. Bethesda, Md.

Bowman, R. E. 1984. Food of silver hake, *Merluccius bilinearis. Fishery Bulletin, U.S.* 82 (1): 21–35.

Bozeman, E. L., Jr., and M. J. Van Den Avyle. 1989. *Species profiles: Life histories and environmental requirements of coastal fishes and invertebrates (South Atlantic)—alewife and blueback herring.* U.S. Fish and Wildlife Service, Office of Biological Services, FWS/OBS-82/11.111. U.S. Army Corps of Engineers TR ED-82-4.

Branstetter, S., J. A. Musick, and J. A. Colvocoresses.

1987. A comparison of the age and growth of the tiger shark, *Galeocerdo cuvieri,* from off Virginia and the northwestern Gulf of Mexico. *Fishery Bulletin, U.S.* 85 (2): 269–279.

Breitburg, D. L. 1989. Demersal schooling prior to settlement by larvae of the naked goby. *Environmental Biology of Fishes* 26 (2): 97–103.

Briggs, J. C. 1993. New genus and species of clingfish (Gobiesocidae) from southern Australia. *Copeia* 1993 (1): 196–199.

Brill, J. 1991. Killifish habitats of the New York metropolitan area. *Journal of American Killifish Association* 24 (3): 105–112.

Brown, N.J. 1981. Reproductive biology and recreational fishery for spotted seatrout, *Cynoscion nebulosus,* in Texas and Virginia. Master's thesis, College of William and Mary, Williamsburg, Va.

Buckley, J. 1984. *Habitat Suitability Index Models: Larval and juvenile red drum.* U.S. Fish and Wildlife Service, Office of Biological Services, FWS/OBS-82/10.74.

Burgess, W. E. 1978. *Butterflyfishes of the world.* TFH Publications, Jersey City, N.J.

Byrne, D. M. 1978. Life history of the spotfin killifish, *Fundulus luciae* (Pisces: Cyprinodontidae), in Fox Creek Marsh, Virginia. *Estuaries* 1 (4): 211–227.

Caldwell, D. K. 1955. Offshore records of the triple-tail, *Lobotes surinamensis,* in the Gulf of Mexico. *Copeia* 1955 (2): 152–153.

———. 1962a. Development and distribution of the short bigeye, *Pseudopriacanthus altus* (Gill), in the western North Atlantic. *Fishery Bulletin, U.S.* 62 (1): 103–150.

———. 1962b. Western Atlantic fishes of the family Priacanthidae. *Copeia* 1962 (2): 417–424.

Caldwell, M. C. 1962c. Development and distribution of larval and juvenile fishes of the family Mullidae of the western North Atlantic. *Fishery Bulletin, U.S.* 62 (3): 403–457.

Carle, K. J., and P. A. Hastings. 1982. Selection of meiofaunal prey by the darter goby, *Gobionellus boleosoma* (Gobiidae). *Estuaries* 5 (4): 316–318.

Caruso, J. H. 1981. The systematics and distribution of the lophiid anglerfishes: 1, A revision of the genus *Lophiodes* with the description of two new species. *Copeia* 1981 (3): 522–549.

———. 1983. The systematics and distribution of the lophiid anglerfishes: 2, Revisions of the genera *Lophiomus* and *Lophius. Copeia* 1983 (1): 11–30.

Casey, J. G., H. L. Pratt Jr., and C. E. Stillwell. 1985. Age and growth of the sandbar shark *(Carcharhinus plumbeus)* from the western North Atlantic. *Canadian Journal of Fisheries and Aquatic Sciences* 42:963–975.

Chao, L. N. 1978. *A basis for classifying western Atlantic Sciaenidae (Teleostei: Perciformes).* Northeast Fisheries Center, National Marine Fisheries Service, National Oceanic and Atmospheric Administration, Department of Commerce, Technical Series Report 415.

Chao, L. N., and J. A. Musick. 1977. Life history, feeding habits, and functional morphology of juvenile sciaenid fishes in the York River Estuary, Virginia. *Fishery Bulletin, U.S.* 75 (4): 657–702.

Chapleau, F. 1988. Comparative osteology and intergeneric relationships of the tongue soles (Pisces; Pleuronectiformes; Cynoglossidae). *Canadian Journal of Zoology* 66:1214–1232.

———. 1993. Pleuronectiform relationships: A cladistic reassessment. *Bulletin of Marine Science* 52 (1): 516–540.

Chapleau, F., and A. Keast. 1988. A phylogenetic reassessment of the monophyletic status of the family Soleidae, with comments on the suborder Soleoidei (Pisces; Pleuronectiformes). *Canadian Journal of Zoology* 66:2797–2810.

Chidester, F. E. 1920. The behavior of *Fundulus heteroclitus* on the salt marshes of New Jersey. *American Naturalist* 54:551–557.

Chittenden, M. E., Jr. 1975. Dynamics of American shad, *Alosa sapidissima,* runs in the Delaware River. *Fishery Bulletin, U.S.* 73 (4): 487–494.

———. 1976. Weight loss, mortality, feeding, and residence of adult American shad, *Alosa sapidissima,* in fresh water. *Fishery Bulletin, U.S.* 74 (1): 151–157.

Chittenden, M. E., Jr., L. R. Barbieri, and C. M. Jones. 1993. Spatial and temporal occurrence of Spanish mackerel in Chesapeake Bay. *Fishery Bulletin, U.S.* 91 (1): 151–158.

Coad, B. W., and G. Power. 1973. Life history notes and variation in the freshwater fourspine stickleback, *Apeltes quadracus* (Mitchill), near Sept-Iles, Quebec. *Naturaliste Canadien* 100:247–251.

Cohen, D. M., T. Inada, T. Iwamoto, and N. Scialabba. 1990. *FAO species catalogue.* Vol. 10, *Gadiform fishes of the world: An annotated and illustrated catalogue of cods, hakes, grenadiers, and other gadiform fishes known to date.* Food and Agriculture Organization of the United Nations, Fisheries Synopsis 125. Rome.

Cole, C. F. 1967. A study of the eastern johnny darter, *Etheostoma olmstedi* Storer (Teleostei, Percidae). *Chesapeake Science* 8 (1): 28–51.

Collette, B. B., and L. N. Chao. 1975. Systematics and morphology of the bonitos *(Sarda)* and their relatives (Scombridae, Sardini). *Fishery Bulletin, U.S.* 73 (4): 516–625.

Collette, B. B., and C. E. Nauen. 1983. *FAO species catalogue.* Vol. 2, *Scombrids of the world: An annotated and illustrated catalogue of tunas, mackerels, bonitos, and related species known to date.* Food and Agriculture Organization of the United Nations, Fisheries Synopsis 125. Rome.

Collette, B. B., and J. L. Russo. 1984. Morphology, systematics, and biology of the Spanish mackerels (*Scomberomorus*, Scomberidae). *Fishery Bulletin, U.S.* 82 (4): 545–692.

Collette, B. B., G. E. McGowen, N. V. Parin, and S. Mito. 1984. Beloniformes: Development and relationships. In *Ontogeny and systematics of fishes,* Special Publication 1, ed. H. G. Moser, W. J. Richards, D. M. Cohen, M. P. Fahay, A. W. Kendall Jr., and S. L. Richardson, 335–354. American Society of Ichthyologists and Herpetologists, Lawrence, Kans.

Collins, M. R., D. J. Schmidt, C. W. Waltz, and J. L. Pickney. 1989. Age and growth of king mackerel, *Scomberomorus cavalla,* from the Atlantic coast of the United States. *Fishery Bulletin, U.S.* 87 (1): 49–61.

Compagno, L. J. V. 1984a. *FAO species catalogue. Vol. 4, Sharks of the world: An annotated and illustrated catalogue of shark species known to date.* Pt. 1, *Hexanchiformes to Lamniformes.* Food and Agriculture Organization of the United Nations, Fisheries Synopsis 125. Rome.

———. 1984b. *FAO species catalogue. Vol. 4, Sharks of the world: An annotated and illustrated catalogue of shark species known to date.* Pt. 2, *Carcharhiniformes.* Food and Agriculture Organization of the United Nations, Fisheries Synopsis 125. Rome.

Comyns, B. H., and G. C. Grant. 1993. Identification and distribution of *Urophycis* and *Phycis* (Pisces: Gadidae) larvae and pelagic juveniles in the U.S. Middle Atlantic Bight. *Fishery Bulletin, U.S.* 91 (2): 210–223.

Conover, D. O., and S. A. Murawski. 1982. Offshore winter migration of the Atlantic silverside, *Menidia menidia. Fishery Bulletin, U.S.* 80 (1): 145–150.

Courtenay, W. R., Jr. 1971. Sexual dimorphism of the sound producing mechanism of the striped cusk-eel, *Rissola marginata* (Pisces: Ophidiidae). *Copeia* 1971 (2): 259–268.

Cowan, J. H., Jr., R. S. Birdsong, E. D. Houde, J. S. Priest, W. C. Sharp, and G. B. Mateja. 1992. Enclosure experiments on survival and growth of black drum eggs and larvae in lower Chesapeake Bay. *Estuaries* 15 (3): 392–402.

Cowen, R. K., L. Chiarella, C. Gomez, and M. Bell. 1991. Distribution, age, and lateral plate variation of larval sticklebacks *(Gasterosteus)* off the Atlantic coast of New Jersey, New York, and southern New England. *Canadian Journal of Fisheries and Aquatic Sciences* 48:1679–1684.

Crabtree, R. E., and D. P. Middaugh. 1982. Oyster shell size and the selection of spawning sites by *Chasmodes bosquianus, Hypleurochilus geminatus, Hypsoblennius ionthas* (Pisces, Blenniidae), and *Gobiosoma bosci*

(Pisces, Gobiidae) in two South Carolina estuaries. *Estuaries* 5 (2): 150–155.

Cressey, R. F., and E. A. Lachner. 1970. The parasitic copepod diet and life history of diskfish (Echeneidae). *Copeia* 1970 (2): 310–318.

Dadswell, M. J., B. D. Taubert, T. S. Squiers, D. Marchette, and J. Buckley. 1984. Synopsis of biological data on shortnose sturgeon, *Acipenser brevirostrum* Lesueur 1818. Northeast Fisheries Center, National Marine Fisheries Service, National Oceanic and Atmospheric Administration, Department of Commerce, Technical Series Report 14.

Dahlberg, M. D., and J. C. Conyers. 1973. An ecological study of *Gobiosoma bosci* and *G. ginsburgi* (Pisces, Gobiidae) on the Georgia coast. *Fishery Bulletin, U.S.* 71 (2): 279–287.

Danie, D. S., J. G. Trial, and J. G. Stanley. 1984. *Species profiles: Life histories and environmental requirements of coastal fishes and invertebrates (North Atlantic)—Atlantic salmon.* U.S. Fish and Wildlife Service, Office of Biological Services, FWS/OBS-82/11.22. U.S. Army Corps of Engineers TR EL-82-4.

Daniel, L. B., III, and J. E. Graves. 1994. Morphometric and genetic identification of eggs of spring-spawning sciaenids in lower Chesapeake Bay. *Fishery Bulletin, U.S.* 92 (2): 254–261.

Darcy, G. H. 1985a. *Synopsis of biological data on the spottail pinfish, Diplodus holbrooki (Pisces: Sparidae).* Northeast Fisheries Center, National Marine Fisheries Service, National Oceanic and Atmospheric Administration, Department of Commerce, Technical Series Report 19.

———. 1985b. *Synopsis of biological data on the pinfish, Lagodon rhomboides (Pisces: Sparidae).* Northeast Fisheries Center, National Marine Fisheries Service, National Oceanic and Atmospheric Administration, Department of Commerce, Technical Series Report 23.

Dawson, C. E. 1958. *A study of the biology and life history of the spot, Leiostomus xanthurus Lacepède, with special reference to South Carolina.* Bears Bluff Laboratory Contribution 28. Charleston, S.C.

———. 1969. *Studies on the gobies of Mississippi Sound and adjacent waters, 2.* Publications, Gulf Coast Research Laboratory, Museum. Ocean Springs, Miss.

———. 1982. Family Syngnathidae: Subfamilies Doryrhamphinae and Syngnathinae. In *Fishes of the western North Atlantic,* Sears Foundation for Marine Research, Memoir 1, pt. 8, 1–172. Yale University, New Haven, Conn.

Deckert, G. D., and D. W. Greenfield. 1987. A review of the western Atlantic species of the genera *Diapterus* and *Eugerres* (Pisces: Gerreidae). *Copeia* 1987 (1): 182–194.

Dentzau, M. W., and M. E. Chittenden. 1990. Reproduction, movements, and apparent population dynamics of the Atlantic threadfin *Polydactylus octonemus* in the Gulf of Mexico. *Fishery Bulletin, U.S.* 88 (3): 439–462.

DeSylva, D. 1984. Sphyraenoidei: Development and relationships. In *Ontogeny and systematics of fishes,* Special Publication 1, ed. H. G. Moser et al., 534–540. American Society of Ichthyologists and Herpetologists, Lawrence, Kans.

DeVane, J. C., Jr. 1978. Food of king mackerel, *Scomberomorus cavalla,* in Onslow Bay, North Carolina. *Transactions of the American Fisheries Society* 107 (4): 583–586.

Dick, M. M. 1964. Suborder Esocoidea. In *Fishes of the western North Atlantic,* Sears Foundation for Marine Research, Memoir 1, pt. 4, 550–560. Yale University, New Haven, Conn.

Dovel, W., J. A. Mihursky, and A. J. McErlean. 1969. Life history aspects of the hogchoker, *Trinectes maculatus,* in the Patuxent River Estuary, Maryland. *Chesapeake Science* 10 (2): 123–129.

DuBuit, M. H. 1991. Food and feeding of saithe (*Pollachius virens* L.) off Scotland. *Fisheries Research* 12 (1991): 307–323.

Dymond, J. R. 1963. Family Salmonidae. In *Fishes of the western North Atlantic,* Sears Foundation for Marine Research, Memoir 1, pt. 3, 457–502. Yale University, New Haven, Conn.

Eddy, S., and J. C. Underhill. 1978. *How to know the freshwater fishes.* 3d ed. William C. Brown, Dubuque, Iowa.

Edwards, E. A., G. Gebhart, and O. E. Maughan. 1983. *Habitat Suitability Index Models: Smallmouth bass.* U.S. Fish and Wildlife Service, Office of Biological Services, FWS/OBS-82/10.36.

Ellis, R. 1975. *The book of sharks.* Grosset and Dunlap, New York.

Eschmeyer, W. N. 1990. *Catalog of the genera of recent fishes.* California Academy of Sciences, San Francisco.

Fagade, S. O., and C. I. O. Olaniyan. 1973. The food and feeding interrelationships of the fishes in the Lagos Lagoon. *Journal of Fish Biology* 5:205–225.

Fahay, M. P. 1974. Occurrence of silver hake, *Merluccius bilinearis,* eggs and larvae along the Middle Atlantic continental shelf during 1966. *Fishery Bulletin, U.S.* 72 (3): 813–830.

———. 1975. *An annotated list of larval and juvenile fishes captured with surface-towed meter net in the South Atlantic Bight during four RV Dolphin cruises between May 1967 and February 1968.* Northeast Fisheries Center, National Marine Fisheries Service, National Oceanic and Atmospheric Administration, Department of Commerce, Technical Series Report 685.

———. 1983. Guide to the early stages of marine fishes

occurring in the western North Atlantic Ocean, Cape Hatteras to the southern Scotian Shelf. *Journal of Northwest Atlantic Fishery Science* 4:1–423.

———. 1992. Development and distribution of cusk eel eggs and larvae in the Middle Atlantic Bight with a description of *Ophidion robinsi* n. sp. (Teleostei: Ophidiidae). *Copeia* 1992 (3): 799–819.

Fahay, M. P., and K. W. Able. 1989. White hake, *Urophycis tenuis,* in the Gulf of Maine: Spawning seasonality, habitat use, and growth in young-of-the-year, and relationships to the Scotian Shelf population. *Canadian Journal of Zoology* 67:1715–1724.

Fay, C. W., R. J. Neves, and G. B. Pardue. 1983. *Species profiles: Life histories and environmental requirements of coastal fishes and invertebrates (Mid-Atlantic Bight)— Atlantic silverside.* U.S. Fish and Wildlife Service, Office of Biological Services, FWS/OBS-82/11.10. U.S. Army Corps of Engineers TR EL-82-4.

Fine, M. L. 1975. Sexual dimorphism of the growth rate of the swimbladder of the toadfish, *Opsanus tau. Copeia* 1975 (3): 483–490.

Fischer, W., ed. 1978. *FAO species identification sheets for fishery purposes: Western central Atlantic, fishing area 31.* Vols. 1–7. Food and Agriculture Organization of the United Nations, Rome.

Fischer, W., G. Bianchi, and W. B. Scott, eds. 1981. *FAO species identification sheets for fishery purposes: Eastern central Atlantic, fishing areas 34, 47 (in part).* Vols. 1–7. Canada Funds-in-Trust, Ottawa; Department of Fisheries and Oceans, Canada; by arrangement with the Food and Agriculture Organization of the United Nations.

Fritz, R. L. 1962. *Silver hake.* U.S. Fish and Wildlife Service, Bureau of Commercial Fisheries, Fishery Leaflet 538.

Fritzsche, R. A. 1978. *Development of fishes of the Mid-Atlantic Bight: An atlas of egg, larval, and juvenile stages.* Vol. 5, *Chaetodontidae through Ophidiidae.* U.S. Fish and Wildlife Service, Office of Biological Services, FWS/OBS-78/12.

———. 1982. Osteichthyes. In *Synopsis and classification of living organisms,* vol. 2, 858–944. McGraw-Hill, New York.

Gilbert, C. R. 1989. *Species profiles: Life histories and environmental requirements of coastal fishes and invertebrates (Mid-Atlantic Bight)—Atlantic and shortnose sturgeons.* U.S. Fish and Wildlife Service, Office of Biological Services, FWS/OBS-82/11.122. U.S. Army Corps of Engineers TR EL-82-4.

Ginsburg, I. 1931. Juvenile and sex characters of *Evorthodus lyricus* (family Gobiidae). *Fishery Bulletin, U.S.* 47 (1): 117–124.

———. 1932. A revision of the genus *Gobionellus* (family Gobiidae). *Bulletin, Bingham Oceanographic Collection, Yale University* 4 (2): 1–51.

———. 1952. Flounders of the genus *Paralichthys* and related genera in American waters. *Fishery Bulletin, U.S.* 52 (2): 267–351.

Gorham, S. W., and D. E. McAllister. 1974. The shortnose sturgeon, *Acipenser brevirostrum*, in the Saint John River, New Brunswick, Canada: A rare and possibly endangered species. *Syllogeus* 5.

Govoni, J. J., and J. V. Merriner. 1978. The occurrence of ladyfish, *Elops saurus*, larvae in low-salinity waters and another record for Chesapeake Bay. *Estuaries* 1 (3): 205–206.

Grant, G. C., and J. E. Olney. 1991. Distribution of striped bass, *Morone saxatilis* (Walbaum), eggs and larvae in major Virginia rivers. *Fishery Bulletin, U.S.* 89 (1): 187–193.

Graves, J. E., J. R. McDowell, and M. L. Jones. 1992. A genetic analysis of weakfish, *Cynoscion regalis*, stock structure along the mid-Atlantic coast. *Fishery Bulletin, U.S.* 90 (3): 469–475.

Gutherz, E. J. 1967. *Field guide to the flatfishes of the family Bothidae in the western North Atlantic.* U.S. Fish and Wildlife Service, Bureau of Commercial Fisheries, Circular 263.

Hales, L. S., and M. J. Van Den Avyle. 1989. *Species profiles: Life histories and environmental requirements of coastal fishes and invertebrates (South Atlantic)—spot.* U.S. Fish and Wildlife Service, Office of Biological Services, FWS/OBS-82/11.91. U.S. Army Corps of Engineers TR EL-82-4.

Halliday, R. G. 1991. Marine distribution of the sea lamprey *(Petromyzon marinus)* in the northwest Atlantic. *Canadian Journal of Fisheries and Aquatic Sciences* 48:832–842.

Hardy, J. D., Jr. 1978a. *Development of fishes of the Mid-Atlantic Bight: An atlas of egg, larval, and juvenile stages.* Vol. 2, *Anguillidae through Syngnathidae.* U.S. Fish and Wildlife Service, Office of Biological Services, FWS/OBS-78/12.

———. 1978b. *Development of fishes of the Mid-Atlantic Bight: An atlas of egg, larval, and juvenile stages.* Vol. 3, *Aphredoderidae through Rachycentridae.* U.S. Fish and Wildlife Service, Office of Biological Services, FWS/OBS-78/12.

Hare, J. A., and R. K. Cowen. 1993. Ecological and evolutionary implications of the larval transport and reproductive strategy of bluefish *(Pomatomus saltatrix).* *Marine Ecology, Progress Series* 98:1–16.

Harrington, R. W., Jr., and E. S. Harrington. 1972. Food of female marsh killifish, *Fundulus confluentus* Goode and Bean, in Florida. *American Midland Naturalist* 87 (2): 492–502.

Hassler, T. J. 1987. *Species profiles: Life histories and environmental requirements of coastal fishes and invertebrates (Pacific Southwest)—coho salmon.* U.S. Fish and Wildlife Service, Office of Biological Services, FWS/

OBS-82/11.70. U.S. Army Corps of Engineers TR EL-82-4.

Haven, D. S. 1957. Distribution, growth, and availability of juvenile croaker, *Micropogon undulatus*, in Virginia. *Ecology* 38 (1): 88–97.

Hayse, J. W. 1990. Feeding habits, age, growth, and reproduction of Atlantic spadefish *Chaetodipterus faber* (Pisces: Ephippidae) in South Carolina. *Fishery Bulletin, U.S.* 88 (1): 67–83.

Heemstra, P. C., and J. E. Randall. 1993. *FAO species catalogue.* Vol. 16, *Groupers of the world: An annotated and illustrated catalogue of the grouper, rockcod, hind, coral grouper, and lyretail species known to date.* Food and Agriculture Organization of the United Nations, Fisheries Synopsis 125. Rome.

Hildebrand, S. F. 1963a. Clupeidae. In *Fishes of the western North Atlantic,* Sears Foundation for Marine Research, Memoir 1, pt. 3, 257–385, 397–442, 452–454. Yale University, New Haven, Conn.

———. 1963b. Elopidae. In *Fishes of the western North Atlantic,* Sears Foundation for Marine Research, Memoir 1, pt. 3, 111–131. Yale University, New Haven, Conn.

———. 1963c. Engraulidae. In *Fishes of the western North Atlantic,* Sears Foundation for Marine Research, Memoir 1, pt. 3, 152–249. Yale University, New Haven, Conn.

Hildebrand, S. F., and L. E. Cable. 1938. Further notes on the development and life history of some teleosts at Beaufort, N.C. *Bulletin of the U.S. Bureau of Fisheries* 48 (24): 504–642.

Hildebrand, S. F., and W. C. Schroeder. 1928. Fishes of Chesapeake Bay. *Bulletin of the U.S. Bureau of Fisheries* 43 (1): 1–366.

Hill, J., J. W. Evans, and M. J. Van Den Avyle. 1989. *Species profiles: Life histories and environmental requirements of coastal fishes and invertebrates (South Atlantic)—striped bass.* U.S. Fish and Wildlife Service, Office of Biological Services, FWS/OBS-82/11.118. U.S. Army Corps of Engineers TR EL-82-4.

Hoff, J. G. 1976. Contribution to the biology of the seaboard goby, *Gobiosoma ginsburgi*. *Copeia* 1976 (2): 385–386.

Hood, P. B., K. W. Able, and C. B. Grimes. 1988. Biology of the conger eel, *Conger oceanicus*, in the Mid-Atlantic Bight: 1, Distribution, age, growth and reproduction. *Marine Biology* 98:587–596.

Horn, M. H. 1970. Systematics and biology of the stromateoid fishes of the genus *Peprilus*. *Bulletin, Museum of Comparative Zoology at Harvard University* 149 (5): 165–261.

Hostetter, E. B., and T. A. Munroe. 1993. Age, growth, and reproduction of tautog *Tautoga onitis* (Labridae: Perciformes) from coastal waters of Virginia. *Fishery Bulletin, U.S.* 91 (1): 45–64.

Jenkins, R. E., and N. M. Burkhead. 1994. *Freshwater fishes of Virginia.* American Fisheries Society, Bethesda, Md.

Jenkins, R. E., and J. A. Musick. 1979. Freshwater and marine fishes. In *Endangered and threatened plants and animals of Virginia,* Virginia Polytechnic Institute and State University, Sea Grant Program, Publication VPI-SG-79-13, ed. D. W. Linzey, 319–373. Blacksburg.

Jensen, A. C. 1966. Life history of the spiny dogfish. *Fishery Bulletin, U.S.* 65:527–554.

Johnson, G. D. 1978. *Development of fishes of the Mid-Atlantic Bight: An atlas of egg, larval, and juvenile stages.* Vol. 4, *Carangidae through Ephippidae.* U.S. Fish and Wildlife Service, Office of Biological Services, FWS/OBS-78/12.

———. 1980. The limits and relationships of the Lutjanidae and associated families. *Bulletin of the Scripps Institution of Oceanography* 24:1–114.

Jones, P. W., F. D. Martin, and J. D. Hardy Jr. 1978. *Development of fishes of the Mid-Atlantic Bight: An atlas of egg, larval, and juvenile stages.* Vol. 1, *Acipenseridae through Ictaluridae.* U.S. Fish and Wildlife Service, Office of Biological Services, FWS/OBS-78/12.

Jones, P. W., H. J. Speir, N. H. Butowski, R. O'Reilly, L. Gillingham, and E. Smoller. 1988. *Chesapeake Bay fisheries: Status, trends, priorities, and data needs.* Maryland Department of Natural Resources, Tidewater Division, and the Virginia Marine Resources Commission, Annapolis.

Joseph, E. B. 1972. The status of sciaenid stocks of the middle Atlantic coast. *Chesapeake Science* 13 (2): 87–100.

Joseph, E. B., J. J. Norcross, and W. H. Massman. 1964. Spawning of the cobia, *Rachycentron canadum,* in the Chesapeake Bay area, with observations of juvenile specimens. *Chesapeake Science* 5 (1–2): 67–71.

Keefe, M. 1993. Patterns of metamorphosis in summer flounder, *Paralichthys dentatus. Journal of Fish Biology* 42:713–728.

Kelso, W. E. 1979. Predation on soft-shell clams, *Mya arenaria,* by the common mummichog, *Fundulus heteroclitus. Estuaries* 2 (4): 249–254.

Kendall, A. W. 1977. *Biological and fisheries data on black sea bass, Centropristis striata (Linnaeus).* Sandy Hook Laboratory, Northeast Fisheries Center, National Marine Fisheries Service, National Oceanic and Atmospheric Administration, Department of Commerce, Technical Series Report 7.

Kendall, A. W., Jr., and L. A. Walford. 1979. Sources and distribution of bluefish, *Pomatomus saltatrix,* larvae and juveniles off the east coast of the United States. *Fishery Bulletin, U.S.* 77 (1): 213–227.

Kerschner, B. A., Peterson, M. S., and R. G. Gilmore Jr. 1985. Ecotopic and ontogenetic trophic variation in

mojarras (Pisces: Gerreidae). *Estuaries* 8 (3): 311–322.

Kostecki, P. T. 1984. *Habitat Suitability Index Models: Spotted seatrout.* U.S. Fish and Wildlife Service, Office of Biological Services, FWS/OBS-82/10.75.

Krueger, W. H. 1961. Meristic variation in the fourspine stickleback, *Apeltes quadracus. Copeia* 1961 (4): 442–450.

Lachner, E. A. 1954. A revision of the goatfish genus *Upeneus* with descriptions of two new species. *Proceedings of U.S. National Museum* 103:497–532.

Lagler, K. F., J. E. Bardach, R. R. Miller, and D. R. M. Passino. 1977. *Ichthyology.* 2d ed. John Wiley and Sons, New York.

Lazzari, M. A., and K. W. Able. 1990. Northern pipefish, *Syngnathus fuscus,* occurrences over the Mid-Atlantic Bight continental shelf: Evidence of seasonal migration. *Environmental Biology of Fishes* 27: 177–185.

Lee, D. S., S. P. Platania, C. R. Gilbert, R. Franz, and A. Norden. 1981. A revised list of the freshwater fishes of Maryland and Delaware. *Proceedings of the Southeastern Fisheries Council* 3 (3): 1–10.

Lee, L. A., and J. W. Terrell. 1987. *Habitat Suitability Index Models: Flathead catfish.* U.S. Fish and Wildlife Service, Office of Biological Services, FWS/OBS-82/10.152.

Leslie, A. J., and D. J. Stewart. 1986. Systematics and distributional ecology of *Etropus* (Pisces, Bothidae) on the Atlantic Coast of the United States with description of a new species. *Copeia* 1986 (1): 140–156.

Liem, A. H., and W. B. Scott. 1966. *Fishes of the Atlantic coast of Canada.* Fisheries Research Board of Canada, Bulletin 155. Ottawa.

Lippson, A. J., and R. L. Moran. 1974. *Manual for identification of early developmental stages of fishes of the Potomac River Estuary.* Maryland Department of Natural Resources, Power Plant Siting Program PPSP-MP-13. Baltimore.

Livingston, R. J. 1984. Trophic response of fishes to habitat variability in coastal seagrass systems. *Ecology* 65 (4): 1258–1275.

Luczkovich, J. J., G. M. Watters, and B. L. Olla. 1991. Seasonal variation in usage of a common shelter resource by juvenile snailfish *(Liparis inquilinus)* and red hake *(Urophycis chuss). Copeia* 1991 (4): 1104–1109.

Lugger, O. 1877. Additions to the list of fishes of Maryland, published in report, January 1, 1876. In *Report, Commissioner of Fisheries of Maryland, 1877,* 57–94. Baltimore.

Luo, J., and J. A. Musick. 1991. Reproductive biology of the bay anchovy in Chesapeake Bay. *Transactions of the American Fisheries Society* 120 (6): 701–710.

MacKenzie, C., L. S. Weiss-Glanz, and J. R. Moring. 1985. *Species profiles: Life histories and environmental requirements of coastal fishes and invertebrates (Mid-Atlantic Bight)—American shad.* U.S. Fish and Wildlife Service, Office of Biological Services, FWS/OBS-82/11.37. U.S. Army Corps of Engineers TR EL-82-4.

Manooch, C. S. 1984. *Fisherman's guide: Fishes of the southeastern United States.* North Carolina State Museum of Natural History, Raleigh.

Mansueti, R. J. 1960. Restriction of very young red drum, *Sciaenops ocellatus,* to shallow estuarine waters of Chesapeake Bay in late autumn. *Chesapeake Science* 1 (3–4): 207–210.

———. 1961a. Age, growth, and movements of the striped bass, *Roccus saxatilis,* taken in size selective fishing gear in Maryland. *Chesapeake Science* 1 (1–2): 9–36.

———. 1961b. Movement, reproduction, and mortality of the white perch, *Roccus americanus,* in the Patuxent Estuary, Maryland. *Chesapeake Science* 2 (3–4): 142–205.

———. 1962. The Atlantic bonito, *Sarda sarda,* in northern Chesapeake Bay and comments on the seaside fishery of Maryland. *Chesapeake Science* 3 (1): 47–49.

———. 1964. Eggs, larvae, and young of the white perch, *Roccus americanus,* with comments on its ecology in the estuary. *Chesapeake Science* 5 (1–2): 3–45.

Mansueti, A. J., and J. D. Hardy Jr. 1967. *Development of fishes of the Chesapeake Bay region: An atlas of egg, larval, and juvenile stages.* Natural Resources Institute, University of Maryland, Solomons.

Mansueti, R. J., and A. J. Mansueti. 1962. Little tunny, *Euthynnus alletteratus,* in northern Chesapeake Bay, Maryland, with illustrations of its skeleton. *Chesapeake Science* 3 (4): 257–263.

Martin, F. D. 1972. Factors influencing local distribution of *Cyprinodon variegatus* (Pisces: Cyprinodontidae). *Transactions of the American Fisheries Society* 1:89–93.

Martin, F. D., and G. E. Drewry. 1978. *Development of fishes of the Mid-Atlantic Bight: An atlas of egg, larval, and juvenile stages.* Vol. 6, *Stromateidae through Ogcocephalidae.* U.S. Fish and Wildlife Service, Office of Biological Services, FWS/OBS-78/12.

Massmann, W. H. 1954. Marine fishes in fresh and brackish waters of Virginia rivers. *Ecology* 35 (1): 75–78.

———. 1957. New and recent records of fishes in Chesapeake Bay. *Copeia* 1957 (2): 156–157.

———. 1960. Additional records for new fishes in Chesapeake Bay. *Copeia* 1960 (1): 70.

———. 1963. Age and size composition of weakfish, *Cynoscion regalis,* from pound nets in Chesapeake Bay, Virginia, 1954–1958. *Chesapeake Science* 4 (1): 43–51.

Massmann, W. H., and A. L. Pacheco. 1960. Disappearance of young Atlantic croakers from the York River, Virginia. *Transactions of the American Fisheries Society* 89 (2): 154–159.

———. 1961. Movement of striped bass tagged in Virginia waters of Chesapeake Bay. *Chesapeake Science* 1 (1–2): 37–44.

Matheson, R. E., Jr. 1981. The distribution of the flagfin mojarra, *Eucinostomus melanopterus* (Pisces: Gerreidae), with ecological notes on Texas and Florida populations. *Northeast Gulf Science* 5 (1): 63–66.

Matheson, R. E., Jr., and J. D. McEachran. 1984. Taxonomic studies of the *Eucinostomus argenteus* complex (Pisces: Gerreidae): Preliminary studies of external morphology. *Copeia* 1984 (4): 893–902.

McBride, R. S., and D. O. Conover. 1991. Recruitment of young-of-the-year bluefish, *Pomatomus saltatrix,* to the New York Bight: Variation in abundance and growth of spring-and summer-spawned cohorts. *Marine Ecology, Progress Series* 78 (3): 205–216.

McClane, A. J., ed. 1965. *McClane's standard fishing encyclopedia.* Holt, Rinehart and Winston, New York.

McCleave, J. D., and M. J. Miller. 1994. Spawning of *Conger oceanicus* and *Conger triporiceps* (Congridae) in the Sargasso Sea and subsequent distribution of leptocephali. *Environmental Biology of Fishes* 39: 339–355.

McCosker, J. E., E. B. Böhlke, and J. E. Böhlke. 1989. Family Ophichthidae. In *Fishes of the western North Atlantic,* Sears Foundation for Marine Research, Memoir 1, pt. 9, 254–412. Yale University, New Haven, Conn.

McEachran, J. D. 1982. Chondrichthyes. In *Synopsis and classification of living organisms,* vol. 2, 831–844. McGraw-Hill, New York.

McEachran, J. D., and J. Davis. 1970. Age and growth of the striped searobin. *Transactions of the American Fisheries Society* 99 (2): 343–352.

McEachran, J. D., and C. O. Martin. 1977. Possible occurrence of character displacement in the sympatric skates *Raja erinacea* and *R. ocellata* (Pisces: Rajidae). *Environmental Biology of Fishes* 2 (1): 121–130.

McEachran, J. D., and J. A. Musick. 1975. Distribution and relative abundance of seven species of skates (Pisces: Rajidae) which occur between Nova Scotia and Cape Hatteras. *Fishery Bulletin, U.S.* 73 (1): 110–136.

McEachran, J. D., D. Boesch, and J. A. Musick. 1976. Food division within two sympatric species of skates (Pisces: Rajidae). *Marine Biology* 73:110–136.

Medved, R. J., and J. A. Marshall. 1981. Feeding behavior and biology of young sandbar sharks, *Carcharhinus plumbeus* (Pisces, Carcharhinidae), in Chincoteague Bay, Virginia. *Fishery Bulletin, U.S.* 79 (4): 441–447.

Mercer, L. P. 1983. *A biological and fisheries profile of weakfish, Cynoscion regalis.* North Carolina Division of Marine Fisheries, Special Scientific Report 39. Morehead City, N.C.

———. 1984a. *A biological and fisheries profile of red drum, Sciaenops ocellatus.* North Carolina Division of Marine Fisheries, Special Scientific Report 41. Morehead City, N.C.

———. 1984b. *A biological and fisheries profile of the spotted seatrout, Cynoscion nebulosus.* North Carolina Division of Marine Fisheries, Special Scientific Report 40. Morehead City, N.C.

Merriner, J. V. 1976. Aspects of the reproductive biology of the weakfish, *Cynoscion regalis* (Sciaenidae), in North Carolina. *Fishery Bulletin, U.S.* 74 (1): 18–26.

Meyer, T. L., R. A. Cooper, and R. W. Langston. 1979. Relative abundance, behavior, and food habits of the American sand lance, *Ammodytes americanus,* from the Gulf of Maine. *Fishery Bulletin, U.S.* 77 (2): 243–254.

Middaugh, D. P. 1981. Reproductive ecology and spawning periodicity of the Atlantic silverside, *Menidia menidia* (Pisces: Atherinidae). *Copeia* 1981 (4): 766–776.

Miller, R. R. 1950. A review of the American clupeid fishes of the genus *Dorosoma. Proceedings of U.S. National Museum* 100 (3267): 387–410.

———. 1963. Genus *Dorosoma.* In *Fishes of the western North Atlantic,* Sears Foundation for Marine Research, Memoir 1, pt. 3, 443–454. Yale University, New Haven, Conn.

Morse, W. W. 1977. *Biological and fisheries data on scup, Stenotomus chrysops (Linnaeus).* Northeast Fisheries Center, National Marine Fisheries Service, National Oceanic and Atmospheric Administration, Department of Commerce, Technical Series Report 12.

———. 1980. Maturity, spawning, and fecundity of Atlantic croaker, *Micropogonias undulatus,* occurring north of Cape Hatteras, North Carolina. *Fishery Bulletin, U.S.* 78 (1): 190–195.

Morse, W. W., M. P. Fahay, and W. G. Smith. 1987. *MARMAP surveys of the continental shelf from Cape Hatteras, North Carolina, to Cape Sable, Nova Scotia (1977–1984): Atlas 2, Annual distribution patterns of fish larvae.* National Oceanic and Atmospheric Administration, Department of Commerce, Technical Memorandum NMFS-F/NEC-47.

Morton, T. 1989. *Species profiles: Life histories and environmental requirements of coastal fishes and invertebrates (Mid-Atlantic Bight)—bay anchovy.* U.S. Fish and Wildlife Service, Office of Biological Services,

FWS/OBS-82/11.97. U.S. Army Corps of Engineers TR EL-82-4.

Muncy, R. J., and W. M. Wingo. 1983. *Species profiles: Life histories and environmental requirements of coastal fishes and invertebrates (Gulf of Mexico)—sea catfish and gafftopsail catfish.* U.S. Fish and Wildlife Service, Office of Biological Services, FWS/OBS-82/11.5. U.S. Army Corps of Engineers TR EL-82-4.

Munroe, T. A. 1987. A systematic revision of Atlantic tonguefishes (*Symphurus:* Cynoglossidae: Pleuronectiformes), with a preliminary hypothesis of species group relationships. Ph.D. diss., College of William and Mary, Williamsburg, Va.

Murawski, S. A., D. G. Frank, and S. Chang. 1978. *Biological and fisheries data on butterfish, Peprilus triacanthus (Peck).* Sandy Hook Laboratory, Northeast Fisheries Center, National Marine Fisheries Service, National Oceanic and Atmospheric Administration, Department of Commerce, Technical Series Report 6.

Murphy, M. D., and R. G. Taylor. 1990. Reproduction, growth, and mortality of red drum *Sciaenops ocellatus* in Florida waters. *Fishery Bulletin, U.S.* 88 (4): 531–542.

Musick, J. A. 1972. Fishes of Chesapeake Bay and the adjacent coastal plain. In *A check list of the biota of lower Chesapeake Bay,* Virginia Institute of Marine Science, Special Scientific Report 65, comp. M. L. Wass et al., 175–212. Gloucester Point.

———. 1973. A meristic and morphometric comparison of the hakes *Urophycis chuss* and *U. tenuis* (Pisces: Gadidae). *Fishery Bulletin, U.S.* 71 (4): 479–448.

———. 1974. Seasonal distribution of sibling hakes, *Urophycis chuss* and *U. tenuis* (Pisces: Gadidae), in New England. *Fishery Bulletin, U.S.* 72 (3): 481–495.

Musick, J. A., and L. P. Mercer. 1977. Seasonal distribution of black sea bass, *Centropristis striata,* in the Mid-Atlantic Bight, with comments on the ecology and fisheries of the species. *Transactions of the American Fisheries Society* 106 (1): 12–25.

Musick, J. A., S. Branstetter, and J. A. Colvocoresses. 1993. Trends in shark abundance from 1974 to 1991 for the Chesapeake Bight region of the U.S. mid-Atlantic coast. In *Conservation biology of elasmobranchs,* National Marine Fisheries Service, National Oceanic and Atmospheric Administration, Department of Commerce, Technical Series Report 115, ed. S. Branstetter, 1–18.

Musick, J. A., R. E. Jenkins, and N. M. Burkhead. 1994. Sturgeons, family Acipenseridae. In *Freshwater fishes of Virginia,* ed. R. E. Jenkins and N. M. Burkhead, 183–194. American Fisheries Society, Bethesda, Md.

Nakamura, I., and N. V. Parin. 1993. *FAO species cata-*

logue. Vol. 15, *Snake mackerels and cutlassfishes of the world.* Food and Agriculture Organization of the United Nations, Fisheries Synopsis 125. Rome.

Nammack, M. F., J. A. Musick, and J. A. Colvocoresses. 1985. Life history of the spiny dogfish off the northeastern United States. *Transactions of the American Fisheries Society* 114:367–376.

Nelson, D. M., E. A. Irlandi, L. R. Settle, M. E. Monaco, and L. C. Coston-Clements. 1991. *Distribution and abundance of fishes and invertebrates in southeast fisheries.* Estuarine Living Marine Resources Report 9. Strategic Environmental Assessments Division, National Oceanic and Atmospheric Administration, National Ocean Service, Rockville, Md.

Nelson, J. S. 1968. Salinity tolerance of brook sticklebacks, *Culaea inconstans,* freshwater ninespine sticklebacks, *Pungitius pungitius,* and freshwater fourspine sticklebacks, *Apeltes quadracus. Canadian Journal of Zoology* 46:663–667.

———. 1994. *Fishes of the world.* 3d ed. John Wiley and Sons, New York.

Nizinski, M. S., B. B. Collette, and B. B. Washington. 1990. Separation of two species of sand lances, *Ammodytes americanus* and *A. dubius,* in the western North Atlantic. *Fishery Bulletin, U.S.* 88 (2): 241–255.

Norcross, B. L., and H. M. Austin. 1981. *Climate scale environmental factors affecting year class fluctuations of Chesapeake Bay croakers, Micropogonias undulatus.* Virginia Institute of Marine Science, Special Scientific Report 110. Gloucester Point.

Norcross, B. L., and D. Hata. 1990. Seasonal composition of finfish in waters behind the Virginia Barrier Islands. *Virginia Journal of Science* 41 (4A): 441–461.

Norcross, J. J., S. L. Richardson, W. H. Massmann, and E. B. Joseph. 1974. Development of young bluefish *(Pomatomus saltatrix)* and distribution of eggs and young in Virginian coastal waters. *Transactions of the American Fisheries Society* 103:477–497.

Notarbartolo-di-Sciara, G., and E. V. Hillyear. 1989. Mobulid rays off eastern Venezuela (Chondrichthyes, Mobulidae). *Copeia* 1989 (3): 607–614.

Nyman, R. M., and D. O. Conover. 1988. The relation between spawning season and the recruitment of young-of-the-year bluefish, *Pomatomus saltatrix,* to New York. *Fishery Bulletin, U.S.* 86 (2): 237–250.

Olla, B. L., and C. Samet. 1977. Courtship and spawning behavior of the tautog, *Tautoga onitis* (Pisces: Labridae), under laboratory conditions. *Fishery Bulletin, U.S.* 75 (4): 585–599.

Olla, B. L., A. J. Bejda, and A. D. Martin. 1974. Daily activity, movements, feeding, and seasonal occurrence in the tautog, *Tautoga onitis. Fishery Bulletin, U.S.* 72 (1): 27–35.

———. 1975. Activity, movements, and feeding behavior of the cunner, *Tautogolabrus adspersus,* and a comparison with food habits with young tautog, *Tautoga onitis,* off Long Island, New York. *Fishery Bulletin, U.S.* 73 (4): 895–900.

———. 1979. Seasonal dispersal and habitat selection of cunner, *Tautogolabrus adspersus,* and young tautog, *Tautoga onitis,* in Fire Island Inlet, Long Island, New York. *Fishery Bulletin, U.S.* 77 (2): 255–261.

Olla, B. L., C. Samet, and A. L. Studholme. 1981. Correlates between number of mates, shelter availability, and reproductive behavior in the tautog, *Tautoga onitis. Marine Biology* 62 (4): 239–248.

Olney, J. E. 1983. Eggs and larvae of the bay anchovy, *Anchoa mitchilli,* and the weakfish, *Cynoscion regalis,* in lower Chesapeake Bay with notes on associated ichthyoplankton. *Estuaries* 6 (1): 20–35.

Olney, J. E., and G. W. Boehlert. 1988. Nearshore ichthyoplankton associated with seagrass beds in the lower Chesapeake Bay. *Marine Ecology, Progress Series* 45 (1–2): 33–43.

Olney, J. E., and G. C. Grant. 1976. Early planktonic larvae of blackcheek tonguefish, *Symphurus plagiusa* (Pisces: Cynoglossidae), in the lower Chesapeake Bay. *Chesapeake Science* 17:229–237.

O'Neil, S. P., and M. P. Weinstein. 1987. Feeding habits of spot, *Leiostomus xanthurus,* in polyhaline versus meso-oligohaline tidal creeks and shoals. *Fishery Bulletin, U.S.* 86 (4): 785–796.

Orth, R. J., and K. L. Heck Jr. 1980. Structural components of eelgrass *(Zostera marina)* meadows in the lower Chesapeake Bay—fishes. *Estuaries* 3 (4): 278–288.

Pacheco, A. L. 1962. Age and growth of spot in the lower Chesapeake Bay, with notes on distribution and abundance of juveniles in the York River system. *Chesapeake Science* 3 (1): 18–28.

Page, L. M. 1983. *Handbook of darters.* TFH Publications, Neptune City, N.J.

Page, L. M., and B. M. Burr. 1991. *A field guide to freshwater fishes of North America north of Mexico.* Houghton Mifflin, Boston.

Parsons, G. P., and K. A. Killam. 1991. Activity patterns of the bonnethead shark, *Sphyrna tiburo* (Linnaeus). *Journal of Aquariculture and Aquatic Sciences* 6 (4): 8–13.

Pflieger, W. L. 1975. *The fishes of Missouri.* Missouri Department of Conservation, Jefferson City.

Pietsch, T. W., and C. P. Zabetian. 1990. Osteology and interrelationships of the sand lances (Teleostei: Ammodytidae). *Copeia* 1990 (1): 78–100.

Pottern, G. B., M. T. Huish, and J. H. Kerby. 1989. *Species profiles: Life histories and environmental requirements of coastal fishes and invertebrates (Mid-Atlantic*

Bight)—bluefish. U.S. Fish and Wildlife Service, Office of Biological Services, FWS/OBS-82/11.94. U.S. Army Corps of Engineers TR EL-82-4.

Powell, A. B., and H. R. Gordy. 1980. Eggs and larval development of the spot, *Leiostomus xanthurus* (Sciaenidae). *Fishery Bulletin, U.S.* 78 (4): 701–714.

Powles, H. 1980. Description of larval silver perch, *Bairdiella chrysoura,* banded drum, *Larimus fasciatus,* and star drum, *Stellifer lanceolatus* (Sciaenidae). *Fishery Bulletin, U.S.* 78 (1): 119–136.

Powles, H., and B. W. Stender. 1978. *Taxonomic data on the early life history stages of Sciaenidae of the South Atlantic Bight of the United States.* South Carolina Marine Resources Center, Technical Report 31. Charleston.

Raleigh, R. F., L. D. Zuckerman, and P. C. Nelson. 1986. *Habitat Suitability Index Models and Instream Flow Suitability Curves: Brown trout.* U.S. Fish and Wildlife Service, Office of Biological Services, FWS/OBS-82/10.124.

Ralph, D. E. 1982. *Biological and fisheries data on northern kingfish, Menticirrhus saxatilis (Bloch and Schneider).* Sandy Hook Laboratory, Northeast Fisheries Center, National Marine Fisheries Service, National Oceanic and Atmospheric Administration, Department of Commerce, Technical Series Report 27.

Randall, J. E. 1967. Food habits of reef fishes of the West Indies. *University of Miami Studies in Tropical Oceanography* 5:665–847.

———. 1983. *Caribbean reef fishes.* TFH Publications, Neptune City, N.J.

———. 1992. Review of the biology of the tiger shark *(Galeocerdo cuvier). Australian Journal of Marine and Freshwater Research* 43:21–31.

Raney, E. C. 1952. The life history of the striped bass, *Roccus saxatilis* (Walbaum). *Bulletin, Bingham Oceanographic Collection, Yale University* 14 (1): 5–97.

Raney, E. C., R. H. Backus, R. W. Crawford, and C. R. Robins. 1953. Reproductive behavior in *Cyprinodon variegatus* Lacepède, in Florida. *Zoologica* 38 (2): 97–104.

Reintjes, J. W. 1969. *Synopsis of biological data on the Atlantic menhaden, Brevoortia tyrannus.* U.S. Fish and Wildlife Service, Circular 320.

Richards, C. E. 1963. First record of four fishes from Chesapeake Bay, and observations of other fishes during 1962. *Copeia* 1963 (3): 584–585.

———. 1967. Age, growth, and fecundity of the cobia, *Rachycentron canadum,* from Chesapeake Bay and adjacent mid-Atlantic waters. *Transactions of the American Fisheries Society* 96 (3): 343–350.

———. 1970. A first record of *Kyphosus incisor* (Cuvier) for Chesapeake Bay, Va. *Chesapeake Science* 11: 66–67.

Richards, S. W., J. M. Mann, and J. A. Walker. 1979. Comparison of spawning seasons, age, growth rates, and food of two sympatric species of searobins, *Prionotus carolinus* and *Prionotus evolans,* from Long Island Sound. *Estuaries* 2 (4): 255–268.

Richardson, S. L., and E. B. Joseph. 1973. Larvae and young of western North Atlantic bothid flatfishes *Etropus microstomus* and *Citharichthys arctifrons* in the Chesapeake Bight. *Fishery Bulletin, U.S.* 71 (3): 735–767.

———. 1975. Occurrence of larvae of the green goby, *Microgobius thalassinus,* in the York River, Virginia. *Chesapeake Science* 16 (3): 215–218.

Robins, C. R., G. C. Ray, and J. Douglass. 1986. *A field guide to Atlantic coast fishes of North America.* Houghton Mifflin, Boston.

Robins, C. R., R. M. Bailey, C. E. Bond, J. R. Brooker, E. A. Lachner, R. N. Lea, and W. B. Scott. 1991. *Common and scientific names of fishes from the United States and Canada.* 5th ed. American Fisheries Society, Special Publication 20. Bethesda, Md.

Robinson, P. F., and F. J. Schwartz. 1968. Toxicity of the northern puffer, *Sphoeroides maculatus,* in the Chesapeake Bay and its environs. *Chesapeake Science* 9 (2): 136–143.

Rogers, S. G., and M. J. Van Den Avyle. 1983. *Species profiles: Life histories and environmental requirements of coastal fishes and invertebrates (Mid-Atlantic Bight)— summer flounder.* U.S. Fish and Wildlife Service, Office of Biological Services, FWS/OBS-82/11.15. U.S. Army Corps of Engineers TR EL-82-4.

Ross, S. W. 1984. Reproduction of the banded drum, *Larimus fasciatus,* in North Carolina. *Fishery Bulletin, U.S.* 82 (2): 227–235.

———. 1988. Age, growth, and mortality of Atlantic croaker in North Carolina, with comments on population dynamics. *Transactions of the American Fisheries Society* 117:461–473.

———. 1989. Diet of the banded drum in North Carolina. *Transactions of the American Fisheries Society* 118:680–686.

Russell, M., M. Grace, and E. J. Gutherz. 1992. *Field guide to the searobins (Prionotus and Bellator) in the western North Atlantic.* Southeast Fisheries Center, National Marine Fisheries Service, National Oceanic and Atmospheric Administration, Department of Commerce, Technical Series Report 107.

St. Pierre, R. A., and J. Davis. 1972. Age, growth, and mortality of the white perch, *Morone americana,* in the James and York Rivers, Virginia. *Chesapeake Science* 13 (4): 272–281.

Schwartz, F. J. 1961. Fishes of Chincoteague and Sinepuxent bays. *American Midland Naturalist* 65 (2): 384–408.

———. 1971. Biology of *Microgobius thalassinus* (Pisces: Gobiidae), a sponge-inhabiting goby of Chesapeake Bay, with range extensions of two goby associates. *Chesapeake Science* 12 (3): 156–166.

———. 1974. Movements of the oyster toadfish (Pisces: Batrachoididae) about Solomons Island, Maryland. *Chesapeake Science* 15 (3): 155–159.

———. 1990. Length-weight, age and growth, and landings observations for sheepshead *Archosargus probatocephalus* from North Carolina. *Fishery Bulletin, U.S.* 88 (4): 829–832.

Schwartz, F. J., and B. W. Dutcher. 1963. Age, growth, and food of the oyster toadfish near Solomons Island, Maryland. *Transactions of the American Fisheries Society* 92:170–173.

Scott, W. B., and E. J. Crossman. 1973. *Freshwater fishes of Canada*. Fisheries Research Board of Canada, Bulletin 184. Ottawa.

Shaffer, R. V., and E. L. Nakamura. 1989. *Synopsis of biological data on cobia, Rachycentron canadum (Pisces: Rachycentridae)*. National Marine Fisheries Service, National Oceanic and Atmospheric Administration, Department of Commerce, Technical Series Report 82.

Shenker, J. M., D. J. Hepner, P. E. Frere, L. E. Currence, and W. W. Wakefield. 1983. Upriver migration and abundance of naked goby *(Gobiosoma bosci)* larvae in the Patuxent River estuary, Maryland. *Estuaries* 6 (1): 36–42.

Sheperd, G. R., and C. B. Grimes. 1983. Geographic and historic variation in growth of weakfish, *Cynoscion regalis*, in the Middle Atlantic Bight. *Fishery Bulletin, U.S.* 81 (4): 803–813.

———. 1984. Reproduction of weakfish, *Cynoscion regalis*, in the New York Bight and evidence for geographically specific life history characteristics. *Fishery Bulletin, U.S.* 82 (3): 501–511.

Smith, C. L. 1971. A revision of the American groupers: *Epinephelus* and allied genera. *Bulletin of the American Museum of Natural History* 146 (2): 67–242.

———. 1985. *The inland fishes of New York State*. New York State Department of Environmental Conservation, Albany.

Smith, D. G. 1989a. Family Anguillidae. In *Fishes of the western North Atlantic*, Sears Foundation for Marine Research, Memoir 1, pt. 9, 25–47. Yale University, New Haven, Conn.

———. 1989b. Family Congridae. In *Fishes of the western North Atlantic*, Sears Foundation for Marine Research, Memoir 1, pt. 9, 60–567. Yale University, New Haven, Conn.

———. 1989c. Order Elopiformes. In *Fishes of the western North Atlantic*, Sears Foundation for Marine Research, Memoir 1, pt. 9, 961–981. Yale University, New Haven, Conn.

Smith, J. W., and J. V. Merriner. 1987. Age and growth, movements, and distribution of the cownose ray, *Rhinoptera bonasus*, in Chesapeake Bay. *Estuaries* 10 (2): 153–164.

Smith, J. W., and C. A. Wenner. 1985. Biology of the southern kingfish in the South Atlantic Bight. *Transactions of the American Fisheries Society* 114:356–366.

Smith, P. W. 1979. *The fishes of Illinois*. University of Illinois Press, Urbana.

Smith, W. G. 1972. The distribution of summer flounder, *Paralichthys dentatus*, eggs and larvae on the continental shelf between Cape Cod and Cape Lookout, 1965–66. *Fishery Bulletin, U.S.* 71 (3): 527–548.

Smith, W. G., and A. Wells. 1977. *Biological and fisheries data on striped bass, Morone saxatilis (Walbaum)*. Sandy Hook Laboratory, Northeast Fisheries Center, National Marine Fisheries Service, National Oceanic and Atmospheric Administration, Department of Commerce, Technical Series Report 4.

Smith, W. G., P. Berrien, and T. Potthoff. 1994. Spawning patterns of bluefish, *Pomatomus saltatrix*, in the northeast continental shelf ecosystem. *Bulletin of Marine Science* 54 (1): 8–16.

Smith-Vaniz, W. F. 1980. Revision of western Atlantic species of the blenniid fish genus *Hypsoblennius*. *Proceedings of the Academy of Natural Sciences of Philadelphia* 132:285–305.

Smith-Vaniz, W. F., and J. C. Staiger. 1973. Comparative revision of *Scomberoides, Oligoplites, Parona*, and *Hypacanthus* with comments on the phylogenetic position of *Campogramma* (Pisces: Carangidae). *Proceedings of the California Academy of Sciences*, 4th ser., 39 (13): 185–256.

Snelson, F. F., S. E. Williams-Hooper, and T. H. Schmid. 1988. Reproduction and ecology of the Atlantic stingray, *Dasyatis sabina*, in Florida coastal lagoons. *Copeia* 1988 (3): 729–739.

Sogard, S. M., K. W. Able, and M. P. Fahay. 1992. Early life history of the tautog *Tautoga onitis* in the Mid-Atlantic Bight. *Fishery Bulletin, U.S.* 90 (3): 529–539.

Springer, V. G. 1959. Blenniid fishes of the genus *Chasmodes*. *Texas Journal of Science* 11 (3): 321–334.

Starck, W. A., II. 1971. *Biology of the gray snapper, Lutjanus griseus (Linnaeus), in the Florida Keys*. University of Miami Studies in Tropical Oceanography, 10.

Starnes, W. C. 1988. Revision, phylogeny, and biogeographic comments on the circumtropical marine percoid fish family Priacanthidae. *Bulletin of Marine Science* 43 (2): 117–203.

Stickney, R. R. 1976. Food habits of Georgia estuarine fishes: 2, *Symphurus plagiusa* (Pleuronectiformes: Cynoglossidae). *Transactions of the American Fisheries Society* 105:202–207.

Stone, S. L., T. A. Lowery, J. D. Field, C. D. Williams,

D. M. Nelson, S. H. Jury, M. E. Monaco, and L. Andreasen. 1994. *Distribution and abundance of fishes and invertebrates in Mid-Atlantic estuaries.* Estuarine Living Marine Resources Report 12. Strategic Environmental Assessments Division, National Oceanic and Atmospheric Administration, National Ocean Service, Silver Spring, Md.

Stoner, A. W., and R. J. Livingston. 1984. Ontogenetic patterns in diet and feeding morphology in sympatric sparid fishes from seagrass meadows. *Copeia* 1984 (1): 174–187.

Strasburg, D. W. 1959. Notes on the diet and correlating structures of some central Pacific echeneid fishes. *Copeia* 1959 (3): 244–248.

Stuber, R. J., G. Gebhart, and O. E. Maughan. 1982. *Habitat Suitability Index Models: Largemouth bass.* U.S. Fish and Wildlife Service, Office of Biological Services, FWS/OBS-82/10.16.

Suttkus, R. D. 1963. Order Lepisostei. In *Fishes of the western North Atlantic,* Sears Foundation for Marine Research, Memoir 1, pt. 3, 61–88. Yale University, New Haven, Conn.

Swink, W. D. 1990. Effect of lake trout size on survival after a single sea lamprey attack. *Transactions of the American Fisheries Society* 119 (6): 996–1002.

———. 1991. Host-size selection by parasitic lampreys. *Transactions of the American Fisheries Society* 120 (5): 637–643.

Szedlmayer, S. T., K. W. Able, and R. A. Rountree. 1992. Growth and temperature induced mortality of young-of-the-year summer flounder, *Paralichthys dentatus,* in southern New Jersey. *Copeia* 1992 (1): 120–128.

Teaf, C. M., and T. C. Lewis. 1987. Seasonal occurrence of multiple caudal spines in the Atlantic stingray, *Dasyatis sabina* (Pisces: Dasyatidae). *Copeia* 1987 (1): 224–227.

Tolley, S. G. 1987. Association of young *Chloroscombrus chrysurus* (Pisces: Carangidae) with the jellyfish *Aurelia aurita. Copeia* 1987 (1): 216–219.

Tucker, J. W. 1982. Larval development of *Citharichthys cornutus, C. gymnorhinus, C. spilopterus, Etropus crossotus* (Bothidae), with notes on larval occurrence. *Fishery Bulletin, U.S.* 80 (1): 35–73.

Twomey, K. A., K. L. Williamson, and P. C. Nelson. 1984. *Habitat Suitability Index Models: White sucker.* U.S. Fish and Wildlife Service, Office of Biological Services, FWS/OBS-82/10.64.

Uhler, P. R., and O. Lugger. 1876. List of the fishes of Maryland. In *Report, Commissioner of Fisheries of Maryland, 1876,* 81–208. Annapolis.

Van Den Avyle, M. J. 1984. *Species profiles: Life histories and environmental requirements of coastal fishes and invertebrates (South Atlantic)—Atlantic sturgeon.* U.S. Fish and Wildlife Service, Office of Biological Ser-vices FWS/OBS-82/11.25. U.S. Army Corps of Engineers TR EL-82-4.

Vanicek, D. 1961. Life history of the quillback and high-fin carpsuckers in the Des Moines River. *Proceedings of the Iowa Academy of Science* 58:238–246.

Vari, R. P. 1982. The seahorses (subfamily Hippocampinae). In *Fishes of the western North Atlantic,* Sears Foundation for Marine Research, Memoir 1, pt. 8, 173–189. Yale University, New Haven, Conn.

Vincent, A. 1990. A seahorse father makes a good mother. *Natural History* (December): 34–42.

Virginia Marine Resources Commission. 1990. *1989 VMRC Finfish Stock Assessment Program: Biological sampling of commercial fish harvests.* Virginia Marine Resources Commission, Newport News.

Vladykov, V. D., and J. R. Greeley. 1963. Acipenseroidei. In *Fishes of the western North Atlantic,* Sears Foundation for Marine Research, Memoir 1, pt. 3, 24–60. Yale University, New Haven, Conn.

Walford, L. A. 1946. New southern record for Atlantic halibut. *Copeia* 1946 (2): 100–101.

Wallace, D.C. 1971. Age, growth, year class strength, and survival rates of the white perch, *Morone americana* (Gmelin), in the Delaware River in the vicinity of Artificial Island. *Chesapeake Science* 12:205–218.

Waring, G. T. 1984. Age, growth, and mortality of the little skate off the northeast coast of the United States. *Transactions of the American Fisheries Society* 113:314–321.

Warkentine, B. E., and J. W. Rachlin. 1989. Winter off-shore diet of the Atlantic silverside, *Menidia menidia. Copeia* 1989 (1): 195–198.

Warlen, S. M., and A. J. Chester. 1985. Age, growth, and distribution of larval spot, *Leiostomus xanthurus,* off North Carolina. *Fishery Bulletin, U.S.* 83 (4): 587–599.

Weinstein, M. P. 1981. Biology of adult sciaenids. In *Sciaenids: Territorial sea demersal resources,* Proceedings of the Sixth Annual Marine Recreational Fisheries Symposium, Houston, Texas, ed. H. Clepper, 125–138.

———. 1983. Population dynamics of an estuarine-dependent fish, the spot *(Leiostomus xanthurus),* along a tidal creek–seagrass meadow coenocline. *Canadian Journal of Fisheries and Aquatic Sciences* 40: 1633–1638.

———. 1986. *Habitat Suitability Index Models: Inland silverside.* U.S. Fish and Wildlife Service, Office of Biological Services, FWS/OBS-82/10.120.

Weinstein, M. P., and M. P. Walters. 1981. Growth, survival, and production in young-of-year population of *Leiostomus xanthurus* Lacepède residing in tidal creeks. *Estuaries* 4 (3): 185–197.

Weinstein, M. P., S. L. Weiss, R. G. Hodson, and L. R. Gerry. 1980. Retention of three taxa of postlarval fishes in an intensively flushed tidal estuary, Cape Fear River, North Carolina. *Fishery Bulletin, U.S.* 78 (2): 419–436.

Weisberg, S. B. 1986. Competition and coexistence among four estuarine species of *Fundulus. American Zoologist* 26 (1): 249–257.

Welsh, W. W., and C. M. Breder Jr. 1923. Contributions to life histories of Sciaenidae of the Eastern United States coast. *Bulletin of the U.S. Bureau of Fisheries* 39:141–201.

Wenner, C. A., W. A. Roumillat, and C. W. Waltz. 1986. Contributions to the life history of the black sea bass, *Centropristis striata,* off the southeastern United States. *Fishery Bulletin, U.S.* 84 (4): 723–741.

White, M. L., and M. E. Chittenden Jr. 1977. Age determination, reproduction, and population dynamics of the Atlantic croaker, *Micropogonias undulatus. Fishery Bulletin, U.S.* 75 (1): 109–123.

Whitehead, P. J. P. 1985. *FAO species catalogue.* Vol. 7, *Clupeoid fishes of the world: An annotated and illustrated catalogue of the herrings, sardines, pilchards, sprats, anchovies, and wolf-herrings.* Pt. 1, *Chirocentridae, Clupeidae, and Pristigasteridae.* Food and Agriculture Organization of the United Nations, Fisheries Synopsis 125. Rome.

Whitehead, P. J. P., M. L. Bauchot, J. C. Hureau, J. Nielsen, and E. Tortonese, eds. 1984. *Fishes of the north-eastern Atlantic and the Mediterranean.* Vol. 1. UNESCO, Paris.

———, eds. 1986a. *Fishes of the north-eastern Atlantic and the Mediterranean.* Vol. 2. UNESCO.

———, eds. 1986b. *Fishes of the north-eastern Atlantic and the Mediterranean.* Vol. 3. UNESCO.

Whitehead, P. J. P., G. J. Nelson, and T. Wongratana. 1985. *FAO species catalogue.* Vol. 7, *Clupeoid fishes of the world: An annotated and illustrated catalogue of the herrings, sardines, pilchards, sprats, anchovies, and wolf-herrings.* Pt. 2, *Engraulididae.* Food and Agriculture Organization of the United Nations, Fisheries Synopsis 125. Rome.

Wilk, S. J. 1977. *Biological and fisheries data on bluefish, Pomatomus saltatrix (Linnaeus).* Northeast Fisheries Center, National Marine Fisheries Service, National Oceanic and Atmospheric Administration, Department of Commerce, Technical Series Report 11.

Williams, J. T. 1983. Taxonomy and ecology of the genus *Chasmodes* (Pisces: Blenniidae) with a discussion of its zoogeography. *Bulletin of the Florida State Museum, Biological Science* 29 (2): 65–101.

Williamson, K. L., and P. C. Nelson. 1985. *Habitat Suitability Index Models and Instream Flow Suitability Curves: Gizzard shad.* U.S. Department of the Interior, Fish and Wildlife Service, Office of Biological Services, FWS/OBS-82/10.112.

Illustration Credits

When known, the artist's name and the date are provided for the classic illustrations from the late 1800s and early 1900s.

FAO 4   Compagno, L. J. V. 1984. *FAO species catalogue*. Vol. 4, *Sharks of the world: An annotated and illustrated catalogue of shark species known to date*. Pt. 1, *Hexanchiformes to Lamniformes*. Pt. 2, *Carcharhiniformes*. Food and Agriculture Organization of the United Nations, Fisheries Synopsis 125. Rome.

FAO 10   Cohen, D. M., T. Inada, T. Iwamoto, and N. Scialabba. 1990. *FAO species catalogue*. Vol. 10, *Gadiform fishes of the world: An annotated and illustrated catalogue of cods, hakes, grenadiers, and other gadiform fishes known to date*. Food and Agriculture Organization of the United Nations, Fisheries Synopsis 125. Rome.

FAO 16   Heemstra, P. C., and J. E. Randall. 1993. *FAO species catalogue*. Vol. 16, *Groupers of the world: An annotated and illustrated catalogue of the grouper, rockcod, hind, coral grouper, and lyretail species known to date*. Food and Agriculture Organization of the United Nations, Fisheries Synopsis 125. Rome.

FAO 31   Fischer, W., ed. 1978. *FAO species identification sheets for fishery purposes: Western central Atlantic, fishing area 31*. Vols. 1–7. Food and Agriculture Organization of the United Nations, Rome.

FAO 34   Fischer, W., G. Bianchi, and W. B. Scott, eds. 1981. *FAO species identification sheets for fishery purposes: Eastern central Atlantic, fishing areas 34, 47 (in part)*. Vols. 1–7. Canada Funds-in-Trust, Ottawa; Department of Fisheries and Oceans, Canada; by arrangement with the Food and Agriculture Organization of the United Nations.

INHS   Ilinois Natural History Survey

NCSMNS   North Carolina State Museum of Natural Sciences

NMNH   Division of Fishes, National Museum of Natural History, Smithsonian Institution

NYSDEC   New York State Department of Environmental Conservation

PLATE 1. From the Coastwatch Program, U.S. National Oceanic and Atmospheric Administration (NOAA). Mosaicked from 1988 and 1989 images and edited by David A. Hastings of NOAA's National Geophysical Data Center.

PLATE 2. From NMNH. Illustrated by J. H. Richard, 1880.

PLATE 3. From NMNH. Illustrated by Charles B. Hudson, 1896.

PLATE 4. From NMNH. Illustrated by A. H. Baldwin[?], 1898.

PLATE 5. From NMNH. Illustrated by Charles B. Hudson, 1896.

PLATE 6. From NMNH. 1898.

PLATE 7. From NMNH. Illustrated by Sherman Foote Denton.

PLATE 8. From NMNH. Illustrated by Sherman Foote Denton.

PLATE 9. From NMNH. Illustrated by Sherman Foote Denton.

PLATE 10. From NMNH. Illustrated by E. A. Woodbury, 1883.

PLATE 11. From NMNH. Illustrated by Sherman Foote Denton.

PLATE 12. From INHS.

PLATE 13. From INHS.

PLATE 14. From INHS.

PLATE 15. From NMNH. Illustrated by Charles B. Hudson, 1896.

PLATE 16. From NMNH. Illustrated by Charles B. Hudson, 1896.

PLATE 17. From NMNH. Illustrated by Charles B. Hudson, 1896.

PLATE 18. From NMNH. Illustrated by Charles B. Hudson, 1896.

PLATE 19. From NMNH. Illustrated by A. H. Baldwin, 1899.

PLATE 20. From NMNH. Illustrated by Sherman Foote Denton, 1888.

PLATE 21. From NMNH. Illustrated by Charles B. Hudson, 1896.

PLATE 22. From NMNH. Illustrated by Sherman Foote Denton.

PLATE 23. From NMNH. Illustrated by Charles B. Hudson, 1898.

PLATE 24. From NMNH. 1888.

PLATE 25. From NMNH. Illustrated by Charles B. Hudson, 1896.

PLATE 26. From NMNH. Illustrated by Charles B. Hudson, 1896.

PLATE 27. From NMNH. Illustrated by Charles B. Hudson, 1896.

PLATE 28. From NMNH. Illustrated by Sherman Foote Denton, 1888.

PLATE 29. From NMNH. Illustrated by Sherman Foote Denton, 1888.

PLATE 30. From NYSDEC. Illustrated by Sherman Foote Denton. Slide transparency provided by Victor Springer.

PLATE 31. From NMNH. Illustrated by Charles B. Hudson.

PLATE 32. From NMNH. Illustrated by Charles B. Hudson, 1896.

PLATE 33. From NMNH. Illustrated by A. H. Baldwin, 1898.

PLATE 34. From NMNH. Illustrated by A. H. Baldwin, 1898.

PLATE 35. From NYSDEC. Illustrated by Sherman Foote Denton.

PLATE 36. From NMNH. Illustrated by Sherman Foote Denton, 1888.

PLATE 37. From NYSDEC. Illustrated by Sherman Foote Denton.

PLATE 38. From NMNH. Illustrated by Charles B. Hudson, 1897.

PLATE 39. From NMNH. Illustrated by A. H. Baldwin, 1899.

PLATE 40. From NMNH. Illustrated by A. H. Baldwin, 1898.

PLATE 41. From NMNH. Illustrated by Sherman Foote Denton.

PLATE 42. From INHS.

PLATE 43. From NYSDEC. Illustrated by Sherman Foote Denton.

PLATE 44. From NMNH. Illustrated by Charles B. Hudson, 1896.

PLATE 45. From NYSDEC. Illustrated by Sherman Foote Denton.

PLATE 46. From NMNH. Illustrated by Charles B. Hudson, 1897.

PLATE 47. From NMNH. Illustrated by Sherman Foote Denton, 1888.

PLATE 48. From NYSDEC. Illustrated by Sherman Foote Denton. Slide transparency provided by Victor Springer.

PLATE 49. From NMNH. Illustrated by Charles B. Hudson, 1896.

FIGURE 1. From U.S. Environmental Protection Agency.

FIGURE 2. Reprinted from FAO 31.

FIGURE 3. Reprinted from FAO 34.

FIGURE 4. Reprinted from FAO 31.

FIGURE 5. Reprinted from FAO 31.

FIGURE 6. Courtesy of the Sears Foundation for Marine Research, Yale University.

FIGURE 7. From NMNH.

FIGURE 8. From NMNH. 1881.

FIGURE 9. Reprinted from FAO 31.

FIGURE 10. Reprinted from FAO 31.

FIGURE 11. Reprinted from FAO 31.

FIGURE 12. Reprinted from FAO 31.

FIGURE 13. Reprinted from FAO 31.

FIGURE 14. From NMNH. 1883.

FIGURE 15. Reprinted from FAO 31.

FIGURE 16. Reprinted from FAO 34.

FIGURE 17. Reprinted from FAO 4.

FIGURE 18. Reprinted from FAO 31.

FIGURE 19. Reprinted from FAO 31.

FIGURE 20. Reprinted from FAO 31.

FIGURE 21. Reprinted from FAO 31.

FIGURE 22. Reprinted from FAO 34.

FIGURE 23. Reprinted from FAO 31.

FIGURE 24. Reprinted from FAO 34.

FIGURE 25. From NMNH. Illustrated by H. L. Todd, 1879.

FIGURE 26. From NMNH. Illustrated by H. L. Todd[?], 1885.

FIGURE 27. From NMNH. Illustrated by H. L. Todd[?].

FIGURE 28. From NMNH. Illustrated by H. L. Todd[?].

FIGURE 29. Reprinted from FAO 34.

FIGURE 30. Reprinted from FAO 34.

FIGURE 31. Reprinted from FAO 31.

FIGURE 32. Reprinted from FAO 34.

FIGURE 33. From NMNH. Illustrated by H. L. Todd.

FIGURE 34. Courtesy of the Sears Foundation for Marine Research, Yale University.

FIGURE 35. From NMNH. Illustrated by A. H. Baldwin, 1894.

FIGURE 36. Courtesy of the Sears Foundation for Marine Research, Yale University.

FIGURE 37. Courtesy of the Sears Foundation for Marine Research, Yale University.

FIGURE 38. Courtesy of the Sears Foundation for Marine Research, Yale University.

FIGURE 39. From NMNH. Illustrated by H. L. Todd.

FIGURE 40. From NCSMNS. Illustrated by Renaldo Kuhler.

FIGURE 41. From INHS.

FIGURE 42. From NMNH.

FIGURE 43. From NMNH.

FIGURE 44. From NMNH.

FIGURE 45. From NMNH. Illustrated by Charles B. Hudson, 1896.

FIGURE 46. From NMNH.

FIGURE 47. Reprinted from FAO 31.

FIGURE 48. Reprinted from FAO 31.

FIGURE 49. Reprinted from FAO 31.

FIGURE 50. Reprinted from FAO 31.

FIGURE 51. Courtesy of the Sears Foundation for Marine Research, Yale University.

FIGURE 52. From NMNH. Illustrated by Ann S. Green.

FIGURE 53. From NMNH. Illustrated by H. L. Todd, 1883.

FIGURE 54. From NMNH. 1897.

FIGURE 55. From NMNH.

FIGURE 56. From NMNH. Illustrated by H. L. Todd.

FIGURE 57. From NMNH. 1898.

FIGURE 58. From NMNH. 1880.

FIGURE 59. From NMNH. 1880.

FIGURE 60. From NMNH. 1883.

FIGURE 61. From NMNH. Illustrated by J. W. Gehringer.

FIGURE 62. From NCSMNS. Illustrated by Renaldo Kuhler.

FIGURE 63. From NMNH. Illustrated by H. L. Todd.

FIGURE 64. From NCSMNS. Illustrated by Renaldo Kuhler.

FIGURE 65. From NCSMNS. Illustrated by Renaldo Kuhler.

FIGURE 66. From NCSMNS. Illustrated by Renaldo Kuhler.

FIGURE 67. From NMNH.

FIGURE 68. From NCSMNS. Illustrated by Renaldo Kuhler.

FIGURE 69. From NCSMNS. Illustrated by Renaldo Kuhler.

FIGURE 70. From NCSMNS. Illustrated by Renaldo Kuhler.

FIGURE 71. From NCSMNS. Illustrated by Renaldo Kuhler.

FIGURE 72. From NMNH. 1880.

FIGURE 73. From NMNH. Illustrated by H. L. Todd.

FIGURE 74. From NMNH. Illustrated by M. Smith, 1884.

FIGURE 75. From INHS.

FIGURE 76. From INHS.

FIGURE 77. From INHS.

FIGURE 78. From NMNH.

FIGURE 79. From INHS.

FIGURE 80. From NMNH.

FIGURE 81. From U.S. Fish and Wildlife Service.

FIGURE 82. From NMNH.

FIGURE 83. From NCSMNS. Illustrated by Renaldo Kuhler.

FIGURE 84. Reprinted from W. B. Scott and E. J. Crossman, *Freshwater fishes of Canada,* Fisheries Research Board of Canada, Bulletin 184 (Ottawa, 1973).

FIGURE 85. Courtesy of the Sears Foundation for Marine Research, Yale University.

FIGURE 86. From NMNH. Illustrated by Louella E. Cable.

FIGURE 87. Reprinted from S. Runyan, "Early development of the clingfish, *Gobiesox strumosus* Cope," *Chesapeake Science* 2, nos. 3–4 (1961): 113.

FIGURE 88. From NMNH.

FIGURE 89. Reprinted from FAO 31.

FIGURE 90. Reprinted from FAO 10.

FIGURE 91. From NMNH.

FIGURE 92. Reprinted from FAO 31.

FIGURE 93. Reprinted from FAO 10.

FIGURE 94. From NMNH.

FIGURE 95. From NMNH. 1879.

FIGURE 96. Reprinted from FAO 31.

FIGURE 97. Reprinted from FAO 31.

FIGURE 98. Reprinted from FAO 31.

FIGURE 99. Reprinted from FAO 31.

FIGURE 100. From Bruce B. Collette. Illustrated by Mildred Carrington.

FIGURE 101. Reprinted from FAO 31.

FIGURE 102. From NMNH. Illustrated by A. H. Baldwin.

FIGURE 103. From NMNH. Illustrated by W. L. Haines, 1887.

FIGURE 104. From NMNH. Illustrated by A. H. Baldwin.

FIGURE 105. From NMNH. Illustrated by A. H. Baldwin.

FIGURE 106. From NMNH. (*a*) Illustrated by H. L. Todd. (*b*) Illustrated by Charles B. Hudson, 1896.

FIGURE 107. From NMNH. Illustrated by A. H. Baldwin.

FIGURE 108. From NMNH. Illustrated by A. H. Baldwin.

FIGURE 109. From NMNH.

FIGURE 110. From NMNH.

FIGURE 111. From NMNH. Illustrated by A. H. Baldwin.

FIGURE 112. From NMNH. Illustrated by A. H. Baldwin, 1891.

FIGURE 113. From NMNH. Illustrated by H. L. Todd.

FIGURE 114. From NMNH.

FIGURE 115. From NMNH.

FIGURE 116. From NMNH. Illustrated by H. L. Todd.

FIGURE 117. From John D. McEachran. Illustrated by Janice D. Fechhelm.

FIGURE 118. From John D. McEachran. Illustrated by Janice D. Fechhelm.

FIGURE 119. From NMNH.

FIGURE 120. From NMNH.

FIGURE 121. From NMNH.

FIGURE 122. From NMNH. 1879.

FIGURE 123. From NMNH. 1879.

FIGURE 124. From NMNH.

FIGURE 125. From NMNH.

FIGURE 126. Reprinted from FAO 31.

FIGURE 127. Reprinted from FAO 31.

FIGURE 128. Reprinted from FAO 31.

FIGURE 129. Reprinted from FAO 31.

FIGURE 130. Reprinted from FAO 31.

FIGURE 131. Reprinted from FAO 31.

FIGURE 132. Reprinted from FAO 31.

FIGURE 133. From NMNH. Illustrated by A. H. Baldwin, 1907.

FIGURE 134. Reprinted from FAO 31.

FIGURE 135. Reprinted from FAO 31.

FIGURE 136. Reprinted from FAO 31.

FIGURE 137. Reprinted from FAO 31.

FIGURE 138. Reprinted from FAO 31.

FIGURE 139. Reprinted from FAO 31.

FIGURE 140. From NMNH.

FIGURE 141. From NMNH. 1880.

FIGURE 142. From NMNH.

FIGURE 143. From NMNH.

FIGURE 144. Reprinted from FAO 31.

FIGURE 145. Reprinted from FAO 31.

FIGURE 146. From NMNH. 1879.

FIGURE 147. From NMNH. 1884.

FIGURE 148. Reprinted from FAO 31.

FIGURE 149. Reprinted from FAO 31.

FIGURE 150. From NMNH.

FIGURE 151. From NMNH.

FIGURE 152. Reprinted from FAO 31.

FIGURE 153. From NMNH.

FIGURE 154. Reprinted from FAO 31.

FIGURE 155. From NMNH. 1881.

FIGURE 156. Reprinted from FAO 31.

FIGURE 157. Reprinted from FAO 31.

FIGURE 158. From NMNH.

FIGURE 159. From NMNH.

FIGURE 160. From NMNH.

FIGURE 161. Reprinted from FAO 31.

FIGURE 162. From NMNH. 1887.

FIGURE 163. From NMNH.

FIGURE 164. From NMNH. Illustrated by H. L. Todd, 1886.

FIGURE 165. From NMNH. 1880.

FIGURE 166. From NMNH.

FIGURE 167. From NMNH. Illustrated by H. L. Todd, 1879.

FIGURE 168. From NMNH.

FIGURE 169. From NMNH. Illustrated by H. L. Todd.

FIGURE 170. From NMNH. 1880.

FIGURE 171. From NMNH.

FIGURE 172. Reprinted from FAO 34.

FIGURE 173. From NMNH.

FIGURE 174. From NMNH. 1880.

FIGURE 175. Reprinted from FAO 31.

FIGURE 176. From NMNH. 1881.

FIGURE 177. From NMNH. 1881.

FIGURE 178. Reprinted from FAO 31.

FIGURE 179. From NMNH. Illustrated by A. H. Baldwin, 1893.

FIGURE 180. From NMNH. 1884.

FIGURE 181. From NMNH. 1881.

FIGURE 182. From NMNH. Illustrated by H. L. Todd.

FIGURE 183. From NMNH. Illustrated by H. L. Todd.

FIGURE 184. From NMNH. Illustrated by Louella E. Cable, 1929.

FIGURE 185. From NMNH.

FIGURE 186. From NMNH.

FIGURE 187. Reprinted from FAO 31.

FIGURE 188. Reprinted from FAO 31.

FIGURE 189. From NMNH. 1881.

FIGURE 190. From NMNH. Illustrated by H. L. Todd.

FIGURE 191. From NMNH. Illustrated by Charles B. Hudson, 1896.

FIGURE 192. Reprinted from FAO 31.

FIGURE 193. From NCSMNS. Illustrated by Renaldo Kuhler.

FIGURE 194. From NMNH.

FIGURE 195. From NMNH. Illustrated by A. H. Baldwin, 1907.

FIGURE 196. From NMNH. Illustrated by Louise Nash, 1925.

FIGURE 197. From NMNH. Illustrated by Louise Nash, 1925.

FIGURE 198. From NMNH. 1878.

FIGURE 199. From NMNH. Illustrated by A. H. Baldwin, 1898.

FIGURE 200. From NCSMNS. Illustrated by Renaldo Kuhler.

FIGURE 201. From NMNH. 1878.

FIGURE 202. Reprinted from FAO 31.

FIGURE 203. From NMNH. Illustrated by M. M. Smith, 1884.

FIGURE 204. From NMNH.

FIGURE 205. From NMNH. Illustrated by W. S. Haines.

FIGURE 206. From NMNH.

FIGURE 207. From Florida Department of Environmental Protection. Illustrated by Diane Peebles.

FIGURE 208. From Florida Department of Environmental Protection. Illustrated by Diane Peebles.

FIGURE 209. Reprinted from FAO 31.

FIGURE 210. From NMNH. Illustrated by Sherman Foote Denton, 1888.

FIGURE 211. From NMNH. Illustrated by H. L. Todd, 1883.

FIGURE 212. From NMNH. 1881.

FIGURE 213. From NMNH. 1881.

FIGURE 214. Reprinted from FAO 31.

FIGURE 215. From NMNH.

FIGURE 216. Reprinted from FAO 31.

FIGURE 217. From NMNH. 1882.

FIGURE 218. From NMNH. 1878.

FIGURE 219. From NMNH. Illustrated by H. L. Todd, 1878.

FIGURE 220. From NMNH.

FIGURE 221. From NMNH. Illustrated by H. L. Todd, 1879.

FIGURE 222. From NMNH. Illustrated by H. L. Todd. 1879.

FIGURE 223. From NMNH.

FIGURE 224. From INHS.

FIGURE 225. From NMNH.

FIGURE 226. From NMNH. 1878.

FIGURE 227. From NCSMNS. Illustrated by Renaldo Kuhler.

FIGURE 228. From NCSMNS. Illustrated by Renaldo Kuhler.

FIGURE 229. From NMNH. 1879.

FIGURE 230. From NMNH.

FIGURE 231. From NMNH. 1880.

FIGURE 232. From NMNH.

FIGURE 233. From NMNH. From NYSDEC. Illustrated by Sherman Foote Denton.

FIGURE 234. Reprinted from FAO 16.

FIGURE 235. *(a)* From NMNH. 1880. *(b)* Reprinted from FAO 16.

FIGURE 236. Reprinted from FAO 31.

FIGURE 237. From NMNH.

FIGURE 238. From NMNH.

FIGURE 239. From NMNH.

FIGURE 240. From NMNH. 1879.

FIGURE 241. From NMNH.

FIGURE 242. From NMNH. 1878.

FIGURE 243. From NMNH.

FIGURE 244. From NMNH.

FIGURE 245. From NMNH.

FIGURE 246. From NMNH. Illustrated by K. Ito, 1912.

FIGURE 247. From NMNH.

FIGURE 248. Reprinted from FAO 31.

FIGURE 249. From NMNH. 1879.

FIGURE 250. From NMNH.

FIGURE 251. From NMNH. Illustrated by H. L. Todd, 1885.

FIGURE 252. From NMNH. Illustrated by W. S. Haines.

FIGURE 253. From NMNH. Illustrated by H. L. Todd, 1884.

Index

Page numbers for taxon descriptions are in boldface; those for illustrations are in italics. Page numbers for names in identification keys are marked with the letter "k"; the letter "t" marks page numbers for names in tables.

sharks
sheep
28
shin